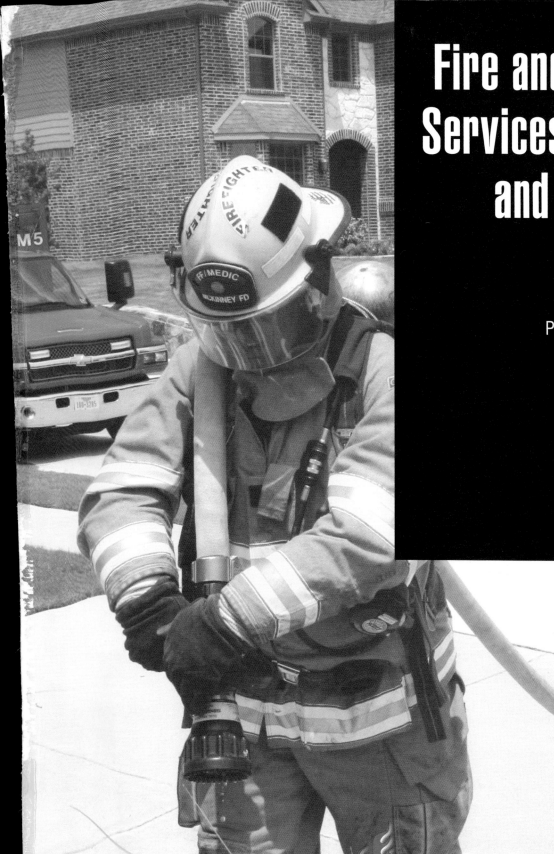

Fire and Emergency Services and Terminology

Fifth Edition

Jeff Fortney
Project Manager/Senior Editor

Clint Clausing
Senior Editor

Elkie Burnside
Instructional Developer

Pam Powell
Contract Writer

ifsta

Validated by the International Fire Service Training Association

Published by
Fire Protection Publications • Oklahoma State University

The International Fire Service Training Association

The International Fire Service Training Association (IFSTA) was established in 1934 as a *nonprofit educational association of fire fighting personnel who are dedicated to upgrading fire fighting techniques and safety through training.* To carry out the mission of IFSTA, Fire Protection Publications was established as an entity of Oklahoma State University. Fire Protection Publications' primary function is to publish and disseminate training texts as proposed and validated by IFSTA. As a secondary function, Fire Protection Publications researches, acquires, produces, and markets high-quality learning and teaching aids as consistent with IFSTA's mission.

The IFSTA Validation Conference is held the second full week in July. Committees of technical experts meet and work at the conference addressing the current standards of the National Fire Protection Association® and other standard-making groups as applicable. The Validation Conference brings together individuals from several related and allied fields, such as:

- Key fire department executives and training officers
- Educators from colleges and universities
- Representatives from governmental agencies
- Delegates of firefighter associations and industrial organizations

Committee members are not paid nor are they reimbursed for their expenses by IFSTA or Fire Protection Publications. They participate because of commitment to the fire service and its future through training. Being on a committee is prestigious in the fire service community, and committee members are acknowledged leaders in their fields. This unique feature provides a close relationship between the International Fire Service Training Association and fire protection agencies, which helps to correlate the efforts of all concerned.

IFSTA manuals are now the official teaching texts of most of the states and provinces of North America. Additionally, numerous U.S. and Canadian government agencies as well as other English-speaking countries have officially accepted the IFSTA manuals.

ISBN 978-0-87939-403-5   *Library of Congress Control Number: 2010942571*

Fifth Edition, First Printing, February 2011   *Printed in the United States of America*

10   9   8   7   6   5   4   3   2   1

If you need additional information concerning the International Fire Service Training Association (IFSTA) or Fire Protection Publications, contact:

Customer Service, Fire Protection Publications, Oklahoma State University
930 North Willis, Stillwater, OK 74078-8045
800-654-4055   Fax: 405-744-8204

For assistance with training materials, to recommend material for inclusion in an IFSTA manual, or to ask questions or comment on manual content, contact:

Editorial Department, Fire Protection Publications, Oklahoma State University
930 North Willis, Stillwater, OK 74078-8045
405-744-4111   Fax: 405-744-4112   E-mail: editors@osufpp.org

Chapter Summary

Table of Contents

X

List of Tables

Preface

This fifth edition of **Fire and Emergency Services Orientation and Terminology** is written to provide information for newcomers about the history, organization, and work of the fire service. It will assist the newcomer in meeting some of the objectives outlined in NFPA® 1001, *Standard for Fire Fighter Professional Qualifications,* 2008 edition. It will also help the newcomer learn the objectives outlined in the FESHE *Principles of Emergency Services* course.

Acknowledgments and special thanks are extended to the members of the material review committee who contributed their time, wisdom, and knowledge to the development of this new fifth edition of **Fire and Emergency Services Orientation and Terminology.**

IFSTA Fire and Emergency Services Orientation and Terminology Fifth Edition Validation Committee

Chair

Rick McIntyre, CFO
Fire Chief
City of Jacksonville Fire Department
Jacksonville, NC

Vice-Chair/Secretary

Mark Butterfield
Faculty Member/Instructor
Hutchinson Community College Fire Science
Hutchinson, KS

Contract Writer

Pamela Powell
Technical Writer and Editor
Sheldonville, MA

Committee Members

John Blaschik, Jr.
Commissioner
East Haddam Fire Department
East Haddam, CT

Heidi Heavner
Fire/Rescue Training Specialist
North Carolina Office of State Fire Marshal
Raleigh, NC

Frank A. Carter II
Consultant
Ergometrics and Applied Personnel Research
Lynnwood, WA

Howard C. Holt
Captain
Oakland Fire Department
Oakland, CA

Brent Foss
Deputy Fire Chief
DeForest Area Fire & EMS
DeForest, WI

Merlin Klassen
Instructor
Lakeland College
Edmonton, AB, Canada

Committee Members (continued)

John D. Reed, Jr.
Battalion Chief
Fulton County Fire Rescue Department
Atlanta, GA

Derrick Sawyer
Battalion Chief
Philadelphia Fire Department
Philadelphia, PA

Don Turno
Fire Protection Engineering / Program Manager
Savannah River Nuclear Solutions
Aiken, SC

Special thanks are given to Pamela Powell for her skillful writing, editing, and expertise. Grateful thanks are also extended to the following organizations and individuals who contributed information, photographs, and technical assistance that were instrumental in the development of this manual:

American Emergency Vehicles (AEV)

Biomarine, Incorporated
    J. Douglas Anderson

Collin College, McKinney, TX
    Pat McAuliff

Congressional Fire Service Institute
    William M. Webb, Executive Director

Federal Emergency Management Agency
    Dianna Gee

Fireman's Hall Museum, Philadelphia, PA
    Henry J. Magee, Curator

Fulton County (GA) Fire Rescue Department
    John Reed, Jr., Battalion Chief
    Dennis L. Martin
    Reginald I. King
    William J. Gazawky, Jr.
    Christopher Price
    Terrance Williams

Johnson County RFD #1, Clarksville, AR
    Dayna Hilton

Lake Ozark (MO) Fire District

Las Vegas (NV) Fire and Rescue

McKinney (TX) Fire Department
    Mark Wallace, Fire Chief
    Ron Moore, Training Officer
    Jared Mounger
    Troy Underwood

National Fallen Firefighters Foundation (NFFF)

National Institute for Occupational Safety and Health (NIOSH)

National Institute of Standards and Technology (NIST)

National Fire Academy and United States Fire Administration
    Robert Neale
    Tom Olshanski

The Nethercutt Collection, Sylmar, CA
    Jack Nethercutt
    Lori Thornhill

Neutronics, Inc.
    Doug Anderson

Ontario Office of the Fire Marshal
    Bev Gilbert
    Sophie Greco
    Carol Jones-Simmons
    Martha Murphy

Philadelphia (PA) Fire Department
    Derrick Sawyer, Battalion Chief

Stillwater (OK) Fire Department
    Marion Blackwell, Fire Chief
    Rex Mott, Assistant Chief of Operations
    Trent Hawkins, Fire Marshall
    Robert Black, Training Officer
    Eric Seeliger, Battalion Chief
    Jay Willis, Battalion Chief
    Terry Essary
    Morris German
    Chad Hane
    Todd Hinkle
    Todd Jones
    Kevin Roach
    James Roe
    Tyler Sparks
    Steve Sylvester

Stillwater (OK) Office of Emergency Management
    Rob Hill
    Joe Minnick

Tulsa (OK) Fire Department
    R.B. Ellis,
    Jerry Gibbens

United States Coast Guard
    Petty Officer 3rd Class Lauren Downs

United States Navy
    Chief Mass Communication Specialist
    Bill Mesta

Steve Baker
Robert Billen
Ted Boothroyd
Frank A. Carter II
Wayne Chapdlaine
Chas Fagan
Dick Giles
Donny Howard
Ron Jeffers
Edwin A. Jones, USAFR
John Lewis
Steve Loftin

Very special thanks are also extended to the faculty and staff of the Oklahoma Fire Service Training's Professional Skills Center for their timely and efficient assistance on this manual.

    Bryan West
    Rudee Cryer
    Dusty Harkin
    Rhett Strain
    Brad Talley
    Chris Tivis

Last, but certainly not least, gratitude is also extended to the members of the Fire Protection Publications **Fire and Emergency Services Orientation and Terminology**, 5th Edition, Project Team whose contributions made the final publication of this manual possible.

Fire and Emergency Services Orientation and Terminology, 5th Edition, Project Team

Project Manager
Jeff Fortney, Senior Editor

Instructional Developer
Elkie Burnside, Instructional Developer

Technical Writer
Pamela A. Powell

Sheldonville, MA

Editorial Reviewer
Clint Clausing, Senior Editor

Technical Reviewer
Tim Stemple, Fire Chief

Air Force Plant 4

Production Manager
Ann Moffat, Coordinator,

Publications Production

Illustrators and Layout Designers
Errick Braggs, Senior Graphic Designer

Ben Brock, Senior Graphic Designer

Missy Hannan, Senior Graphic Designer

Ruth Mudroch, Senior Graphic Designer

Clint Parker, Senior Graphic Designer

Curriculum Development
Andrea Haken, Instructional Developer

Elkie Burnside, Instructional Developer

FPP Photography
Jeff Fortney, Senior Editor

Ed Kirtley, IFSTA Projects and Curriculum Coordinator

Fred Stowell, Senior Editor

Mike Sturzenbecker, Senior Editor

Mike Wieder, Managing Editor

Editorial Assistant
Tara Gladden

Library Researchers
Susan F. Walker, FPP Librarian

Chris Hayden, Graduate Assistant

Research Technicians
Gabriel Ramirez

The IFSTA Executive Board at the time of validation of the **Fire and Emergency Services Orientation and Terminology** manual was as follows:

IFSTA Executive Board

Executive Board Chair

Jeffrey Morrissette
State Fire Administrator
Commission on Fire Prevention and Control
Windsor Locks, CT

Vice Chair

Paul Valentine
Fire Marshal
Mt. Prospect Fire Department
Mt. Prospect, IL

Executive Director

Mike Wieder
Fire Protection Publications
Oklahoma State University
Stillwater, OK

Board Members

Stephen Ashbrock
Fire Chief
Madeira & Indian Hill Fire Department
Cincinnati, OH

Steve Austin
Project Manager
Cumberland Valley Volunteer Fireman's Association
Newark, DE

Roxanne Bercik
Assistant Chief
Los Angeles Fire Department
Long Beach, CA

Mary Cameli
Assistant Chief
City of Mesa Fire Department
Mesa, AZ

Bradd Clark
Fire Chief
Owasso Fire Department
Owasso, OK

Chief Dennis Compton
National Fallen Firefighters Foundation
Mesa & Phoenix, AZ

Frank L. Cotton
Battalion Chief
Memphis Fire Department
Memphis, TN

Chief George Dunkel
Special Districts Association of Oregon
St. Helens, OR

John Hoglund
Director Emeritus
Maryland Fire & Rescue Institute
College Park, MD

Wes Kitchel
Captain
Santa Rosa Fire Department
Santa Rosa, CA

Introduction

Introduction Contents

Introduction

From a broad perspective, the purpose of the fire service is to protect life and property from the effects of fire and other hazards. This is accomplished by such activities as fire prevention, fire suppression, public fire education, fire investigation, hazardous materials mitigation, and emergency medical services. Obviously, firefighters today do much more than fight fires. Most of them are trained to provide emergency medical care, and many are additionally trained in special skills such as water rescue, heavy rescue, hazardous materials response, and disaster response. All of these areas require intensive training if firefighters are to respond efficiently and safely. For example, emergency medical incidents must be handled much like hazardous materials incidents in order to protect both victims and rescuers.

New firefighters must become acquainted with all of the responsibilities of their job. They must understand the organizational structure of their departments and learn how their departments interact with other local, state, or provincial agencies. It is also useful if the firefighter understands some of the history associated with the fire service.

Firefighter candidates can enter the fire service several ways. They may be hired by one of the career departments that protect larger communities throughout North America. However, the majority of new firefighters are those who join the ranks of the volunteer service. Volunteer fire departments protect the major portion of North America. Others may join industrial fire brigades. Regardless of the mode of entry, all firefighters need proper orientation and training in basic skills.

Purpose and Scope

The purpose of this manual is to meet the learning outcomes of the National Fire Academy (NFA) Fire and Emergency Services Higher Education (FESHE) *Principles of Emergency Services* course. In addition, information in the manual addresses numerous requisite knowledge items identified in Chapter 5, Fire Fighter I, and Chapter 6, Fire Fighter II, of NFPA® 1001, *Standard for Fire Fighter Professional Qualifications*.

The scope of this manual is to acquaint new firefighters with the history, traditions, terminology, organization, and operation of the fire and emergency services. In addition, the manual contains typical job and operation descriptions that should provide insight into the inner workings of the fire service. An extensive fire and emergency services glossary is included.

Manual Organization

The 5th edition of **Fire and Emergency Services Orientation and Terminology** gathers the knowledge, skills, and abilities listed into 10 chapters. The chapters include:

Chapter 1   Fire and Emergency Services as a Career

Chapter 2   Roles of Fire and Emergency Services Personnel

Chapter 3   Early Traditions and History

Chapter 4   Fire Investigation, Fire Prevention, and Public Fire and Life Safety Education

Chapter 5   Scientific Terminology

Chapter 6   Building Construction

Chapter 7   Fire Detection, Alarm, and Suppression Systems

Chapter 8   Roles of Public and Private Support Organizations

Chapter 9   Fire and Emergency Services Apparatus, Equipment, and Facilities

Chapter 10   Fire Department Organization and Management

Learning objectives located at the beginning of each chapter will assist the reader in focusing on the appropriate topic and knowledge. The Fire and Emergency Services Higher Education (FESHE) *Principles of Emergency Services* course outcomes and the Job Performance Reguirement (JPR) numbers of the JPRs are also listed at the beginning of chapters where they are referenced. **Appendix A** contains a guide that coordinates the FESHE *Principles of Emergency Services* course outcomes to the chapter and page number that relates to the requirements. Appendix A also contains a list of NFPA® 1001 Chapters 5 and 6 JPRs correlated to the chapters and pages where they are referenced.

Study questions are located at the end of each chapter to ensure that the reader has a good comprehension of the material in the chapter. The questions are based on the learning objectives. Please note that these questions should not be used for certification or course examinations. **Appendix B** provides a description of the Candidate Physical Ability Test (CPAT) program. **Appendix C** contains the article: *Prehospital 9-1-1 Emergency Medical Response: The Role of the United States Fire Service in Delivery and Coordination.* **Appendix D** lists the 16 Firefighter Life Safety Initiatives developed by the Firefighter Life Safety Summit in 2004. **Appendix E** contains a sample Incident Command System (ICS) organizational chart.

Resources

Additional educational resources to supplement this manual are available from the International Fire Service Training Association (IFSTA) and Fire Protection Publications (FPP). These resources include an instructional packaged composed of chapter lessonplans, PowerPoint® presentations, and test questions.

Terminology

IFSTA has traditionally provided training materials that are used throughout the U.S. and Canada. In recent years, the sales of IFSTA materials have expanded into a truly international market and resulted in the translation of materials into German, French, Spanish, Japanese, Hebrew, Turkish, and Italian. Writing the manuals, therefore, requires the use of *Global English* that consists of words and terms that can be easily translated into multiple languages and cultures.

This manual is written with the global market as well as the North American market in mind. Traditional fire service terminology, referred to as *jargon*, must give way to more precise descriptions and definitions. Where jargon is appropriate, it will be used along with its definition. The glossary at the end of the manual will also assist the reader in understanding words that may not have their roots in the fire and emergency services. The sources for the definitions of fire-and-emergency-services-related terms will be the *NFPA® Dictionary of Terms*.

NFPA® Copyright Permission

One of the basic purposes of IFSTA manuals is to allow fire service personnel and their departments to meet the requirements set forth by NFPA® codes and standards. These NFPA® documents may be referred to throughout this manual. References to information from NFPA® codes and standards are used with permission from National Fire Protection Association®, Quincy, MA 02169. This referenced material is not the complete and official position of the National Fire Protection Association® on the referenced subject which is represented only by the standard in its entirety.

Key Information

Various types of information in this book are given in shaded boxes marked by symbols or icons. See the following examples:

Information

Information boxes give facts that are complete in themselves but belong with the text discussion. It is information that may need more emphasis or separation. They can be summaries of points, examples, calculations, scenarios, or lists of advantages/disadvantages.

Safety Alert

Safety alerts provide additional emphasis on matters of safety.

Three key signal words are found in the book: **WARNING, CAUTION,** and **NOTE.** Definitions and examples of each are as follows:

- **WARNING** indicates information that could result in death or serious injury. See the following example:

> **WARNING!**
> Any clothing saturated with a cryogenic material must be removed immediately, particularly if the vapors are flammable or oxidizing. The industrial fire brigade member could not escape flames from clothing-trapped vapors if the vapors were to ignite.

- **CAUTION** indicates important information or data that fire and emergency services members need to be aware of in order to perform their duties safely. See the following example:

> **CAUTION**
> All personnel working at hazardous materials incidents must use appropriate personal protective equipment, including appropriate respiratory protection equipment.

- **NOTE** indicates important operational information that helps explain why a particular recommendation is given or describes optional methods for certain procedures. See the following example:

NOTE: *Vapor* is a gaseous form of a substance that is normally in a solid or liquid state at room temperature and pressure. It is formed by evaporation from a liquid or sublimation from a solid.

Notice on Use of State and Province

In order to keep sentences uncluttered and easy to read, the word "state" will be used to represent both state and provincial level governments. This usage is applied to this manual for the purposes of brevity and is not intended to address or show preference for only one nation's method of identifying regional governments within its borders.

Fire and Emergency Services as a Career

Chapter Contents

Photo courtesy of Dick Giles.

chapter 1

Key Terms

FESHE Outcomes

This chapter provides information that addresses the outcomes for the Fire and Emergency Services Higher Education (FESHE) *Principles of Emergency Services* course.

3. Differentiate between fire service training and education and explain the value of higher education to the professionalization of the fire service.

5. Identify fire protection and emergency-service careers in both the public and private sector.

11. Recognize the components of career preparation and goal setting.

12. Describe the importance of wellness and fitness as it relates to emergency services.

NFPA® Job Performance Requirements

This chapter provides information that addresses the following job performance requirements of NFPA® 1001, *Standard for Fire Fighter Professional Qualifications* (2008)

5.1.1

Fire and Emergency Services as a Career

Learning Objectives

After reading this chapter, students will be able to:

1. Identify fire protection and emergency-service careers in both the public and private sector.

2. Recognize the components of career preparation and goal setting.

3. Describe the importance of wellness and fitness as it relates to emergency services.

4. Differentiate between fire service training and education, and fire protection certificate program and fire service degree programs.

5. Explain the value of education in the fire service.

6. Summarize the career firefighter selection process.

7. Describe the volunteer firefighter selection process.

Chapter 1
Fire and Emergency Services as a Career

Case History

Tim Nyhan is a senior in high school and is planning his future. He does well in the classroom, and would like a job that lets him go to college part time. He's healthy, physically fit, and good with his hands. Some of his friends are enlisting in the military, but Tim would prefer to live closer to his large extended family. He likes the idea of public service and would be interested in helping the town where he grew up.

The guidance counselor at Tim's school mentioned the fire service as a career possibility. Tim thought that the fire service sounded challenging and exciting – and he welcomed the physical demands that the fire service would put on him. He decided to look into it.

Figure 1.1 Firefighters fighting a structure fire. *Courtesy of Dick Giles.*

Fire fighting is one of the world's most honored but hazardous occupations. It is the duty of every firefighter and every fire department to save lives and to reduce injury and property loss **(Figure 1.1)**. By becoming firefighters, people join a profession that is rich in the heritage of dedication, unselfish sacrifice, and inspired human action. The firefighter's job is not comfortable or easy; it is a profession that exposes an individual to a high level of personal stress and danger. Fire fighting requires a high level of skill, a high sense of personal dedication, and a genuine desire to help people.

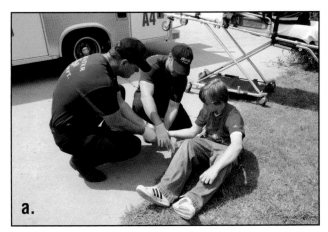

Figures 1.2a - c Firefighters respond to all types of emergencies, including emergency medical responses, water rescues, and aircraft incidents.

There is an old adage that states: "People learn from their mistakes." In the fire service, waiting to learn from mistakes can be fatal. Proper training helps firefighters become proficient in their occupation. However, it is virtually impossible for a firefighter to become completely trained in all areas because the firefighter's education and training cover such a broad spectrum of subjects. Training must remain an ongoing process for all fire service members, for as long as they serve.

Fire and Emergency Services Culture

Whenever there is an emergency, the fire department is one of the first entities called to the scene. In any emergency, there will be hard, fast work required that drains a firefighter's energy and tests his or her endurance. Emergencies involve not only fires but also such incidents as medical emergencies, cave-ins, building collapses, motor vehicle accidents, aircraft crashes, tornadoes, hazardous materials incidents, civil disturbances, terrorist attacks, rescue operations, explosions, and water incidents **(Figures 1.2 a - c)**. The list of potential emergencies is unlimited.

Firefighters are public servants who are expected to calmly evaluate the situation and bring it to a successful conclusion. As a result of their efforts, firefighters come to know sincere thanks, human kindness, misunderstanding, frustration, sadness, helplessness, and disappointment. They will see and know unrestricted emotion, destruction, foolishness, pain, and death. From the first time an emergency situation is encountered until the last day of service, firefighters are expected by the public to perform heroically. Firefighters are not extraordinary -- they are ordinary people who often find themselves in extraordinary situations.

Safety Alert

In the fire service, safety is "job one." In addition to their responsibilities to the public, firefighters are accountable for their own safety and for the safety of their fellow firefighters.

Types of Fire Service Positions

There are several types of fire departments: career, volunteer, combination, paid-on-call, and public safety. Career fire departments primarily protect larger towns and cities. Volunteer fire departments are most commonly found in small and rural communities, although volunteers may supplement career personnel in larger communities. Volunteer fire departments and their firefighters greatly outnumber career departments and their firefighters. In all, it is estimated that there are over 30,000 public fire departments in North America. In the United States, 14 percent of all departments are all career or mostly career but protect 61 percent of the U.S. population, while 86 percent of all departments are mostly volunteer or all volunteer and protect 39 percent of the population **(Figure 1.3)** In addition to public fire departments, large private industries – especially those with extensive facilities or hazardous materials or processes – have their own fire departments.

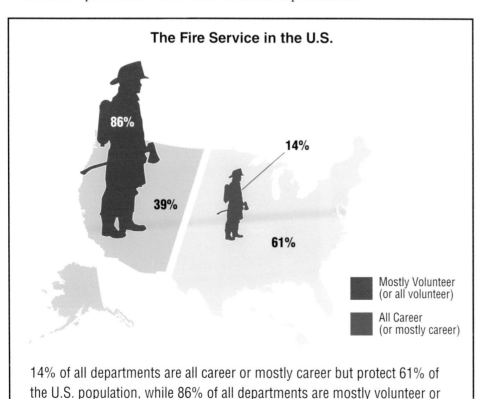

Figure 1.3 The differences between career (or mostly career) fire departments and volunteer departments in terms of percentage of departments and percentage of the population protected.

Career Firefighter —Person whose primary employment is as a firefighter within a fire department.

Regardless of the type of fire department or whether the jurisdiction is public or private, the department must be adequately staffed in order to function. Some firefighters are **career firefighters,** indicating that is their full-time job. Other firefighters may be paid per call or on a strictly voluntary basis and receive no compensation at all. In this context, the term *professional* refers to a level of competence or expertise and may apply equally to those firefighters who are paid for their services and to volunteers. A department may be fully staffed with career personnel, with volunteer personnel, or with a combination of career and volunteer personnel.

Career Departments

Career Fire Department — Fire department composed of full-time, paid personnel.

Most larger cities, and some medium-sized cities, counties, and fire protection districts operate full-time, **career fire departments** — that is, the jurisdiction maintains facilities and equipment to support fire protection and employs firefighters and other personnel to provide fire protection and related services. The firefighters are paid a salary, usually based on an hourly rate, and they work for the department as their principal place of employment. Some firefighters may receive incentives in the form of wage increases for achieving certain fire service or EMS certifications, fire department rank/position, longevity, and college hours or degrees.

Another characteristic of career fire departments is that their fire stations are staffed around the clock. Emergency response personnel live in the fire stations while they are on duty (**Figures 1.4 a and b**). Some career departments employ personnel on a part-time basis to supplement the response force during peak emergency periods based on the time of day, the day of the week, or the season. The department may also maintain administrative offices that work more conventional business hours.

NOTE: See the section on Work Schedules later in this chapter for more information about firefighter schedules.

Figures 1.4a and b In departments where fire stations are staffed around the clock, firefighters work, eat, relax, and study together while they are on duty.

Figure 1.5 The fire station of a volunteer fire department.

Volunteer Departments

Another classification of fire department is the volunteer organization. This type of structure is principally found in smaller towns and rural communities. A **volunteer fire department** may operate as a department of the local government, but some are totally independent from government agencies within the areas they serve. In some cases, a town may provide a facility to be used as a fire station and buy and maintain fire-suppression equipment **(Figure 1.5)**. In other cases, the volunteer organization meets its expenses without support from municipal funds. Money may come from donations, subscription fees paid by people in the community, billing for all or part of response costs, and fund-raising events, such as bake sales, pancake breakfasts, dinners, dances, or fairs.

Oversight of the volunteer organization comes from the local entity that supports the department or from an independent association or governing board. However, some volunteer organizations are corporations governed by boards of directors. In most cases, volunteer organizations do not maintain staffed fire stations, and **volunteer firefighters** respond from home or work to emergencies when summoned by pagers, telephone calls, or a community signal. Designated personnel go to the fire station and drive the apparatus to the emergency scene, while others may report to the fire station or directly to the scene. Most communities in the United States receive fire protection through volunteer fire organizations.

Combination Departments

A **combination fire department** can take different forms. For example, a mostly volunteer organization may pay drivers or may pay part of the salary of a telecommunicator while law enforcement pays the rest. In another form of combination department, a career department may also maintain a cadre of volunteers trained in areas such as fire suppression, rescue, emergency medical care, or scene control. In some combination departments, there are more paid firefighters than volunteer firefighters. In some, the highest-ranking officer is a volunteer and exerts primary control over the department; in others, a career chief exercises control. So, the distribution of responsibilities and the relative percentages of paid and unpaid personnel can vary greatly from one combination department to another.

Volunteer Fire Department — Organization of part-time firefighters who may receive monetary compensation for on-call time or fire fighting duty time.

Volunteer Firefighter — Active member of a fire department who may receive monetary compensation for on-call time and/or fire fighting duty time. *Also spelled* Volunteer Fire Fighter.

Combination Fire Department — Organization in which some of the firefighters receive pay while other personnel serve on a voluntary basis. In Canada, a combination fire department is called a Composite Department.

Combination departments provide staffing and receive funding in accordance with the dominant aspect of their organization — that is, combination departments that are operated primarily as full-time, career departments tend to staff their stations around the clock and use budgeted tax dollars to fund their operations, while those that are primarily volunteer organizations tend to have no one or only limited numbers of personnel residing in their fire stations.

Paid-On-Call Departments

Some firefighters work on an on-call basis. Under this structure, a firefighter does not stay at the fire station, but is summoned to the fire station or emergency scene by a mobile telephone call, pager, PDA device, or community signal (such as a siren). **Paid-on-call firefighters** are paid for responding, usually with an hourly wage or with a set fee per response. This approach to compensation may also be used to pay part-time personnel in career or combination departments, or to pay compensated personnel in volunteer departments. In some cases, departments are actually operated on a paid-on-call basis.

Functionally, the paid-on-call department resembles a volunteer organization: the fire stations are minimally staffed and fire-suppression personnel are normally summoned to the emergency scene or fire station by pagers, telephones, or community signals. Fiscally, paid-on-call resembles a career department because most or all paid-on-call department funding comes from a local government agency or association.

Public Safety Departments

In most **public safety departments**, the fire command/management officers, company officers, and apparatus driver/operators are career, fire personnel. On a given shift they may function as police officers or as firefighters according to staffing needs.

Industrial Fire Departments

Some large industrial and manufacturing facilities, as well as facilities with hazardous operations or processes (such as refineries or power generating plants) have their own fire departments, sometimes called **industrial fire departments**, **fire brigades**, **industrial fire brigades**, **emergency response organizations**, or emergency response teams **(Figure 1.6)**. Some industrial fire departments can be quite large.

Industrial firefighters must meet NFPA® 1081, *Standard for Industrial Fire Brigade Member Professional Qualifications.* In addition, industrial fire brigades in the United States must comply with Occupational Safety and Health Administration (OSHA) regulations contained in *CFR 1910.156, Fire Brigades,* which cover the organization, training, and personal protective equipment of industrial fire brigades established by employers.

Like career or volunteer departments, industrial fire departments have a specific structure, membership requirements, rules of conduct, and required training. Standard operating procedures (SOPs) for fire vehicles, water systems, fixed equipment, hose handling and equipment operation, tank firefighting, and inspection of bunker gear also exist. For further information on industrial fire fighting, please refer to IFSTA's **Industrial Emergency Services Training: Incipient Level** and **Industrial Exterior and Structural Fire Brigades** manuals.

Figure 1.6 Members of an industrial fire brigade during a training evolution.

Fire Service Career Information

Personnel entering the fire service often have questions regarding the fire service career field that relate to pay, work schedules, promotions, retirements, and other benefits. While each locality handles these issues differently, we can provide some general information about these topics in the sections that follow.

Pay

Fire service salaries vary by area of the country, municipality, rank within the department, certifications, and length of service. According to CareerBuilder. com, entry level firefighters in the United States typically earn an average of $22,000-30,000 annually. Firefighters in more prosperous jurisdictions and in major metropolitan areas will typically earn more than firefighters in poorer or rural areas.

Work Schedules

Career firefighters work a variety of schedules. Very few work the typical eight-hour shifts found in other professions. Most firefighters work a different, longer scheduled shift. The first thing upon which the work schedule depends is the number of shifts the department uses. Fire departments may have a two-, three-, or four-shift system. Two-shift systems are fairly rare in the public fire service, although much of the American military fire service still operates with two shifts. The most common work schedule for each shift under the two-shift system is a straight 24 hours on duty and 24 hours off duty.

Industrial Fire Brigade — Team of employees organized within a private company, industrial facility, or plant who are assigned to respond to fires and emergencies on that property.

Emergency Response Organization — Fire brigade or emergency medical response team.

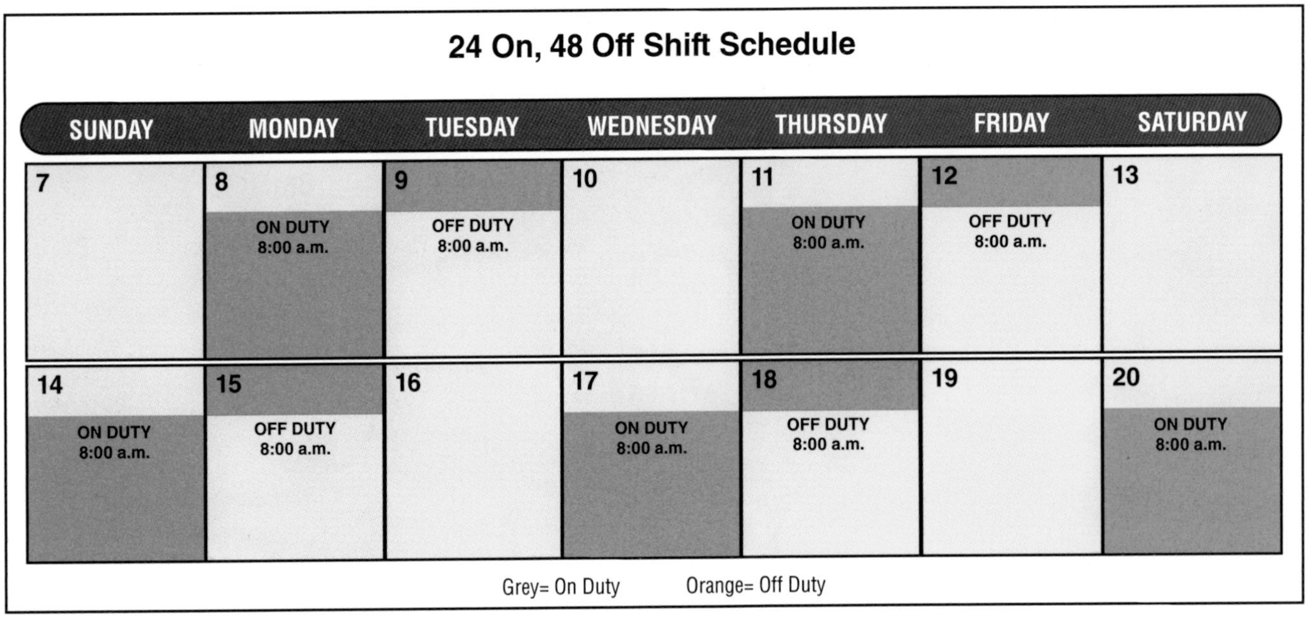

24 On, 48 Off Shift Schedule

SUNDAY	MONDAY	TUESDAY	WEDNESDAY	THURSDAY	FRIDAY	SATURDAY
7	8 ON DUTY 8:00 a.m.	9 OFF DUTY 8:00 a.m.	10	11 ON DUTY 8:00 a.m.	12 OFF DUTY 8:00 a.m.	13
14 ON DUTY 8:00 a.m.	15 OFF DUTY 8:00 a.m.	16	17 ON DUTY 8:00 a.m.	18 OFF DUTY 8:00 a.m.	19	20 ON DUTY 8:00 a.m.

Grey= On Duty   Orange= Off Duty

Figure 1.7 The most common fire department shift is 24 hours on, 48 hours off. Cycle repeats every 3 weeks.

10s and 14s Shift Schedule

SUNDAY	MONDAY	TUESDAY	WEDNESDAY	THURSDAY	FRIDAY	SATURDAY
7	8 ON DUTY 8:00 a.m. / OFF DUTY 6:00 p.m.	9 ON DUTY 8:00 a.m. / OFF DUTY 6:00 p.m.	10 ON DUTY 6:00 p.m.	11 OFF DUTY 8:00 a.m. / ON DUTY 6:00 p.m.	12 OFF DUTY 8:00 a.m.	13
14	15	16 ON DUTY 8:00 a.m. / OFF DUTY 6:00 p.m.	17 ON DUTY 8:00 a.m. / OFF DUTY 6:00 p.m.	18 ON DUTY 6:00 p.m.	19 OFF DUTY 8:00 a.m. / ON DUTY 6:00 p.m.	20 OFF DUTY 8:00 a.m.

Grey= On Duty   Orange= Off Duty

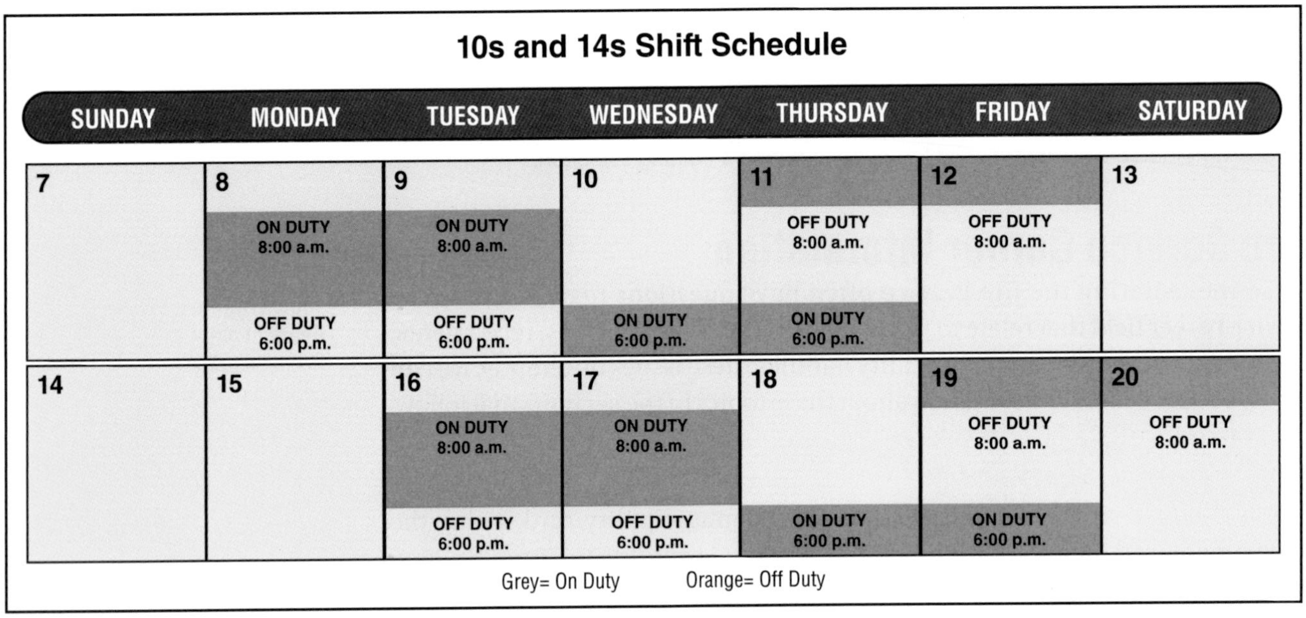

Figure 1.8 In four-platoon systems, a work schedule of 10 hours for day shifts and 14 hours for night shifts is common. Cycle repeats every 3 weeks.

The majority of the North American career fire service operates under the three-platoon system. A variety of work schedules are used under the three-platoon system; however, most revolve around 24-hour work shifts. Although many variations exist, the most common schedule is the straight 24 hours on duty and 48 hours off duty (**Figure 1.7**).

Some cities, particularly large cities with heavy run loads, use a four-platoon system. Most commonly, the four-platoon system revolves around shortened work periods, such as 10-hour day shifts and 14-hour night shifts (or 9 hours and 15 hours) (**Figure 1.8**). Other variations exist, but one common schedule is for a crew to work two day shifts and then two night shifts, followed by four days off. Again, other variations exist.

Volunteer departments may or may not have work schedules. Most smaller departments depend on all volunteers to respond any time they are available. Larger volunteer organizations and those with paid-call firefighters may have personnel assigned to duty crews that respond only during specific times.

Promotion

With promotion comes increased pay and responsibility within the department. Promotion in the fire service was once based largely on seniority. Now, particularly in the career fire service, promotion is often based on acquiring more complex skills and competencies gained through training and education. Typically, an examination or certification measures the candidate's new skills. More information can be found in the Firefighter Certification section later in this chapter and in Chapter 2, Roles of Fire and Emergency Services Personnel, which describes various fire service positions.

Retirement and Other Benefits

A wide variety of retirement programs exist for career and volunteer firefighters. The specifics of each program vary from state to state, from province to province, and from municipality to municipality. Some combination of years of service and age often determines retirement compensation. Many departments adhere to the policy of retirement at 55 years of age with 20 years of service. For those department members who serve over 20 years, increases in retirement pay may be made. Additional benefits may include group health and life insurance coverage and a survivor's benefits package for the spouse or other beneficiary of the retiree. Many departments allow early retirement at a reduced amount of pay.

Volunteer firefighters in most states and provinces are also eligible for certain retirement benefits. These vary widely but are usually linked to the years of service provided by the retiree to the department. These programs are often referred to as Length of Service Awards (LOSA) programs. In some cases, the program funding is supplemented by the county or state government.

In addition to salary and retirement benefits, personnel in career fire departments are likely to receive benefits that may include life and medical insurance, paid vacation and sick leave, uniform allowances, prescription assistance/coverage, and deferred compensation plans. Assistance with certain educational expenses and employee assistance programs that provide access to counseling services for firefighters and their families are also provided. Some or all of the department staff may work for the city under a periodically renewed contract, which is often negotiated on behalf of the workers by a labor union.

Firefighters as Public Figures

Whether volunteers or career, firefighters are public figures and are expected to meet certain standards of responsible behavior, conduct, image, fitness, uniform and dress, human and customer relations, and teamwork. Firefighters rely on each other for their safety and survival which makes it critical that these standards are followed.

Responsible Behaviors for Firefighters

In any profession, adopting a proper attitude is a key factor in an individual's attempt to be successful. Like most occupations, the fire service has its code of ethics and standards of behavior with which compliance is expected. Life in the fire department brings the members close together during working hours. Firefighters eat, live, and spend time together while on duty. Volunteer firefighters also spend a considerable amount of time together during training, emergency incidents, and fundraising. As a result, these groups tend to establish their own values and norms and make social and labor judgments based on the standards formed. The following suggestions may be important for a successful career in the fire service and may also be helpful in providing some basic ideas for a smooth transition into the career field:

Freelancing — Operating independently of the incident commander's command and control.

- *Be sincerely interested in and dedicated to the job* — To properly perform in the fire service, firefighters must have a high degree of personal commitment. Selfish interests have no place in the fire service. Only through a group effort can the protection of the public be accomplished. In many cases, such as interior structural fire fighting, failure to work as a team (**freelancing**) can be deadly. Cooperation is the key - each person must be willing to work in the position assigned and be dedicated to the performance of the duties of that position.

- *Be loyal to the fire department and to fellow firefighters* —Firefighters should understand their department's policies and functions and be prepared to implement and defend them. To fail to do so is a failure to defend oneself. Firefighters are also representatives of the department, and their dress and actions should be a credit to their department. As individuals who depend on each other for safety, firefighters must develop loyalty to the other members of the department and band together.

- *Be aggressive in the pursuit of all education and training opportunities* — Firefighters are never completely trained. A firefighter's training is an ongoing process that lasts until the individual leaves the fire service (**Figure 1.9**). There is no such thing as an "overeducated" firefighter. Individuals participating in the fire fighting profession must display a willingness to obtain as much career education as possible.

- *Guard speech both on and off duty* — As members of the department, firefighters possess information that should not be revealed. Firefighters should use discretion while discussing information that could have a negative effect on the department or individuals on the department. This does not mean, however, that firefighters should not discuss the functions, history, and traditions of the fire service with the public.

- *Be the type of person who inspires confidence and respect* — Firefighters must strive to be honest, fair, and trustworthy when dealing with fellow firefighters and supervisors, and the public. Dependability is a must in the fire service - others rely on it.

- *Be able to accept criticism graciously, and accept praise, honors, and advancement modestly* — There is no perfect firefighter. Everyone makes mistakes. Legitimate and constructive criticism of mistakes is not a cause for anger. In fact, it should be welcomed because improvement is the name of the game. With improvement comes honors and advancement; accept these with humility and in a manner that will not alienate others.

Figure 1.9 Firefighters undergoing rope rescue training.

- *Ask questions* — If any aspect of instruction is unclear, ask the supervisor specific questions concerning those areas in which information is incomplete or not understood. This is the most effective way for an exchange of information to take place.

Health Insurance Portability and Accountability Act (HIPAA)

The Health Insurance Portability and Accountability Act of 1996 (HIPAA) includes safeguards for patient privacy including medical information. As caregivers, members of the fire service should be aware of the need to keep all patient information confidential and never discuss patient information.

Conduct

Members of the fire service must conduct themselves properly in order for the department to function safely as a team in an emergency and to maintain a positive public image. Fire department members should always report for duty in good mental and physical condition, ready to work safely. They should never be permitted to report for duty while impaired by alcohol or any drug. Off-duty members should not appear at any station in an intoxicated condition. Scuffling, horseplay, or any other form of physical encounter incompatible with accepted standards of conduct should be prohibited in or around any fire department facility. Fire department members should avoid swearing and rudeness while on duty. The general rule for new firefighters is to use good judgment and follow fire department protocols when it comes to their behavior.

NOTE: No activity that could compromise firefighter or public safety or lower the public's or the local government's respect for the department can ever be tolerated.

Firefighters are expected to adhere to the following rules of conduct:

- Be ready to perform duties and avoid absences from duty without specific permission from the company officer.
- Arrive on time and prepared for all required training, meetings, or other activities.
- Follow all orders from superiors.
- Be respectful and courteous to all members of the department.
- Be respectful and courteous to the general public.
- Establish and maintain effective working relationships with other firefighters, other public employees, and the general public.

The Firefighter Image

The public's view of the fire service constantly changes. In recent years, the firefighter's image has improved beyond drinking coffee and playing checkers while "waiting for the bell to ring" to being proactive and visible members of the community. New firefighters need to realize that their public image is essential to successfully conducting everyday activities.

Firefighters are often considered the most helpful people in the neighborhood. The qualities that make them firefighters rub off onto their everyday activities and associations. Much is expected of them, and they usually live up to these expectations. Because of public exposure, firefighters should not indulge in behavior that would lower public opinion of them. All in all, the position of a firefighter can be summed up as one in which expectations are high. Firefighters should try to be the type of people of whom their families, the department, and the public can be proud.

Physical Fitness

Firefighters must be able to perform many complex and crucial tasks quickly and without error. At a fire scene, the tasks that need to be accomplished require quick thinking, agility, skill, and speed. These tasks can only be performed effectively if firefighters have the physical ability to perform them. This is why physical conditioning is so important. It is vital that firefighters be in top physical and mental condition, both for their own safety and for the safety of others (**Figure 1.10**).

Medical and physical requirements are usually high for gaining entrance into a fire department. Often these requirements are based on NFPA® 1582, *Standard on Medical Requirements for Fire Fighters*. Recruits are selected and then put through strenuous training in basic firefighter school. After the initial period, however, most departments decrease their physical condition requirements. Only recently have fire departments started to increase their

Figure 1.10 Physical fitness training is an important part of a firefighter's routine.

expectations concerning fitness. While experience can compensate to some degree for the vigor of youth, there is no excuse for older firefighters to be in poor physical condition.

Remaining Physically Fit

Firefighting is physically demanding work. Many firefighter injuries and illnesses are related to poor physical conditioning. Lack of fitness endangers the individual and the team, makes it more difficult to perform fire fighting duties, and decreases the chance of success.

Uniforms and Dress

Appropriate dress is usually defined in the department regulations, which may include requirements for dress uniform, station work clothing, and protective clothing. The dress uniform, sometimes referred to as the Class A uniform, is used for public appearances, special events, parades, inspections, and some social functions. A dress uniform generally consists of a uniform pant and jacket, white shirt for officers, colored shirt for firefighters, tie, black shoes, appropriate department insignia, badge, name tag, and uniform hat.

Figure 1.11 Fire departments may issue different types of uniforms. Shown here are a firefighter in a common station work uniform (left), an officer in a business casual style uniform (center), and a firefighter in a workout uniform (right).

Figure 1.12 Firefighters wearing standard structural fire fighting protective clothing and self-contained breathing apparatus (SCBA) during a training evolution.

Station work clothing comes in several forms (**Figure 1.11**). Work clothes are usually worn while on duty or on special work details. Some departments prefer the uniform-type work clothing. Others wear collared shirts or tee shirts and cotton or flame-resistant trousers. Coveralls may be worn for especially dirty work. Regardless of the style that the fire department chooses, all work uniforms must comply with the requirements set forth in NFPA® 1975, *Standard on Station/Work Uniforms for Fire and Emergency Services*. Additional information on station work uniforms can be found in Chapter 9, Fire and Emergency Services Apparatus, Equipment, and Facilities.

Volunteer firefighters do not usually have the opportunity to wear an approved work uniform when responding to an emergency. However, volunteer departments are encouraged to establish guidelines for proper dress when responding to an alarm. When possible, natural fibers such as cotton or wool are preferred.

All firefighters must wear personal protective clothing when responding to and working at emergencies. Full personal protective clothing consists of a turnout coat and pants, helmet, protective hood, eye protection, hearing protection, boots, and gloves for fire fighting. When working in atmospheres that are hazardous or have the potential to become so, firefighters must wear self-contained breathing apparatus (SCBA) and personal alert safety systems (PASS devices) (**Figure 1.12**). Additional information on personal protective closing and self-contained breathing apparatus can be found in Chapter 9, Fire and Emergency Services Apparatus, Equipment, and Facilities.

Human Relations and Customer Service

Both inside and beyond the fire department firefighters function in a diverse world. Co-workers and the public can be a mosaic of gender, race, religion, socio-economic status, ethnic background, country of origin, sexual preference, and language.

Firefighters must be prepared to work with, cooperate with, and protect all people. Respect for differences is a key part of a successful career and of effective **customer service**.

Effective customer service should generate a feeling that interaction with the fire department is positive, informative, and reassuring: a confidence that all will be well.

Customer Service — Quality of an organization's relationship with individuals who have contact with the organization. There are internal customers such as the various levels of personnel and trainees, and external customers such as other organizations and the public. Customer service is the way these individuals, personnel, and organizations are treated, and their levels of satisfaction.

Figure 1.13 Teamwork is crucial to safe fireground operations.

Teamwork

Teamwork refers to individuals working smoothly together to accomplish a task that is important to the total operation. To work together under conditions where the safety of one member is dependent upon the action of another requires teamwork **(Figure 1.13)**. How the emergency is resolved depends upon teamwork.

A good team has confidence that comes from belief in each team member and in the team. Studying and drilling as a team develops and nurtures this confidence. The strength of the team is the combined strength of each of those firefighters who compose the team. It is possible to evaluate the strength of a team by evaluating the firefighters. Team spirit is the enthusiasm developed through satisfactory teamwork. The contribution of each member of the team is essential to its proper functioning. This includes all facets of ability, confidence, and spirit. Teamwork is based on the following factors:

- Members must have a common desire for success.

- Members should earn the trust of other firefighters.

- Members must demonstrate a high level of personal integrity.

- Members must each contribute to the team.
- Members should know their job function and the job functions of other team members so that they can supplement each other as teammates.
- Members must have two-way communication.
- Members must train together over and over to ensure precision and quickness.

Training and Education

Training and education are required to enter the fire service, to continue in the fire service, and to advance in the fire service. Training is available from the department, county, and state/provincial fire training programs, while colleges and universities and the National Fire Academy provide educational opportunities. Non-traditional training and education is also available. Completion of some courses of study can lead to certificates, certification, or degrees.

The Difference between Training and Education

Training is a supervised activity or process for achieving and maintaining proficiency through instruction and hands-on practice in the operation of equipment and systems that are expected to be used in the performance of assigned duties. Training is also called drilling. **Education**, on the other hand, is a process of teaching, instructing, or training individuals in new skills or additional knowledge or preparing individuals for some kind of action or activity. Education is what teachers do to bring about learning in their students. It may or may not involve formal classroom instruction.

Types of Training

Basically, there are two types of training – classroom study and training drills (**Figures 1.14 a and b**). Classroom study is the fundamental training for acquiring basic knowledge that can be applied to practical applications. A drill is the practical application of classroom techniques and theories and the rehearsal of pre-incident plans, SOPs, and courses of action. The practices are designed to allow firefighters to rehearse safely until a procedure can be performed without error or hesitation. Training is necessary to perfect the fundamentals and execution of the firefighter's duties. These practices are also an important part of the firefighter's protection and safety. Without firefighter drills, precision and perfection are unobtainable and success is impossible.

Departmental Training

The majority of a firefighter's training comes from within his or her fire department. From the career department perspective, a rookie is hired and immediately placed into the department's recruit academy class. In the departmental training academy, the rookie learns the basics of the job so that he or she can then be assigned to a company. Once in the field, a firefighter faces in-service training the rest of his or her career. In-service training comes in many forms, including individual company training, multicompany training sessions,

Figure 1.14a Classroom training imparts valuable knowledge.

Figure 1.14b A live fire training drill allows firefighters to apply what they have learned.

and members returning to the fire department training academy or division for courses. Courses are held to update line personnel on new procedures or equipment and to prepare personnel for promotion.

In larger departments, training activities are coordinated and run through the fire department's training division. The person in charge of the training division is usually called the chief of training. Other personnel, both sworn and civilian, are assigned to the training division as well. Typically, the sworn personnel hold the rank of company officer. Training division personnel are responsible for delivering courses at the academy and coordinating the delivery of company-level training throughout the department.

Small volunteer and career departments may only have one person who is assigned the role of training officer. This person generally has the same responsibilities as the entire training division in the larger departments. In some cases, particularly in very small volunteer departments, the duties of training officer may be in addition to other responsibilities such as those of assistant chief.

Volunteer departments have to pattern their training around the schedules of their members. For this reason, training sessions are often held during the evenings or on weekends. Volunteer departments generally do not have the luxury of sending new members to the same type of recruit academy as their career counterparts. However, new members must not be allowed to respond to emergencies until they have adequate training in the types of activities they will be expected to perform.

Occupational Safety and Health

According to NFPA® 1500, *Standard on Fire Department Occupational Safety and Health Program*, no member (career or volunteer) may be allowed to actively engage in structural fire fighting until he or she has met the requirements contained in NFPA® 1001, *Standard for Fire Fighter Professional Qualifications.*

Figure 1.15 The Alabama Fire College is an example of a state fire service training agency.

County and State/Provincial Fire Training Programs

Many governmental agencies sponsor fire training programs. These training programs may range from occasional seminars to academies with full-time staff and a regular schedule of courses. Training programs are found on the county, parish (Louisiana and Canada), borough (Alaska), and state or provincial levels (**Figure 1.15**).

County, parish, and borough programs are usually found in more populous areas that contain large numbers of small fire departments, particularly volunteer departments. These programs provide a wide variety of basic and advanced courses. In many cases, these courses are comparable to those given at the state academies, and certification may be obtained at the local level.

Many state or provincial fire training programs operate under a university or educational agency, usually vocational. In other cases, the director of fire training operates under the state fire marshal's office. State/provincial fire training agencies may have either a full- or part-time instructional staff. The instructors' responsibilities include assigning and supervising part-time field instructors, developing instructional outlines, developing and producing audiovisual training aids, and monitoring required records.

Many state training agencies have training facilities, and some even provide accommodations in dormitories. Most on-campus courses last a week and cover either a specific subject area or a range of subjects. There are also courses that are offered off- campus and usually are taught by state certified part-time instructors.

Value of Education

The value of a firefighter's education is nearly immeasurable in terms of how it benefits career development. A firefighter usually begins his or her educational experience at the very start of entering the fire service. The rookie begins to study the basics in order to become an entry-level firefighter and first responder. From this point on, it is a constant process of reading, training, studying, practicing, and experiencing skills and scenarios to hone skills and become more proficient. This is a process that never stops. A firefighter can never know everything. This is because the subject matter involved in fire fighting and emergency response is so vast that it is impossible for even the most skilled firefighter to learn everything and retain it without frequently brushing up on skills and information.

Firefighters will also find it beneficial to further their education to a formal level such as associate or bachelor college degrees. Most firefighters come out of these degree programs with the knowledge, skills, and certifications to attain employment in a fire department. Some fire departments even require certain levels of college degrees and/or certifications to be eligible for employment or promotion with a fire department.

Evolving technology is another source and reason for continuous education. Ideas and scenarios are constantly being tried on training grounds and laboratories to improve the safety levels and proficiency of today's firefighters. This is how most of the training that firefighters now receive has come about, either through technology or trial and error (sometimes with tragic errors). Firefighters must always be willing to pay attention and to learn new ways of doing things. They must remain aware of changing procedures and constantly think about safety in their work. The best firefighters must always be willing to learn.

Colleges and Universities

Community and junior colleges throughout North America offer many traditional and online fire science degree programs on either a full- or part-time basis. An associate's degree is normally awarded upon completion of these programs, while some institutions offer a certificate for partial completion.

Also offered are four-year degree programs with emphasis on fire service management, fire protection engineering, or fire protection technology. Some of the more well-known programs of this type in the United States are located at Eastern Kentucky University, Oklahoma State University, the University of Houston-Downtown, University of Maryland, and the University of New Haven. Graduate study programs are available at Oklahoma State University, the University of Maryland, Worcester Polytechnic Institute, Western Oregon University, and Utah Valley University.

There are similar programs in Canada. These programs range from certificates, diplomas, applied degrees, and graduate degrees. The Canadian programs are available in different forms throughout the country. Lakeland College in Alberta is associated with a fire training school and offers an online applied degree.

College fire science programs are usually designed to supplement, not to replace, departmental training. The curriculum design for many such programs emphasizes the arts and sciences, with special courses in fire protection subjects beyond the scope of basic fire training programs. A majority of programs emphasize supervisory and management skills along with fire science. These degree programs are designed to prepare individuals for entry into or promotion within the department. A few colleges emphasize engineering and technology courses with their programs. These programs prepare the individual to participate in the more technical aspects of the fire protection field, such as fire protection system design, building design considerations, and code enforcement.

National Fire Academy (NFA)

The National Fire Academy (NFA) is a center for fire protection related education, information, and expertise. The NFA's aim is to improve the professional development of fire service personnel and allied professionals. The academy, which is operated by the United States Fire Administration (USFA) as part of the Department of Homeland Security, offers a wide variety of courses in the general areas of incident management, fire technology, and fire prevention. These courses are delivered through an on-campus program and an extensive outreach program.

The resident student program consists of courses conducted at the National Emergency Training Center (NETC) in Emmitsburg, Maryland. Students, primarily from the fire service, attend these courses at minimal cost through a stipend program, which pays the cost of tuition, travel, and accommodations in campus dormitories. Most courses are one or two weeks in length and are linked so that the student can advance through different levels in a particular subject or develop expertise in a variety of subjects. The NFA Outreach Program provides for the delivery of short-term (generally two-day) courses to students in locations all over the United States. These courses are usually coordinated through state and local training agencies and are concentrated on weekends to allow maximum participation from both career and volunteer fire service personnel.

Figure 1.16 A firefighter taking an online course.

Non-Traditional Training and Education

Non-traditional training and education can include correspondence or online courses and conferences and seminars. In some cases, it is possible to earn degrees through non-traditional training and education. In other cases, students can earn Continuing Education Units.

Off-campus study through correspondence courses has been available for many years. Many colleges and universities are now using the Internet to offer on-line courses as a means to reach students who may not otherwise take college courses **(Figure 1.16)**. These institutions offer a variety of technical and general education courses over the Internet. Some advantages to such programs include the following:

- Students work on the courses when they can and at their own pace.
- Travel to college/university campuses is reduced.
- The student can take a variety of courses from different institutions in different geographic locations.

Through the NFA's Degrees-at-a-Distance Program, it is possible to complete a bachelor's degree curriculum and earn a degree through on-line study. **Table 1.1 (p. 30)** presents information about colleges and universities that participate in the NFA's Degrees-at-a-Distance program.

A large variety of international, national, state or provincial, regional and county organizations offer conferences and seminars for the fire service. The topics, venues, costs, and quality of instruction varies widely. The best way to determine which offerings are of the highest quality is to talk with people who have attended the same conference or seminar in recent years. Questions to ask include:

- Did the conference or seminar provide good value?
- Did the conference or seminar cover the advertised topics?
- Did the advertised instructors actually teach?
- What was the quality of the instruction?
- What was the quality of the instructional materials?
- What did the students actually learn?
- Were Continuing Education Units provided? (A Continuing Education Unit [CEU] typically represents 10 hours of instruction by an organization recognized by the International Association of Continuing Education and Training.)
- If CEU's are not offered, are certificates of a completion provided?

Firefighter Certification

The term *certification* means to attest authoritatively that an individual has met the qualifications specified in a given standard. The certification of firefighters is important from a liability standpoint. Certification shows that the individual has met the objectives of the applicable standard and should be ready to handle the responsibilities of the job.

The standards that the fire service uses to certify firefighters are developed by the National Fire Protection Association® (NFPA®) and are commonly referred to as the Professional Qualifications (Pro-Qual) Standards. These standards are consensus documents that are developed by other members of the fire service. The following is a list of the professional qualifications standards used by the fire service:

- NFPA® 472, *Standard for Competence of Responders to Hazardous Materials /Weapons of Mass Destruction Incidents*
- NFPA® 1001, *Standard for Fire Fighter Professional Qualifications*
- NFPA® 1002, *Standard for Fire Apparatus Driver/Operator Professional Qualifications*
- NFPA® 1003, *Standard for Airport Fire Fighter Professional Qualifications*
- NFPA® 1006, *Standard for Technical Rescuer Professional Qualifications*
- NFPA® 1021, *Standard for Fire Officer Professional Qualifications*
- NFPA® 1026, *Standard for Incident Management Personnel Professional Qualifications*

Table 1.1
NFA's Degrees-at-a-Distance Institutions

School and Contact Information	Region
Cogswell College 1175 Bordeaux Sunnyvale, CA 94089-1299 (800) 264-7955 http://www.cogswell.edu/firescience.html	Arizona, California, Nevada
Empire State College/SUNY Fire Service Coordinator Center for Distance Learning 111 West Avenue Saratoga Springs, NY 12866 (518) 587-2100, ext. 2300 http://www.esc.edu	Connecticut, Maine, Massachusetts, New Hampshire, New York, Pennsylvania, Rhode Island, Vermont
University of Cincinnati College of Applied Science 2220 Victory Parkway Cincinnati, OH 45206 (513) 556-6583 http://www.uc.edu/cas/firescience	Indiana, Michigan, Minnesota, North Dakota, Ohio, South Dakota, Wisconsin, Florida, Georgia
University of Maryland University College Undergraduate Programs 3501 University Blvd. Adelphi, MD 20783 (800) 888-UMUC (8682) or (301) 985-7000 http://www.umuc.edu/ugp/majors/fscn.html http://www.umuc.edu/distance	Delaware, Maryland, New Jersey, North Carolina, District of Columbia, West Virginia, Virginia
University College University of Memphis 218 Brister Hall Memphis, TN 38152 (901) 678-2716 http://www.uc.memphis.edu/ undergrad-fire-admin.php	Alabama, Arkansas, Kentucky, Mississippi, Tennessee, South Carolina, Louisiana
Western Oregon University Fire Services Administration 345 N. Monmouth Ave Monmouth, OR 97361 (800) 451-5767 or (503) 838-8697 http://www.wou.edu/fsa/	Alaska, Colorado, Hawaii, Idaho, Montana, Oregon, Utah, Washington, Wyoming
Western Illinois University Non-Traditional Programs Horrabin Hall 6 Macomb, IL 61445 (309) 298-1929 http://www.wiu.edu/ses/distance/	Illinois, Iowa, Kansas, Missouri, Nebraska, New Mexico, Oklahoma, Texas

- NFPA® 1031, *Standard for Professional Qualifications for Fire Inspector and Plan Examiner*
- NFPA® 1033, *Standard for Professional Qualifications for Fire Investigator*
- NFPA® 1035, *Standard for Professional Qualifications for Public Fire and Life Safety Educator*
- NFPA® 1037, *Standard for Professional Qualifications for Fire Marshal*
- NFPA® 1041, *Standard for Fire Service Instructor Professional Qualifications*
- NFPA® 1051, *Standard for Wildland Fire Fighter Professional Qualifications*
- NFPA® 1061, *Standard for Professional Qualifications for Public Safety Telecommunicator*
- NFPA® 1071, *Standard for Emergency Vehicle Technician Professional Qualifications*
- NFPA® 1081, *Standard for Industrial Fire Brigade Member Professional Qualifications*
- NFPA® 1521, *Standard for Fire Department Safety Officer*

These standards provide guidelines for state certification agencies and for local departments to use in designing their curricula. Because the standards are minimum requirements, each department must adapt and amend the standards to meet local requirements. In some areas, the national standards may not be adequate to handle the hazards found, and firefighters may need to be trained to a higher level. In such situations, local fire chiefs will determine what to require of their personnel and how to effectively apply the standards to provide the best possible fire protection for the citizens.

To become certified to any of these standards, a firefighter must first complete the required training and then pass a certification examination. The certification examination is conducted by an agency accredited to certify firefighters to these standards. The two organizations that accredit training agencies to certify firefighters are the National Board on Fire Service Professional Qualifications (sometimes called the NBFSPQ or the Pro Board) and the International Fire Service Accreditation Congress (IFSAC).

National Board on Fire Service Professional Qualifications (NBFSPQ or Pro Board)

The National Board on Fire Service Professional Qualifications (NBFSPQ) was an outgrowth of the Joint Council of Fire Service Organizations. NBFSPQ (also known as the Pro Board) was conceived by the Council in 1972 to provide minimum performance standards that can be used to evaluate firefighters' abilities and skills and determine whether they possess the necessary qualifications for that respective level. The NBFSPQ also accredited training agencies that sought to certify firefighters to these standards. In the mid-1980s, the task of developing and maintaining the professional qualifications standards was passed on to the NFPA®, and the NBFSPQ concentrated strictly on accreditation of programs. The NBFSPQ is composed of leaders from some of the organizations that were represented on the Joint Council. At the time this manual was developed, agencies in the United States and Canada were accredited by NBFSPQ to certify firefighters. In addition, some overseas agencies were also

Figure 1.17 The International Fire Service Accreditation Congress (IFSAC) accredits fire certification agencies and is part of Oklahoma State University.

accredited to issue certifications. Further discussion on this topic can be found in Chapter 8, Roles of Public and Private Support Organizations.

International Fire Service Accreditation Congress (IFSAC)

The International Fire Service Accreditation Congress (IFSAC) was created out of a meeting of the National Association of State Directors of Fire Training and Education (now simply the North American Fire Training Directors) in August 1990. IFSAC, which is based at Oklahoma State University (OSU), held its first organizational meeting in February 1991. The purpose of IFSAC is to provide a self-governed, peer-driven system that accredits fire service certification programs and fire-related degree programs **(Figure 1.17)**. IFSAC consists of four sections: Administration, Certificate Assembly, Degree Assembly, and the Congress. Administration is provided by full- and part-time staff at OSU. The Congress is composed of two Assemblies from the agencies representing Certification and Degree Programs.

Career Firefighter Selection Process

Because a firefighter interacts with the public and with other firefighters on a daily basis, the firefighter candidate must possess excellent interpersonal skills in addition to expertise in a wide variety of technical skills. Firefighters must also be trustworthy and ethical. Because training is an essential part of a firefighter's career, he or she must also study training and technical manuals throughout their career. As the firefighter progresses through promotions to officer and management positions, he or she then will have the responsibility to handle personnel matters, including disciplinary actions and disputes between employees. Firefighters also must remain in top physical condition throughout their careers because fire fighting is an extremely physically demanding occupation. Firefighters must also present themselves to the public in a positive way by maintaining a professional appearance and attitude.

Because of the above qualifications, it is essential that every fire department have in place a strict candidate selection process so that the most qualified candidates will be selected to join the fire department. In many cases, there are a large number of applicants for every open position. It is not uncommon for larger cities to have thousands of applicants competing for perhaps a dozen jobs. This is another reason why fire departments must have a selection process that is reliable, efficient, and fair.

The firefighter selection process varies with each fire department or geographical area. This process usually includes an advertisement or announcement, an application, a written examination, a physical agility test, and at least one oral interview **(Figure 1.18)**. In the latter stages of the selection process, a candidate may be required to undergo a physical and/or psychological examination, a thorough background investigation, and a drug test. The results of each phase of the process are compiled, evaluated, and compared to the other candidates' results. This process usually results in a "list" from which the chief of department or other designated representative will use when hiring new recruits. Individuals are usually selected in order of their ranking on that list, or the person doing the hiring may be required to select from a number of candidates whose final scores fall within the top percentage of applicants.

A candidate's final score or rank is usually determined by taking an average of that candidate's performance on the different phases of the examination. Not all phases of the examination process are always weighed equally.

```
┌─────────────────────────────────────────────────────┐
│              Sample Job Announcement                │
│                                                     │
│  Firefighter (Entry Level) – New Sharon, OK         │
│                                                     │
│  Closing Date                                       │
│  8/31/2011                                          │
│                                                     │
│  Description                                        │
│  New Sharon Fire Department is accepting applications to establish │
│  a hiring list for Entry-Level Firefighter.         │
│                                                     │
│  Requirements                                       │
│  Minimum Qualifications                             │
│  • High school graduate/GED or equivalent.          │
│  • Minimum 21 years of age before September 1, 2011. │
│  • Valid Oklahoma state drivers license by date of hire. │
│  • Good driving record, must provide copy of driving record for │
│    previous three years at time of application.     │
│  • Candidates must be able to communicate effectively in English, │
│    both verbally and in writing.                    │
│  • Fire service experience is not required to apply. Successful │
│    candidates will attend the Oklahoma State Firefighter Recruit │
│    Academy (attendance may be waived with proof of recent │
│    completion, NSFD discretion).                    │
│                                                     │
│  Preferred Qualifications                           │
│  • Firefighting experience.                         │
│  • Recent successful completion of Oklahoma State Firefighter │
│    Recruit Academy.                                 │
│                                                     │
│  Interested candidates may apply by submitting a City of New Sharon │
│  Application, in person, by mail or facsimile to the following address: │
│  City of New Sharon Human Resources,                │
│  Municipal Building Room 222                        │
│  930 N. Main Street, New Sharon, OK 74078.          │
│  EO/Affirmative Action Employer                     │
└─────────────────────────────────────────────────────┘
```

Figure 1.18 An example of an announcement seeking firefighter applicants.

For example, the written portion of the examination might be weighted 50 percent, with the agility and oral tests each weighted at 25 percent. In some cases, military veterans or candidates who reside in the city or town in which the position is located are given additional points. There is often a period of several days to several months between each phase of the examination process, with the candidates being notified in writing of the dates for each part of the examination.

Recruitment

Career and volunteer fire departments typically must advertise to gather a pool of qualified applicants for firefighter positions. These departments use various media, including their websites, to get their recruiting announcements out. Public service announcements on radio stations and television channels are another method. Recruiting ads in local, regional, national, and trade newspapers are another. The Internet is rapidly becoming a major component in the firefighter recruitment process.

Fire Cadet/Explorer Scout Programs

Fire Cadet and Explorer Scout programs are designed to involve the youth of a community in the fire department, expose them to a possible career in the fire service, and allow them to participate in their department under controlled conditions with supervision provided by members of the department. These programs generally accept young people aged 14 to 21. Often, cadets/explorers who reach the age of adulthood (age defined by state/provincial law) are then eligible to join the department as a full member.

Many departments, career and volunteer, actively support Fire Cadet/Explorer Scout programs because they serve as recruitment programs. Fire service personnel advise the cadets/explorers, conduct training programs in fire service subjects, and serve as mentors for these potential future firefighters. The departments provide a meeting place, tools, equipment, protective clothing, and workers' compensation coverage for those personnel serving as advisors to the program.

Although cadets/explorers are not allowed to fight fires, most of them can participate in fire department ride-along programs. Cadets may perform support roles at emergency operations or other fire department activities. Depending on their level of training and experience, cadets/explorers may participate in facility and equipment maintenance, setting up mobile kitchens, assisting with salvage and overhaul operations, and loading equipment.

Figure 1.19 Physical training, such as jogging, can help applicants prepare for the physical agility test.

Preparation

Fire departments, particularly in desirable urban or suburban locations, sometimes have a large pool of applicants – far larger than the number who can be accepted. For this reason, candidates should enter a period of preparation to be able to better compete for a prized slot in a recruit class. Preparation can range from physical training to excel in the health and physical fitness requirements, earning an associate's degree or certification as a firefighter before applying for a position, or gaining certification as an EMT or EMS first responder **(Figure 1.19)**. Participating in practice interviews or internship or ride-along programs are other forms of preparation.

Application

The first step in the selection process usually requires that the candidates complete an employment application. Prerequisites for applying vary with each department. Most departments require that all applicants be at least 18 years of age, hold a valid driver's license, and have a high school diploma or Graduate Equivalency Diploma (GED). Some departments have more stringent pre-employment requirements, such as requiring that all applicants be certified to NFPA® 1001, *Standard for Fire Fighter Professional Qualifications*, or as emergency medical technicians, either at a basic or paramedic level. Others may require that applicants already have an associate's degree or be certified hazardous materials technicians. Still other departments may require that the applicants hold a commercial driver's license or be otherwise qualified and licensed to drive and operate fire apparatus.

Written Examination

After all employment applications have been reviewed and processed, the written test or examination is usually the first phase of the firefighter examination process. The written test is usually created by an independent testing or personnel agency contracted by the fire department conducting the test and is almost exclusively a multiple-choice test. Most written tests are designed so that a candidate who has no experience in the fire service will still be able to score well. Written tests might present some of the following types of problems to the candidate: math, reading comprehension, mechanical aptitude, recognition/observation, and psychological comparisons.

Math

The firefighter's job may require performing mathematical calculations. These calculations often must be performed quickly and *in your head* while on the fireground. A fire apparatus driver or engineer would have to calculate such information as pump discharge pressures or friction loss calculations for different sizes of hose. The written test often addresses math problems in the form of word problems relating to fire department situations. The word problem is then broken down into a mathematical equation that must be solved.

Reading Comprehension

Firefighters are required to train throughout their careers. Much of this training involves studying various written materials and books. Many written tests require that the candidate read and comprehend a selection of material, usually ranging from several paragraphs to several volumes in length. The candidate must then answer questions relating to the content of that paragraph. This type of test determines the candidate's ability to mentally retain written information or to recognize content that is of particular importance.

Mechanical Aptitude

Firefighters must operate a variety of different types of tools and equipment, both power and hand-operated. Firefighters are also often faced with situations that require them to have a basic understanding of the way things work mechanically and must have the ability to adapt and improvise in situations where they might not have the appropriate tools or training. Because of this need to understand how tools work, many written tests include some type of mechanical aptitude or reasoning section. These questions usually consist of a diagram or illustration in which the candidate must determine the effect or outcome of some event. For example, a series of gears are shown, and the candidate must determine in which direction a certain gear will turn. In another question, various shaped cylinders are shown and the candidate must decide which cylinder would hold the greatest amount of fluid, etc.

Recognition/Observation

When faced with a fire, a firefighter must be able to quickly observe a building's features and take note of the conditions in order to begin to formulate a plan for attacking the fire. Even more important is the ability to evaluate possible hazards and know how to avoid them. The firefighter must also take notice of placement of windows, doors, or other areas of refuge in case the fire fighting crew must evacuate the building in case of emergency. This is part of the process that is known as size-up.

To evaluate a candidate's ability to recognize and remember details, some written tests require that the candidates study an illustration – usually of a burning building – for a pre-determined period of time (usually 1 minute). When the test proctor calls time, the candidates must turn the picture over or hand it in. The candidates must then answer a number of questions about the illustration, such as, "How many windows are in the bedroom?" or "What time does the living room clock say?" Another variation of this type of test is when the proctor reads aloud a passage and the candidates must then answer questions about the content of that passage.

Psychological (Comparisons)

Firefighters deal with several types of stress, ranging from accident scenes, to living with other firefighters in the station. For this reason, it is important that firefighter candidates be psychologically compatible with firefighting. In psychological screening, for example, the candidate must choose between two statements, deciding which statement he most agrees with, such as, "I prefer to work independently," or "It is more efficient to work as a team."

Physical Ability Test

The physical ability test, commonly known as the *agility* test, measures the candidate's physical strength and aerobic condition. Because firefighters are often called upon to perform extremely strenuous tasks under very adverse conditions, it is essential that they be in excellent physical condition. A physical agility test is most often used to evaluate a candidate's suitability.

The types of evolutions that the candidates must perform vary widely with each jurisdiction. These tests are designed to approximate as closely as possible the physical tasks that must be performed by firefighters. Some of these tests are given on a *pass/fail* basis, while others are timed and scored accordingly. In some cases the individual events are performed and scored separately, and in others the events are performed consecutively and timed or scored as a single event. These tests are usually very physically demanding, and it is important that candidates prepare well in advance of the test date to prevent injury and avoid failure. Often the fire department sponsoring the test will provide an explanation of all that will be required weeks in advance so that candidates have time to fully prepare themselves.

Candidate Physical Ability Test (CPAT) program

The widely used Candidate Physical Ability Test (CPAT) was jointly developed by the International Association of Fire Chiefs and the International Association of Fire Fighters. The CPAT exam is comprised of eight stations that must be completed in one continuous sequence. It is a pass/fail evaluation. The maximum time allowed for passing is 10 minutes and 20 seconds. CPAT has been validated as an acceptable method for testing the physical requirements for being a firefighter. **Appendix B** lists the elements of the CPAT.

During the entire test, the candidate must wear long pants, appropriate footwear, a safety helmet with chin strap, gloves and a 50-pound (22.68 kg) weighted vest to simulate the weight of personal protective equipment with self-contained breathing apparatus (SCBA). An additional 25 pounds (11.34 kg) (12.5 lbs. per shoulder [5.67 kg]) will be added during the first event, but will be removed at the completion of that event. Watches and loose or restrictive jewelry may not be worn during the test.

The events are placed in a sequence that best simulates fire scene events, while allowing an 85-foot (25.9 m) walk between events. This walk allows for approximately 20 seconds to recover and regroup before the next event. Running is not allowed between events. The events are as follows:

- Stair climb
- Hose drag
- Equipment carry
- Ladder raise and extension
- Forcible entry
- Search
- Rescue
- Ceiling breach and pull

Interview Process

Candidates who successfully complete the written examination and the physical agility test then participate in an interview process. As described below, the interview process consists of an initial oral interview that is sometimes followed by a second interview.

Oral Interview

For many candidates, the most difficult part of the examination process is the oral interview, commonly referred to as the oral board. It can be an extremely unnerving experience to walk into a room and sit before a panel of several interviewers, all of whom are not only evaluating the candidate's answers to their questions, but are also judging him or her based on dress, appearance, and attitude.

To maintain fairness, all candidates are asked the same questions in the same order. Candidates are rated on their responses to each question. At the conclusion of the interview, the interviewers will often consult with each other and "compare notes" so as to arrive at a final score for the candidate. This helps to eliminate subjectivity on the part of the interviewers.

Second Interview

Candidates who score highly after completing the written, agility, and oral exams are sometimes asked to return for an additional interview, sometimes known as the Chief's Interview. This interview may be conducted by the fire chief or members of the staff. This interview is usually not scored, but rather is held so that the interviewers can get a better idea of a candidate's suitability for the position. If the interviewers agree that a candidate is suitable for employment, that candidate would then likely move on to the final stages of the process, which may include a physical examination, psychological evaluation, background check, or any combination of these.

Probationary Period

Firefighter candidates in both career and volunteer departments can expect to serve a probationary period that typically lasts a minimum of one to three years. During the probationary period, the candidate is expected to attend formal training classes in fire fighting, first aid, and hazardous materials. If the candidate cannot or does not meet the fire department's training requirements, the candidate may be terminated or asked to resign his or her position with the fire department. The intent of the probationary period is for the candidate to show a desire to be a member of the fire service. A candidate who has not demonstrated that desire may be asked to resign at any time during the probationary period.

Volunteer Firefighter Selection Process

While there are always a very large number of men and women eager to work as paid firefighters, members of volunteer fire departments are often harder to recruit and retain. The selection process for volunteer fire departments often differs greatly from the process for career selection. Prior experience or certification is not usually necessary to become a member of a volunteer organization, as this experience is gained and certifications are obtained throughout an individual's service in the department. There is normally not a written test or physical agility test, but an interested party might have to complete an application or submit a letter of interest to the fire chief. Applicants to a volunteer department may be required to interview with the chief or a committee of department members.

Because volunteer firefighters represent the department to the community in which they serve, it is equally important for them to be able to be held to a high standard of ethics and professionalism. For this reason, many volunteer fire departments today will subject an interested candidate to as strict a background check as one that may be administered to those vying for a career firefighter position.

Chapter Summary

Whether a firefighter is a member of a paid department or a volunteer department, the job is a demanding one. Firefighters are expected to work well as a team and to be willing to undergo continual training in basic and new skills. Because the job of firefighter has grown over the years to include emergency medical response, hazardous materials mitigation, rescue, and response to terrorist attacks, firefighters must be willing to learn new skills as the department's mission expands.

The successful firefighter candidate will be one who is in good physical condition and who is willing to study and work hard. Because emergency response activities demand intense work under uncontrolled conditions, firefighters must be willing to work and train to be part of a team – for their safety as well as the safety of the public they serve. They must also remember that they represent a very public organization and behave professionally to avoid tarnishing the image of the department. The firefighter who is committed to education will find many opportunities to learn new skills and concepts at the local, state, and even national levels.

Review Questions

1. Compare and contrast fire protection and emergency service careers in both the public and private sector.

2. What are the main differences between fire service training and fire service education?

3. How is a fire protection certificate program different from a fire service degree program?

4. What effect does changing technology have on education for fire and emergency services personnel?

5. What are good sources for continued training for fire and emergency services personnel?

6. How can setting goals help fire and emergency services personnel achieve advancement during his or her career?

7. How do wellness and fitness affect an applicant's chances of earning a spot in the fire department?

8. Why do veteran firefighters need to maintain a certain level of fitness?

Roles of Fire and Emergency Services Personnel

Chapter Contents

Key Terms

FESHE Outcomes

This chapter provides information that addresses the outcomes for the Fire and Emergency Services Higher Education (FESHE) *Principles of Emergency Services* course.

5.   Identify fire protection and emergency-service careers in both the public and private sector.

NFPA® Job Performance Requirements

This chapter provides information that addresses the following job performance requirements (JPRs) of NFPA® 1001, *Standard for Fire Fighter Professional Qualifications* (2008).

5.1.1

6.1.1

Roles of Fire and Emergency Services Personnel

Learning Objectives

After reading this chapter, students will be able to:

1. Distinguish between the different types of fire companies.

2. Identify the duties of fire suppression (operations) personnel.

3. Define the roles of training division personnel.

4. Recognize possible positions for fire service administration.

5. List special operations personnel duties.

6. Explain how fire prevention (community risk reduction) personnel assist in building community fire safety.

7. Compare and contrast the duties of emergency medical services personnel.

8. Describe the role emergency management personnel have in community safety planning.

9. Recognize other fire department personnel who assist in carrying out the broad mission of the fire department.

Chapter 2
Roles of Fire and Emergency Services Personnel

Case History

The graduation ceremonies to mark the end of the rookie academy had been awesome. The new firefighters were proud of what they had accomplished – and could tell that their applauding family and friends were proud, too.

The fire chief looked very impressive in her Class A uniform. In her graduation speech, she not only welcomed the newest firefighters to the department, but also talked about the different career paths that were now open to them. Some firefighters would be assigned to engine companies, while others would go to a truck or rescue squad. Some would find fulfillment as shift firefighters until retirement. Other new graduates would advance their technical skills by becoming driver/operators, haz mat technicians, special rescue technicians, or fire investigators. Somewhere in the graduating class were future company officers, assistant chiefs, and maybe even a fire chief.

For the moment, though, the newly graduated firefighters could not wait to use their new knowledge and skills in their first fire company.

There is more to a fire department than putting out fires. New firefighters soon realize that roles exist for fire department personnel other than riding the apparatus, pulling hoselines, or raising ladders. This chapter describes the organization and duties of fire companies and also defines many of the other roles (such as training and administration, special operations, fire prevention or community risk reduction, emergency medical services, emergency management, and other roles) commonly found within the fire service. Depending on local requirements and customs, additional specialized personnel may be used. The duties and requirements of these positions will vary depending on local needs and procedures.

Fire Companies

The standard operating unit of a fire department is the **company**. A company consists of a group of firefighters assigned to a particular piece of fire apparatus. The number of personnel varies depending upon:

- The type of company
- The size of apparatus
- The number of personnel available

Company — (1) Basic fire fighting organizational unit consisting of firefighters and apparatus; headed by a company officer. (2) Term that embraces the whole crew of a vessel.

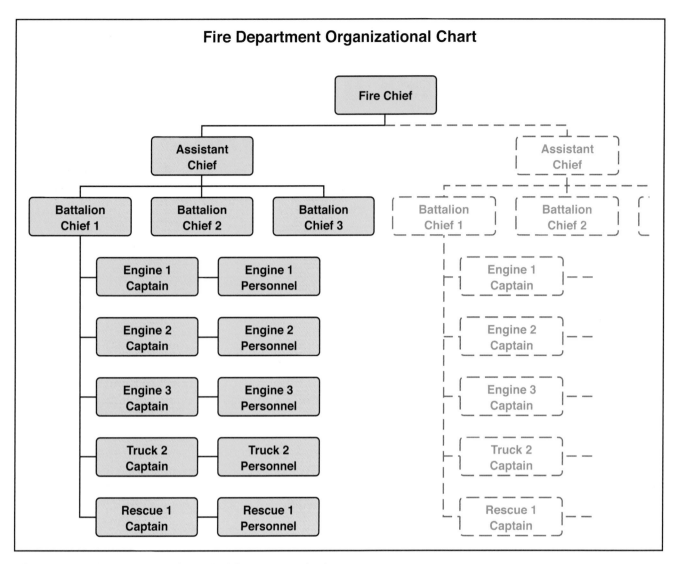

Figure 2.1 The organization of a typical fire company is shown.

Company Officer —
Individual responsible for command of a company. This designation is not specific to any particular fire department rank (may be a firefighter, lieutenant, captain, or chief officer if responsible for command of a single company).

A company consists of a **company officer**, a **fire apparatus driver/operator**, and one or more firefighters supervised by a Battalion Chief or District Chief (**Figure 2.1**). A fire company is organized, equipped, and trained for a definite function. The specific functions and duties of a fire company of the same type may vary in different localities because of the inherent hazards of the area, the size of the department, and the scope of the department's activities. A small fire department may have only one fire company to carry out the functions that would normally be performed by several companies in a larger city. A group of fire companies assigned to work together constitutes a **task force** (assorted types of units) or **strike team** (a group of similar units). Apparatus and assigned groups have considerable influence on how, when, and where each company operates. The type of apparatus and equipment corresponds to the purpose and duty of the fire company. The following general descriptions of the three types of fire companies – engine, truck, and rescue squad – illustrate how fire companies are organized and how they operate.

Figure 2.2 Members of an engine company fighting a training fire.

Engine Company

The basic role of the **engine company** in structural fire fighting is to deploy hoselines for fire attack and exposure protection. Stretching and operating hoselines into structures, operating portable master stream devices from outside the structure, or supplying water to aerial apparatus that are operating elevated master stream devices are all methods of deploying hoselines (**Figure 2.2**). While engine company members may also perform rescue, forcible entry, or other functions while preparing to make a fire attack, these are more typically the responsibility of a truck company.

The engine company is responsible for the primary fire attack on nonstructural fires such as automobiles, trash dumpsters, and natural cover fires. Depending on local policies, the engine company may also respond to medical emergencies, automobile or industrial accidents, and citizen assist calls.

Truck (Ladder) Company

The role of the **truck (ladder) company** in structural fire fighting is to perform forcible entry, search and rescue, ventilation, salvage and overhaul, control of utilities, and to provide access to upper levels (**Figure 2.3, p. 46**). In many cases, it is necessary for the truck company to perform two of these functions simultaneously, splitting the crew to handle the various jobs. Truck companies can place ground ladders in addition to the apparatus's main aerial device. The truck company may also be required to operate an elevated master stream for fire attack or exposure protection.

In some municipalities, the truck company responds to medical emergencies and citizen assist calls. Because the aerial apparatus has a large amount of compartmentation, many departments have the truck company carry rescue equipment and perform rescue operations such as vehicle extrications and specialty rescues.

Fire Apparatus Driver/ Operator — Firefighter who is charged with the responsibility of operating fire apparatus to, during, and from the scene of a fire operation, or at any other time the apparatus is in use. The driver/operator is also responsible for routine maintenance of the apparatus and any equipment carried on the apparatus. This is typically the first step in the fire department promotional chain. *Also known as* Chauffeur, Driver/Operator, or Engineer.

Battalion Chief — Chief officer assigned to command a fire department battalion. *Also known as* District Chief.

Task Force — (1) Group of individuals convened to analyze, investigate, or solve a particular problem. (2) Group of resources, with common communications and a leader, temporarily assembled for a specific mission. An example would be a group of firefighters and equipment assigned to a special task, such as backfiring; consists of three engines, a dozer, a hand crew, and a task force leader. (3) Any combination of single resources, within a reasonable span of control, assembled for a particular tactical need with common communications and a leader.

Strike Team — Specified combinations of the same kind and type of resources with common communications and a leader; usually composed of either engines, hand crews, or bulldozers, but may be composed of any resource of the same kind and type. Exception — *see* Enhanced Strike Team.

Engine Company — Group of firefighters assigned to a fire department pumper who are primarily responsible for providing water supply and attack lines for fire extinguishment.

Truck Company — Group of firefighters assigned to a fire department aerial apparatus; primarily responsible for search and rescue, ventilation, salvage and overhaul, forcible entry, and other fireground support functions. *Also known as* Ladder Company.

Rescue Company — Specialized unit of people and equipment dedicated to performing rescue and extrication operations at the scene of an emergency. *Also known as* Rescue Squad or Rescue Truck.

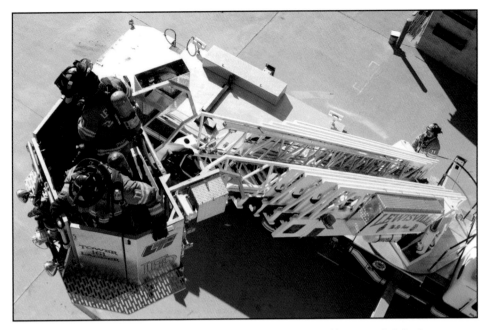

Figure 2.3 Truck company personnel being raised to a roof in an aerial device.

Rescue Squad/Company

The role of the **rescue squad or company** varies from department to department. Typically, its primary responsibility is the removal of victims from areas of danger or entrapment including vehicle extrications, industrial and agricultural extrications, trench and structural collapse rescues, and high-angle (rope) rescues (**Figure 2.4**). Frequently, the rescue company is assigned to respond on structural fires as well. The duties of the rescue company on the fireground vary depending on departmental procedures and what is needed at the scene. The rescue company often assists engine or truck companies, performs first aid on patients, refills air cylinders, provides floodlighting, or performs other duties. In some departments (particularly smaller or volunteer departments) rescue or squad companies may also perform duties of a ladder or truck company.

Fire Suppression (Operations) Personnel

The primary mission of the fire and emergency services is community risk reduction, including fire prevention. However, when all else fails and a fire starts, it is the job of the fire department to extinguish it. As fire departments have improved over time, they have learned that certain functions must be accomplished in a coordinated manner for successful fire fighting. These fire suppression functions include:

- Rescue
- Exposure protection
- Fire confinement
- Fire extinguishment
- Salvage and overhaul
- Ventilation
- Securing utilities
- Fire cause determination

Figure 2.4 A rescue squad member performing a vehicle extrication procedure.

Conducting these operations are the primary objectives of suppression personnel. By providing these functions, firefighters can control fire. The major personnel positions held by fire suppression personnel are:

- Firefighter
- Fire apparatus driver/operator
- Company officer
- Battalion or district chief

Firefighter

Fire fighting requires skill in preventing, combating, and extinguishing fires; answering emergency calls; and operating and/or maintaining fire department equipment, apparatus, and quarters. The work involves extensive training in performing fire fighting and rescue activities. **Firefighters** are required to learn and participate in operating apparatus and performing hazardous tasks under emergency conditions – all of which require strenuous exertion with hazards such as smoke and cramped surroundings wearing full personal protective equipment (PPE) (**Figure 2.5, p. 48**). Although fire fighting and rescue work are the most difficult and hazardous aspects of a firefighter's work, a significant portion of time is spent on performing routine activities, such as inspections, training, and station duties. The following are some of the typical duties of a firefighter:

Firefighter — Active member of the fire department. *Also spelled* Fire Fighter.

Figure 2.5 Firefighters must wear personal protective equipment (PPE) and self-contained breathing apparatus (SCBA) during fire fighting operations.

- Attend training courses; read and study assigned materials on topics such as fire behavior and extinguishment, hazardous materials, fire prevention, and safety.
- Don PPE.
- Respond to fire alarms with the company, operate fire fighting equipment, lay and connect hose, maneuver nozzles and direct fire streams, raise and climb ladders, use fire extinguishers and all fire fighting hand tools.
- Ventilate burning buildings.
- Remove people from danger and administer first aid.
- Perform salvage and overhaul operations.
- Relay instructions, orders, and information and give locations of alarms received from the dispatcher.
- Exercise precautions to avoid injury and to avoid unnecessary damage to or loss of property.
- Ensure safekeeping and proper care of all fire department property.
- Perform assigned fire inspections.
- Assist the public with general fire safety questions

A firefighter needs to have certain knowledge and skills that allow him or her to function effectively in the position. For the firefighter to function effectively, he or she is required to meet the following requirements:

- Meet the requirements set forth in NFPA® 1001, *Standard for Fire Fighter Professional Qualifications*.

- Know department organization, operation, and procedures.

- Know the district or city street system and physical layout.

- Meet minimum health and physical fitness standards in NFPA® 1500, *Standard on Fire Department Occupational Safety and Health Program*, NFPA® 1582, *Standard on Comprehensive Occupational Medical Program for Fire Departments*, and NFPA® 1583, *Standard on Health-Related Fitness Programs for Fire Department Members,* or as determined by the Authority Having Jurisdiction (AHJ).

- Climb ladders and work at considerable heights.

- Learn a wide variety of fire fighting and rescue duties within a reasonable working probationary period.

- Understand and follow oral and written instructions.

- Perform assigned equipment and station maintenance duties.

Figure 2.6 The driver/operator is responsible for driving the apparatus safely, positioning it at the scene, and operating fire pumps to supply water for fire fighting.

Fire Apparatus Driver/Operator

The fire apparatus driver/operator position is typically the first level of promotion in the fire department's organizational chain of command. A driver/operator has the responsibilities of a firefighter and the additional general duties related to the care and use of departmental equipment and property. A driver/operator is responsible for safely driving assigned fire apparatus to and from fire and emergency scenes and for operating pumps, aerial devices, or other mechanical equipment as required (**Figure 2.6**). Work is usually performed under the direction of a company officer. A driver/operator is expected to perform the following duties:

- Drive assigned fire fighting apparatus to and from emergencies or other assigned activities; operate its pumps, aerial device, and other mechanical equipment as required, and keep accurate inventory of tools and equipment on the apparatus.

- Clean and service the assigned apparatus, keep the apparatus ready, report mechanical failures or difficulties to the proper person, and help the department's apparatus technician or mechanic make minor apparatus repairs.

- Perform general fire fighting duties as assigned and participate in company inspections.

- Attend appropriate training sessions and instruct relief driver in equipment operation.

- Act in a supervisory capacity over the company in the absence of the company officer.

A fire apparatus driver/operator is one of the most important members of the company. Because of the technical requirements for the position, an operator must be trained to a higher level than a firefighter. To be eligible for the apparatus driver/operator position, a firefighter must meet the following requirements:

- Meet the requirements for Fire Fighter I in NFPA® 1001 and the appropriate requirements contained in NFPA® 1002, *Standard for Fire Apparatus Driver/ Operator Professional Qualifications.*

- Be legally licensed within the state or province to operate heavy vehicles.

- Know the location of streets, fire alarm boxes, and fire hydrants and know the types of building construction in the district.

- Know the mechanical principles involved in operating fire apparatus and allied equipment.

- Know the rules and regulations of the fire department.

- Know modern fire fighting, fire prevention practices, and first aid.

- Understand and follow oral and written instructions, react quickly in emergencies, and display proper judgment in making work decisions.

- Make quick, mental mathematical calculations involving water flow formulas.

- Operate mechanical and automotive fire equipment.

For more information on fire apparatus driver/operators, see the IFSTA **Pumping Apparatus Driver/Operator** and **Aerial Apparatus Driver/Operator Handbooks**.

Company Officer

The company officer supervises a fire company in the station and at the fire scene. The authority for this position is delegated from the chief officer. The work includes responsibility for proper maintenance and operation of the fire station and fire fighting equipment.

The company officer performs a wide variety of fire fighting and related duties, including inspections of equipment, personnel, and public buildings. Routine duties are performed with independence within established regula-

Figure 2.7 A company officer directing crew members at an emergency scene.

tions but under the general direction of a chief officer. Observation of work in progress, results obtained, and inspections of quarters and equipment are all used to evaluate company officers. Depending on the structure of the fire department, the company officer holds the rank of lieutenant, captain, major, or a similar title.

A company officer is expected to perform the following duties:

- Respond to all fire and emergency alarms assigned to the company, advise the driver/operator on the route to follow, evaluate the scene conditions, and direct the company's initial actions.

- Perform size-up.

- Direct and assist subordinates at the emergency scene unless command is assumed by a chief officer or other officer operating within the Incident Management System (IMS) (**Figure 2.7**).

- Call for second or higher alarm as needed, based on size-up.

- Inspect conditions at the fire scene to prevent re-ignition and to assist in determining fire cause.

- Provide for safe crew operations and provide safety for citizens.

- Inspect apparatus, equipment, grounds, and station to ensure proper order and condition.

- Inspect public buildings, businesses, hospitals, schools, and places of public assembly for fire hazards or conditions dangerous to life and property; give fire prevention and community risk reduction presentations; and assist in fire cause determination.

- Prepare and conduct employee-training courses and perform special duties in the training school.
- Handle administrative and/or personnel matters as required.
- Assign daily non-emergency work at station.
- Complete various types of reports dealing with incidents.

The job requirements for company officers are extensive because of their tremendous responsibilities. Because the company officer is the leader, expectations of the person in this position are extremely high. Many fire service leaders view the company officer as the most important cog in the fire department's wheel of success. It is important to note that the company officer is the first level of supervision in the department's command and structure.

A company officer needs the following qualifications:

- Ability to meet the appropriate requirements in NFPA® 1021, *Standard for Fire Officer Professional Qualifications*
- Considerable knowledge of streets, principal buildings, fire hydrants, and fire alarm boxes in the city
- Considerable knowledge of the principles and practices of fire fighting, fire prevention, and first aid, and the ability to apply them
- Ability to evaluate emergency situations, recognize danger, and take immediate action to protect life and property
- Ability to inspect buildings, recognize and determine fire or other hazardous conditions, and make written and oral reports of such conditions with recommendations for their correction

For more information on the role of a company officer, refer to the IFSTA **Fire and Emergency Services Company Officer** manual.

Battalion/District Chief

The role of the battalion or district chief (referred to here as the battalion chief) varies depending on the size of the fire department. In small departments, the battalion chief may actually be the shift commander in charge of all duty crews. For the purpose of this chapter, a battalion chief is the first level of chief officer in a large department. The battalion chief is assigned the responsibility of supervising a group of fire companies during emergency and non-emergency situations in a specified geographical region of the city (**Figure 2.8**). Typically, each battalion chief supervises several fire companies or administrative sections. In many departments, the battalion chief responds to incidents that require the response of three or more companies. A battalion chief is required to perform the following duties:

- Supervise all fire fighting and rescue activities within the battalion during an assigned tour of duty, review records and reports of operations, and take appropriate corrective action when required.
- Inspect fire stations, equipment, and apparatus and make recommendations or issue orders to comply with established departmental standards of condition and appearance.
- Provide direction to the company officers of the battalion and handle administrative or personnel matters when required.

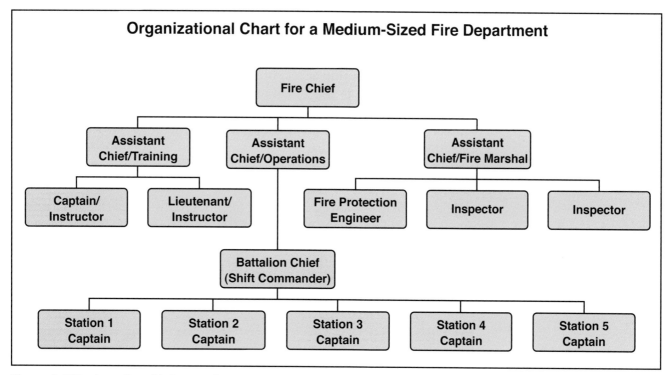

Organizational Chart for a Medium-Sized Fire Department

Figure 2.8 The battalion chief supervises several companies.

- Provide assistance to other battalion chiefs in the event of a multiple-alarm emergency in their district.
- Assist higher chief officers with special projects and requests for help or information when required.

Because the battalion chief is the first level of chief officer, the person holding this position must have exemplary technical and administrative skills. A battalion chief's qualifications include:

- Ability to meet the appropriate requirements in NFPA® 1021, *Standard for Fire Officer Professional Qualifications*
- Ability to evaluate fires, recognize danger, use sound judgment, and react calmly in emergencies
- Thorough knowledge of fire fighting and rescue tactics and strategy; ability to organize the emergency scene through the use of the department's incident management system
- Extensive knowledge of the rules and regulations of the fire department, geography of the city, location of streets, and the nature and location of hazardous premises, principal buildings, fire hydrants, and fire alarm boxes in the city

Training Division Personnel

Firefighters responding to an emergency must be properly prepared to perform safely and effectively. The protection of lives of the civilians and fellow firefighters, the prevention of serious injury to civilians and firefighters, and the protection of property all depend upon firefighters accomplishing their tasks expediently and efficiently. The training that new firefighters receive is one of the most important aspects of job preparation. Training includes demanding classroom work, acquiring new physical skills, and supervised practice under realistic conditions.

A firefighter's training never ends. Even the firefighter who has been with the department for 20 years has something to learn. New firefighting technology, strategies, and tactics have to be learned. New building materials and technology present new challenges. It is imperative that the fire service remain aware of these changes. Staying current is accomplished only with frequent and intense training that is constantly improved and updated to make it more effective.

The size of the training staff is dependent on the size of the department. Small departments may have a single training officer who acts as both the administrator and trainer. Larger departments have a chief of training and instructors to carry out the delivery. This section details the roles of the instructor and the administrator of training programs (the training officer).

Figure 2.9 Fire and emergency services instructors deliver both classroom and hands-on training.

Instructor

Instructor — Individual deemed qualified by the authority having jurisdiction to deliver instruction and training in fire and emergency services; charged with the responsibility to conduct the class, direct the instructional process, teach skills, impart new information, lead discussions, and cause learning to take place.

The **instructor** is responsible for the actual delivery of the training courses to the other members of the department (**Figure 2.9**). These courses could be entry (recruit) level, recurrent training, or advanced training and may be delivered at a training center or in the field. The instructor takes direction from the chief of training and is expected to perform the following duties:

● Deliver prepared training courses using a variety of classroom delivery methods and practical exercises.

● Prepare curriculum for new courses at the request of the chief of training.

● Monitor practical exercises for safety hazards, and correct them immediately when noted.

- File appropriate paperwork to record the progress and completion of course work for all students.

  The instructor must have the following qualifications:

- Ability to meet the appropriate requirements contained in NFPA® 1041, *Standard for Fire Service Instructor Professional Qualifications*

- Knowledge of the fire department's operating procedures and the ability to convey them with the training material

- Good verbal communications skills

- Thorough knowledge of all the skills and theories conveyed to the class

  For more information on the role of a fire service instructor, see the IFSTA **Fire and Emergency Services Instructor** manual.

Training Officer (Chief of Training/Drillmaster)

Of primary importance to most departments is the intradepartmental training they establish and conduct. The **training officer** (sometimes called the *chief of training* or *drillmaster*) actually runs the program. The training officer's responsibilities involve the administration of all fire department training activities. Typically, the training officer reports directly to the fire chief.

The training officer is expected to perform the following duties:

- Plan, organize, and supervise the work of subordinate instructors.

- Determine the need for new training material and evaluate new training techniques, methods, and procedures.

- Conduct risk assessments on all practical training drills and assure the safety of all firefighters during training exercises.

- Research and secure necessary resources to conduct training exercises and classes.

- Oversee the maintenance of department personnel training records.

- Oversee the maintenance of training facilities and equipment.

  The training officer must have the following qualifications:

- Ability to meet the appropriate requirements contained in NFPA® 1041, *Standard for Fire Service Instructor Professional Qualifications*

- Extensive background in educational theory and methodology

- Knowledge of the fire department's record-keeping system

- Ability to interact with the other administrators of the department and convert their concerns into appropriate training courses

Training Officer — Individual responsible for running a fire department's training program, to include the administration of all training activities; typically reports directly to the fire chief. *Also known as* Chief of Training or Drillmaster.

Administration

Every organization requires leadership. In the fire department, that leadership is provided by the personnel assigned to the Administration section. Particularly in larger departments, the Administration division includes a group for personnel service and a grants administrator. Other administrative positions include:

- Human resources/personnel services

- Grants administrator
- Safety officer
- Public information officer
- Assistant or deputy chief
- Fire chief

Because the safety of the department personnel is paramount to the organization, the department must provide for the safety of the department members by staffing or assigning a Safety Officer position. In addition, the department must maintain a positive relationship with the community and the media, so that is the role of the Public Information Officer (PIO). Assistant/Deputy Chiefs serve a vital role within the department's management staff by assuming command during the absence of the chief and by responding to major incidents. The Fire Chief provides the strategic planning for the department and bears the ultimate responsibility for the success or failure of the organization.

Human Resources/Personnel Services

Sometimes working in cooperation with municipal civil service, the fire department's human resources/personnel group is responsible for functions such as:

- Recruitment and hiring of uniformed and non-uniformed personnel
- Salary and promotion practices
- Management of benefits such as insurance (health, dental, life, disability, long-term care) and retirement
- Disciplinary actions
- Maintenance of accurate personnel records
- Supervision of certain civilian positions, such as physician, chaplain, and employee assistance program personnel.

Grants Administrator

Fire departments – especially those that serve the largest metropolitan areas and the smallest rural communities – often seek monetary gifts called grants to help offset the costs of the many services that fire departments provide. Grants can come from local, state, or provincial, national, or even international organizations. Some of these organizations are governmental, some are foundations or other non-profits; some are corporate, and some are civic (such as the Kiwanis or Lions). In recent years in the United States, the Assistance to Firefighters Grants (AFG) from the Federal Emergency Management Agency have increased the availability of grant funds.

The job of a grants administrator is to:

- Identify sources of grant funding for fire department programs.
- Prepare and submit proposals to potential funders, in accordance with funder and fire department guidelines and regulations.
- Monitor spending to assure that it is appropriate to the grant, legal, ethical, and in accordance with funder and department guidelines and regulations.
- Prepare and submit required reports.

Safety Officer

The **safety officer** is charged with overseeing a fire department's occupational safety and health program. Depending on the department, this individual may hold the rank of company officer or battalion chief, or could be a civilian employee. The safety officer must be well respected and able to work effectively with all members of the department from the fire chief to recruits.

The safety officer is required to perform the following duties:

- Formulate and administer the department's occupational safety and health program.
- Maintain an accident investigation and record-keeping system.
- Coordinate safety inspections of all department equipment, apparatus, and facilities.
- Respond to emergency incidents to view operations with the goal of maintaining crew safety, coordinate with the incident commander, and stop or modify operations when serious safety concerns arise (**Figure 2.10**).
- Perform research and provide recommendations on new equipment, apparatus, and facilities in relation to safety issues.

Because the position of safety officer has a variety of duties, this individual needs the following qualifications:

- Ability to meet the requirements established by NFPA® 1521, *Standard for Fire Department Safety Officer*
- Extensive knowledge of emergency operations, building construction, hazardous materials, and incident management
- Ability to effectively communicate with members at all levels of the department
- Ability to carry out research projects, document results, and maintain an effective record-keeping system for firefighter safety and health

For more information on the role of a safety officer, see the IFSTA **Fire Department Safety Officer** manual.

Safety Officer — (1) Fire officer whose primary function is to administrate safety within the entire scope of fire department operations. *Also known as* Health and Safety Officer. (2) Member of the IMS command staff responsible to the incident commander for monitoring and assessing hazardous and unsafe conditions and developing measures for assessing personnel safety on an incident. *Also known as* Incident Safety Officer.

Figure 2.10 An incident safety officer should be assigned to each emergency response.

Public Information Officer (PIO)

The **public information officer** (or information officer) is responsible for maintaining a positive relationship between the fire department, the media, and the general public. Depending on the department, this individual may hold the rank of company officer or battalion chief, or the individual could be a civilian employee.

The PIO is required to perform the following duties:

- Act as the department's primary contact with media representatives.
- Coordinate all departmental news releases and public service announcements.
- Respond to major emergency incidents to act as a liaison between the incident commander and the news media (**Figure 2.11, p. 58**).
- Serve as a departmental spokesperson before neighborhood, civic, and other groups.

Public Information Officer (PIO) — Member of the command staff responsible for interfacing with the media, public, or other agencies requiring information direct from the incident scene. *Also known as* Information Officer (IO).

Figure 2.11 The public information officer is responsible for relaying information about the emergency incident to the media.

Because the PIO is often the only direct view that the public has of the fire department, it is important that this individual have the following qualifications:

- Ability to meet the requirements established by NFPA® 1035, *Standard for Professional Qualifications for Public Fire and Life Safety Educator*

- Ability to effectively convey information to the media and the general public, using easily understood terms, often without a script or advance preparation

- Ability to discriminate between information that can be released and confidential information that should not be released

- Ability to maintain excellent rapport with all members of the fire department, news media, and general public

- Have excellent written and verbal communication skills

For more information on the role of a public information officer, see the IFSTA **Public Information Officer** manual.

Assistant/Deputy Chief

Fire departments usually have one or more assistant or deputy chiefs. These titles are used interchangeably from department to department. An assistant chief is part of the fire department senior management staff. Typically, a fire department has several assistant chiefs, each one assigned a specific function or portion of the department to manage. Some of the roles assigned to an assistant chief include operations, administration, special operations, fire prevention (community risk reduction), resources, or planning.

Figure 2.12 An assistant chief serving as the incident commander of an emergency.

The assistant chief is expected to perform the following duties:

- Supervise the operation of the division of the department to which he or she is assigned.

- Respond to major emergency incidents, when required, and assist in the command structure as needed (**Figure 2.12**).

- Provide input to or carry out the major administrative duties of the fire department. This includes activities such as budgeting, policy development, research and planning, personnel matters, and community relations.

- Assume the duties of the fire chief when required.

To successfully complete the duties of an assistant chief, the individual needs to have a wide variety of personal and professional abilities. The position of assistant chief should require the following qualifications:

- Ability to assume the duties of the chief when the chief is absent

- Ability to meet the appropriate requirements in NFPA® 1021, *Standard for Fire Officer Professional Qualifications*

- A college degree or some education above the high school level; many departments require an advanced degree

- Extensive knowledge of the fire department's administrative structure and process

- Excellent written and oral communication skills

- Thorough knowledge of fire fighting and rescue tactics and strategy; ability to organize the emergency scene through the use of the department's incident management system

For additional information about the role and duties of the assistant chief, refer to the IFSTA **Chief Officer** manual.

Fire Chief/Chief of Department

The fire **chief** or **chief of department** is the chief executive officer of the fire department. The fire chief is ultimately responsible for all operations within the fire department. In turn, the fire chief is responsible to the city manager, mayor, council, district board members, and the members of the fire department. In some jurisdictions, the position is known as the **fire commissioner**. Although the responsibilities remain the same, the activities of the fire chief vary depending on the size of the fire department. In small departments, the fire chief has a close interaction with line personnel and may handle functions that would be delegated to assistant chiefs in larger departments **(Figure 2.13)**. In large departments, the chief is primarily an administrator.

The fire chief is expected to perform the following duties:

- Interact with the heads of other city departments and local government officials.
- Respond to major incidents when required and assist in the command structure as needed.
- Provide leadership and direction to all members of the fire department.
- Participate directly in the city or county budgeting process.
- Develop policy, plans, and objectives for the department.

Figure 2.13 A chief officer arriving at an incident scene.

The position of fire chief is one that presents a great challenge. To meet this challenge, a person must be fully prepared for the job. Some of the requirements for the position of fire chief include:

- Ability to meet the appropriate requirements in NFPA® 1021, *Standard for Fire Officer Professional Qualifications*

- A college degree or some education above the high school level

- Extensive knowledge of the fire department's administrative structure and process

- Excellent written and oral communication skills

- Thorough knowledge of fire fighting and rescue tactics and strategy; ability to organize the emergency scene through the use of the department's incident management system

- Ability to deal with local government officials and processes

- Personnel skills, including labor negotiations skills for paid union departments

For more information about the role of the chief officer, consult IFSTA's **Chief Officer** manual.

Special Operations Personnel

If fire departments only provided standard structural fire protection to their communities, the line positions discussed to this point in the chapter would cover all personnel. However, this is not the case in most modern fire departments, which provide a wide variety of services. These special services require personnel who are trained in special skills. In many cases, these individuals serve as both regular firefighters and specialists in a particular discipline. This section addresses three types of special operations personnel: the airport firefighter, hazardous materials technician, and the technical rescuer. In addition, the section introduces the marine, wildland, and industrial or brigade firefighters.

Airport Firefighter

Aircraft rescue and fire fighting (ARFF) work involves responsibility for protecting life and property, controlling fire hazards, and performing general duties related to airport operations and aircraft safety. **Airport firefighters** are responsible for driving fire apparatus to and from fire scenes, standing by during aircraft emergency landings, handling fuel spills on the airfield, and performing fire fighting and rescue procedures on downed aircraft (**Figure 2.14, p. 62**).

In some cases, airport firefighters also provide conventional fire protection and emergency medical services to the airport facility. The following are duties of the airport firefighter:

- Respond to all fires and standby alarms at an airport; position equipment according to prearranged runway positions; take into consideration the type of aircraft, number of passengers, wind, and other factors.

- Perform rescue, fire fighting, and first aid duties in connection with aircraft emergencies.

Airport Firefighter — Firefighter trained to prevent, control, or extinguish fires that are in or adjacent to aircraft. *Also known as* ARFF Firefighter.

Figure 2.14 Airport firefighters during a live fire training evolution.

Figure 2.15 An aircraft rescue and fire fighting (ARFF) apparatus is positioned to discharge its extinguishing agent on an aircraft.

- Operate aircraft rescue and fire fighting vehicles, fire pumps, turret nozzles, and foam, dry chemical, and water extinguishers (**Figure 2.15**).

- Use specialized tools specific to aircraft emergencies.

- Perform structural fire fighting, emergency medical services, fire prevention duties, and other functions as required on the airport property.

- Attend training courses and drills as required.

Airport firefighters must have all the skills of a structural firefighter and those specific to aircraft and airports. Airport firefighters must have the following special qualifications:

- Ability to meet the requirements in NFPA® 1001, *Standard for Fire Fighter Professional Qualifications*, and NFPA® 1003, *Standard for Airport Fire Fighter Professional Qualifications*

- Knowledge of the proper use and care of aircraft rescue and fire fighting equipment

- Knowledge of modern fire fighting methods used in aircraft rescue and fire fighting, structural fire fighting, and the fundamentals of first aid

- Ability to cope firmly with emergencies with maximum effectiveness

- Ability to analyze situations quickly and objectively and to determine the proper course of action

- Ability to learn and apply correct techniques to combat airfield and aircraft fires

- Skill in driving and operating aircraft rescue and fire fighting vehicles, fire trucks, and related equipment

- Knowledge of aircraft types and characteristics

- Knowledge of the airport facility and its rules and regulations

The IFSTA **Aircraft Rescue and Fire Fighting** manual provides additional information on the role of an airport firefighter.

Hazardous Materials Technician

Hazardous materials can be found in every community, and all fire departments must be prepared to handle hazardous materials emergencies. Some departments do this by using regular engine, truck, and rescue company personnel to handle the incidents. Others have dedicated hazardous materials response units and teams to control such emergencies. In most cases, the **hazardous materials technician** is a firefighter who has received additional, specialized training on the topic.

The hazardous materials technician is expected to perform the following duties:

- Conduct fire safety/hazardous materials inspections for compliance with applicable codes and standards.

- Respond to and assist with the mitigation of hazardous materials incidents (**Figure 2.16**).

- Assist with the development of departmental programs related to hazardous materials.

- Participate in extensive specialized hazardous materials training.

The serious health and safety threats posed by many hazardous materials emergencies require that personnel assigned to mitigate these emergencies be extremely competent. The hazardous materials technician must have the following major qualifications:

- The ability to meet the requirements of NFPA® 472, *Standard for Competence of Responders to Hazardous Materials/Weapons of Mass Destruction Incidents*

Hazardous Material — Any substance or material that poses an unreasonable risk to health, safety, property, and/or the environment if it is not properly controlled during handling, storage manufacture, processing, packaging, use, disposal, or transportation.

Hazardous Materials Technician — Individual trained to use specialized protective clothing and control equipment to control the release of a hazardous material. Hazardous materials technicians can specialize in four areas: Cargo Tank Specialty, Intermodal Tank Specialty, Marine Tank Vessel Specialty, and Tank Car Specialty.

Figure 2.16 Hazardous materials technicians at a hazmat incident. *Courtesy of Steve Baker.*

- Extensive knowledge in chemistry and other physical sciences
- Knowledge of specific departmental operating procedures for hazardous materials incidents (which can include chemical, biological, nuclear, and ordnance incidents)

The IFSTA **Hazardous Materials for First Responders** and **Hazardous Materials: Managing the Incident** manuals provide additional information in this area.

Technical Rescuer (Special Rescue Technician or Technical Rescue Specialist)

Some of the challenging rescue situations a fire department may have to respond to include the following:

- High- and low-angle (rope) rescue
- Trench collapse
- Confined space entry
- Industrial extrication
- Agricultural extrication
- Transportation extrication (**Figure 2.17**)
- Cave or mine rescue
- Structural collapse
- SCUBA/swift water rescue

Some departments choose to have different teams for each type of potential emergency. Other departments have one team of specialized personnel, known as the rescue company or heavy rescue squad, who handle all rescue situations. The **technical rescuer** is expected to perform the following duties:

- Respond to special rescue situations, fires, and other emergencies in accordance to fire department standard operating procedures.
- Maintain rescue equipment in a state of readiness.
- Participate in special training sessions.
- Provide input to department administrators on equipment needs and specifications.

Most technical rescuers are firefighters who have been trained to a higher level for these particular rescue situations. The technical rescuer needs the following qualifications:

- Ability to meet the requirements in NFPA® 1001, *Standard for Fire Fighter Professional Qualifications, and* NFPA® 1006, *Standard for Technical Rescuer Professional Qualifications*
- Specialized training on the equipment and methods used for special rescue situations to which the individual will be assigned
- Mechanical aptitude to adapt to the conditions presented by particular situations

The IFSTA **Principles of Vehicle Extrication**, **Fire Service Search and Rescue**, and **Technical Rescue for Structural Collapse** manuals contain more information for special rescue personnel.

Technical Rescuer — Individual who has been trained to perform or direct a variety of unique and/or complex rescue situations, such as rope rescues (low- and high-angle), confined space, trench and excavation, structural collapse, mine and tunnel, and other rescue types. *Also known as* Special Rescue Technician or Technical Rescue Specialist.

Wildland Fire — Unplanned, unwanted, and uncontrolled fire in vegetative fuels such as grass, brush, or timberland involving uncultivated lands; requires suppression action and may threaten structures or other improvements. *Also known as* Ground Cover Fire, Ground Fire, Natural Cover Fire, Vegetation Fire, or Wildfire.

Figure 2.18 Marine firefighters combating a fire aboard a small vessel. *Courtesy of John Lewis.*

Figure 2.17 Technical rescuers practicing vehicle extrication techniques.

Marine, Wildland, and Industrial Firefighters

In addition to the special operations personnel described above, other firefighters choose to become marine, wildland, or industrial firefighters. Marine firefighters are land-based firefighters who specialize in fire suppression operations in the marine domain, which includes large and small vessels (including vessels such as houseboats), marinas, piers, docks, and wharves **(Figure 2.18)**. Professional qualifications for such firefighters are covered by NFPA® 1005, *Standard for Professional Qualifications for Marine Fire Fighting for Land-Based Fire Fighters*. The IFSTA **Marine Fire Fighting for Land-Based Firefighters** manual provides additional information on this subject.

Wildland firefighters use special skills and equipment to suppress **wildland fires (Figure 2.19, p. 66)**. Professional qualifications for wildland firefighters are described by NFPA® 1051, *Standard for Wildland Fire Fighter Professional Qualifications*, which describes four levels of advanced training and responsibility.

Industrial firefighters, unlike most firefighters who serve in a public fire department, are employed by private companies — such as refineries or manufacturing plants — whose operations and processes make an on-site **industrial fire department** necessary. Industrial firefighters are members of an industrial fire department, compared to members of an **industrial fire brigade (Figure 2.20, p. 66)**. IFSTA's **Industrial Emergency Services Training: Incipient Level** and **Industrial Exterior and Structural Fire Brigades** manuals provide additional information on this subject.

Industrial Fire Department — Full-time emergency response organization providing fire suppression, rescue, and related activities at a commercial, institutional, or industrial facility or facilities under the same ownership and management. While the industrial fire department is generally trained and equipped for specialized operations based on site-specific hazards present at the facility, it may also respond off-site under a mutual aid agreement.

Industrial Fire Brigade — Team of employees organized within a private company, industrial facility, or plant who are assigned to respond to fires and emergencies on that property.

Figure 2.19 Wildland firefighters working a fire line.

Figure 2.20 Industrial fire brigade members practicing foam application techniques.

Fire Prevention (Community Risk Reduction) Personnel

The **fire prevention** or *community risk reduction* division is extremely important to the fire department's overall purpose of public protection. In fact, some would argue that this should be the largest section of a department. An effective fire prevention program not only protects the community, but also decreases the need for suppression activities, thereby reducing the cost and risk of extinguishing fire. An effective fire prevention program, however, requires aggressiveness and enterprising action to make it successful. For a fire department to be complete, it must have a competent fire prevention program.

An assistant chief or other staff officer of the department typically heads the fire prevention division of a fire department. Depending on local customs, this person may be called the assistant chief in charge of fire prevention or the **fire marshal (Figure 2.21)**. The qualifications for fire marshal are contained in NFPA® 1037, *Standard for Professional Qualifications for Fire Marshal*. The fire marshal has subordinate officers to fill the various roles within the division. Depending on local customs, fire prevention personnel may be sworn members of the fire department or they may be civilian employees.

The fire prevention division generally includes four major responsibilities:

- Fire prevention/inspection
- Fire investigation
- Public fire and life safety education
- Fire protection/building plans examination

Figure 2.21 An assistant chief of fire prevention oversees the fire prevention program.

Fire Inspector

The **fire inspector**, sometimes called a fire code enforcement officer or fire prevention officer, conducts technical and supervisory work in the fire prevention program. The work involves supervising and participating in field enforcement of local and state or provincial fire prevention laws and ordinances (**Figure 2.22, p. 68**). Considerable effort is required to correct fire hazards, and emphasis is placed on public assembly inspections and those areas (such as industrial occupancies) where special hazards are present. The work allows considerable latitude for independent judgment and is reviewed by observing the results.

Fire Prevention — (1) Part of the science of fire protection that deals with preventing the outbreak of fire by eliminating fire hazards through such activities as inspection, code enforcement, education, and investigation programs. (2) Division of a fire department responsible for conducting fire prevention programs of inspection, code enforcement, education, and investigation. *Also known as* Fire Prevention Bureau.

Fire Marshal — Highest fire prevention officer of a state, province, county, or municipality. In Canada, this officer is *also known as* the Fire Commissioner.

Fire Inspector — Fire personnel assigned to inspect property with the purpose of enforcing fire regulations.

Figure 2.22 A fire inspector preparing to inspect a hotel under construction.

A fire inspector is expected to perform duties such as:

- Assist the fire chief or fire marshal in planning and implementing the local fire prevention program.

- Inspect places of public assembly, such as halls, auditoriums, theaters, businesses, and industrial establishments, for existing or potential fire hazards and order correction of dangerous conditions.

- Conduct plans reviews.

- Receive complaints on fire hazards, investigate them, and recommend or order methods of correction.

- Inspect schools for fire hazards, conduct fire drills, and give presentations to students on fire hazards and drill procedures.

- Cooperate with inspectors or field service workers of other municipal departments when making inspections to correct or remove hazards involving structural, electrical, and utility service safety.

- Cooperate with and assist fire companies in district fire prevention and inspection activities.

- Prepare reports of inspections and maintain files on all records.

The fire inspector is obviously responsible for a wide range of duties. To effectively perform these functions, the inspector must have the following qualifications:

- Ability to meet the requirements in NFPA® 1031, *Standard for Professional Qualifications for Fire Inspector and Plan Examiner*

- Thorough knowledge of fire safety laws, fire hazards, and methods of fire prevention

- Knowledge of the principles and practices of building construction and maintenance

- Ability to recognize existing and potential fire and casualty hazards in a wide variety of structures and installations

- Ability to establish and maintain effective working relationships with property owners, other employees, and the general public

- Ability to express factual information clearly and concisely, both orally and in writing

- Ability to enforce rules and regulations firmly, tactfully, and impartially

The IFSTA **Fire Inspection and Code Enforcement** manual provides additional information on this subject.

Fire Investigator

Fire Investigator — Public or private sector individual tasked with discovering the origin and cause of a fire, as well as who may be responsible or liable for a fire.

The purpose of a fire investigation is to determine the cause of the fire. The results are then used to settle insurance claims, prosecute criminals, and protect the innocent. The responsibility of fire investigations may fall on several different sources. A fire department may handle the fire investigations in its area with specially trained personnel. The state or provincial fire marshal's office usually provides a **fire investigator** for areas that do not have their own personnel. Large cities may use police and fire personnel to form a strike force. Many state police forces organize fire and arson investigation teams. Federal agencies, such as the Bureau of Alcohol, Tobacco, Firearms, and Explosives (commonly called ATF) or the Federal Bureau of Investigations (FBI), may provide assistance on large incidents. In Canada, this would include the Royal Canadian Mounted Police (RCMP), local policing authority, or fire commissioner's office.

The field of fire investigation has become highly technical. It is now possible to discover information that a few years ago would have been impossible to discover. The use of computer modeling and fire testing, for example, has improved the accuracy of many investigations. A fire investigator is responsible for determining the cause of all assigned fires, regardless of size. An **arson investigator** is needed to answer specific questions once the fire cause is determined to be arson.

The job functions and requirements are similar because each investigator must make analytic judgments based on the remains at the fire scene. A fire or arson investigator is expected to perform the following duties:

- Respond to the fire scene as part of routine duties or respond when summoned.

- Make preliminary observations of the location, including the exterior of the fire area, the condition of the involved location, and the position of surrounding objects.

- Conduct the investigation of the fire area, and use all available means to determine the origin of the fire, the fire cause, and the results (**Figure 2.23**).

- Attempt to determine the sequence of events by using evidence, technical data, outside agencies, and witnesses.

- Appear in court to express an expert opinion about the fire cause and the results of investigations.

- Participate in arson awareness and prevention programs.

Arson Investigator — Public sector fire investigator who primarily investigates intentionally set fires; may be tasked with locating and arresting arsonists and interviewing suspects. May also have limited law enforcement powers, such as the power of arrest and authorization to carry a weapon.

Figure 2.23 A fire investigator taking photos at the scene of a suspicious fire.

A fire or arson investigator must have the following qualifications:

- Ability to meet the requirements in NFPA® 1033, *Standard for Professional Qualifications Fire Investigator*
- Thorough knowledge of all applicable areas of fire science, including fire chemistry, fuel types, burn patterns, and ignition sources
- Thorough knowledge of fire environment, including building construction, utility services, motor vehicles, and weather
- Ability to do strenuous activity, see well, and perceive colors accurately
- Ability to make pertinent observations and to take complete and coherent notes
- Ability to use tools, cameras, gas detection devices, microscopes, and other technical equipment efficiently and correctly
- Ability to converse and work with property owners, other agencies, witnesses, and the general public
- Ability to express factual information clearly and concisely, both orally and in writing

The IFSTA **Fire Investigator** manual provides additional information on this subject.

Figure 2.24 A fire and life safety educator preparing to deliver a training program on installing child safety seats. *Courtesy of Beverley Walker.*

Public Fire and Life Safety Educator

Public fire and life safety education consists of informing the public about fire hazards, life safety issues, fire causes, precautions, and actions to take during a fire. To reduce fires in the community, the public fire and life safety educator should focus on fire prevention in the home. The public is encouraged to use smoke detectors, fire extinguishers, and exit drills. Through these efforts, the loss of life and property is reduced. The public fire and life safety educator is the hub of the public fire education program (**Figure 2.24**).

The public fire and life safety educator is required to perform the following duties:

- Assist the fire chief and fire marshal in planning and implementing the local public fire education program.
- Design and develop training aids to use in public demonstrations and learning sessions.
- Work with newspapers, radio, and television to disseminate information to the public, in cooperation with the Public Information Officer (PIO).
- Develop flyers and pamphlets that contain pertinent information.
- Conduct education activities for the public.
- Provide information to firefighters about public fire and life safety education so that they can effectively represent the department's program.

A public fire and life safety educator needs the following qualifications:

- Ability to meet the requirements in NFPA® 1035, *Standard for Professional Qualifications Public Fire and Life Safety Educator*
- Thorough knowledge of current fire education principles and techniques
- Knowledge of human motivation and how to make the information desirable to learn

- Ability to work with news media professionals
- Ability to effectively communicate and to present oneself professionally
- Ability to portray confidence and to present an image acceptable to the public

Difference between Fire and Life Safety Educator and Public Information Officer

Some people confuse the roles of the fire and life safety educator and those of the public information officer. In part, this may be because both positions are covered by NFPA® 1035, *Standard for Professional Qualifications Fire and Life Safety Educator*, and the personnel who perform these duties may be from the same section of a fire department. In some departments, a single person serves as both fire and life safety educator and public information officer.

While both of these duties involve the public, their specific functions are different. Fire and life safety educators conduct training sessions with the public that cover a broad spectrum of fire prevention, fire safety, risk reduction, and life safety topics. The public information officer serves as a liaison for providing information between the fire department, the media, and the public.

For more information on public fire education and the responsibility of the educator, see the IFSTA **Fire and Life Safety Educator** manual.

Fire Protection Engineer/Building Plans Examiner

The use of **fire protection engineers (FPEs)** and building plans examiners by municipal fire departments has increased significantly. In some cases, the fire protection engineer is responsible for building plans review to assure compliance with fire and safety codes and standards.

FPEs are typically civilian employees who have an educational background in one of the following: fire protection engineering, safety engineering, civil engineering, mechanical engineering, or engineering technology. Primarily, the FPE acts as a consultant to the upper administration of the department. FPEs are used in both the operations and prevention sections of a department, although it is more common for the FPE to work in the prevention section. In operations, the FPE provides assistance in research and planning, purchasing equipment and apparatus, facilities specifications, hazardous materials problems and responses, water supply issues, and emergency scene safety. FPEs often handle building plans reviews, fire protection systems plans reviews, systems tests, apparatus access issues, and other fire prevention and code enforcement concerns.

The typical duties of a fire protection engineer or plans examiner include the following:

- Review site and building plans, note code violations, and make recommendations for changes (**Figure 2.25, p. 72**).
- Review fire protection systems plans, note deficiencies, and make recommendations for improving systems.

Fire Protection Engineer (FPE) — Graduate of an accredited institution of higher education who has specialized in engineering science related to fire protection.

Figure 2.25 A plans examiner reviewing a set of building plans.

- Inspect, review, and test fire protection systems.
- Consult with those involved in preliminary planning for building construction or change and give advice on current legal requirements.
- Interact with officials of all departments involved in regulating construction and use.
- Provide assistance in issues related to the municipal water supply system.
- Perform research, assist in planning functions, prepare specifications, and perform other services as required by operations personnel.

A fire protection engineer must have the following two qualifications:

1. College degree in one of the following: fire protection engineering, safety engineering, civil engineering, mechanical engineering, or engineering technology

2. Appropriate professional registry (often called licensing) such as a Professional Engineer (PE), a Certified Safety Professional (CSP), or a Canadian Registered Safety Professional (CRSP)

A building plans examiner must meet the requirements in NFPA® 1031, *Standard for Professional Qualifications for Fire Inspector and Plan Examiner.* Both fire protection engineers and building plans examiners must have:

- Thorough knowledge of all applicable state or provincial and local laws and codes concerning fire protection
- Ability to review and evaluate plans and proposals for fire hazards
- Ability to provide appropriate recommendations relating to the review and evaluation process
- Ability to communicate appropriate recommendations relating to the review and evaluation process
- Ability to effectively communicate orally and in writing
- Ability to establish working relationships with members of other regulatory agencies
- Ability to provide information on a burning building's structural condition, on water hydraulics problems, and on the nature of hazardous materials involved in an incident

More information about the plans review process can be found in the IFSTA **Plans Examiner** manual.

Emergency Medical Services Personnel

The fire department's role in the **emergency medical service** has increased significantly since the late 1920's, when firefighters from a few fire departments gave aid to citizens who were experiencing breathing problems and heart attack symptoms. By the early 1960's, the techniques of emergency life support were being perfected, and public demand for these services rose. By the 1970's, a few departments started to use specialized paramedic technicians to provide advanced life support for patients of accidents and illness working under direction of a physician or medical director. These services were provided to complement the ambulance and first aid service that many departments already provided.

Today, the fire service's involvement in providing emergency medical services (EMS) is dependent on local needs and practices. Departments that provide first response to EMS incidents have trained first aid responders on regular fire companies such as engines, trucks, or squads. These personnel may be trained as a first responder, emergency medical technician (EMT), or paramedic (**Figure 2.26, p. 74**). The ambulance that responds to transport the patient also has trained crew members on board. Some departments use civilian EMS personnel, while other departments cross-train firefighters in EMS. For example:

- Some fire departments still do not have any responsibility for EMS.
- Some departments provide first response to priority calls.
- Some departments provide first response to all calls.
- Many departments handle all the EMS responsibilities for their districts, including the transport of patients to the hospital.

The following sections highlight the capabilities of personnel who are trained to the first responder, emergency medical technician, or paramedic levels. Remember that in most cases EMS duties are performed in addition to those of a firefighter.

First Responder

The primary function of the **first responder** is to sustain life until more highly trained medical personnel arrive. In most states, a first responder has minimal emergency care training, equipment and limited tools to gain access to the patient; in other states, the "first responder" is a certified EMT. The first responder is not usually responsible for transporting the patient to the hospital.

The first responder is responsible for treating patients with medical conditions or injuries. The job consists of stabilizing the patient. Some of these conditions treated by the first responder include but are not limited to:

- Respiratory distress or arrest
- Heart attack or cardiac arrest
- Extensive bleeding
- Poisoning
- Shock

Emergency Medical Services (EMS) — Initial medical evaluation/treatment provided to employees and others who become ill or are injured. These services may be provided by an in-house emergency response team or by an outside provider.

First Responder (EMS) — (1) First person arriving at the scene of an accident or medical emergency who is trained to administer first aid and basic life support. (2) Level of emergency medical training, between first aider and emergency medical technician levels, that is recognized by the authority having jurisdiction (AHJ).

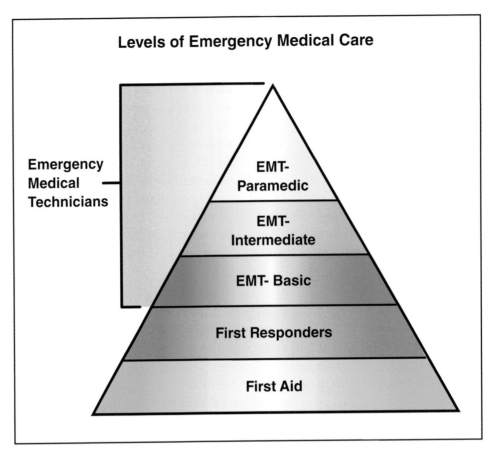

Figure 2.26 Levels of Emergency Medical Care.

- Emergency childbirth
- Substance abuse
- Stroke
- Diabetic coma and insulin shock
- Fractures
- Seizures
- Animal bites
- Severe exposure and burns

The first responder is trained to apply emergency **first aid** to those having any of these listed conditions and he or she is effectively equipped to do so. For more details, see the Brady/IFSTA **Fire Service First Responder** manual. The National Highway Traffic Safety Administration (NHTSA) has also developed a curriculum for first responders.

Emergency Medical Technician

The **emergency medical technician** (EMT) provides **basic life support** (BLS) for those whose lives are in danger. The EMT has been trained in a program of at least 120 hours and certified proficient by a regulatory agency. As compared to the first responder, the EMT is responsible for providing more care to the patient and will have significantly more training and equipment to do so. The EMT may also be responsible for transporting the patient. **Appendix C** contains the report, *Prehospital 9-1-1 Emergency Medical Response: The Role of the United States Fire Service in Delivery and Coordination.*

First Aid — Immediate medical care given to a patient until he or she can be transported to a medical facility.

Emergency Medical Technician (EMT) — Professional-level provider of basic life support emergency medical care. Requires certification by some authority.

Basic Life Support (BLS) — Emergency medical treatment administered without the use of adjunctive equipment; includes maintenance of airway, breathing, and circulation, as well as basic bandaging and splinting.

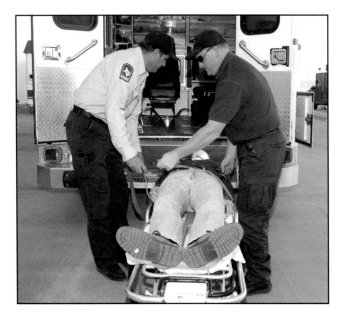

Figure 2.27 EMTs preparing a patient for transport to a nearby medical facility.

The EMT is expected to perform the duties of the first responder, plus the following:

- Conduct examinations to determine the extent of illness or injury.
- Stabilize the patient before taking him or her to a hospital (**Figure 2.27**):
- Maintain patient's respiration.
  - Use mechanical aids like suction and oxygen equipment to aid breathing.
  - Take blood pressure and other vital signs.
  - Dress and bandage wounds.
  - Immobilize fractures in all areas of the body.
- Use proper methods for moving patients to the ambulance.
- Transport patients safely to the hospital while taking proper care of them.
- Extricate patients from automobiles and other sources of entrapment.

  NOTE: Extrication may be performed by other firefighters or a rescue team.
- Maintain proper control over the accident scene until police arrive.
- Be familiar with and use proper communication procedures.
- Maintain proper records of activities.

These listed duties are those expected of a basic level EMT. Many jurisdictions have certification levels for EMTs that exceed these minimums. EMTs that are certified to these advanced levels may provide more advanced care than the basic level EMTs. For example, most EMT-Basics are trained in the use of automatic external defibrillators (AEDs), and EMT- Intermediates are trained to use semi-automatic external defibrillators (SAEDs), start IV's, and administer some medications. In some jurisdictions EMTs are the first level of **advanced life support**.

For additional information, see the Brady/IFSTA **Fire Service Emergency Care** manual.

Advanced Life Support (ALS) — Advanced medical skills performed by trained medical personnel, such as the administration of medications, or airway management procedures to save a patient's life.

Paramedic

A **paramedic** is the highest patient care position within the emergency medical service. In many jurisdictions, paramedic is the first level of advanced life support (ALS). At a minimum, paramedics must complete a training program and be certified by a regulatory agency in the state. This training will consist of 800 or more hours, depending on the jurisdiction. The program includes course work, practical instruction, and a field internship. Paramedics work under the supervision of a physician.

Compared to the first responder and EMT, the paramedic maintains the most responsibility for patient care. Paramedics handle incidents similar to those handled by EMTs, but they are able to provide ALS whereas EMTs are limited to BLS. Thus, the paramedic's knowledge must be more in-depth. To be competent, paramedics must be able to perform the following duties:

- Recognize and assess medical emergencies.
- Decide priorities of medical treatment and communicate necessary data to the responsible physician.
- Follow the directions of the physician concerning treatment and report the progress of treatment.
- Function and exercise judgment in stabilizing the patient when out of contact with the physician; formal protocols (standing orders) may be established by medical command and must be followed by the paramedic in these situations.
- Administer intravenous fluids and drugs, including narcotics.
- Perform airway management, including intubation.
- Direct the proper transport of the patient.
- Maintain proper records.
- Maintain emergency equipment and supplies.

Paramedics also accompany patients to the hospital. During the trip, paramedics stay in contact with the hospital to handle situations as they arise.

EMS Chief/Officer

The emergency medical services chief or officer supervises an EMS company in the station and at the emergency scene. The authority for this position is delegated from the department's chief officer. The work includes responsibility for proper maintenance and operation of the fire station and EMS equipment.

The EMS officer performs a wide variety of EMS and related duties, including inspections of equipment, personnel, and public buildings. Routine duties are performed with independence within established regulations but under the general direction of a fire department chief officer. The EMS officer is evaluated by observation of work in progress, by results obtained, and by inspections of quarters and equipment. Depending on the structure of the fire department, the EMS officer holds the rank of lieutenant, captain, major, or a similar title. An EMS officer is expected to perform the following duties:

- Reviews pre-hospital care reports.
- Maintains files on assigned EMS personnel to ensure current certification in accordance with county and state/provincial standards.

- Coordinates and schedules continuing education opportunities including field care audits, field observations, ride-alongs, attendance at required meetings, interaction with base hospitals and other agencies.
- Prepares statistical and EMS program reports.
- Establishes and maintains rapport with ambulance providers, city and county EMS agencies, and other interfacing agencies.
- Develops and updates fire department EMS procedures as required.
- Attends or arranges for EMS related meetings, such as the Emergency Medical Care Committee, Pre-hospital Care Board, and Base Hospital Committees.
- Prepares and assists with the administration of the department EMS program budget.
- Purchases, evaluates, and inventories emergency medical supplies and equipment.
- Develops and arranges EMS drills, multicasualty-incident exercises, and EMS critiques to maintain personnel skills and training.
- Responds on major incidents and acts in ICS staff roles, as assigned.
- Acts as the Infection Control Officer for the department.
- Provides on-scene supervision and evaluation of fire department personnel on medical emergencies.

The job requirements for EMS officers are extensive because of their tremendous responsibilities. Because the EMS officer is the leader, expectations of the person in this position are extremely high. An EMS officer must have the following qualifications:

- Knowledge of local and state/provincial laws and regulations relating to emergency medical services and pre-hospital care
- Knowledge of common and/or specific practices and procedures employed in emergency medical services and paramedic programs
- Knowledge of management of emergency response programs and organizations, particularly in regard to fire department operations
- Knowledge of training methodology and techniques, data collection and analysis, medical quality improvement programs, and case reviews
- Knowledge of personnel practices and administration
- Ability and skill to plan, organize, assign, coordinate, direct and evaluate work of subordinates
- Ability and skill to read, interpret, and apply applicable medical policies, protocols, and procedures
- Ability and skill to develop and maintain cooperative working relationships with a variety of agencies, boards, commissions, and committees with varying interests and political agendas
- Ability and skill to perform and instruct a wide variety of EMS procedures in both field and emergency room settings
- Ability to triage
- Possess a valid driver's license
- Current ALS and BLS certificates
- State/provincial or national paramedic certificate or R.N. license

Emergency Management Personnel

Emergency (or disaster) management is the specialized discipline of anticipating various types of natural or human-made risks and planning to limit their consequences. The risks of interest to emergency management include:

- Mass casualty
- Weather-related disasters
- Earthquake or other natural disasters
- Industrial disasters
- Environmental disasters
- Major hazardous materials incident
- Mass evacuation
- Pandemic, epidemic, or quarantine
- Acts of terror

Emergency management activities take place on the national, state or provincial, county, and local levels. Because fire departments respond to all sorts of disasters, they increasingly either employ fire emergency management personnel or work closely with emergency management personnel from other public agencies, local corporations, or other providers (such as the Red Cross or Salvation Army). Emergency management personnel include the emergency management specialist (also called an emergency manager or emergency management planner) **(Figure 2.28)**.

According to the United States Bureau of Labor Statistics, emergency management specialists or emergency managers have special training to prepare them to coordinate disaster response or crisis management activities, provide disaster preparedness training, and prepare emergency plans and procedures for natural (e.g., hurricanes, floods, earthquakes), wartime, or technological

Figure 2.28 Emergency managers working in a command post during a series of large wildland fires.

(e.g., nuclear power plant emergencies, hazardous materials spills) disasters or hostage situations. Many emergency management professionals earn (and many employers require) certifications such as Certified Emergency Manager (CEM) and Certified Business Continuity Professional (CBCP).

Other Fire Department Personnel

In order to carry out the broad mission of the fire department, other personnel, such as telecommunicators, information technology personnel, facilities management personnel, and apparatus and equipment maintenance personnel are required. This section describes some of these personnel.

Telecommunications/Dispatch Personnel

The radio communications system of the fire department is the operation's central nervous system. The backbone of this system is the **telecommunicator** who operates the system (**Figure 2.29**). Telecommunicators may be civilians or sworn members of the department and typically work 8- to 12-hour shifts. Some departments have their telecommunicators work the same shifts as the line companies. In many cases, a regional dispatch center processes calls for several communities or departments.

Telecommunicator — Person who works in the telecommunications center and processes information from the public and from emergency responders. *Formerly known as* Dispatcher. *Also known as* Emergency Communications Technician.

Communications Technology

The field of emergency communications has been drastically influenced by changes in communications technology. In addition to voice and TDD (hearing impaired) calls, some emergency communications centers are now able to communicate via email or even text message. Some centers can geographically locate 911 callers using GPS coordinates provided by cellular phones or data provided by cellular towers. Systems such as Reverse 911 allow emergency communications centers to contact all residents within a geographical area to provide emergency information in an "outbound" fashion. Some systems use automatic vehicle locators (AVLs) to pinpoint emergency apparatus on a map, making it possible to dispatch units closest to the scene of an emergency. As communication technologies continue to evolve, so too will emergency communications.

The duties of the telecommunicator include the following:

- Take emergency and non-emergency phone calls and process the information appropriately.

- Dispatch the appropriate units to handle reported emergencies.

Figure 2.29 Telecommunicators receive emergency calls from the public and dispatch emergency responders.

- Maintain contact with companies that are in service and provide communications assistance when required.
- Follow departmental guidelines to relocate non-assigned companies to fill empty stations during an extended incident.
- Follow departmental policy in relaying information to the media.
- Record all information according to departmental policy.

The telecommunicator must have the following qualifications:

- Ability to meet the appropriate requirements contained in NFPA® 1061, *Standard for Professional Qualifications for Public Safety Telecommunicator*
- Where necessary, be EMD (Emergency Medical Dispatch) qualified
- Ability to communicate clearly and concisely
- Ability to remain calm during stressful situations
- Knowledge of fire department standard operating procedures for company assignment and relocation
- Ability to operate communications equipment, including radios, telephones, computers, fire alarm equipment, and recording equipment
- Ability to operate a computer

For more information on the role of a public safety telecommunicator, refer to the IFSTA **Telecommunicator** manual.

Information Technology Personnel

Like other complex organizations, especially those that deal with complicated situations, fire departments rely on information technology and on information technology (IT) professionals to maintain and troubleshoot hardware and software.

Depending on the size of a fire department, services such as IT personnel, facilities management, and fleet maintenance may fall under the fire department's "umbrella" or may be provided by other municipal departments (i.e. fleet services, building maintenance, etc.). Examples of information technology used in the fire and emergency medical service environment include:

- Computer-aided dispatch
- Vehicle location systems
- Mapping
- Telemetry of patient information to and from hospitals
- Shift scheduling

Facilities Management Personnel

The fire department operates a wide variety of facilities. Volunteer fire departments not only operate their facilities, but can also own them. Fire department facilities include:

- Cooking, sleeping, and laundry quarters in fire stations
- Bays for storing apparatus and other vehicles
- Apparatus and vehicle fueling and maintenance facilities

- Equipment storage and maintenance facilities
- Work out areas and equipment, either located in fire stations or elsewhere
- Classrooms
- Outdoor training areas
- Offices

Each of these types of areas requires functioning utilities (electricity, water, plumbing), HVAC, housekeeping and groundskeeping, short- and long-term maintenance, and security. Providing such services is the role of facilities maintenance personnel. These personnel can be facilities managers or skilled or semi-skilled tradespeople who may be employed by the fire department, the city, or a combination.

Apparatus and/or Equipment Maintenance Personnel

To keep the fire department running properly, maintenance personnel are required for the testing and preventive maintenance of fire apparatus and equipment. In some jurisdictions, the department carries out its maintenance and repair. In other jurisdictions, the maintenance facility or "shop" services all city departments. Wherever they work, maintenance personnel need specialized training in apparatus, in addition to being able to maintain such fire equipment as pumps, aerial devices, and generators. Fire equipment maintenance personnel are responsible for maintaining all portable equipment on the apparatus.

The following are typical duties for apparatus maintenance personnel:

- Perform routine maintenance on all mechanical components of the vehicle (**Figure 2.30, p. 82**).
- Perform repairs on all mechanical components of the vehicle.
- Repair damage to the body of the vehicle as required.
- Maintain and repair all fire-related portions of the apparatus, including fire pumps and aerial devices.
- Perform service tests on aerial devices and fire pumps.
- Inspect the vehicle according to state or provincial requirements.
- Maintain records of all work performed on each apparatus.

Apparatus maintenance personnel should have the following qualifications:

- Ability to meet the appropriate requirements contained in NFPA® 1071, *Standard for* **Emergency Vehicle Technician** *Standard for EVT Professional Qualifications*
- Certification by an organization such as the National Association of Emergency Vehicle Technicians (NAEVT)
- Appropriate automotive mechanic certification for the types of vehicles to be worked on
- Training in the maintenance of equipment specific to fire apparatus
- Certification to perform state or provincial inspections
- Ability to operate towing vehicles if required

Emergency Vehicle Technician (EVT) — Individual trained to perform emergency response vehicle inspections, diagnostic testing, maintenance, repair procedures, and operational testing. The NFPA® recognizes three levels of EVTs.

Figure 2.30 Vehicle maintenance personnel work closely with driver/operators to ensure emergency response vehicles are well maintained.

The typical duties for equipment maintenance personnel include the following:

- Maintain portable equipment such as hose, ladders, SCBAs, hand and power tools, and lighting or electrical equipment

- Service test equipment after repairs or on an annual basis as required by applicable standards

- Stock extra parts for potential repairs

- Maintain a record system for recording repairs and testing fire alarms communications

  Equipment maintenance personnel should have the following qualifications:

- Knowledge of the proper repair and testing procedures for all equipment

- Appropriate licenses and training for equipment

- Manufacturer's certification for servicing specialized equipment such as SCBA

- Ability to analyze equipment for problems

Chapter Summary

The fire department's mission once was fairly straightforward: Protect lives and property from unwanted fire. Beginning in the 1970s, however, the fire service also began providing basic (and now advanced) emergency medical care. Fire department involvement in hazardous materials incidents and a variety of other technological and natural disasters also began to increase. Not surprisingly, fire service personnel can prepare themselves for many highly technical subspecialties. In addition, the fire service offers a definite career ladder for those interested in fire service management.

Review Questions

1. What duties will a Rescue Squad/Company perform that a Truck Company will not?

2. Why could the title and roles of a Battalion/District Chief vary?

3. What officer is charged with overseeing a fire department's occupational safety and health program?

4. What are four possible types of special operations positions in which a firefighter can specialize?

5. What positions typically make up the fire prevention (community risk reduction) division in a fire department?

6. What are the four types of Emergency Medical Service personnel that could be a part of the fire department?

7. What personnel roles can be filled by sworn civilians or outside contractors depending on the size of the department?

8. What role will emergency management personnel play in community safety planning?

Early Traditions and History

Chapter Contents

Key Terms

FESHE Outcomes

This chapter provides information that addresses the outcomes for the Fire and Emergency Services Higher Education (FESHE) *Principles of Emergency Services* course.

1. Illustrate and explain the history and culture of the fire service.

Early Traditions and History

Learning Objectives

After reading this chapter, students will be able to:

1. Describe the early history of fire services.

2. Discuss fire protection in early America.

3. Explain how the growth of the volunteer fire service affects modern-day fire and emergency services.

4. Describe how the age of steam affects modern-day fire and emergency services.

5. Identify key developments from the chemical engine and early ladder trucks that are still used in modern-day fire and emergency services.

6. Tell how improvements to protective clothing and self-contained breathing apparatus impact modern-day fire practices.

7. Indicate how developments in gasoline- and diesel-powered equipment has changed modern-day fire practices.

8. Explain how the modern-day philosophy of public safety is impacted by historic fires in North America.

9. Explain how the modern-day philosophy of firefighter safety is impacted by historic fires in North America.

Chapter 3
Early Traditions and History

Case History

Being a firefighter was as much a part of the Andrews' family tradition as popcorn on Saturday night. Grandpa Jack signed on as a volunteer on his 18th birthday in 1960, without a physical or written exam. (There were some junior members who were even younger.) He enjoyed the weekly drills where he learned about hose handling, ladder climbing, and all the other skills of firefighting. Those two-three hour classes were harder than he expected. Live-fire training, special weekend classes at the state fire academy, and the occasional visit to highly hazardous locations like the magnesium factory expanded upon Jack's firefighter training. He had some pretty exciting experiences and loved to talk about them.

It is Jed's turn now to follow Grandpa Jack's footsteps. But his path will be different. He plans to gain experience as a volunteer and then try to get a position at one of the nearby career departments. Both as a volunteer and paid firefighter, he will need to pass a rigorous physical fitness test and written exam. Some paid departments require thorough interviews, background checks, drug screening, and even national certification before hiring. But Jed does not mind working at things until he gets them right. And the advanced training for EMT, haz mat, and trench rescue sounds like something he would like to try. He will be a good firefighter.

According to archeologists, man's first use of fire occurred around 500,000 BCE. Primitive man's first introduction to fire probably came from fires started by lightning or volcanoes, and these mysterious and powerful forces created many superstitions and myths about fire. One of these myths was that because fire had been created by a supernatural force or being, it would be sacrilegious to allow it to burn out. As people learned to use fire, the need for keeping a particular fire lit became unimportant and its mystic powers declined. People learned that a controlled fire kept them warm, gave them security and light, and served as a focal point for the nightly gathering. They also learned that an uncontrolled fire could do them physical harm and destroy their property. Recorded in history are many instances where entire villages and cities were destroyed by fire, either by accident or as an ancient method of warfare.

Early Fire Services

The earliest known organized firefighters protected the city of Rome. Many great fires destroyed large portions of Rome in 24 BCE. This led Emperor Caesar Augustus to form the *familia publica,* a group of 600 servants stationed by the city's gates for the express purpose of fighting fires. In 6 BCE, after another disastrous fire, Emperor Augustus instituted the *Corps of Vigiles,* which was to protect Rome for the next 500 years. Vigiles were a night patrol of slaves who checked for fires and alerted the town if a fire was discovered. The vigiles, correctly dressed and equipped with buckets and axes, also fought fires and enforced fire prevention. The Corps warned all households that fires could be caused through negligence and instructed occupants to keep water in their rooms. They also had the authority to lash offenders. Rome was divided into districts and protected by about 7,000 vigiles. A ranking was used to organize the Corps into officers and ordinary firefighters – an organization similar to that used by today's larger fire departments.

The First Fire Pump

When was the first **fire pump** invented? The exact date is unknown. Where people were concentrated in an urban area, the problem of fire became so acute that some methods of fire prevention or fire extinguishment had to be devised.

A Roman writer who is generally assumed to have lived in the Third Century BCE described a fire pump that expelled water to a great height. He gave an exact description of the machine, which consisted of two brass cylinders with carefully fitted pistons that sucked water through valves at the base and pushed it through outlet valves into a chamber. As the water rose in the chamber, it compressed the air inside, forcing the water to eject in a steady stream through a pipe and nozzle. Long handles operated the pistons. It is assumed that the vigiles used these machines. Pieces of these machines have been excavated at many Roman sites. An Alexandrian Greek named Ctesibius has been given credit for inventing this pump, which was known as a *siphona*. This simple, double-force device remained the basic mechanical method that operated hand pumps until modern times (**Figure 3.1**).

With the fall of Rome, the vigiles and the fire pump were forgotten in the Middle Ages. With their passing went an organized and well-equipped fire department that Europe would not know again for another thousand years.

Fire Pump — (1) Water pump used in private fire protection to provide water supply to installed fire protection systems. (2) Water pump on a piece of fire apparatus. (3) Centrifugal or reciprocating pump that supplies seawater to all fire hose connections aboard a ship.

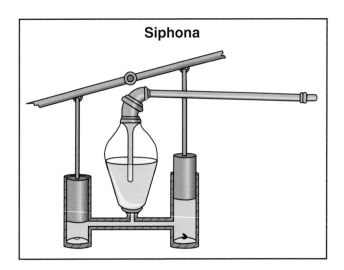

Figure 3.1 The first fire pump was hand operated and worked as a double-force pump.

Extinguishing Techniques

Although people learned early that water was the cheapest, most plentiful, and best agent for extinguishing fire, there were several interesting earlier beliefs and techniques. In Japan, if fire threatened the emperor's palace, hundreds of people carrying huge fans would line the walls of the palace. They would attempt to fan flying embers away from the palace while the building on fire burned to the ground. In the seventh century, some people believed that ringing church bells in reverse would control large fires. The ringing was not entirely mystical because it did serve to warn inhabitants that something was amiss. People would run to the church and be available for fire fighting. This method was later used to summon volunteer firefighters, and it persisted in some communities until the twentieth century.

Fire Laws and Ordinances

No known records exist of any organized fire fighting in the eleventh and twelfth centuries, and fire continued to destroy large cities and villages. The church bells would ring their reverse peals, and the inhabitants would hurry to the outbreak to render what disorganized assistance they could.

There were laws and ordinances passed in an attempt to prevent fires. When the Normans conquered England in 1066, one of William the Conqueror's laws of the land required that all fires in the household had to be extinguished at nightfall. The simplest way of extinguishing a fire on the open hearth was to put a metal cover over it and exclude the air. In Norman French, this fire cover was called a *couvre feu*, which in English became the word *curfew*. The evening bell that tolled lights out was known as the curfew bell. It was to toll in parts of England for the next 800 years, long after its original purpose had been forgotten.

In 1189, the first lord mayor of London issued the following order: *Each house should be built of stone, and the roof should be covered with slate or burnt tile.* The dangerous thatched roof was banned. **Party walls** at least 16 feet (5 m) high and 3 feet (1 m) in breadth were to be provided between places at shared cost to both parties. The citizens were to provide ladders and a barrelful of water before their doors. Fire hooks were to be provided to remove burning thatch and to hook into the gables or other structural members and pull down the house to create a fire break. Some hooks were large, and horses could be harnessed to them to pull down a building. Some houses were built with an iron ring in the gable into which the fire hook could be inserted (**Figure 3.2, p. 90**). The **fire hook** was an old fire tool dating from Roman times and was used until the twentieth century, mostly in Europe. The early ladder trucks carried the fire hooks, and the term "hook and ladder truck" evolved from this ancient fire fighting tool.

Causes of Fire

During the seventeenth century, some of the main causes of fire in England were unsafe chimneys, careless methods of carrying burning sticks or peat from a neighbor's house to relight a fire, and incendiarism. Congestion, thatched roofs, and wooden buildings were probably the greatest fire hazards. Narrow streets allowed quick transfer of radiated heat, and the unorganized methods of fighting fire could not prevent the many *conflagrations* that occurred (**see Info Box**).

Party Wall — Dividing wall that stands between two adjoining buildings or units, often on the property line, and is common to both buildings. A party wall is almost always a load-bearing wall and usually serves as a fire wall.

Fire Hook — Hook, on the end of a rope or pole, used to pull combustible roofing materials such as thatch from burning buildings. These devices could also be used to hook into the gables of a building, or a ring installed on the gable, to pull that end of a building down. Because these hooks were carried on early ladder trucks, these trucks became known as "hook and ladder companies." The pike pole is a modern variation of the fire hook.

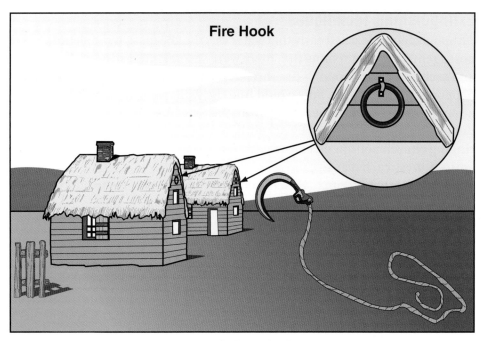

Figure 3.2 Fire hooks could pull thatch off of a roof or be attached to a ring set in the gable of a house and used to pull a building down.

Conflagration

A **conflagration** is a large, uncontrollable fire covering a considerable area and crossing natural fire barriers such as streets; usually involves buildings in more than one block, requires major resource commitments, and causes a large loss. Major wildland fires can also be considered conflagrations.

Britain's First Fire Brigade

The great turning point in fire fighting history occurred in September, 1666. London suffered a conflagration that raged for four days and destroyed more than 80 percent of the city. The fire was fought with buckets, hooks, *fire squirts* (**see Info Box**), and some primitive fire engines. Lead and wooden water pipes in the streets served as the water supply.

Syringes as Fire Fighting Tools

In the sixteenth century, syringes were used as fire fighting tools. These syringes were referred to as fire squirts and the larger ones were sometimes mounted on wheels (**Figure 3.3**). Both the large and small syringes were operated by placing hands on the holding handles midway up the barrel, putting the end of the plunger rod against the chest, and pulling the barrel toward the chest.

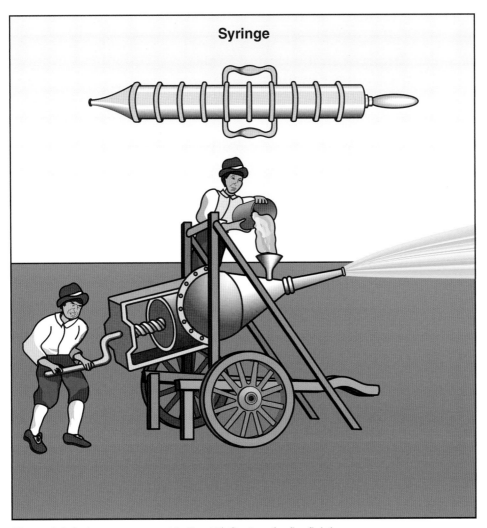

Syringe

Figure 3.3 Syringes were used in the 16ᵗʰ Century for fire fighting.

Fire Mark - Distinctive metal or wooden marker once produced by insurance companies for identifying their policyholders' buildings.

After the so-called Great Fire of London in 1666, officials there passed a code of building regulations. The city authorities recommended many new proposals to improve fire fighting methods, but their suggestions were not acted upon. The theory of the "hand of God" in fire disasters had such a hold on citizens' mentality that their thoughts never turned to skilled fire brigades, or when they did, the cost was considered too high. As a result of this fire, the first fire insurance company was formed. The creation of the fire insurance company was to have a major effect on the fire service of Britain, whose traditions and ideas spread later to North America.

If the authorities were cautious about forming proper fire brigades, the businessmen who ran the fire insurance companies were not. These owners realized that it was bad business to allow the destruction of their assets with the haphazard fire fighting that authorities provided. Therefore, they were soon advertising that they had qualified firefighters who were always ready when a fire occurred. Buildings they insured were provided with **fire marks**, which featured the fire insurance company's design on a plaque (**Figures 3.4**). The fire mark had to be posted in a prominent place because the fire brigades would only respond to buildings displaying their company's mark. In this manner, Britain developed its first organized fire brigades.

Figures 3.4 Insurance companies used fire marks such as this one to indicate those buildings that their fire brigade would attempt extinguishment should a fire occur.

Development of the Fire Engine

It was not until the Sixteenth Century that the writings of the ancient Romans and Greeks were translated, and fire engines were rediscovered. Unfortunately, the discovery was not put to use then, and more than a century passed before people began to experiment with fire engines again. Curiously enough, when pumps using the early *siphona* principle for throwing water were reinvented throughout Europe, they were thought to be a new idea, and each inventor believed the creation unique. By the time fire engines came into use in North America, the *siphona* principle was recognized and understood. The failure of so many of the earliest machines was due more to mechanical imperfection or clumsiness than to errors in design.

The London fire and the competition between insurance companies' fire brigades hastened the development of the fire engine. Manufacturers also received a boost from Holland. Amsterdam's municipal fire brigades had 60 fire engines. Its captain, Jan van der Heijden, was an accomplished engineer who invented a new engine. He also invented fire hose, pieces of leather sewn together to form a tube. This hose was used to supply the pumping engine, eliminating the need for bucket brigades. In addition, buckets were no longer needed to fill the engine's water reservoir. A close attack with a jet was now possible instead of the impractical long shot of a swiveling gooseneck mounted on the engine.

A suction hose and device for drawing water were also invented, but it would be many years before other firefighters realized the value of these fire fighting advancements. In 1690, Mr. van der Heijden produced a book explaining his new machine: *A Description of the Newly Invented and Patented Fire Engines with Flexible Hose, and Their Manner of Extinguishing Fires, by Their Inventor Jan van der Heijden*. The book included many pictures and demonstrated the advantages of the close attack.

By the end of the Seventeenth Century in England, several manufacturers were producing fire engines and competition was becoming heated. The best engines at this time appeared to be copies of the Dutch engine. In 1721, Richard Newsham developed an engine that became very popular (**Figure 3.5**). This mechanical fire apparatus consisted of a rectangular box or tub mounted on wheels. The bucket brigade poured water into the water reservoir while the men on the pump handles supplied the power to produce water pressure. The engine was rugged and practical, and the working parts were beautifully made and balanced.

Figure 3.5 A Newsham pumper circa 1764. *Courtesy of Fireman's Hall Museum.*

Newsham was the first to place the long wooden handle bars, known as the "**brakes**," along the sides of the engine. The brakes were made of oak – smooth, round, and just thick enough to permit a firm grip. Some models had brakes up to 15 feet (5 m) long, extending well beyond the body at both ends. As many as ten men could stand side by side and operate these brakes. The firefighters standing on both sides of the machine worked the brakes up and down like a seesaw, which moved a metal beam that operated the piston pump. A big nozzle or gooseneck, much like the deck gun on modern fire apparatus, was mounted on the engine. The engine was placed in front of the burning building, and the big nozzle shot a stream into the fire, which was a big improvement over men using buckets to throw water at the fire. The stream was fairly steady and provided enough pressure to force water up to a window or roof. In his advertising pamphlet, Newsham claimed that his engine could send a stream 165 feet (50 m) high. Newsham's engine was capable of providing a continuous stream of water while other engines provided only intermittent streams.

The Newsham engine was the first *hand tub apparatus.* Over time, many improvements were made on his design. Engines were produced with bent axles that put the body nearer the ground, making it easier to operate the brakes. Some models had treadles on top, allowing firefighters, while standing, to use their legs to assist in pumping. There were refinements in the swiveling gooseneck, but one of the biggest improvements was the development of the suction hose and a special three-way fitting. This improvement made it possible to fill the tub either by drafting water from a nearby well or reservoir or by using the old **bucket brigade** method. Many of these sturdy machines are on display in museums today.

Brakes – Long wooden handles on early hand pump fire engines that firefighters moved up and down to pump water from the reservoir to the pump's discharge.

Bucket Brigade — Early fire fighting technique in which people formed two lines between a fire and a water source. One line (usually composed of men) would pass buckets of water toward the fire to be applied onto the fire, and the other line (composed of women and children) would return the empty buckets to be refilled.

Figure 3.6 Bucket brigades were formed with one line of men to advance the full pails of water and a second line of women and children to return the empty pails.

Fire Protection in Early America

A disastrous fire contributed to the failure of Jamestown, the first English settlement in America. The new settlers were unprepared for the cold winters, and large fireplaces and chimneys made of wood or wooden reeds lines with mortar were common features in their homes. In 1608, Jamestown had the first recorded major fire in the New World. It burned down every house in the settlement and destroyed clothes and private provisions. Exposure to the severe winter and Indian attacks forced the suffering inhabitants to return to England.

Fire continued to plague the early settlers. Europeans arrived at such a pace that taking care of their immediate needs left little time for town planning. Protection from the weather was their first concern, and fire protection was given little thought as the towns expanded aimlessly forward. Organized fire fighting consisted of the town leaders issuing commands and giving authority to pull down burning houses that would threaten the town.

Another form of organized fire protection was the bucket brigade. Villagers would form two lines between the water supply and the fire (**Figure 3.6**). Men would form one line from the water source to the fire, passing full buckets of water. Women and children would form another line to pass empty buckets back to the water supply. The bucket brigade system became ineffective when some mothers began to station their daughters opposite desirable young men in the line. This matchmaking practice decreased the efficiency of the operation. Placing the lines of people back to back solved this problem.

First Fire Personnel in North America

By the early 1600s, people known as **fire wards**, **fire wardens**, and surveyors of buildings had begun providing fire protection in the growing cities of North America. America's fastest-growing city, Boston, experienced fire almost from its founding. In 1631, only eight months after it was settled, the city had its first major fire. After the fire, city leaders issued orders that no man should build

Fire Wards — Individuals appointed by the city of Boston after 1631 in an attempt to prevent fires. They were provided badges and staffs of office and assigned to different parts of the city. Similar to the fire wardens of New Amsterdam and other early American cities.

Fire Wardens — Individuals appointed by the city of New Amsterdam and other early American cities in an attempt to prevent fires by inspecting chimneys and hearths. They were empowered to cite residents for failing to meet the city fire codes. Similar to the fire wards of early Boston.

his chimney with wood or roof his house with thatch. However, this order did not solve the problem. Fire wards were appointed in different sections of the town and were outfitted with badges and five-foot staffs headed with a spire six inches long. The staff may have been painted red and designated the bearer as the person in charge of fire fighting activities.

In 1647, Peter Stuyvesant, the new Dutch governor of New Amsterdam (later called New York), arrived from Amsterdam. The new governor reorganized the government, surveyed and mapped the area, established a building code, and appointed a group of men as fire masters. Although they had no special authority while a fire was in progress, they did form the first fire organization in America – Surveyors of Buildings. From early evening until dawn, these men patrolled the streets carrying wooden noisemakers, called rattlers, to arouse the people in case of fire. They also performed fire prevention work and imposed fines on violators. People did not always follow the law and some hazards were overlooked, but the tough governor kept the town more fire safe and free from disastrous fires than many other towns in America.

Stuyvesant brought the fire protection ideas from his native country, Holland, during the Dutch Golden Age when the wealth of the East Indies poured into the city of Amsterdam, and the merchants built their magnificent, tall houses along the canals. Where there is great wealth, the fire risk is generally given serious consideration, and Amsterdam formed a municipal fire brigade.

Before the first fire departments were established, places like New Amsterdam began appointing men known as fire wardens whose job was to inspect chimneys and fire hearths. People were forbidden to lay straw or other combustible material in their homes or close outside them. Fines could be levied for failure to keep chimneys clean, for failure to keep a leather bucket at hand, or for failure to keep combustibles a safe distance from the house. In 1685, a public chimney sweep was appointed. His rates were fixed according to the height of the house. Eventually, these approaches became what we now know as incident management (see Chapter 10).

First Fire Departments

As the 21st Century began, there were more than 30,000 fire departments in the United States and approximately 3,500 fire departments in Canada. These departments had begun modestly enough just after the turn of the 18th Century as mutual fire societies and then volunteer fire companies, as described in the sections that follow.

Mutual Fire Society of Boston

In 1717, Boston established America's first fire department. Boston was years ahead of other cities in establishing a fire department because the terrible fires that the city had experienced made engines, buckets, and other fire equipment vital to its existence. At this time, New York and Philadelphia did not even have any engines in service. In spite of the increased protection, the fear of another conflagration led some Boston homeowners to band together, and on September 30, 1718, the first fire society was formed. This was the beginning of the age of the **volunteer firefighter** who was to play an important role in American history. In that same year, the first, more-advanced fire engine arrived in Boston from England.

Volunteer Firefighter — Active member of a fire department who may not receive monetary compensation for his/her time spent performing fire fighting operations. *Also spelled* Volunteer Fire Fighter.

Figure 3.7 The bed key was a very important early fire fighting tool. If firefighters could quickly dismantle a bed and carry it outside, they could save one of the family's most valuable possessions.

The *mutual fire societies* operated independently and volunteered assistance to the regular Boston firefighters. The limited membership carried a small booklet listing the location of each member's home and place of business. Each member responded to a fire alarm with personal equipment, which consisted of a bucket and a bag bearing the society's emblems, a bed key, and a screwdriver. Because the bed was the most valuable item in a house, the bed key was used to take the bed apart in case of fire (**Figure 3.7**). If the fire was in or near a member's building, members would rush to the scene, make sure all lives were safe, dismantle the bed with bed keys, fill their bags with the valuables, carry them to safety, and then assist in the fire fighting. After the fire, a member would stand guard against pilfering and admit only recognized members and firefighters for salvage work. The fire societies proved valuable, and within a few years, Boston had several neighborhood organizations that held regular meetings and had rules that fixed fines for nonattendance at fires or meetings.

Philadelphia: Union Volunteer Fire Company

Benjamin Franklin moved to Philadelphia at a young age. After a devastating fire there in 1730, Franklin began doing research on fire prevention. On February 2, 1735, after returning from a trip to Boston, he wrote an article about fire protection for his newspaper, *The Pennsylvania Gazette*. In the article, he mentioned the Mutual Fire Society of Boston and told how this organization was helping fight fires. The following year, Franklin and several of his friends established the first fire organization in Philadelphia, the Union Volunteer Fire Company, patterning it after the Boston Mutual Fire Society (**Figure 3.8**). The Union Volunteer Fire Company responded to any fire calls in its vicinity, unlike the Boston Mutual Fire Society, which responded only to members' properties. There was soon such an overwhelming response that Franklin divided the department into additional companies – the beginning of a fire department.

New York Volunteer Department

In 1737, the Volunteer Department of the City of New York was formed with 35 members. By 1784, it consisted of 15 engines and two hook and ladder companies. In 1786, the fire department of the city of New York was completely reorganized; membership was increased, and districts were created and placed under the leadership of several men. Every volunteer company wanted to be the best, fastest, and the most handsome in the department or its district. The New Yorkers decorated their machines with gleaming metal, used high-gloss paint, and hired well-known artists to execute elaborate paintings (**Figure 3.9**). The scenes were usually mythological or patriotic in nature, and many of the

Figure 3.8 A portrait of Benjamin Franklin, *Father of the Fire Service* © 1994 by Chas Fagan. *Courtesy of the Congressional Fire Services Institute.*

Figure 3.9 Volunteer fire companies in the late 1700s showed their pride by elaborately decorating and painting their engines.

scenes still exist in museums today. The volunteers also dressed in colorful uniforms for parades and public contests between companies.

The fire department continued to grow and by the early 1800s had 25 engines numbered, named, nicknamed, and manned with 10 to 20 men each, depending on the size, the weight, and to some extent the location of the machine. The department also had a chief engineer and six assistant engineers. The companies continued to function on their own while the chiefs did nothing but occasionally inspect the apparatus.

This all changed in 1811, when Tommy Franklin became chief engineer and assumed the role of active chief of the entire department. Because of his sincere personality and leadership, his position was accepted, and all company foremen followed to his orders without acception. (The foreman was in charge of a company and was elected to this position by the men of his company.) Franklin's successors had little trouble continuing with the same authority. For 25 years, New York was the only North American city to have a fire department under a unified command.

First Fire Insurance Companies

In its earliest North American form, the fire insurance company not only insured against fires, but actually responded to them. Like much of the innovation in the North American colonies, fire insurance companies trace their roots to the city of Philadelphia – and the vision of Benjamin Franklin.

Figure 3.10 The first successful American fire insurance company, known as the Philadelphia Contributorship of the Assurance of Houses from Loss by Fire, used the "hand in hand" mark. This symbol is still in use today.

The Philadelphia Contributorship of the Assurance of Houses from Loss by Fire

The first successful American fire insurance company was founded in 1752 by Benjamin Franklin and several other businessmen. This company was known as the Philadelphia Contributionship of the Assurance of Houses from Loss by Fire. The company's fire mark was called the "hand in hand" because it showed the right hands of four men gripping one another's wrists as a sign of unity and strength. The number of the insurance policy would appear beneath the fire mark. The "hand in hand" symbol is still in use today by the same fire insurance company, which is now known as The Contributionship Companies (**Figure 3.10**).

Mutual Assurance Company

Ben Franklin believed that trees attracted lightning, so insurance companies refused to insure buildings that were close to trees. Eventually, part of the Philadelphia Contributorship split off to form the Mutual Assurance Company. Its fire mark – a green tree – was issued in 1784. It symbolized the fact that they were willing to issue insurance policies on buildings that were near trees.

Because towns had no permanent firefighters and volunteers received no pay, insurance companies or town treasuries would authorize pay to the first-arriving firefighters who put water on a fire. This incentive set in place the fierce rivalries that developed among volunteers in later years.

Early American Fire Equipment

As America's population and fire departments grew, so did their demand for the most advanced equipment of the day. While the fire engine was the first American fire equipment to be developed, fire extinguishers and alarm and communications systems soon followed.

Development of American Fire Engines

Following a disastrous conflagration in 1653, the Bostonian leaders signed a contract with Joseph Jynks to build an apparatus for fire fighting. This contract was the first mention of any kind of fire apparatus in America, but no description of the engine or record of its construction and delivery exists. American merchants had high praise for an apparatus they had seen at work in London, so in 1676 authorities ordered one. Before the order reached England, however, Boston suffered another conflagration. The type of apparatus ordered was never described, although it was thought to be of the hand-tub type. When it finally arrived in 1678, thirteen men were appointed to keep it in proper repair and ready condition, tow it to fires, and operate the pump. Thomas Atkins was appointed chief engineer, and he and his men were promised pay for their work.

New York imported the first Newsham engines from England in 1731, and Thomas Lote, a New York cooper (barrelmaker) and boat builder, manufactured the first successful fire engine in America. It was delivered to the city in 1743 and was nicknamed "Old Brass Backs" because of the lavish use of brass on the box of the engine (**Figure 3.11**).

Figure 3.11 The first fire engine built in the United States was delivered to New York City in 1743 by Thomas Lote.

New York-Style Hand Engines

The competitive spirit of New York's firefighters gave them the impetus to develop better and more powerful hand tubs. A style of hand engine evolved that used Newsham's principle of the side stroke. This new engine became known as the "New York" style of hand engine . The city of New York started replacing its antiquated machines with this new, powerful "gooseneck" engine that was to become New York's most popular engine and the most publicized style of hand engine (**Figure 3.12, p. 100**). The gooseneck engine – so named because of the prominent bend in the pipe that protruded from the air chamber – was too heavy and bulky for quick maneuvering and too large for narrow passages. These problems caused firefighters to experiment with threading a hose instead of a nozzle to the gooseneck pipe and running a line to a strategic point closer to the fire. This method, called leading hose, was another technological advancement in fire fighting (**Figure 3.13, p. 100**). Instead of spotting the engine directly in front of the fire, firefighters could fight fires in narrow streets and alleys. If they wished, they could even enter and attack the fire from inside the building. In the beginning, the engines carried only a small amount of hose. Leading hose led to the development of more powerful engines and improved water systems.

Piano-Type Engines

From the gooseneck design the more powerful piano-type engines were developed. They were so called because the boxlike body resembled a piano. A development on the piano style was the permanent attachment of the suction hose, which was placed in such a way that it was referred to as a "squirrel tail"

Figure 3.12 The New York style engine was famous for its gooseneck discharge on top of the machine.

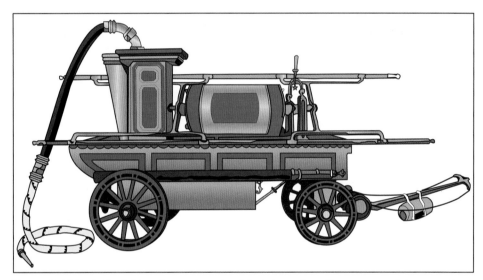

Figure 3.13 Early firefighters began to extend their hose from the gooseneck-type engine. From this practice, leading hose came into use.

(**Figure 3.14**). Other developments led to a style called the Shanghai (a variation on the Philadelphia style). Yet another type had its pump arranged in such a way that men seated on the body could apply their strength in a rowing manner.

Other Hand Engines

Soon manufacturers all over the young American nation were developing machines. One engine became known as the "coffee mill," a rotary-type engine with a crank on each side of the machine that operated it. Another unique rotary engine popularly known as the "cider mill" was operated like the capstan of a ship with the men pushing the bar by walking around the engine (**Figure 3.15**). Richard Mason built the first successful engine made in Philadelphia, and in 1794, Pat Lyon began producing the renowned Philadelphia-style engine (**Figure 3.16**), a powerful, efficient, reliable, double-piston, double-deck, end-stroke engine that is considered by many to have been the best and most successful hand engine developed in this country. Meanwhile, William C. Hunneman

Figure 3.14 The piano-style pumper was distinct because of the preconnected "squirrel-tail" suction hose.

Figure 3.15 The "cider mill" was powered by firefighters walking around the engine.

Figure 3.16 The Philadelphia-style engine developed in 1794 was an excellent double-piston pump, note the elaborate decoration.

Figure 3.17 The Hunneman hand tub was used extensively in New England because its compact size made it easy to maneuver.

of Boston, Massachusetts, was making an excellent end-stroke machine that was small, compact, and easily handled. The Hunneman machine, as it was called, was very serviceable, not only in Boston's narrow streets but also in smaller towns and villages (**Figure 3.17**).

Improvements in Hand Engines

Hand engines continued to become more powerful, bulkier, and heavier. Many of the machines were custom built with variations in design, and other manufacturers copied and improved upon their power plants. It was fortunate that the suction hose replaced the bucket brigade as a way to get water into the chamber of the engine because more and more manpower was needed to work the handles or brakes of the pumping engine. As the hand tubs were

Figure 3.18 The long brakes on each side of this engine allowed many men to operate this apparatus.

improved, the small handles were lengthened until they ran the entire length of the engine, providing room for 15 or more men on each side (**Figure 3.18**). Operating these engines usually reduced the crew to exhaustion in a matter of minutes. When one crew was completely worn out, a fresh crew would step in while the first crew rested and had refreshments – some of which came from a brown jug.

Hand engines were normally operated at about 60 strokes a minute. They were sometimes speeded up to 120 strokes a minute, and on one occasion, it was recorded that the men pushed up to 170 strokes a minute. A stroke consisted of a full up-and-down motion of the brakes. At the normal pace, men could last at the brakes for about 10 minutes, but when the engine was being pushed hard, 1 to 3 minutes was all that a man could work. Firefighters frequently suffered painful injuries, such as torn fingers and broken arms, when the crews rapidly changed places while the engine was being operated at high speed.

Engines were sometimes referred to as having pump cylinders of a certain class. In different engines, the size of the pump cylinder varied from 5 to 10 inches (254 mm to 129 mm) in diameter; the stroke of the piston rods varied from 8 to 18 inches (203 mm to 457 mm); and the length of the brakes was from 16 to 25 feet (4.9 m to 7.6 m). A first-class engine, which would be one with 9- or 10-inch (229 mm or 254 mm) cylinders, would require 40 to 60 men to haul and operate.

Fire Extinguishers

The first fire extinguishers were simply buckets filled with water. Because there were few methods to fight fire, homeowners were responsible for keeping buckets of water filled and ready in order to protect themselves and their neighbors if a fire broke out. Squire Boone, brother of pioneer Daniel Boone, developed the first portable extinguisher in 1778. He succeeded in pushing water out of a gun barrel to extinguish flaming arrows.

Despite Boone's ingenious invention, the first fire extinguisher was not patented until sometime in the 1870s. Many historians report that Alanson Crane patented the first fixed location extinguisher in 1863. Other historians state that it was not until 1872 that Thomas J. Martin patented the fire extinguisher. These extinguishers contained water and were only effective on fires containing wood, paper, cloth, and so on – what are now called Class A fuels.

Later fire extinguishers contained foam or carbon tetrachloride as their active ingredient. All have been declared obsolete for any of the following reasons:

- The extinguisher cannot be turned off once it is activated.
- The extinguishing agent is more corrosive than water.
- The extinguisher is potentially dangerous to the operator during use.
- The agent tank may have corroded over the years, which may result in a violent failure when the tank becomes pressurized, also resulting in injury or death.

Modern Fire Extinguishers

Today's extinguishers contain water, antifreeze, carbon dioxide, dry chemical, dry powder, foam, and clean agents. A portable fire extinguisher is rated according to its intended use and fire fighting capability on the five classes of fire (A, B, C, D, and K). The type and amount of agent contained in the extinguisher and the extinguisher's design determine the amount of fire an extinguisher is able to extinguish for a particular class of fire (**Figure 3.19**).

Alarm and Communication Systems

Emergency public communication has evolved hand-in-hand with the establishment and capabilities of emergency response services. From the earliest beginnings, the outbreak of fire naturally produced a commotion among the populace. The raising of the cry of "Fire!" served to warn the people and mobilize everyone for the common interest of helping their fellow citizens. Eventually, the public would understand an alert as the sounding of devices in a specific manner. Some of the different means used were the ringing of bells from churches and around town – even the firing of pistols or cannons was used to alert the public.

Figure 3.19 An example of a modern extinguisher. The pictures on the instruction plate identify the types of fire for which the extinguisher is suited.

Town Crier

The *town crier* was perhaps the first organized method of notifying the public of emergencies and other situations. Originally, the *town crier* was a delegated citizen who made rounds at dusk, lighting the street lamps. In the morning, the crier would again make the rounds and extinguish the lamps. If, during these rounds, the crier noticed any unusual activity, such as a burglary or a fire, the crier would run up and down the streets notifying the community (**Figure 3.20, p. 104**).

Figure 3.20 Fire rattles such as this one were used by a town crier to alert citizens that a fire had been spotted. *Courtesy of Fireman's Hall Museum.*

As time went by, the responsibilities of the town crier expanded. Many larger communities selected several individuals who supervised the town during all hours of the day and night. The move to 24-hour-a-day coverage dramatically improved the ability of the crier to discover problems early. In time, police patrols or watchmen would replace the need for the town crier, as did the advances in alarm notification devices.

History of the Fire Service Bugle

A fire ground is a noisy place and, in times past, bugles or trumpets were used to amplify an officer's voice giving orders. Gradually, the bugle came to signify rank in the fire service — a practice that continues to the present day. Generally, fire service rank insignia consists of a single bugle, two parallel bugles, or two to five crossed bugles. The more bugles, the more "voice" or rank the individual holds.

Watchmen and Watchtowers

Eventually town criers became known as *watchmen*. The watchmen were usually located in a tower in the center of town – the *watchtower*. Watchmen retained the responsibility to warn citizens in the event of a fire or other emergency. The means of notification varied from place to place, but one thing was constant: when notified, the public would respond, either with a bucket brigade or in some law enforcement capacity. In more recent years, the wildland fire protection agencies have made widespread use of the watchtower.

In the early days, it was unlikely that a burning house would be saved. However, because of the early notification from the watchmen, rescue and fire-spread prevention efforts saved many lives.

Telegraph Alarm Systems

The first technological innovation in the notification of emergency responders came in 1847 with the introduction of a wired telegraph system. The telegraph system allowed emergency responders, specifically the fire department, to be notified immediately when an emergency occurred. Local governments operated dedicated separate networks that were initially used for notification only. Early on, these telegraph lines connected only several devices within a locale for the remote sounding of bells or whistles.

With advances in electromechanical inventions between 1835 and 1848, a means for long-distance communication was a historic occurrence. Devices were developed in which electric impulses could be sent over wire by making or breaking circuits and activating devices on each end. Messages could then be carried between points as Morse code was employed. A longer distance medium, initially with limited availability, produced a rapid communication system tying the country together. Further expansion with the opening of neighborhood "district telegraph offices" gave the public access to this communication.

The first technological innovation in the notification of firefighters for emergencies came in June 1845 when Dr. William Francis Channing adapted Morse code for his patented fire alarm system. When John Nelson Gamewell realized the amount of money to be earned from the alarm system, he raised enough money to buy the patent rights for the entire United States. By 1904, 95 percent of the fire alarms in the country were Gamewell alarm systems.

Boston became the first city to use a fire alarm telegraph system when the City Council appropriated money to construct the first fire alarm telegraph system in the world. The system went into service in 1852.

As the concept expanded, street boxes accessible to the public became common and resulted in municipal fire alarm systems (**Figures 3.21**). These circuits were then extended into firehouses instead of other public offices. A landmark advancement occurred with the first viable communication system. Fire departments could begin to establish centers for receiving and transmitting alarms. At first these boxes only indicated a district for the fire's location. Eventually, however, street boxes would send their location as a specific number.

Figures 3.21 An example of a street type pull station box used to send telegraph alarms to fire department receiving panels.

Most telegraph box systems were discontinued as the telephone became the more popular means of communication. However, some telegraph box systems are still in use today, particularly on the East Coast of the United States. They are used also as circuits from building alarm systems and private fire alarm companies.

Telephone Systems

Another great advance in emergency warning came with the introduction and widespread use of public telephone systems. At first, the caller would speak to an operator working for the local telephone company and the operator would then notify or connect the call to the proper authority. This system worked well for awhile, but it soon became obvious that public safety agencies needed to receive calls under their supervision. The immense growth of private telephones urgently spurred technology for automated dialing exchanges, which allowed calls to be placed directly to specific agencies without going through telephone company switchboards and losing valuable time. The telephone became – and remains today – the primary method for notifying response personnel of an emergency (**Figure 3.22, p. 106**).

igure 3.22 Today's modern telecommunications centers use telephones and computers to communicate with citizens and emergency responders.

The advent of widespread telephone use also allowed public safety response personnel to ask questions of the people actually reporting the situation. The great increase in preresponse information allowed emergency managers to make more informed and appropriate response decisions.

Universal Emergency Telephone Number — Typically an easy to remember and dial 3-digit telephone number that can be used to access emergency services personnel in the event of an emergency. 9-1-1 is the common universal emergency telephone number in the U.S. and Canada. In the United Kingdom, this number is 9-9-9; in other nations in the European Union, it is 1-1-2. *Also known as* Emergency Services Number, Emergency Telephone Number, or Universal Number.

Public Safety Answering Point (PSAP) — Facility or location at which 9-1-1 calls are answered, either by direct calling, rerouting, or diversion.

Universal Emergency Number

The idea of a **universal emergency telephone number** was brought back to the United States from Europe after World War II. The first 9-1-1 system began operation on February 16, 1968, in Haleyville, Alabama. The system continues to be improved today. New technology has made Enhanced 9-1-1 (E-9-1-1) possible, giving telecommunicators information about a caller, such as phone number and/or address, and can be preprogrammed to indicate the appropriate emergency service to call even if that person cannot ask for help. While 9-1-1 is not yet in use everywhere in the United States, its widespread adoption by many communities nationwide is an improvement in ease of public notification of emergency responders.

Use of the universal number has had a great impact on the organization of emergency communications. Directing all calls to a single number has brought about the widespread development of combined communications centers. Before use of the universal number, each service could operate its own dispatch functions. These **Public Safety Answering Points (PSAPs)**, usually operated by law enforcement agencies, may serve regional areas composed of many agencies. Individual agencies not participating in the consolidated centers receive calls transferred from the PSAP.

Radio Communications

Probably the greatest improvement in emergency communications has been radio communications. The function of radio differs somewhat from the equipment and systems described previously. Radio performs more as a dispatching and communication means than it does as a reporting or notification system. "Wireless" radio was a great advance over relying on street boxes or telephones for actual two-way communication. Radio provided the biggest enhancement to fire service communications because resources could be effectively used and managed when out in the field. It is impossible to imagine today's emergency services functioning without the use of radios.

Law enforcement agencies were the first to use wireless radios in the early 1920s. These early systems used coded transmissions (such as "10-4" for "I understand."). Codes were established for a number of things, including location, crime classification, and personal descriptions. In 1922, the Detroit Police Department began using the first voice radio system. Their radios were actually receivers only. Upon receipt of a transmission, the officer had to stop at a telephone to report back to the station. In 1938, the Connecticut State Police became the first law enforcement agency to use FM (frequency modulation) two-way police radios.

The fire service followed the police in the use of radio communication; radio receivers were installed in fireboats and in chiefs' vehicles. Fire service radio usage began in a segment of the public AM (a broadcast system using amplitude modulation) broadcast band, advanced through public safety AM, and finally into FM. Several decades ago, FCC regulations mandated the separation of police and fire frequency bands. Frequency allocation that began on the low bands has moved to the higher UHF bands and most recently, the 800 MHz frequencies. Radio networks today are extensive because of the availability of portable radios and the multiple frequencies for the various needs of the service.

Radio dispatching has come into widespread usage. Telephones and telegraph have become secondary systems. The equipment consists of tone-activated receivers in the stations for selective or group alerting. Toning out the station opens speakers for dispatch announcements and can be used to turn on nightlights and other features. Microwave networks are also used to link the station radios to the telecommunication center rather than transmitting over the normal radio frequency. A correctly engineered and maintained system will have the necessary equipment to ensure reliability and avoid interruption. Receivers can be placed in the residences of chief officers, off-duty members, volunteers, and allied agencies for alerting. Pagers on the radio frequency can also be used to alert staff or line personnel when they are away from quarters or are off duty.

Advances in radio technology are increasing the telecommunicators' abilities to transmit to responders the information they receive from telephone calls. The 800 MHz trunked radios, geopositioning or other automatic vehicle location systems, mobile data terminals, and cellular phones have a significant impact on public safety communications.

Pagers

The idea of an alerting receiver, or pager, has long been associated with the fire or EMS service. Just as the two-way radio brings up the image of a law enforcement unit, the image most associated with a pager is that of a volunteer firefighter busy at work at another job being alerted to an emergency via the pager.

The earliest pagers used for public safety were tone-only pagers. These pagers reacted to a radio signal and set off a tone. The user of the pager then needed to go to a phone or radio and call dispatch or some preprogrammed number to find out the nature of the service being requested. The pager told the user that something was happening that needed attention, but the user had to do other things to find out what exactly was needed.

The next advance in pagers was the tone and voice pager that functions identically to the alerting receivers and home monitors. With this pager, a tone alerts the user to pay attention to the pager. A voice message is then transmitted, giving the details of the call and response instructions.

The next advancement in paging was the display pager, a pager that actually displays letters, numbers, and words instead of just giving an audible alert followed by a voice message. Some display pagers are only able to display a phone number to call, but recent developments have created display pagers that can display text messages. The latest pager is a display pager with the ability to acknowledge the receipt of a message. Some preprogrammed response messages can be built into the pager, and the recipient selects the appropriate preprogrammed message to respond to the page.

The pager has moved beyond a simple alerting device, in essence, to a simple Mobile Data Terminal (MDT). Because of the advent of two-way paging, the user now has the ability to at least acknowledge receipt of the message – not unlike the preprogrammed keys and limited abilities of the early MDT. The Insurance Services Office (ISO), an organization that rates community fire protection (see Chapter 8) has set conditions where paging systems may be accepted as an emergency alerting system.

Personal Alerting Systems

Almost identical to the radio with tone alert, personal alerting systems are used by volunteer or part-time fire personnel at home, in the office, and occasionally in the car. These devices, which are often the size of a large book, such as a dictionary, function like the radio receiver in a fire station. Basically, they are set up to monitor a given radio frequency. An encoded tone (normally an audible tone) opens the audio speaker on the unit which in turn activates an audible tone in the unit that alerts the user that an audio message will follow. This message contains the information regarding the fire call. Some units require someone to reset them so that they will be ready to activate for the next call out. Others, however, have an automatic reset feature that resets after a certain amount of time.

These units, which generally preceded the widespread use of pagers by volunteer and part-time firefighters, are a vast improvement over some of the other alerting methods. Some full-time agencies use these units to call off-duty personnel for major fires or events. Some full-time agencies use these small units to serve as the station-alerting device instead of using other radio receivers in the fire stations. Because these units are produced by such radio manufacturers as Plectron, Motorola, E.F. Johnson, and Regency, many of them are known by their maker's name rather than as an alerting receiver. There is also a type of reverse 9-1-1 that can call any given number of programmed phone numbers, cell, office and home and give a voice message and alert first responders and the public to an emergency.

Figure 3.23 An example of a mobile data and communications system device in use.

Mobile Data Communications Systems (MDCS)

Mobile data devices can send messages to and from a telecommunicator. These messages can be preformatted dispatch incidents, or they could be directed text messages such as e-mail or information from databases sent to the terminal. Newer models allow access to Global Positioning Satellite (GPS) mapping data, weather data, and fire department pre-fire plans. The field unit can send preprogrammed messages, such as status messages, to the telecommunicator. It can send a text message or make a query of a database such as the National Crime Information Center (NCIC) and associated state records for vehicles and persons. Usually, the devices have the ability to send messages to other devices on the same system.

The primary reasons for using mobile data devices are that they reduce the amount of voice traffic on the other radio frequencies, and they offer secure or private communications between the field unit and the telecommunicator. The devices themselves have varied from large terminal devices to very small compact devices. Today, these devices may be fixed installations where the computer is mounted in a specific vehicle and not intended to move from unit to unit. Or, they may be laptop computers, which plug into docking stations in the cars so that they can use vehicle power and an external antenna to support their operation **(Figure 3.23)**. There are even handheld portable units that can function as terminal devices. The term now used to denote this system is **Mobile Data Communications System (MDCS)**, which indicates that it is a system that supports a variety of communications devices.

Mobile Data Communications System (MDCS) — Allows for data exchange and private communications between other mobile data terminal (MDT) units.

While MDCS systems generally have been popular with law enforcement officers, their cost has slowed their growth and use by the fire service. The flexibility of the newer systems with laptop computers may bring the price down to a level where there will be a large-scale deployment of these units in most public safety units. Handheld devices such as smart phones are the logical extension of the bugles of earlier days.

Growth of the Volunteer Fire Service

From their earliest days, those who settled in the rugged New World were adventurers. By the time of the Revolutionary War, North Americans were ready to fight to protect themselves and their homes. The progression from volunteers, patriots, and competitors to membership in the first fire department hose company seemed entirely natural.

Volunteers, Patriots, and Competitors

After the Revolutionary War, volunteer fire fighting spread throughout the country. Upon returning home, many veterans joined a fire company. A large number of these companies became veterans' organizations with the engine house as their clubroom. The reward for the first-arriving company changed from pay to pride. As companies became better organized, the men and their equipment grew more splendidly decorated, and, as a result, rivalries between companies increased. Feelings of exhilaration and self-satisfaction over serving one's community and doing a worthwhile job well became the incentive. Many famous Americans, such as George Washington, John Hancock, Alexander Hamilton, Samuel Adams, and Paul Revere served as volunteer firefighters. With all the color and excitement of a volunteer firefighter's life, each company had a long list of young hopefuls waiting for an opening in the limited membership. The age of the American volunteer firefighter began.

America was growing, and many changes were taking place in the volunteer fire service. Cities improved building regulations and water systems. Ingenuity produced bigger and better fire engines to replace the worn-out Newsham engines. Firefighters, cobblers, harness makers, and other enterprising businessmen started making leather hose, fire bell signals, fire fighting tools, and uniforms. Because of the urgent need for more and better protection in the growing cities, nearly all of the new equipment and new methods of fire fighting were introduced in Boston, Philadelphia, and New York, but were subsequently adopted in smaller towns.

The creation, development, and competitive spirit of the American volunteer firefighter system influenced the fire service in several ways. The zeal to beat rival companies led manufacturers and firefighters to work continuously at developing new and better apparatus, equipment, and methods of fire fighting. Firefighters practiced making fast turnouts to fires, drilled to save time in putting engines to work, and experimented with the bunking-out system (sleeping at the station). It was also during these early years that firefighters emerged as heroes. Their daring rescues and their heroic stands before fires were captured in song and verse, as well as in the drawings of Currier and Ives. Soon every young boy in America wanted to be a firefighter when he grew up. The firefighter's exciting and colorful job was one of major interest to the townspeople, who would gather to watch firefighters in action. Competitive pumping contests would bring cheers and encouragement for local favorites.

Early volunteers were selected carefully and underwent a thorough character investigation and trial period before the company accepted them. Most of the members were men of means – merchants, manufacturers, and professionals – who kept their fire companies as socially exclusive as a private country club. To be a firefighter was to be somebody, and everybody who was anybody usually joined. The volunteers were expected to endure both cold and hot weather; the hazards of fire, smoke, and falling walls; and physical exhaustion. Every fire was a challenge and the volunteers reveled in fighting it. The status of belonging to a fire company, the teamwork, and the pride in the beautiful machinery made membership in the company very desirable.

Every member was responsible to the company, the fire department, and the city. A chief engineer and his assistants headed the fire department. The man in charge of a company was referred to as the foreman. Expulsion and fines were used to maintain proper discipline, and the men worked under a rigid set of rules. The money collected went into a fund to help keep their equipment in proper shape and to finance picnics, clambakes, dances, banquets, parades, and other social functions. Fines of various amounts were levied for the following:

- Nonattendance at a fire
- Not wearing the badge and fire cap
- Absence from regular meetings or weekly engine washings
- Talking politics
- Profanity
- Intoxication
- Smoking or chewing in the engine house
- Shoving on the engine while on the run
- Failure to return to the house with the engine after a fire

It was the competitive rivalry with other fire companies that generated the greatest excitement for the volunteer. His engine was the best and his company was the toughest, the strongest, the smartest, the first to reach the fire, and the most efficient at extinguishing it. If two companies happened to meet when responding to a fire, a foot race generally ensued. Nothing stood in the way of the running volunteers and their rigs. When the streets were hazardous, the race too heated, or the only way to pass another company was to take to the smoother sidewalks, they did so, knocking over all pedestrians who got in their way. If the water supply was a long distance from the fire and water had to be relayed by one engine pumping to another, the first engine tried to pump hard enough to deliver more water into the box of the second engine than its crew could pump into the hose leading to the fire. When the box of the second engine began overflowing, the engine was referred to as being "washed" and was one of the greatest insults an engine crew could receive. When one engine had washed another, some members of the crew would stop pumping to cheer and slap each other on the back while others would saunter down to

Figure 3.24 Larger hand engines could require as many as 50 men to pull them.

the washed engine to add a few more verbal insults. This generally resulted in a few fist fights. In the following days, more fights would break out because the members of the first engine would go around town bragging about the disgrace of the washed company. Those early volunteers were as competitive as they were dedicated, a culture that continues to this day.

As the hand engines improved in power, they increased in size, and enormous numbers of men were needed to operate them. Men pulled the heavy apparatus to the fire and worked the pumps. There were no horses used to pull apparatus, no steam, and no motors at that time — manpower did it all. The first firefighters to arrive at the fire house took hold of the drag ropes and got the machine rolling. As more men caught up and got a grip on the ropes, they sped up until they were running with their apparatus. Practice was required at the drag ropes. If the men were too closely spaced, they were likely to trip and cause a dangerous pileup while their heavy machine came rumbling toward them. In spite of practice and prudence, there were ditches, cobblestones, and other obstacles to throw a firefighter off his feet. To see a hand tub coming down the street with 50 men on the ropes, bell ringing, and everyone shouting, was an unforgettable sight (**Figure 3.24**).

Rowdiness increased when the firefighters not only wanted to be the first to arrive at the fire scene, but also wanted to be the first to put water on the fire. Some resorted to employing a youngster to dash to fires with an empty barrel to put over the nearest fire plug. The youngster would sit innocently upon the barrel until his or her company arrived. These street-wise youngsters became known as "plug-uglies," and the battle for fire plugs would sometimes rage while the fire burned unheeded.

By the middle of the nineteenth century, rowdy behavior began to spread in the larger cities. It started with social outcasts and tougher elements in the cities, who resented the fact that they were not acceptable for the volunteer life of social prominence, the glorified heroics, and the toughness and manliness of the job. Gangs would wait in alleys and dark streets to pounce upon the alarm-answering firefighters, engage them in fights, and try to overturn their apparatus and damage their equipment. The heated rivalries and the troubles they caused did not reach a peak until the cities' growing pains started a deterioration of the volunteer system.

During the Nineteenth Century, the large number of immigrants escaping famines, political unrest, and depressions in other countries swelled the nation's cities. By 1835, the city of New York began to assume the proportions of a great metropolis and to display the problems of all large cities. The number and size of fire companies had to be increased to deal with the growing numbers of fires and the increased manpower needed to operate the larger machines. East Side toughs managed to infiltrate the ranks of volunteers and became public nuisances by engaging in drunken brawls, street riots, and dangerous heroics at fires. The political forces at City Hall who supported the gangs because of their friendship and political support hampered fire departments' efforts to curtail these behaviors.

First Hose Company

The large cities developed a water system using bored-out crude logs that were tapered and fitted together. Every half block or so a wooden plug was inserted into this water system, and this plug was removed to obtain water. From this system came the term **fire plug**. Philadelphia put into service the first successful water system. Philadelphia's volunteers developed a new piece of apparatus, the hose wagon, to take advantage of this new system (**Figures 3.25**).

Hose No. 1, with a limited membership of twenty members, became the first hose company in America. The volunteers designed their hose reel (which later became a horse-drawn hose wagon) and paid to have it built. They purchased

Fire Plug — Wooden plug inserted into holes drilled into early wooden water main systems; when the plug was removed, water could be obtained for fire fighting purposes. Fire hydrants evolved from fire plugs.

Figure 3.25 When water systems were first developed, hose wagons were developed to make maximum use of the systems.

all the equipment, which included 600 feet (180 m) of hose, nozzles, axes, and candle-burning lanterns. Members of Hose No. 1 also erected a building to house their apparatus. They had an understanding with Engine 1 that they would supply them with water. On one occasion when Engine 1 was late, the hose company connected to the water supply and placed an effective stream of water on the fire without the need for an engine. The hose company became popular, and soon other hose companies were established.

Rivalry between hose companies emerged. When one hose company copied Hose No. 1, the original company attached a bell to its apparatus so that it could be distinguished from the other company. This design, too, was copied, and soon everyone had bells on their fire apparatus. Thus began the alarm signal for apparatus.

Flexible hose had been used since the time of the ancient Greeks, who used the intestines of oxen. The leather hose invented in Holland was made of cowhide, sewn together carefully like the leg of a fine boot, and had brass fittings on both ends so that it could be coupled to other hose. When pressure was applied to the hose, water would sometimes burst through the cracks and seams, resulting in a poor water supply at the nozzle. Despite these problems, firefighters realized they had a necessary and effective tool. The members of Hose No. 1 were an inventive group, and two of its members developed the riveted hose — a great improvement over the leaky sewed hose and a major advancement in fire fighting.

During the era of the bucket brigade, water came from wells, ponds, streams, lakes, and cisterns. Bucket brigades filled most early hand engines. Some early water systems had such weak pressure that they functioned only as a distribution system for the bucket brigades. The ability to draw or suction water had been known for years, but the American builders and volunteers did not actually use it until 1819. The New York machines were furnished with suction hose and old machines altered so that they could use them. As the water system improved, the box of the hand engine could receive water from a hydrant. Some companies would carry a section of hose for this purpose. With the development of its suction ability, the engine started carrying a hard, noncollapsible suction hose to draw water. Water systems kept improving and some maintained enough pressure to allow a hose company to attach directly to the hydrant and have a good working line. Engines were needed only to maintain pressure for long distances and heights.

The Age of Steam

The colorful era of the hand-operated machine drew to a close with the development of the steam engine. The development of early steam engines can be dated back to 1829 in London. In America, the construction of two workable steam engines in 1840 marked the beginning of the end of the tumultuous days of the huge 80-man volunteer fire company. In 1840, the New York insurance companies first commissioned Paul Hodge to build a steamer. A year later, his steamer, which was self-propelled and had a horizontal boiler, was ready to be put to its first test (**Figure 3.26**). The test for the Hodge engine was successful in that it put a stream of water over the cupola of City Hall. However, it was also a failure because the volunteer firefighters refused to cooperate with the steamer and used trickery to make its performance look poor. The Insurance

Figure 3.26 The first steamer, built by Paul Hodge in 1841, failed its initial test.

Companies were not deceived by the volunteer firefighters, but they did realize that they were dependent upon these volunteer companies to handle 99 percent of the fire fighting in the city. Eventually, the Hodge engine was sold to power a box factory.

A Swedish engineer, Captain John Ericsson, who later designed the *USS Monitor* (the first ironclad steamship in the U.S. Navy), designed the second steamer. As a mechanical engineer, John Ericsson was a designer and inventor of many devices, including the *USS Monitor,* improved propellers, and a "hot air engine" that used hot air in place of steam as a propellant. His prize-winning fire engine was never used, however, because again the volunteers disapproved of the machine. The rejection of these engines was not serious at the time because the hand-operated engines with their multitudes of men could handle the fires that occurred. The situation did become serious when the wild fights between rival fire companies became so intense that on many occasions a fire would burn uncontrolled.

It was after one of these fights that city authorities in Cincinnati, realizing that something must be done, purchased a Latta steam engine (**Figure 3.27, p. 116**). The firefighters at first launched a brutal physical attack on the machine until a group of outraged citizens came to the rescue of the steamer. The Latta engine remained on the job, and Cincinnati later became the first all-steam fire department in America. In 1853, Cincinnati also became the first fully paid fire department. By 1857, St. Louis would also have a fully paid department.

After the acceptance of steam engines at Cincinnati, other cities began purchasing steam engines as rapidly as they became available. As steam became popular, improvements were made. Some of the first steamers were self-propelled, but they were not very successful because they were slow and hard to steer.

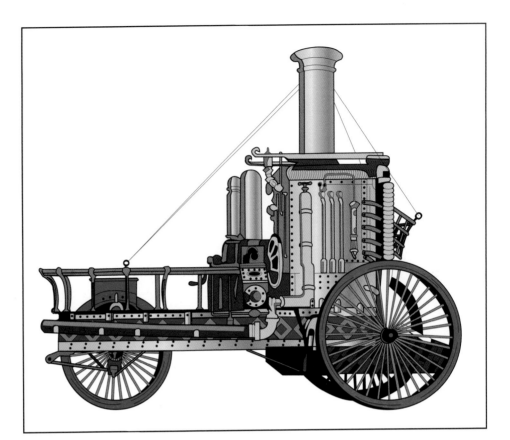

Figure 3.27 The rivalry between volunteer companies led to the purchase of steam engines like the popular Latta.

Gangs of men pulled the steamer to the fire, but this also proved to be too slow. It was soon discovered that the most efficient way to get a heavy steamer to a fire was to pull it with a team of two or more powerful horses (**Figure 3.28**). The use of horses in the fire service also brought about the use of dogs. Because a large number of horses were being stolen, dogs were housed with the horses in order to alert the owner to any problems. It was also discovered that horses would run faster if dogs were leading the way. Dogs would clear the road for the fire apparatus and chase away stray dogs that could scare the horses. Dogs of all types were used for this purpose, but the Dalmatian proved to be the best. Dalmatians formed a special bond with the horses and seemed to have an inherent love for running with horse-drawn carriages. Dalmatians can still be found in a few fire stations, where they are beloved mascots (**Figure 3.29**).

The problem of how to have the steam engine ready to start pumping when it arrived at the fire was ingeniously solved. The steamer's boiler was kept connected to a stationary boiler (also known as a donkey boiler) in the station and hot water circulated through the steamer's boiler at all times. When an alarm sounded, this connection had to be released before the apparatus rolled. The stoker would ignite a bound pack of matches on a piece of sandpaper attached to the boiler and thrust this blazing torch into the firebox. The torch ignited a bed of excelsior and about two bushels of pine kindling wood; thus, the stoker usually had a fire going before the steamer had traveled very far. When the steamer arrived at the fire, the stoker would decide whether or not the fire in the firebox was needed. If the building appeared to be involved or flames were visible, he would throw in some cannel coal from his storage bin. Cannel coal is a hot, quick-burning fuel that gave the engineer quick steam. When the hookup was made and the hose laid, the nozzleman would call for

Figure 3.28 Horse drawn steamers were developed due to the heavy weight of the apparatus and a lack of manpower.

Figure 3.29 The Dalmatian has long been a symbol associated with the fire service.

water and the engineer would ease open the throttle. The pistons moved, the flywheel turned, and black smoke flecked with hot sparks emerged from the stack. Suddenly the machinery gained speed. The pistons flashed up and down, the flywheel became a blur, and the smoke from the stack rose higher. The engineer with his oilcan attended the rhythmic, powerful machine.

Meanwhile, the men at the nozzle braced themselves as the water burst out from the hose in a powerful stream. The horses were unhitched and led away from the steamer because showers of glowing coals could easily burn their hides. The horses would also become unmanageable if they remained harnessed because of the action and vigor the steam engine produced.

The stoker at the engine monitored the supply of cannel coal. If it were a big fire, the supply would soon be exhausted. When the supply became low, the stoker would give a blast on the steamer's whistle – a signal for more coal. A coal wagon would then rush to the steamer and the driver would toss a couple of gunnysacks full of coal into the fire box. He would then stand by waiting for the signal of another steamer's whistle.

Chemical Engines and Ladder Trucks

As fire departments continued to improve, the first fire extinguishing agent – water – was supplemented with new chemical agents and apparatus, which proved particularly useful in responding to small fires. As fire extinguishment capabilities improved, fire departments could also include the support operations such as search and rescue, and ventilation and overhaul. Ladder companies performed the support operations which included carrying and raising ladders, operating related specialized equipment, and being knowledgable about a variety of evolutions and procedures.

Figure 3.30 An example of a chemical apparatus which was the forerunner of units with a booster tank.

Chemical Engine

Soon after the development of the steamer came the first chemical apparatus, generally a two-horse vehicle. It carried one to four 50-gallon (189 L) tanks of soda (sodium bicarbonate) and a carbonic acid preparation. When the operator mixed these two ingredients by operating a front-mounted crank, a strong stream was delivered through a 3/4-inch (19 mm) or 1-inch (25 mm) hose. The carbonic acid caused a chemical reaction that produced carbon dioxide gas that in turn created sufficient pressure to expel the water. These small streams were used to extinguish fires in hard-to-reach places or to extinguish a fire in its beginning phase (**Figure 3.30**).

The chemical engine sometimes used to respond behind the steamers and extinguish the small fires that the boiler sparks caused. Following the steamers was a disadvantage because the faster chemical apparatus was intended to be the first at the fire to extinguish it in its early stages. The chemical company probably extinguished more fires than the steamer, but it was not used as often on large fires except to patrol the surrounding areas and extinguish small fires caused by flying brands. Rubber or chemical hose lines were developed for use with these apparatus.

Ladder Trucks

Because ladder work and **ladder companies** did not develop as rapidly as fire engines, one has to speculate on the difficulties of early rescue work. The demand to improve ladders did not occur until the increase of multiple-storied buildings.

Early ladder companies consisted of a group of men whose duties, when the alarm sounded, were to rush to specified locations in the city and retrieve ladders, ropes, hooks, and other equipment stored there. Two men, who had

Ladder Company — Group of firefighters assigned to a fire department aerial apparatus equipped with a compliment of ladders; primarily responsible for search and rescue, ventilation, salvage and overhaul, forcible entry, and other fireground support functions. *Also known as* Truck Company.

Figure 3.31 Hand-drawn ladder trucks were developed to assist in rescues.

spent many hours practicing to avoid the discomforts and injuries that could occur while running with a long ladder, usually carried longer ladders. Later, hand-drawn hook and ladder trucks that carried several ladders of different lengths were developed (**Figure 3.31**). As ladder lengths increased, it became more difficult to steer the long, bulky apparatus down the streets and especially around corners. Installing a second tillering device on the rear wheels solved this problem.

Manpower had always been used to raise the 65- or 75-foot (20 m or 23 m) extension ladders. These ladders were extremely heavy and took a long time to remove from the truck and raise against a building. Because their bases were never secure, these tall ladders were also hazardous. Daniel Hayes, a former New York City firefighter and master mechanic on the San Francisco Fire Department, devised a method of attaching the base of the tall ladder to the truck bed and lifting its great weight mechanically. The San Francisco firefighters helped him build and experiment with the mechanism. By 1870, they had perfected an apparatus known as the Hayes Aerial, the first aerial ladder truck. Hand cranks were manually used to raise the aerial ladder. This procedure was later succeeded by a set of springs packed in cylinders, then by compressed air, and finally by hydraulic pressure or power from the gasoline truck motor. The ladder truck was further developed to carry several different lengths of ground ladders and assorted equipment, and it soon became the number one lifesaving piece of fire equipment.

Pompier Ladder and Life Net

As late as the 1970s, common fire department equipment included the now rarely used pompier ladder and life net. The pompier is a scaling ladder with a single beam and a large curved metal hook that can be put over windowsills for climbing and was used to provide fire department access into upper floors (**Figure 3.32**). The life net is a canvas device with a folding circular metal frame and spring action used to catch persons who jump from buildings; it is not considered safe or effective for jumps from above the fourth floor of a building.

Figure 3.32 A pompier ladder once used by firefighters to scale the outside of tall buildings. *Courtesy of Frank Carter.*

Protective Clothing and Self-Contained Breathing Apparatus (SCBA)

The steam engine, the chemical engine, and the aerial ladder were not the only improvements in the fire service. The need for horse stalls, which housed the fire equipment, and the firefighters' living quarters caused a change in fire station design. Many stations were two stories high, with the sleeping quarters on the second floor. Sliding poles were introduced in the 1870s for a quick descent to the apparatus floor. Daniel Lawler, a New York firefighter invented the first poles, which were made of wood. In the larger cities, "bunking out" was becoming more popular and regular shifts of firefighters were being used for this purpose. During this time of innovation, protective clothing and self-contained breathing apparatus (SCBA) were introduced.

Figure 3.33a An old style fire helmet.

Figure 3.33b A firefighter wearing a modern style fire helmet.

Protective Clothing

All the larger departments during the early 1800s adopted standard uniforms. The protective leather fire helmet was used as early as 1740 and evolved to its now-famous shape over the next 60 years. By 1820, the helmet had the front shield that displayed the engine number and the brim had the familiar rear extended scoop to carry water off the helmet and protect the back of the firefighter's neck from falling hot brands. The helmet could also be reversed and the scoop used to protect the face if necessary. Special treatment of the leather made these helmets very durable. Although some NFPA® compliant leather helmets are still used today, plastic and fiberglass helmets are more common (**Figures 3.33a and b**).

Early protective clothing was made of wool or other natural fibers. This clothing was very heavy, particularly when wet. It also placed a tremendous amount of heat stress on those who wore it. Eventually, rubber coats became the norm. Although they did a better job of keeping the firefighters dry beneath the protective clothing, the rubber coats subjected the firefighters to quick fatigue, and the trend reverted back toward woven fibers. For a long time, clothing constructed of heavy cotton duck canvas material was the norm. This material, however, was not very flame resistant which led to the development of manufactured fibers used in today's protective clothing such as Nomex® fire resistant material and PBI Gold® polybenzimidazole fiber.

SCBA Equipment

Historical records indicate that the recognition of the need for respiratory protection (**respirators**) for firefighters dates back close to 2,000 years. More than 2,000 years ago, Pliny, a Roman writer, made reference to the use of loose-fitting animal bladders to protect Roman miners against inhalation of red oxides of lead. Both artist/inventor Leonardo da Vinci (1452-1519) and Bernardino Ramazzini (1633-1714), the founder of the discipline of occupational medicine, recognized the need for respiratory protection against hazardous atmospheres.

During the 1700s, the original ancestors of modern respiratory protection devices were developed. Although the designs have changed drastically in the past 300 years, the performance of the respirators is still based on the following two basic principles:

1. Purifying the ambient air by removing contaminants

2. Providing clean breathing air from an uncontaminated source

In 1814, the first air-purifying filter (a filter in a rigid container) was developed. Activated charcoals began to be used as a filtration medium in 1854. Galibert later developed the concept of "rebreathing." He applied it to his design for a respiratory protection device in 1864 in England **(Figures 3.34)**. An early patent for an air-purifying mask in the U.S. was issued in 1872 to Peter Ackerman of Bangor, Maine. For several years, the London Fire Brigade used a facepiece that Captain E. M. Shaw designed coupled with a canister that Professor John Tyndall designed in 1890. Dreager masks were used in mines in the late 1800s and early 1900s and were also used by firefighters. The Shaw design was the forerunner of the Type N, Universal gas mask canister that many fire departments used until the late 1960s.

Many improvements in air-purifying masks, both particulate filter and oxygen rebreathers, have been made since the end of World War II. Most changes have been generated by workplace safety regulations such as those resulting from the Occupational Safety and Health Act, enacted in 1970. To address these requirements, manufacturers of respiratory protection equipment have developed filter systems and masks to meet the specific hazards outlined in the regulations. The same technology that created some hazards has also helped create types of protection against these hazards. For example, fine glass fibers that can create a breathing hazard have made the construction of high-efficiency filters possible. Other developments include smaller, better fitting facepieces with improved fields of vision, lower profile masks that interface with other types of head and eye protection, and filters that provide specific levels of protection.

The development of air-supplied systems began in the late 1700s. The first known self-contained breathing apparatus (SCBA) was developed in Germany in 1795 **(see Info Box, p. 122)**. About 1830, the Vienna Fire Brigade began using a container made of sheet iron that carried atmospheric air. In 1877 in England, the French mining engineer Henri Fayol developed an apparatus that may

Respirator — Device designed to protect the wearer from inhaling harmful air contaminants. The two main categories of respirators are air-purifying respirators, which use cartridges or filters to remove contaminants, and air-supplied respirators, such as SCBAs and airline respirators, which provide an alternate supply of fresh air.

Figure 3.34 An early model of SCBA.

have been the first pressure-demand device. The unit had a bellows-type air bag filled with clean air capped with a lead lid. The weight of the lid forced air to the user's mouthpiece for breathing and also supplied air to a lamp to keep it burning in an oxygen-deficient atmosphere.

Self-Contained Breathing Apparatus (SCBA)

As used by the contemporary fire service, *Self-Contained Breathing Apparatus (SCBA)* is a respirator worn by the user that supplies a breathable atmosphere that is either carried in, or generated by, the apparatus and is independent of the ambient atmosphere. Respiratory protection is worn in all atmospheres that are considered to be Immediately Dangerous to Life and Health (IDLH). SCBAs are also known as *Air Masks* or *Air Packs*.

In Britain, the use of breathing apparatus (BA) increased in the 1930s and 1940s. At that time, two BAs were carried on all fire service apparatus, and two men on each crew were trained in their use. The BAs were used primarily for search and rescue but were also to be worn "if the smoke is thick" or there was "burning electrical insulation." By 1960, BA training was provided for all personnel with 18 months service. Ultralightweight air cylinders were introduced into service in 1969.

The United States had very few dependable manufacturers of protective breathing devices before World War I. As late as 1910, many cities required firefighters to have beards at least 6 inches (152 mm) long. Firefighters would dip their beards into buckets of water, fold them into their mouths, and use them as smoke filters for breathing.

The earliest known American-made SCBA was LaCour's device in 1863. This apparatus was similar to Galibert's SCBA. LaCour's device used a leather air bag containing two tubes leading from the bag to the mouth. One tube went into the top of the bag for inhaling oxygen and the other tube went into the bottom of the bag for exhaling carbon dioxide. Smoke hoods containing compressed air or oxygen were also manufactured during this time period.

Early Attitudes Regarding SCBA Usage

In the past, firefighters were reluctant to use SCBA due to peer pressure and mistaken competitiveness. In those days, firefighters liked to call themselves "smoke-eaters" or "leather lungs." There has been a culture shift from bravado to safety and health awareness regarding SCBA. Now, the fire and emergency services know that smoke can lead to lung cancer, heart disease, and other serious health conditions. Firefighters should *always* use SCBA for their own safety.

Supplied air equipment was developed for the U.S. fire service in the late 1800s and saw limited use at fires until the adoption of SCBA for respiratory protection. For instance, in 1892, Merriman's Smoke Mask featured an air hose located inside a water hose. Moistened-sponge devices for cooling and filtering inhaled air were also commonly used. The Nealy Smoke Mask of 1877 had sponges that were kept moist from water contained in a boat on the user's chest.

The first SCBA to be approved in the United States was the Gibbs closed-circuit oxygen breathing apparatus that the Mine Safety Appliances Company developed. This device, the forerunner of today's equipment, was the first to use a completely lung-governed principle of operation. The Gibbs apparatus was primarily used in the early 1920s.

The use of air-supplied respiratory protection equipment in the fire service in North America dates from the 1950s. The early SCBAs were expensive, and fire department administrations did not view them as necessary. Units were usually placed on ladder trucks and used only for search, rescue, and ventilation. Engine companies were rarely equipped with SCBAs and then only with one or two units.

The need for air-supplied respiratory protection equipment only became apparent with the increase in hazardous materials in the environment. Plastics and synthetic materials in homes, chemicals and petroleum products in warehouses and on highways, and the use of flammable and toxic materials in manufacturing led to the creation of government regulations for their manufacture, handling, and disposal. These regulations culminated in the creation of the Occupational Safety and Health Administration (OSHA) in 1970. Although originally intended to regulate private industry, the laws have been applied subsequently to the public sector and to the fire and emergency services.

With the increasing hazards and new government regulations, the fire service began to increase its use of air-supplied systems, in particular SCBA. Fire departments equipped all fire apparatus with one SCBA per crew member during a given work shift. Training in respiratory protection was provided, first for existing employees and then for new personnel in recruit classes. Annual medical evaluations and physical fitness programs were also inaugurated to ensure that personnel could operate in hazardous environments while using SCBA. By the 1990s, individual facepieces were issued to fire department members, spare air cylinders were carried on all apparatus, and protocols were in place that required the wearing of respiratory protection whenever personnel were engaged in interior fire fighting or when entering a potentially hazardous or unknown atmosphere.

Technological changes paralleled the increasing use of air-supplied respiratory protection equipment (**Figure 3.35, p. 124**). Equipment changes include the following:

- Use of fire-retardant material on the harness system and hoses
- Increased capacity air cylinders
- Use of lightweight materials to reduce weight and bulkiness
- Integrated personal alert safety system (PASS) devices
- Heat- and fire-resistant material for facepieces
- Integrated facepiece and helmet systems

Figure 3.35 Firefighters wearing modern SCBA during a training evolution.

- Shift from negative-pressure to positive-pressure type regulators
- Development of quick-fill systems
- Development of buddy-breathing adapters
- Improved communications systems integrated with the breathing air system

Gasoline-and Diesel-Powered Equipment

The beginning of the twentieth century saw a dramatic change in fire service apparatus — the gasoline-powered engine. The automobile was becoming a popular mode of travel, and it was only natural that this technology would soon be adapted to fire fighting. Eventually, it appeared that steamers and all the other horse-drawn apparatus would go the way of the tub engines. Like the change from hand-operated engines to steam, the transition to gasoline power was gradual because the steamer had finally become the backbone of fire fighting. Tradition and sentimentality had settled in. Firefighters and the public had become attached to their fine horses. They took pride in the speed with which they came out of their stalls for the quick hitch. No sputtering, smelly motor with its lack of soul could take the place of horses for some old-timers.

The gasoline engine finally replaced horses, but did not supersede the steam engine until years later. The advantages of the motor-driven apparatus were recognized, especially when a long-distance fire run was necessary — a run that would soon tire out horses. At first, engineers were unsuccessful in making a reliable piece of equipment with a shifting mechanism that would transfer the gasoline engine's power from road gear to pump gear. Failures and breakdowns were frequent enough that many fire chiefs still demanded steam. Many departments compromised by building gasoline-powered tractors on the front of their steamers (**Figure 3.36**). In this way they could travel to the fire using gasoline power and then pump using steam.

Figure 3.36 Early motorized fire apparatus used the tractors to pull steam powered fire engines to the fire scene. *Courtesy of the Nethercutt Collection.*

Figure 3.37 Eventually manufacturers were able to develop engines that could propel the apparatus and the fire pump. *Courtesy of Ron Jeffers.*

Engineering continued to improve. Soon, the manufacturers developed reliable and powerful pumps that were driven by the same motor that propelled the vehicle. These arrived in time to replace the motorized steamers as they wore out. The noble and picturesque steamers joined the hand pumpers as museum pieces. The 1930s ushered in even more advances in pumping apparatus with greater reliability and capabilities (**Figure 3.37**). Today, the motor-pumping engine, be it gasoline or a more powerful diesel engine, is in universal use (**see Info Box**).

Types of Pumpers

Pumpers can be either Class A, the now obsolete Class B, or the pumper/tender; details as follow:

- ***Pumper, Class A*** — Pumper that delivers its rated capacity of at least 750 gpm (2 8939 L/min) at 150 psi (1 034 kPa) net pump pressure at a lift of not more than 10 feet (3 m) with a motor speed of not more than 80 percent of the certified peak of the brake horsepower curve; will deliver 70 percent of rated capacity at 200 psi (1 379 kPa) and 50 percent of rated capacity at 250 psi (1 724 kPa).

- ***Pumper, Class B*** — Pumper that delivers its rated capacity at 120 psi (828 kPa) net pump pressure at a lift of not more than 10 feet (3 m) with a motor speed of not more than 80 percent of the certified peak of the brake horsepower curve; will deliver 50 percent of its rated capacity at 200 psi (1 379 kPa) and 33 percent of its rated capacity at 250 psi (1 724 kPa). Class B pumps have not been manufactured since the mid-1950s.

- ***Pumper/tender*** — Mobile water supply apparatus equipped with a fire pump. In some jurisdictions, this term is used to differentiate a fire pump equipped mobile water supply apparatus whose main pur pose is to attack the fire; formerly called pumper/tanker

Figure 3.38 Today's modern pumper features a powerful pump, large water storage, a full complement of hose, and a large variety of fire fighting tools and equipment. *Courtesy of Ron Jeffers.*

Today's pumper comes close to being a complete fire department on wheels. Powerful pumps have been developed in compact sizes, allowing room for the pumper to carry a large amount of hose, and eliminating the need for the hose wagon. Today's pumper can also carry its own water supply with a small hose reel for putting out smaller fires, eliminating the need for the old chemical wagon. Although it did not eliminate the ladder truck and other specialized equipment, the pumper does carry smaller ladders and some forcible entry tools. On today's apparatus, firefighters carry all the practical tools of the past plus those that have recently come into use (**Figure 3.38**).

Impact of Historic Fires on Public Safety in North America

History is of no use to us if we do not use it to make the future better. This chapter has described how fire experiences have led to improvements in fire protection. Many of today's improvements in fire protection and code enforcement are the result of tragedies that occurred yesterday. This section examines some of those tragedies.

Although there have been a number of conflagrations in the U.S. that destroyed substantial sections of communities (Charleston, South Carolina, burned down four times between 1700 and 1779 alone), no fire is marked in history like the Great Chicago Fire of October 9, 1871. Although legend has it that Mrs. O'Leary's cow kicked over a kerosene lamp that set fire to the straw in the barn, most historians now believe that it was a neighbor boy who accidentally started the fire. The resulting fire blackened 2,100 acres, destroyed over 17,000 buildings, left 100,000 people homeless, and killed 250 people. Out of this fire rose a national interest in preventing its repetition. In celebrating its 40th anniversary in 1911, the Fire Marshal's Association of North America sponsored the first Fire Prevention Day on October 9, 1911. In 1920, President Woodrow Wilson declared October 9 as "Fire Prevention Day." Since 1922, the National Fire Protection Association® (NFPA®) has established Fire Prevention Week around this date. To this day, that week remains the focal point for the exchange of fire prevention information in North America.

Between 1903 and 1911, there were four major fires that led to the appointment of the NFPA® Committee on Safety to Life. These fires were as follows:

- Boyertown, Pennsylvania — Rhoades Opera House (1908, 170 deaths)
- Chicago, Illinois — Iroquois Theater (1903, 602 deaths)

- Collinwood, Ohio — Lakeview Grammar School (1908, 175 deaths)
- New York, New York — Triangle Shirtwaist Factory (1911, 145 deaths)

The work of this committee led to the preparation of standards for the construction of stairways and fire escapes, for fire drills in various occupancies, and for the construction and arrangement of exit facilities for factories, schools, etc., which form the basis of the present code.

In 1937, a fire at the Consolidated School in New London, Texas (294 deaths) illustrated the need for state laws to protect public buildings not subject to municipal ordinance and inspection. In the 1940s, a string of multiple-death fires in hotels and public buildings focused national attention on the need for adequate exits and other fire safety features. Among these fires were the following:

- Natchez, Mississippi — The Rhythm Club (1940, 207 deaths)
- Boston, Massachusetts — Coconut Grove Club (1942, 492 deaths)
- Chicago, Illinois — La Salle Hotel (1946, 61 deaths)
- Dubuque, Iowa — Hotel Canfield (1946, 19 deaths)
- Atlanta, Georgia — Winecoff Hotel (1946, 119 deaths)

In particular, the Coconut Grove Fire led to increased research into the use of combustible materials in public spaces. The spread of fire across combustible decorations and furnishings was a major contributor to the magnitude of this fire.

In 1944, 168 people were killed when the Ringling Brothers and Barnum and Bailey Circus tent caught fire in Hartford, Connecticut. This fire led to the development of NFPA® 102, *Standard for Grandstands, Folding and Telescopic Seating, Tents, and Membrane Structures.*

Three hospital fires moved hospital administrators and fire prevention officials across the nation to assess the quality of construction and fire protection systems in hospitals. The three hospitals involved were:

- St. Anthony's Hospital in Effingham, Illinois (1949, 74 deaths)
- Mercy Hospital in Davenport, Iowa (1950, 41 deaths)
- Hospital in Hartford, Connecticut (1961, 16 deaths)

The Our Lady of the Angels Grade School fire in Chicago on December 1, 1958, (95 deaths) probably resulted in the swiftest action in the wake of any major fire since World War II. Within days of the fire, state and local officials throughout the nation ordered fire inspections of schools. Within one year, it was reported that major improvements in life safety had been made in 16,500 schools across the nation.

Fires that have occurred in more recent years continue to influence code development and enforcement and the consciousness of the public about fire hazards. Two high-rise fires in New York City in 1970 led to the adoption of a comprehensive fire code for high-rise buildings in that city. Even fires without loss of life, such as the 1982 K-Mart warehouse fire in Falls Township, Pennsylvania, have had substantial impact on regulations for the bulk storage and high-rack storage of flammable and combustible goods.

The following fires are still having an effect on life safety code work:

- Beverly Hills Supper Club in Southgate, Kentucky, (1977, 165 deaths)
- MGM Grand Hotel in Las Vegas, Nevada, (1980, 85 deaths)
- Happy Land Social Club in New York City (1990, 87 deaths)
- DuPont Plaza Hotel and Casino in San Juan, Puerto Rico (1986, 97 deaths)
- Hamlet, North Carolina food processing plant (1991, 25 deaths)
- Station Nightclub in Warwick, Rhode Island (2003, 100 deaths)

Canada has also experienced significant fires that had an effect on building codes and standards, regulations for hazardous materials storage and shipping, mandatory smoke alarm usage, marine fire safety regulations, and implementing improved fire and life safety education programs. These include the following events:

- The Great Fire of 1877, Saint John, New Brunswick (1877, 19 deaths)
- Great Fire of 1904, Toronto, Ontario (1904, no deaths)
- Parliament Buildings Fire, Ottawa, Ontario (1916, 7 deaths)
- Laurier Palace Theatre Fire Montreal, Quebec (1927, 78 deaths, mostly children)
- S.S. Noronic Fire, Toronto, Ontario (1949, final death toll was never precisely determined but ranges from 118 to 139 deaths)
- Family Residence Fire, West Lincoln, Ontario (2004, 8 deaths in one family)
- Sunrise Propane Explosion, Toronto, Ontario (2008, 2 deaths, 12,000 people were evacuated)

Impact of Historic Fires on Firefighter Safety In North America

The previous section of this chapter explored how some past fires that killed large numbers of people led to improvements in fire protection and code enforcement. In much the same way, past fires that killed many first responders have led to improvements in firefighter safety.

Fires that have had a particular impact on firefighter safety include:

- Mann Gulch Wildland Fire between Helena and Wolf Creek, Montana (1949, 13 firefighter fatalities, documented in Norman Maclean's book *Young Men and Fire*)
- Boiling Liquid Expanding Vapor Explosion (BLEVE) during a propane transfer operation in Kingman, Arizona (1973, 11 firefighter fatalities)
- One Meridian Plaza High-Rise Fire in Philadelphia, Pennsylvania (1991, three firefighter fatalities)
- Food Plant Fire in Seattle, Washington (1995, four firefighter fatalities)
- Cold Storage Warehouse Fire in Worcester, Massachusetts (1999, six firefighter fatalities)
- Southwest Supermarket Fire in Phoenix, Arizona (2001, 1 fatality)
- World Trade Center Attack and Collapse in New York City (2001, 343 firefighter and paramedic fatalities)
- Sofa Super Store Fire and Collapse in Charleston, South Carolina (2007, 9 firefighter fatalities)

Responding to fires and other emergencies has always been – and still is – a dangerous endeavor. Every year, emergency responders are injured or killed when things go wrong at emergency scenes. In 2008, the U.S. Fire Administration reported 108 firefighter line of duty deaths and the NFPA estimated that there were 79,700 line of duty injuries in the United States.

Fires that have resulted in firefighter fatalities have led to an increased need for safety awareness in the fire station, en route to the scene, and at the emergency site. Rapid Intervention Crews **(see Info Box)**, the "Two In/Two Out" rule, and closed cabs on fire apparatus are the direct result of changes made after firefighter deaths and injuries.

Rapid Intervention Crew (RIC)

A Rapid Intervention Crew (RIC) or Rapid Intervention Team (RIT) consists of two or more fully equipped and immediately available firefighters designated to stand by outside the hazard zone to enter and effect rescue of firefighters inside, if necessary. The RIC concept was created in response to Occupational Safety and Health Administration (OSHA) regulations in the 1990s. For more information see the FPP manual, **Rapid Intervention Teams**.

Although protective gear and apparatus have improved dramatically, a firefighter is now expected to physically exert himself or herself more while carrying more and more equipment. Because firefighters are up to one-third less efficient in their gear and because regular exercise has been shown to substantially reduce injury rates, more and more fire departments now require firefighters to participate in regular aerobic exercise.

Changes in the way firefighters respond to an emergency have also reduced firefighter deaths and injuries. Today's firefighters are expected to ride to the incident seated inside the vehicle with seat belts fastened, not clinging to the tailboard outside. No matter how urgent the emergency call, apparatus drivers are taught to stop or otherwise ensure intersections are clear before proceeding. The apparatus and its crew are of no value if they never make it to the emergency scene; furthermore, additional resources must be diverted to help with a second emergency.

At the fire scene, the Incident Management System is implemented to maintain order and efficiency. Firefighters are trained in the buddy system so that no one ever enters an IDLH atmosphere alone. The OSHA Two In/Two Out requirement enforces the buddy system. Accountability is maintained with removable nametags that are kept on a board until each firefighter exits a structure (IDLH) and checks in. There are a number of different personnel accountability systems used today to determine which firefighters are on duty with each company and to help Incident Commanders determine where each of the firefighters is located at the emergency scene (**Figures 3.39, p. 130**). Rapid Intervention Crews (RIC) are established on incidents as an extra measure of safety for firefighters. They are comprised of firefighters equipped with special training and tools needed to effect a firefighter rescue. A Safety Officer is designated to observe the fire scene; this individual can override any other orders if he or she spots an unsafe condition.

Figures 3.39 A fire officer using a personnel accountability board to track personnel at an incident.

Chapter Summary

Although the fire service has grown and changed greatly from the days when the members of a community fought fire with bucket brigades, the objective remains the same: to protect the lives and property of the citizenry. Today's firefighters are better educated, trained, and equipped than ever, yet they still respond to scenes that are dangerous and unstable. The role of the fire department has grown from much more than fire mitigation to encompass public education, emergency medical response, rescue, hazardous materials response, and even terrorism response. Changes in regulations, construction, and technology have changed the ways in which firefighters operate at the emergency scene, but they still work as a team to accomplish their goals.

Review Questions

1. What was probably one of the first pieces of fire equipment to be invented?

2. How did the invention of the fire engine help lead to the formation of early fire departments?

3. What was the first city in the United States to have a fire department?

4. What effect has developing technology had on emergency notification systems?

5. How have improvements to protective clothing affected modern firefighting practices?

6. How have past tragedies influenced the fields of fire protection and code enforcement today?

Fire Investigation, Fire Prevention, and Public Fire and Life Safety Education

Key Terms

FESHE Outcomes

This chapter provides information that addresses the outcomes for the Fire and Emergency Services Higher Education (FESHE) *Principles of Emergency Services* course.

10. Identify and explain the components of fire prevention including code enforcement, public information, and public and private fire protection systems.

NFPA® Job Performance Requirements

This chapter provides information that addresses the following job performance requirements (JPRs) of NFPA® 1001, *Standard for Fire Fighter Professional Qualifications* (2008).

6.3.4(A)

6.5.1(A)

6.5.2(A)

6.5.3(A)

Learning Objectives

After reading this chapter, students will be able to:

1. Explain the various responsibilities of fire and emergency services personnel regarding fire investigation.

2. Identify the components of fire prevention.

3. Describe the roles of code enforcement, public information, and public and private fire protection systems as they relate to fire prevention.

Chapter 4
Fire Investigation, Fire Prevention, and Public Fire and Life Safety Education

Case History

Maria and Danny graduated from the fire academy together 10 years ago. They'd kept in touch, even though Maria was assigned to a ladder company on the north side, and Danny worked on an engine company downtown. Lately they'd been talking about their futures in the fire service. While they both were happy with their current assignments, they were thinking about what the next step might be.

Maria was technically inclined. She was good at figuring things out and was very observant. Maria also had a good sense of how fire would behave in a specific building. Maria thought that she would be a good fire investigator or fire inspector and decided to learn more about each specialty.

Danny could explain almost anything. He was an outgoing guy and volunteered as a coach for the Little League. Danny was very good with those kids! He thought it was time to learn more about becoming a fire and life safety educator.

Every firefighter has a role to play in fire investigation, **fire prevention**, and fire and life safety education. These three functions are often under the supervision of the **fire marshal** or within a **fire prevention bureau**.

The first part of this chapter contains information on the responsibilities of the firefighter and the fire investigator. A firefighter's observations en route, upon arrival, as well as during and after the fire can assist in a fire investigation and are also covered in this chapter. Steps for securing the fire scene and protecting evidence are often the firefighter's responsibility. The chapter also describes the firefighter's conduct at the scene and legal considerations.

The safest way for both firefighters and the public to deal with fire is to prevent it from occurring in the first place. In the past, some fire service personnel felt that fire prevention and public fire education programs threatened the existence of their departments. Today's fire service embraces these activities because they have been shown to save the lives of citizens and firefighters alike. The increased demands now placed on firefighters and other emergency responders necessitate a clear understanding of, and active participation in, all aspects of public fire prevention and education.

> **Fire Prevention** — (1) Part of the science of fire protection that deals with preventing the outbreak of fire by eliminating fire hazards through such activities as inspection, code enforcement, education, and investigation programs. (2) Division of a fire department responsible for conducting fire prevention programs of inspection, code enforcement, education, and investigation. *Also known as* Fire Prevention Bureau.

> **Fire Marshal** — Highest fire prevention officer of a state, province, county, or municipality. In Canada, this officer is *also known as* the Fire Commissioner.

Fire Prevention Bureau
— Division of the fire department responsible for conducting fire prevention programs of inspection, code enforcement, education, and investigation. *Also known as* Fire Prevention.

Fire Investigator — Public or private sector individual tasked with discovering the origin and cause of a fire, as well as who may be responsible or liable for a fire.

Fire Cause Determination — Process of establishing the cause of a fire incident through careful investigation and analysis of the available evidence.

The chapter continues with an overview of fire prevention and the various types of fire hazards. The next section discusses the two types of fire safety surveys: the pre-incident survey and the residential fire safety survey. The last part of the chapter discusses public fire and life safety education. It provides information on fire safety topics a firefighter may be asked to present to public gatherings or to give as part of a fire station tour. For more information on these topics, refer to IFSTA's **Introduction to Fire Origin and Cause** and **Fire and Life Safety Educator** manuals.

Fire Investigation

Once a fire has occurred, it must be investigated to determine its origin and cause. The result of the **fire cause determination** can then be used to improve fire safety conditions within the community. Typically, the fire chief or fire marshal has the legal responsibility for fire origin and cause determination. The actual investigation is usually conducted by a qualified **fire investigator**.

The cause of a fire is a combination of three factors:

- Fuel that ignites
- Form and source of the heat of ignition
- Act or omission that helped to bring these two factors together

The responsibility for investigation includes both accidental and incendiary (intentionally set) fires. The fire chief relies on the fire officers and firefighters at the scene to make sure that the true and specific origin and cause of the fire can be determined. Proper training enables firefighters to recognize and collect important information by observing the fire and its behavior during the response, upon arrival, when entering the structure, while locating, and when extinguishing the fire. More than anyone else, the firefighter is aware of actual conditions at the fire scene.

The first-arriving firefighters may be able to best answer some important questions about structure fires. For example:

- What were the weather and wind conditions?
- What color was the smoke? The flames?
- Were smoke and flames showing from the inside? Where?
- Did some areas appear to have more fire and smoke damage than others?
- What fire patterns were present? (**Figure 4.1 a, b, and c**)
- Were smoke alarms present? Were they working?
- Were sprinkler systems or other suppression systems present? Did they activate?
- Were the contents of the rooms as they should be? Were the rooms ransacked or unusually bare?
- Were the doors and windows open or closed, locked or unlocked?
- Was there evidence of forced entry prior to the arrival of firefighters?
- Were there indications of unusual fire behavior in more than one area of origin?
- Were vehicles or people present in the area?

Figure 4.1a An example of a V-pattern. *Courtesy of Wayne Chapdlaine.*

Figure 4.1b An example of a U-pattern. *Courtesy of Donny Howard.*

Figure 4.1c An example of a hot gas layers pattern. *Courtesy of Donny Howard.*

- Was there anything or anyone out of place or unusual?
- Did the furniture new or appear to be worn ?

Firefighters must be aware during fireground operations that what they do and how they do it can affect the determination of the origin and cause of the fire. Having an alert and open mind combined with performing judicious and careful overhaul may also uncover and preserve important evidence in accidental and incendiary fires. Without the firefighter's observations and open mind, such evidence might be lost.

It is the responsibility of the fire department to respond to and extinguish a fire as quickly as possible. However, the results of the fire fighting operation may impair an investigator in determining fire origin and cause. The firefighters' actions may move evidence from its original location or completely destroy it. It is extremely important that firefighters take as many precautions as they can to protect evidence while fighting a fire.

Information gathered at the scene is of critical importance to the fire investigator. Investigators are seldom present while firefighters attack a fire, perform overhaul, and interview occupants or witnesses to obtain informa-

Figure 4.2 A fire investigator examining the scene of a fire.

tion. Civil and criminal legal proceedings concerning a particular fire may also become necessary. For these reasons, firefighters must be responsible for noting everything that could point to the origin and cause of a fire.

NOTE: For more information about fire investigation, refer to the IFSTA **Introduction to Fire Origin and Cause** manual and to the **Fire Investigator** manual.

Role of the Investigator

Fire investigators have received special training in determining fire origin and cause, fire pattern recognition, evidence collection and preservation, interviewing techniques, and legal procedures and testimony (**Figure 4.2**). Accredited organizations can offer certification to NFPA® 1033, *Standard for Professional Qualifications for Fire Investigator.* The International Association of Arson Investigators and the National Association of Fire Investigators conduct training and testing to become a certified fire and explosion investigator.

Fire marshals, fire inspectors, or other members of a fire prevention bureau are usually responsible for conducting fire origin and cause investigations beyond the level of the fire company. Firefighters may be questioned by an investigator or asked to assist in some aspect of an investigation.

NOTE: Refer to NFPA® 921, *Guide for Fire and Explosion Investigations*, for further information about conducting fire investigations.

Some fire departments have special fire investigation or **arson** squads. In other departments, fire department and law enforcement personnel work together. There are also a few localities where the police department has sole responsibility for handling a fire investigation. In other areas, the responsibility for origin and cause determination lies with the state fire marshal or another state agency rather than with local agencies. Private companies may conduct separate investigations when a fire involves their property, or an insurance company may conduct an investigation.

Arson — Crime of willfully, maliciously, and intentionally starting an incendiary fire or causing an explosion to destroy one's property or the property of another. Precise legal definitions vary among jurisdictions, wherein it is defined by statutes and judicial decisions.

Observations Made by Emergency Responders

The observations that firefighters make and actions they perform are vital to fire origin and cause investigation. These observations and actions occur at different times throughout an incident. For example, firefighters may not find indications of fire patterns or unusual fire behavior until they perform overhaul. **Overhaul** is the act of checking for and extinguishing hidden fires once the main fire has been extinguished. A thorough search for containers and signs of forcible entry may not be feasible until the fire is extinguished. The important point is that firefighters take steps to protect and preserve evidence as soon as they find it.

Overhaul — Operations conducted once the main body of fire has been extinguished; consists of searching for and extinguishing hidden or remaining fire, placing the building and its contents in a safe condition, determining the cause of the fire, and recognizing and preserving evidence of arson.

Observations En Route

The firefighters' responsibility for gathering information begins when the alarm is received. The firefighter should gather information on the following:

- *Time of day* — Are people and circumstances at the scene as they normally would be at this time of day? For example, is it a time when people might normally be cooking? If a fire is in a dwelling at 3 a.m., the residents would probably be wearing nightclothes, not street clothes. If a fire is in an office building after working hours, the owner or "nine-to-five" employees should have a valid reason for being present at that hour. Are cars present or absent in a driveway or garage when expected?

- *Visible flames and smoke* — Are flames or smoke visible? From which windows? Are the flames and smoke located on the inside or the outside of the structure? Upstairs or downstairs? Which specific location (northwest corner? under the eaves? next to the garage door)? What color are the flames and smoke **(Figure 4.3)**?

Figure 4.3 Firefighters should watch for signs of fire and smoke upon arrival at the scene of a fire. *Courtesy of McKinney (TX) Fire Department.*

- *Weather and natural hazards* — Is it hot, cold, or stormy? Is there lightning, heavy snow, ice, high water, or fog? If the outside temperature is high, the furnace in the structure would not be operating. If the outside temperature is low, the windows normally would not be wide open. Winds can "feed" a fire or move it in unexpected directions. Arsonists sometimes set fires during inclement weather because the fire department's response time may be longer.

- *Barriers* — Are there any barriers such as barricades, fallen trees, cables, trash containers, or vehicles blocking access to hydrants, sprinkler and standpipe connections, streets, and driveways? These situations could indicate an attempt on someone's part to delay fire fighting efforts.

- *People leaving the scene* — Are people leaving the scene? A fire is intriguing to most people; they tend to stay and watch. On the other hand, people leaving the scene in a vehicle or on foot may be suspicious. When a person leaves the scene by vehicle, make note of the color of the vehicle, its approximate year, its model, the body style and condition, and the license plate number. Notice how many occupants are in the vehicle. If a person leaves the scene on foot, note the person's attire, general physical appearance, and any peculiarities such as someone trying to leave undetected, walking briskly, or looking over his shoulder.

Observations Upon Arrival

Additional information that firefighters should gather upon arrival at the scene may include the following:

- *Time of arrival and extent of fire* — Ask the person who reported the fire or other witnesses about the extent of the fire at the time it was discovered and reported. The person who reported the fire can be questioned thoroughly at a later time. Note the locations of smoke columns and flames and determine whether flashover or self-ventilation occurred. If the fire self-ventilated, was it vertical or horizontal?

- *Wind direction and velocity* — Note wind direction and velocity. These factors may have a great effect on the natural path of fire spread.

- *Doors or windows locked or unlocked* — Note the position and condition of doors and windows upon arrival. Before opening doors and windows, determine whether they are locked or unlocked or show any signs of forcible entry such as broken glass or split frames. Sometimes doors and windows are covered with blankets, paint, and paper to delay discovery of the fire.

- *Switches in open or closed position* — Check to see if appliance and light switches are in the open or closed position. Do not change the position of a switch.

- *Location of the fire* — Determine the location of the fire. This information helps to identify the area of origin. Also note whether there were separate, seemingly unconnected fires. If so, the fire might have been set in several locations or spread by trailers (combustible material used to spread fire from one area to another).

- *Containers or cans* — Note metal cans or plastic containers found inside or outside the structure. They may have been used to transport accelerants.

- **Burglary tools** — Note tools such as pry bars and screwdrivers found in unusual areas. They may have been used to enter the facility to set the fire.

- **Familiar faces** — Look for familiar faces in the crowd of bystanders. They may be people who like to watch fires, or they may be habitual firesetters.

Observations During Fire Fighting

Firefighters should continue to observe the following conditions that may help determine the origin and cause of accidental and incendiary fires:

- **Fire patterns** — Note the fire's movement and intensity patterns. These can trace how the fire spread, identify the area of origin or ignition source, and determine the fuel(s) involved. Carefully note areas of irregular burning or locally heavy charring in areas of little fuel.

- **Unusual odors** — Note any unusual odors at the fire scene. Firefighters should always wear self-contained breathing apparatus (SCBA) during fire suppression and overhaul operations, but unusual odors may still be noticeable.

- **Abnormal behavior of fire when water is applied** — Reignition, several rekindles in the same area, or an increase in the intensity of the fire indicate possible accelerant use or the improper storage of flammable liquids. Water applied to fires involving ordinary combustibles usually reduces flame propagation. Water applied to a burning liquid accelerant or other flammable liquid, on the other hand, may cause it to splatter, allowing flame intensity to increase and the fire to spread in several directions.

- **Color of flames and smoke** — Note the color of flames and smoke found at the scene. They can provide a lot of information about what is burning.

- **Obstacles hindering fire fighting** — Note whether doors are tied shut or furniture is placed in doorways and hallways to hinder fire fighting efforts. Holes may be cut in the floors that not only hinder fire suppression activities but also spread the fire.

- **Incendiary devices** — Note pieces of glass, fragments of bottles or containers, and metal parts of electrical or mechanical devices. Most incendiary devices (any device designed and used to start a fire) leave evidence of their existence (**Figure 4.4**). More than one device may be found, and sometimes a faulty functioning device can be found during a thorough search.

- **Trailers** — Note combustible materials such as rolled rags, blankets, newspapers, or ignitable liquid (trailers) that could be used to spread fire from one point to another. Trailers usually leave char or fire patterns and may be used with incendiary ignition devices.

- **Demolition, construction, and structural alterations** — Observe all demolition, construction, and alterations to the structure: removal of plaster or drywall to expose wood; holes made in ceilings, walls, and floors; and fire doors secured in an open position. All of these changes are normal during demolition and construction, but impact fire spread. At the same time, such changes could indicate efforts to abnormally spread or move an incendiary fire quickly through the structure.

Figure 4.4 The remains of an incendiary device that started a fire.

- *Heat intensity* — Look for evidence of high heat intensity, especially in relation to other areas of the same room. This may indicate the presence of polyurethane foam furniture, for example, or the use of accelerants.

- *Fire detection and suppression systems* — Check for the presence of detection and suppression systems, whether the systems appeared to be operable or inoperable, whether the systems operated, and evidence of tampering or intentional damage.

- *Intrusion alarms* — Check intrusion alarms to see whether they have been tampered with or intentionally disabled.

- *Location of fire* — Note ignition sources or possible ignition sources in the area of the fire. Be alert to common ignition sources for accidental fires, such as smoking materials, cooking, and space heaters. Fires in areas remote from normal ignition sources may indicate suspicious activity. Some examples are fires in closets, bathtubs, file drawers, or in the center of the floor.

- *Personal possessions* — Look for the following indicators that preparations were made for a fire: absence or shortage of clothing, furnishings, appliances, food, and dishes; absence of personal possessions such as diplomas, financial papers, and toys; absence of items of sentimental value such as photo albums, special collections, wedding pictures, and heirlooms; absence of pets that would ordinarily be in the structure.

  NOTE: Do not assume too much about a lack of material possessions. A person's economic status may dictate his lifestyle, and some people just do not have as much as others.

- *Housekeeping and household items* — Note whether the structure appears to be well- or poorly-maintained, tidy or cluttered. Observe whether major household items appear to be removed or replaced with junk. Check to see whether major appliances were operable, operating, or disconnected or unplugged; determine why they were in this condition.

- *Equipment or inventory* — Notice the presence or absence of equipment or inventory, fixtures, display cases, equipment, and raw materials.

Responsibilities After the Fire

Firefighters should report all facts concerning the fire to the officer in charge as soon as possible. If requested, the firefighter must be prepared to provide a chronological account (oral or written) of important circumstances personally observed. Report hearsay (such as "*The neighbor told me that he saw the lights flickering for a few days before the fire.*") to the investigator for validation. While hearsay, this information may be very helpful to the investigator.

Written Account of the Incident

A written account can be valuable if the responder must testify in court. Cases often come to trial several years after an incident, and testimony should not rely on memory alone.

Figure 4.5 Firefighters covering furniture with a salvage cover to prevent water damage during fire fighting operations.

Salvage and overhaul are probably the pivotal operations in determining fire origin and cause. Some departments take great pride in their salvage and overhaul work and boast that they leave a building neater, cleaner, and more orderly than it was before the fire **(Figure 4.5)**. This thoroughness in salvage and overhaul is admirable, but it may destroy evidence of where and how a fire started. Salvage and overhaul work should be coordinated with the fire investigator until the area of origin has been determined.

Fire personnel should perform salvage and overhaul carefully. They should not move more debris than is necessary, especially in the area of origin, because it may hamper the investigation. Neither should firefighters throw debris outside into a pile — evidence is buried this way and may be permanently lost.

Conduct and Statements at the Scene

Although firefighters and the fire officer should obtain all information possible pertaining to a fire, they should not attempt to interrogate a potential arson suspect. The moment firefighters suspect someone of arson, a trained investigator should be called to conduct an interview. It is the trained investigator's job to interview an arson suspect. Owners or occupants of the property should be allowed to talk freely if they are inclined to do so, and give them a sympathetic ear. Some valuable information is often gathered this way.

Fire personnel should never make statements of accusation, personal opinion, or probable cause to anyone. The property owner, news media, or other bystanders could hear these opinions and mistake such statements as fact. Careless joking and unauthorized or premature remarks that are published or broadcast can be very embarrassing to the fire department. These remarks often impede the efforts of an investigator to prove malicious intent as the fire cause. A sufficient reply to any question about origin and cause is, "The fire is under investigation."

Media Inquiries and Requests

Only authorized personnel, such as a PIO, should speak with the media. Inquiries to firefighters should be referred to the Incident Commander, directed to the PIO, or directed to the lead investigator.

All photos or videos taken by responding emergency personnel should be considered the property of the fire department and cannot be released or posted without proper authorization. Unauthorized release can open the responder and/or department to criminal or civil liabilities.

After the investigator arrives, personnel should make their statements only to this individual. Any public statement regarding the fire origin and cause should be made only after the investigator and ranking fire officer have agreed to its accuracy and validity and have given permission for it to be released.

Securing the Fire Scene

The most efficient and complete efforts to determine the origin and cause of a fire are wasted unless the building and premises are properly secured and guarded until an investigator has finished evaluating the scene. Firefighters should take care not to contaminate the scene while operating power tools, hoselines, or other equipment.

If an investigator is not immediately available, the premises should be guarded and kept under the control of the fire department until all evidence has been collected. All evidence should be marked, tagged, and photographed at this time because in many instances a search warrant or written consent to search will be needed for further visits to the premises. This duty might be given to law enforcement personnel, depending on local policies and personnel availability, but whenever possible fire department personnel trained in evidence collection and preservation should carry out this duty.

The fire department has the authority to deny access to any building during fire fighting operations and for a reasonable length of time after fire suppression is terminated. Fire department authority ends when the last fire department representative leaves the scene. Further visits to the scene require either the owner's written permission or a search warrant. Fire personnel should be aware of any local laws pertaining to the right of access by owners or occupants.

Fire personnel should not allow anyone to enter a fire scene without the investigator's permission, and an authorized individual should escort all who enter the scene. The escort is necessary both for the visitor's safety and for scene security. During fireground operations and the investigation, make a recorded log of any such entry. The log should show the person's name, the time of entry, the time of departure, and a description of any items the person took from the scene.

The premises can be secured and protected in several ways with the use of few personnel. Areas that are fenced and that have a locked gate can be monitored by one person. At large fire scenes, a full-time guard force is often employed. In some extreme instances, all doors, windows, or other entrances could be completely closed with plywood or similar material. Boarding windows and covering openings also prevents further damage to the building and/or

Figure 4.6 Firefighters boarded up the windows of this building to prevent weather damage.

evidence from weather conditions such as rain, snow, or extreme temperature **(Figure 4.6)**. Covering broken windows and other openings after a fire is also a function of customer service and salvage.

Cordoning the area can also help provide a safe and secure fire scene. With the area cordoned, bystanders are kept at a safe distance from the incident and out of the way of emergency personnel. There are no specific recommended boundaries for the cordon.

Cordoning can be accomplished with rope or specially designed fire and police line tape. It may be attached to signs, utility poles, parking meters, vehicles, or any other objects readily available. Properly securing a fire scene also reduces the possibility of looting or unauthorized entry.

Once the cordon is in place, law enforcement or other authorized personnel should monitor the line to make sure people do not cross it. Be aware of seemingly innocent persons (including curious bystanders and the media) attempting to cross a line. Escort from the scene anyone in the cordoned area who is not a part of the operation. Record any information obtained from them for future reference.

Legal Considerations

As previously stated, firefighters may remain on the location as long as necessary, but once they leave they may be required to get a search warrant to reenter the scene. This is based on the case of Michigan vs. Tyler (436 U.S. 499, 56 L.Ed. 2d 486 [1978]) The U.S. Supreme Court held in that case that *"once in a building [to extinguish a fire], firefighters may seize [without a warrant] evidence of arson that is in plain view . . . [and] officials need no warrant to remain in a building for a reasonable time to investigate the cause of a blaze after it has been extinguished."*

The Court agreed, with modification, with the Michigan State Supreme Court's statement that *"[if] there has been a fire, the blaze extinguished and the firefighters have left the premises, a warrant is required to re-enter and search the premises, unless there is consent . . . ."*

The impact of these decisions is that if there is incendiary evidence, the fire department should leave at least one person on the premises until an investigator arrives. Once all personnel have left the scene, to return later, even with the owner's consent or a search warrant, might be enough to make prosecution impossible or for an appellate court to overturn a conviction.

Figure 4.7 A fire investigator examining a fire-damaged appliance.

Each department should learn the legal opinions that affect its jurisdiction in this regard. These opinions or interpretations can be obtained from the district attorney or state attorney general. The fire department should write a standard operating procedure (SOP) around these opinions.

Protecting and Preserving Evidence

The need to protect and preserve evidence applies to both accidental and incendiary fires, since accidental fires can be the subject of civil litigation. No changes of any kind should be permitted in the evidence other than those absolutely necessary in the extinguishment of the fire. As used here, evidence includes fire scene artifacts that can help determine a fire's origin and cause. Examples of such evidence include the following:

- Burned or scorched large and small appliances **(Figure 4.7)**
- Burned, scorched, or melted electrical outlets and cords
- Extension cords
- Areas of concentrated fire seen early in suppression operations
- Portable space heaters
- Smoke alarms

Firefighters should avoid trampling over and obliterating possible evidence. The same precaution applies to the excessive use of water. Human footprints and tire marks must be protected. Boxes placed over prints prevent dust from blowing over otherwise clear prints and keep them in good condition for either photographs or plaster casts at a later time. Completely or partially burned papers found in a furnace, stove, or fireplace should be protected by immediately closing dampers and other openings. Leave charred documents found in containers such as wastebaskets, small file cabinets, and binders that can be moved easily. Keep these items away from drafts.

After an investigator has properly collected evidence, debris may be removed. Charred materials should be removed to prevent the possibility of rekindle and to help reduce smoke damage.

Fire Prevention

Every public action that a fire service organization takes can have a lasting consequence on the firefighters and the citizens it serves. Firefighters frequently respond to fires and other life-threatening incidents that could have been prevented had the individual(s) involved clearly understood the consequences of the unsafe act or the dangers posed by the hazards involved. The foundation of every successful fire prevention program is grounded in a clear understanding of past problems and current needs. Before any corrective action can be instituted, there must first be a recognition and understanding of the potential risk, need, or condition that is being examined.

Firefighters must direct their efforts at reducing known hazardous conditions or preventing dangerous acts before tragedy strikes. There are many innovative ways to accomplish this task, such as conducting educational presentations, distributing safety brochures, providing news articles, writing public safety announcements (PSAs), or establishing meaningful displays in frequently visited areas. Alerting the news media during or just after a preventable accident can turn a loss into a "teachable moment" that significantly increases public awareness. On such occasions, the department's **public information officer** (PIO) or other officer usually works with media contacts **(Figure 4.8, p. 148)**.

Fire safety surveys in public, commercial, and residential occupancies can have an important effect on community fire prevention and pre-incident planning. *Fire safety surveys* involve those activities that have been planned or legislated to ensure that citizens have a safe physical environment in which to live, work, study, worship, or play. The survey process requires firefighters to become familiar with community structures and to recognize safety hazards quickly **(Figure 4.9, p. 148)**. Observed problems can then be resolved diplomatically.

Fire incident records, which represent the documented fire history of a community, can also further fire prevention efforts. Studying previous incidents, reviewing data obtained from various fire reports, and comparing a community's fire loss experience with state/provincial or national statistics are all ways to gain needed information. Such reviews help identify major fire causes and raise questions about possible solutions.

Another important fire prevention activity is code enforcement inspection. Specially trained **fire inspectors** usually conduct fire inspections, although in

Public Information Officer (PIO) — Member of the command staff responsible for interfacing with the media, public, or other agencies requirig information direct from the incident scene. *Also known as* Information Officer (IO).

Fire Inspector — Fire personnel assigned to inspect property with the purpose of enforcing fire regulations.

Figure 4.8 A public information officer being interviewed by a television news reporter about fire prevention. *Courtesy of Dayna Hilton and Johnson County RFD #1.*

Figure 4.9 A fire inspector conducting a fire safety survey in a residence.

Figures 4.10 A fire inspector and a firefighter conducting a fire code compliance inspection in a commercial property.

some cases engine and truck companies conduct routine inspections **(Figure 4.10)**. Their findings not only make firefighters aware of potential hazards, but also permit inspection personnel to communicate unsafe conditions to building occupants and owners. Any person expected to take a more authoritative role in public safety inspections should be trained to meet the objectives found in NFPA® 1031, *Standard for Professional Qualifications for Fire Inspector and Plan Examiner*. Additional guidance regarding inspection practices can be found in IFSTA's **Fire Inspection and Code Enforcement** manual.

Fire Hazards

A **fire hazard** increases the likelihood of a fire or increases the extent or severity of an existing fire. According to the rules of basic fire chemistry, fire cannot survive without a fuel supply, sufficient heat, oxygen supply, and a self-sustained chemical reaction. Therefore, hazardous fire conditions can be prevented by eliminating one or all of these elements.

NOTE: See Chapter 5, Scientific Terminology, for more information about fire behavior.

Fire Hazard — Any material, condition, or act that contributes to the start of a fire or that increases the extent or severity of fire.

Control of the hazards associated with fuel supply and heat sources are the most manageable. If heat sources are kept separated from fuel supplies, the condition remains safe. Not all fuel supplies can be ignited easily, but misuse of any fuel under extreme heat conditions can lead to a fire. Some common fuel and heat-source hazards include the following:

- *Fuel Hazards such as:*
  - Ordinary combustibles such as wood, cloth, or paper
  - Flammable and combustible gases such as natural gas, liquefied petroleum gas (LPG), and compressed natural gas (CNG)
  - Flammable and combustible liquids such as gasoline, oils, lacquers, or alcohol
  - Chemicals such as nitrates, oxides, or chlorates **(Figure 4.11)**
  - Dusts such as grain, wood, metal, or coal
  - Metals such as magnesium, sodium, or potassium
  - Plastics, resins, and cellulose

Figure 4.11 Bags of nitrates and chlorates represent a fuel hazard.

- *Heat Source Hazards such as:*
  - *Chemical heat energy* — Materials that are improperly stored can result in chemical heat energy. Materials may come in contact with each other and react (oxidizer and reducing agent), or they may decompose and generate heat.
  - *Electrical heat energy* — Poorly maintained or defective electrical appliances, exposed wiring, and lighting are sources of electrical heat sources.
  - *Mechanical heat energy* — Moving parts on machines, such as belts and bearings, are sources of mechanical heating.
  - *Nuclear heat energy* — Heat that is created by fission; not commonly encountered by most firefighters.

Common Fire Hazards

The term *common* could be misleading to some individuals. It refers to the probable frequency of a hazard being found, not to the severity of the hazard. A common fire hazard is a condition that is prevalent in almost all occupancies and increases the likelihood a fire may start. Firefighters need to be alert to the dangers posed by the following common hazards:

- Poor housekeeping and improper storage of packing materials and other combustibles **(Figure 4.12)**
- Defective or improperly used heating, lighting, or power equipment
- Improper use and disposal of cleaning compounds
- Misuse of fumigation substances and flammable or combustible liquids

Poor housekeeping can make it difficult for occupants to evacuate and for firefighters to maneuver through an area. Poor housekeeping also increases the fire load and increases the chance that a flammable or combustible material may come in contact with an ignition source. Clutter also conceals additional fire hazards.

Figure 4.12 A common hazard is poor housekeeping practices which can allow combustible materials to build up.

Improperly functioning heating, lighting, or other electrical equipment can provide an ignition source for nearby combustibles. Cleaning compounds, fumigating substances, and other flammable and combustible liquids that are improperly used and stored can provide a volatile fuel source if an ignition source is present.

An individual's attitude or behaviors – such as whether or not smoke alarms are checked or home escape plans are practiced – can increase or reduce the risk of fire or other emergencies. A comprehensive fire and life safety education program can reduce the risks caused by unsafe personal attitudes or behaviors.

Special Fire Hazards

A *special fire hazard* is one that arises as a result of the processes or operations that are characteristic to the individual occupancy. Commercial, manufacturing, and public-assembly occupancies each have their own special fire hazards as follows:

- ***Commercial Occupancies:***
    - Display or storage of large quantities of products **(Figure 4.13)**
    - Mixed varieties of contents
    - Difficulties in entering occupancies during closed periods
    - Existence of party walls, common attics, cocklofts, and other open voids in multiple occupancies

- ***Manufacturing:***
    - High-hazard processes using volatile substances, oxidizers, or extreme temperatures
    - Flammable liquids in dip tanks, ovens, and dryers

Figure 4.13 These cans of flammable paints and lacquers represent a special fire hazard in commercial occupancies.

- Flammable liquids used in mixing, coating, spraying, and degreasing processes
- High-piled storage of combustible materials
- Operation of vehicles, fork trucks, and other powered equipment inside buildings (use and storage of LPG and other fuels, re-service hazards)
- Large, open areas or high volume areas, such as bays, hangars, and indoor sports fields **(Figure 4.14)**
- Large-scale use of flammable and combustible gases

- *Public Assembly:*
  - Large numbers of people present, sometimes exceeding posted occupant limits
  - Insufficient, blocked, or locked exits
  - Storage of materials in paths of egress
  - Highly combustible interior finishes

Figure 4.14 Aircraft maintenance in this aircraft hangar also poses a special fire hazard.

Rhode Island Station Nightclub Fire

The Station Nightclub fire in Rhode Island that killed 100 people in 2003 is an example of the potential danger of highly combustible finishes. In that fire, foam insulation used for soundproofing ignited. The resulting fire spread extremely rapidly, and the resulting flames and thick smoke prevented patrons from finding the marked fire exits.

Figure 4.15 Target fire hazards include bulk oil refinery and storage facilities such as this one.

Target Hazard Properties

A target hazard is viewed as a facility in which there is a great potential for life or property loss from a fire. These occupancies should receive special attention during surveys. Some examples include the following:

- Shopping centers
- Hospitals
- Theaters
- Nursing homes
- Schools
- Nightclubs and social clubs
- Lumberyards
- Bulk oil storage facilities **(Figure 4.15)**
- Distribution centers, particularly for flammable and combustible commodities
- Rows of frame tenements
- "Big box" stores

Multiple Hazards

A special hazard results from a process. A target hazard is a location. A lumber milling and sales yard could be both a special hazard (from the milling process) and a target hazard.

Facility Surveys

Pre-Incident Survey — Survey of a facility or location made before an emergency occurs in order to prepare for an appropriate emergency response. *Also known as* Preplan.

Fire safety surveys include **pre-incident surveys** and residential fire safety surveys. Pre-incident surveys are used for all nonresidential facilities, such as commercial, industrial, manufacturing, and institutional buildings. Residential safety surveys are used for all types of residences (single-family dwellings, apartments, etc.) All of these surveys are used to make owners and occupants aware of hazards or dangerous conditions. Of course, the owners and occupants must then understand the urgency of the situation and take appropriate action to correct the hazards identified. If they do not, the fire department's efforts may be of little consequence. In addition to assisting occupants, the pre-incident and residential fire safety surveys provide the information used by the fire service for a **pre-incident plan**.

The pre-incident survey in public and commercial occupancies gives "up-front" information required to better assess conditions during any emergency situation that might occur in these occupancies. Such insight is essential if firefighters expect to safely, efficiently, and effectively control fire incidents.

Residential fire safety surveys may be accomplished as part of a house-to-house fire prevention program, or they can be done when requested on an individual basis. Fire departments that provide residential fire safety survey services usually do so as part of a fire and life safety education program.

Firefighters need a wide range of personal and technical skills to conduct fire safety surveys properly. Technical knowledge and skills require firefighters to understand building construction, fire and life safety requirements, common and special hazards, building utilities, energy systems, and various fire protection appliances and systems.

Needed interpersonal skills may include those that enhance communication, mitigation, facilitation, negotiation, or mediation.

Personnel Requirements

In the public's eyes, the firefighter's uniform and badge indicate that the wearer is professionally qualified to discuss important aspects of fire prevention and give reliable advice on correcting fire safety hazards. When performing any public fire prevention activity, the firefighter should project a well-groomed, neat appearance. The uniform should be clean and in good condition. A neat appearance helps to gain the respect of the public and bolsters the fire department's public image.

Firefighters who meet the fire prevention and public fire and life safety education objectives found in NFPA® 1001 will possess a basic understanding of fire prevention principles and can approach their assignments with confidence. Firefighters who perform fire safety surveys are expected to recognize basic hazards and report them through the appropriate channels established within their organizations **(Figure 4.16)**. Although firefighters can offer corrective advice, they are not fully qualified inspectors or public fire and life safety educators, so must remember that their expertise is limited.

Pre-Incident Planning — Act of preparing to manage an incident at a particular location or a particular type of incident before an incident occurs. *Also known as* Prefire Inspection, Prefire Planning, Pre-Incident Inspection, Pre-Incident Survey, or Preplanning.

Pre-Incident Plan — Document, developed during pre-incident planning that contains the operational plan or set procedures for the safe and efficient handling of emergency situations at a given location, such as a specific building or occupancy. *Also known as* Preplan.

Figure 4.16 A firefighter conducting a pre-incident survey in a dry cleaning facility.

Scheduling the Pre-Incident Survey

A primary management challenge of every fire department administrator is how to balance competing demands for the firefighter's time. Fire organizations cannot choose the time when they must respond to emergencies, but they are able to decide where and when to perform fire prevention activities. Because of this choice, the fire department administrators should set a schedule for pre-incident surveys.

The company officer should contact the building owner or occupant ahead of time to arrange for the pre-incident survey. The company officer will inform the owner of the purpose of the survey and find out what day and time would be most suitable. This procedure enables fire safety surveys to be scheduled at a time that will not cause hardship for either occupants or fire company. A survey should never be attempted without proper permission. Commercial surveys are usually made during normal business hours, but night surveys are sometimes necessary because of operating schedules.

Pre-incident surveys provide information about building construction, hazardous materials storage, building layout, special processes, fire notification and suppression features, and occupancy concerns. This knowledge greatly improves fire department operations and substantially improves both firefighter and occupant safety when suppression efforts are required.

An earnest effort by firefighters to create a favorable impression upon the owner helps to establish a courteous and cooperative relationship. Firefighters should enter the premises at the main entrance and contact the individual with whom the survey was scheduled. If necessary, firefighters may have to wait to see the proper individual if this person is busy. Reporting to the person in authority after the survey (exit interview) also shows the owner the importance of the pre-incident planning process.

Conducting the Pre-Incident Survey

After the initial meeting with the owner (or delegate), the survey team should return to the outside of the building to survey the exterior to make certain observations, preliminary notes, and photographs. This external survey provides an overview of the building's layout, and provides the necessary information for drawing the exterior walls on a sketch of the floor plan (layout of each floor of a building). The external survey thus makes the interior survey easier

To make a thorough survey, firefighters must take sufficient time to make notes and take photographs, outlining observed hazards, improper practices, and unsafe conditions. Sketches of the interior layout's functional areas, egress routes, and important features should be drawn (or upgraded on an existing sketch) or photographed. These features could include:

- Fire walls
- Sprinkler valves
- Utility shut-offs
- Location of storage (flammable and combustble materials)
- Stairs
- Fire barriers
- Valve rooms
- Areas of refuge

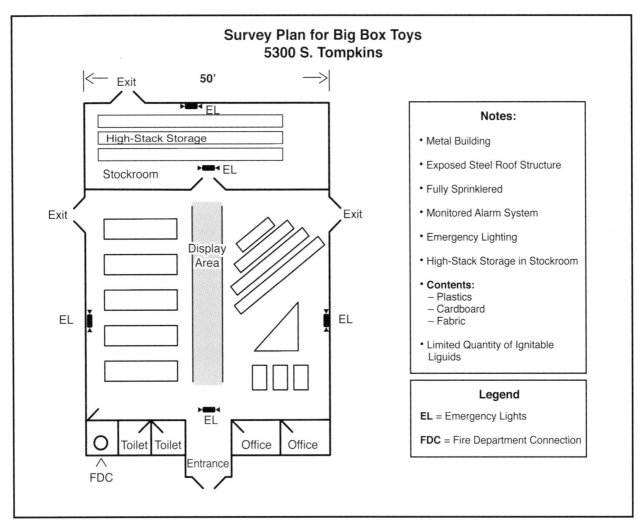

Figure 4.17 An example of a floor plan for a large toy store.

Sketching a facility is particularly important for pre-incident planning. A complete set of notes, photographs, and well-prepared sketches of the building provides dependable information from which a complete report can be written.

In large or complicated buildings, it may be necessary to make more than one visit to complete the survey. If the property includes several buildings, each should be surveyed separately. It is a good idea to start on the roof of the highest building; from here the firefighter can get a general view of the property. A sketch of each floor should be completed before proceeding to the next floor **(Figure 4.17)**. If a floor plan used on a previous survey is available, the survey can proceed more rapidly. Any changes that have been made should be recorded to update the floor plan sketch. Allowing adequate time to discuss the survey results, as well as any fire and life safety concerns, with the owner or occupant usually benefits all concerned.

Firefighters should be particularly observant of hazardous materials (haz mat) commonly used in their response areas. Much of the firefighter's haz mat identification training can be performed at local commercial and industrial facilities. Surveys at these sites allow the firefighter to document the locations of hazardous materials and the physical layout of the plants.

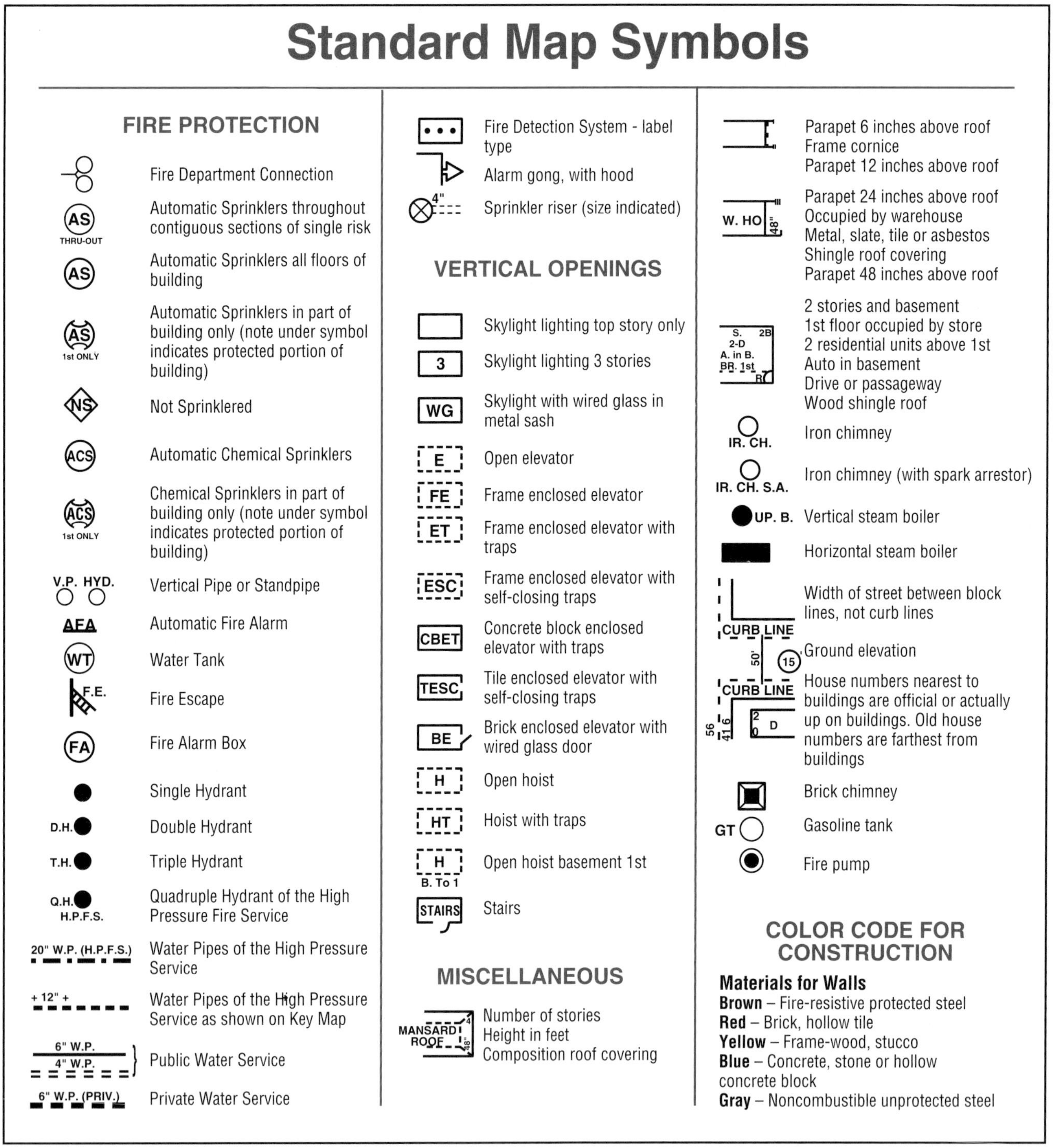

Standard Map Symbols

FIRE PROTECTION

	Fire Department Connection
(AS) THRU-OUT	Automatic Sprinklers throughout contiguous sections of single risk
(AS)	Automatic Sprinklers all floors of building
(AS) 1st ONLY	Automatic Sprinklers in part of building only (note under symbol indicates protected portion of building)
(NS)	Not Sprinklered
(ACS)	Automatic Chemical Sprinklers
(ACS) 1st ONLY	Chemical Sprinklers in part of building only (note under symbol indicates protected portion of building)
V.P. HYD.	Vertical Pipe or Standpipe
AFA	Automatic Fire Alarm
(WT)	Water Tank
F.E.	Fire Escape
(FA)	Fire Alarm Box
●	Single Hydrant
D.H.●	Double Hydrant
T.H.●	Triple Hydrant
Q.H.● H.P.F.S.	Quadruple Hydrant of the High Pressure Fire Service
20" W.P. (H.P.F.S.)	Water Pipes of the High Pressure Service
+ 12" +	Water Pipes of the High Pressure Service as shown on Key Map
6" W.P. 4" W.P.	Public Water Service
6" W.P. (PRIV.)	Private Water Service

Fire Detection System - label type

Alarm gong, with hood

Sprinkler riser (size indicated)

VERTICAL OPENINGS

	Skylight lighting top story only
3	Skylight lighting 3 stories
WG	Skylight with wired glass in metal sash
E	Open elevator
FE	Frame enclosed elevator
ET	Frame enclosed elevator with traps
ESC	Frame enclosed elevator with self-closing traps
CBET	Concrete block enclosed elevator with traps
TESC	Tile enclosed elevator with self-closing traps
BE	Brick enclosed elevator with wired glass door
H	Open hoist
HT	Hoist with traps
H B. To 1	Open hoist basement 1st
STAIRS	Stairs

MISCELLANEOUS

MANSARD ROOF — Number of stories / Height in feet / Composition roof covering

Parapet 6 inches above roof
Frame cornice
Parapet 12 inches above roof

W. HO — Parapet 24 inches above roof
Occupied by warehouse
Metal, slate, tile or asbestos
Shingle roof covering
Parapet 48 inches above roof

2 stories and basement
1st floor occupied by store
2 residential units above 1st
Auto in basement
Drive or passageway
Wood shingle roof

IR. CH. — Iron chimney

IR. CH. S.A. — Iron chimney (with spark arrestor)

UP. B. — Vertical steam boiler

Horizontal steam boiler

CURB LINE — Width of street between block lines, not curb lines

(15) — Ground elevation

CURB LINE — House numbers nearest to buildings are official or actually up on buildings. Old house numbers are farthest from buildings

Brick chimney

GT ○ — Gasoline tank

◉ — Fire pump

COLOR CODE FOR CONSTRUCTION

Materials for Walls
Brown – Fire-resistive protected steel
Red – Brick, hollow tile
Yellow – Frame-wood, stucco
Blue – Concrete, stone or hollow concrete block
Gray – Noncombustible unprotected steel

Figure 4.18 Inspectors should be familiar with common map symbols.

Cleanliness, maintenance, and good housekeeping in haz mat areas are important precautions against fire. It should be recommended that a marking system such as that outlined in NFPA® 704, *Standard System for the Identification of the Hazards of Materials for Emergency Response,* be affixed to the outside of such structures.

Maps and Sketch Making

Maps that convey information relative to construction, fire protection, occupancy, fire loading, special hazards, and other details of building complexes are an asset to fire suppression personnel. Large occupancies or complexes may already have maps that insurance companies have prepared. These maps normally use some form of common map symbols **(Figure 4.18)**.

For buildings where existing maps are not accurate or available, fire department personnel should include a sketch with their survey notes to show the general arrangement of the property with respect to streets, other buildings, and any other important features that will help determine fire fighting procedures. This sketch is commonly called a *plot plan* of the area. A firefighter's sketch of an area frequently constitutes the most informative part of a survey and should be made with neatness and accuracy.

Computer Assisted Pre-Incident Planning

Technology greatly assists the fire service in making and updating pre-incident plans. For example, pre-planning software is available. Digital photos of a facility can be inserted into the plan. Seek the owner's permission for all photos (even exterior shots).

The Exit Interview

Reporting to the person with authority of the building being surveyed can help to maintain a cooperative attitude with the owner **(see Info Box)**. To leave the premises without contacting that person might give the impression that the survey was unimportant. During this interview, a firefighter or the company officer should comment on the conditions found. This is an excellent time to offer specific advice about how to improve safety.

Gathering Additional Information

When speaking with the owner or management, it is a good idea to gain a good understanding about specialized manufacturing or business processes that may relate to fire risk. Also, getting information about the number of employees and working shifts could be useful during an incident. Cooperating with the department's fire prevention bureau is also recommended: the bureau might have information useful to the company and vice versa.

An exit interview also gives firefighters an opportunity to express thanks for the courtesies extended to the fire department and opens the way to explain how firefighters will study these reports from the standpoint of fire fighting procedures. In the final portion of the exit interview, firefighters should answer any questions they can and refer the owner/occupant to the fire marshal's office for further assistance.

Residential Fire Safety Surveys

National statistics annually suggest that over 70 percent of all fires and the vast majority of civilian casualties occur in residences. All fire organizations should make a concerted effort to improve safety in the home setting. Fire safety surveys in existing residential occupancies (particularly one- and two-family dwellings) can only be accomplished on a voluntary basis. Codes typically require inspections for structures that house three or more families, but surveys of other than common areas in these structures may still be at the discretion of the occupants.

When residential fire safety surveys are conducted as part of an organized fire and life safety education program, a great deal of advanced planning and publicity is necessary to gain full acceptance by the community. It must be made clear that the program is a *fire prevention activity* and not a *code enforcement activity*. In other words, the firefighter is coming to make family members aware of safety hazards, not point out code violations. A good rule of thumb is to have two (and only two) firefighters enter the house and remain with the occupant. They should not attempt to enter the bedrooms of the home. For more information, see NFPA® 1452, *Guide for Training Fire Service Personnel to Conduct Dwelling Fire Safety Surveys.*

When firefighters enter the home to conduct a residential fire safety survey, their main objectives should include the following:

- Preventing accidental fires
- Improving life safety conditions
- Helping the owner or occupant to understand and improve existing conditions

Firefighters also gain valuable information when performing residential safety surveys. They become more acquainted with home construction, occupancy conditions, local development trends, streets, hydrants, and water supply locations. Notes on these items and other useful information should be made and discussed during training sessions. While these benefits are helpful, the primary reason for conducting surveys is to reduce hazards associated with loss of life and property.

When conducting the survey, firefighters will find it helpful to use a survey form that lists areas of concern. The form can serve as a guide for firefighters and it can also be used to make summaries of the survey results. These summaries can be copied for the occupant as well.

During the safety survey, firefighters should be alert for the following signs of the most common causes of residential fires:

- Heating appliances
- Cooking procedures
- Smoking materials
- Electrical distribution
- Electrical appliances
- Combustible or flammable liquids

Firefighters must know the common causes of residential fires in order to conduct meaningful residential surveys and make occupants aware of dangerous conditions. For the homeowner or tenant, the residential fire safety survey provides a valuable life safety service. There is no better way for a firefighter to effectively carry out the responsibility of protecting lives and property.

In addition to performing a residential fire safety survey, firefighters should also provide occupants with fire and life safety information. The contemporary fire department is seen as the emergency first responder to all types of emergencies and is often called upon for all-hazard education (discussed more fully below). The safety survey is an excellent opportunity to distribute fire prevention literature, promote exit drills in the home (EDITH), check emergency telephone stickers, discuss smoke alarm and residential sprinkler options, and provide information on safety concerns such as those discussed below.

Smoke Alarm Give-Away Programs and Carbon Monoxide (CO) Detectors

Many fire departments have smoke detector give-away programs where detectors are provided for residents who do not have them. In a similar vein, many departments will swap out old detector batteries with new ones as a free public service.

Carbon monoxide (CO) detectors are becoming as prevalent as smoke detectors. The presence or absence of a CO detector should be noted during a residential safety survey. Some fire departments provide or loan CO detectors on a short-term basis for residents to use while they replace a detector or repair their furnace, for example.

Public Fire and Life Safety Education

Educating the public of all ages to recognize potential hazards and take appropriate corrective action is a fire department function. The teaching of fire survival techniques such as *Stop, Drop, and Roll* or *Crawl Low Under Smoke* can favorably alter behavior and impact life safety **(Figure 4.19, p. 160)**. In recent years, the fire department public education function has grown beyond fire and now encompasses many aspects of safety such as those addressed by NFPA®'s Risk Watch® Program:

- Motor vehicle safety
- Fire and burn prevention
- Choking, suffocation and strangulation prevention
- Poisoning prevention
- Falls prevention
- Firearms injury prevention
- Bike and pedestrian safety
- Water safety

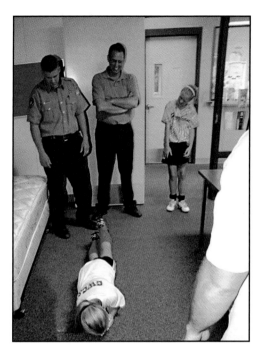

Figure 4.19 A fire and life safety educator watches as a child demonstrates Stop, Drop, and Roll techniques.

Other possible topics may include the following:

- CPR

- Carbon Monoxide detectors

- Installing child safety seats

Child Safety Seats

According to the National Highway Traffic Safety Administration (NHTSA), in the year 2005, all 50 states and the District of Columbia had child occupant protection laws, as well as safety belt laws. These laws vary widely in age requirements, exemptions, enforcement procedures, and penalties. Usage rates vary from state to state and depend upon public attitude, enforcement practices, legal provisions, and public education programs.

The use of child restraint seats has greatly decreased the number of traffic-related injuries and fatalities for younger children. However, traffic crashes still remain the number one cause of unintentional injuries and death for children age 14 and under. In 2000, Safe Kids Worldwide found that 56 percent of children ages 14 and under who were fatally injured in a crash were completely unrestrained. A study conducted by the Safe Kids Worldwide program in 2002 found that 14 percent of children age 14 and under were riding completely unrestrained.

Although this section is not designed to make a firefighter an accomplished speaker or instructor, it presents some basic information that will assist in presenting fire and life safety information to a small group of individuals. When making a fire and life safety presentation, a firefighter can take certain steps to make sure that all the information is presented and that the audience can perform such basic fire and life safety skills as calling the fire department or testing a smoke alarm.

Firefighters who are conducting life safety education should be familiar with the requirements in NFPA® 1035, *Standard for Professional Qualifications for Public Fire and Life Safety Educator*. Firefighters who complete advanced training can earn national certification as a fire and life safety educator. For more information on fire and life safety education, see the IFSTA **Fire and Life Safety Educator** manual.

Presenting Fire and Life Safety Information

The first step in making a presentation is to prepare the audience to learn. This *preparation step* involves gaining the attention of participants and letting them know why the material is important to them. An example of motivating parents during a presentation on smoke alarms might be to appeal to their desire to protect their children. Arousing curiosity, developing interest, and developing a sense of personal involvement on the part of the participants are all part of preparation.

The second step in making a presentation is to actually transfer facts and ideas (make the subject come alive) to the audience. Known as the *presentation step*, this step involves explaining information, using a variety of multi-media visual aids and props (smoke alarm, telephone for dialing 9-1-1, fire alarm pull station), and demonstrating techniques (stop, drop, and roll; crawl low under smoke; alert others to an emergency) **(Figure 4.20)**.

In the third step — perhaps the most important one — the participants use or apply the information they have been taught. This step, known as the *application step*, provides the audience with the opportunity to practice using new ideas, information, techniques, and skills. Whenever possible, each

Figure 4.20 A fire and life safety educator and her partner teach children how to crawl low below smoke and heat. *Courtesy of Dayna Hilton and Johnson County RFD #1.*

person should apply new knowledge by performing the task. For example, the participants could demonstrate how to report a fire, perform the stop, drop, and roll technique, or test a smoke alarm. The firefighter should supervise the application step closely, checking key steps and correcting errors.

Fire and Life Safety Presentation Topics

Firefighters may be asked to assist in or teach a basic fire and life safety class. Some of the topics a firefighter may be asked to present during a fire and life safety presentation include the following:

- Stop, drop, and roll technique
- Home safety practices
- Placing, testing, and maintaining smoke alarms

Stop, Drop, and Roll

Firefighters should do more than simply tell people what to do if their clothing catches on fire. Both adults and children need to be effectively educated with firefighters first demonstrating and then soliciting individuals to perform the action. Demonstrate that if their clothes catch on fire, they must immediately STOP moving, DROP to the ground (covering their face with both hands as they drop), and ROLL over and over until the flames are smothered.

Point out that if someone's clothes catch on fire, an observer may need to assist the person in dropping to the ground and smothering the flames. Coats, rugs, blankets or other heavy cloth items that are close to the victim can be used to help smother the flames. Once the fire is out, cool the area with clean, cold water (if available). Summon emergency medical assistance immediately.

Smoke and Carbon Monoxide (CO) Alarms

Smoke and carbon monoxide alarms provide early warning and facilitate egress for responsive occupants faced with an emergency, especially during sleeping hours. This factor has been the key to survival of residents during fire and CO situations. Because an important part of home safety surveys is to communicate the importance of having working smoke and CO alarms, it is essential that firefighters have a good working knowledge of various residential smoke alarms (**Figure 4.21**).

While an early warning is often credited with saving the lives of a home's occupants, the smoke alarm's warning may have also protected a firefighter from having to enter the burning structure and the Immediately Dangerous to Life and Health (IDLH) environment inside. When smoke alarms are not in the home, a firefighter may be forced to enter the home to rescue the occupants. Fire fighting has been listed as one of the most hazardous occupations in the United States, and search and rescue services significantly increase the possibility of firefighter casualties.

NOTE: For more information, see IFSTA's **Fire Detection and Suppression Systems** manual.

Figure 4.21 A fire and life safety educator examines a smoke alarm during a residential fire safety survey.

Fire Station Tours

Firefighters are frequently required to give tours of the fire station to civilians. These may be spur-of-the-moment visits from people who walk in off the street or scheduled tours with organized groups. **Fire Prevention Week** tours for groups of children are common **(Figure 4.22)**.

Firefighters should consider such tours more than just an opportunity to impress the public. It is important to supplement such visits with a strong safety message and relevant awareness materials. Such an approach not only helps to support fire safety efforts, but also fosters a good image for the fire department. It is a good idea to have several pre-determined topics for each age group or type of tour. This makes the department more consistent in its fire and life safety education message and focuses the knowledge at the appropriate age level.

Figure 4.22 Pre-school age children meet a firefighter during a fire station tour.

Fire Prevention Week — Week proclaimed each year by the President of the United States to commemorate the anniversary of the great Chicago conflagration on October 9, 1871; takes place the week in which October 9 falls.

When visitors are in the station, firefighters should be dressed appropriately. The impression that visitors form while at the station remains in their memories for a very long time, so activities should be productive and *all* areas of the station should be presentable.

Firefighters should answer all questions courteously and to the best of their ability. Fire and life safety information should be passed on to visitors during all station tours. Firefighters must also know and follow the department's policies on safety in the fire station. It may be necessary to explain to visitors that they may not climb on apparatus or don equipment items without department approval and active supervision to avoid the risk of injuries. Young children should not be permitted to handle equipment or don fire helmets lest they strain or injure themselves.

NOTE: Fire department personnel should know and follow all departmental policies about allowing civilians to climb on equipment or don gear.

Never allow visitors, especially children, to roam around the fire station unescorted. Visiting groups should be met by an assigned firefighter or an officer should be assigned to meet visiting groups. This firefighter will carefully explain what steps visitors must take if the firefighters must respond to an alarm during the visit. Special care should be taken to protect curious children or other individuals around shop areas or slide poles. All groups should be kept together and, if necessary, rearranged into smaller groups with a firefighter assigned to each group.

Equipment and apparatus should be demonstrated with considerable caution to ensure that no one gets into a dangerous position. Place a firefighter at each corner of an apparatus to prevent young visitors from getting near the apparatus during demonstrations. Make sure that no wheels of an apparatus are turned until a visual check is performed and maintained. Taking visitors on elevating platforms or aerial ladders should be prohibited. Firefighters should also refrain from sounding sirens or air horns in the presence of children because the decibel levels produced can be detrimental to their hearing.

Station mascots (dogs, cats, etc.) can be potential safety and liability hazards. Excited animals have been known to strike out and bite visitors; therefore, many organizations restrict the presence of animals. If animals are kept in the fire station, they should be cared for by a veterinarian and receive all the necessary inoculations to ensure good health.

Chapter Summary

The role of the fire department extends far beyond responding to and extinguishing fires. Once a fire does occur, firefighters must make not only every effort to extinguish it as quickly and safely as possible, but they must also carefully observe the scene at all times for evidence of the actual cause of the fire. If the fire appears to be of suspicious origin, they must take all steps possible to protect and preserve evidence for fire investigators.

In order to increase safety for both the public and firefighters, it is critical that fire departments act to prevent fires by educating the public in recognizing and reducing hazards and in acting effectively when an emergency occurs. To do this, fire departments must undertake an active program to "spread the word" by building good relationships with individuals, children, and businesses so that they can provide advice and assistance. Conducting pre-incident surveys, conducting fire and life safety education, assisting homeowners and tenants with safety information – are all part of an effort that needs to be ongoing and tailored to the needs of the audience.

Review Questions

1. What position in the fire department usually works to raise public awareness of fire prevention issues?

2. What are two types of documents that help fire prevention efforts by pinpointing observed or past fire safety issues?

3. How does code enforcement inspection help support fire prevention?

4. What are the three steps a Fire and Life Safety Educator should take when presenting to an audience?

5. What two types of surveys are included in fire safety surveys?

6. What is the purpose of a pre-incident survey?

7. Why is it necessary to keep pre-incident surveys updated?

Scientific Terminology

Chapter Contents

Key Terms

FESHE Outcomes

This chapter provides information that addresses the outcomes for the Fire and Emergency Services Higher Education (FESHE) *Principles of Emergency Services* course.

2. Analyze the basic components of fire as a chemical chain reaction, the major phases of fire, and examine the main factors that influence fire spread and fire behavior.

NFPA® Job Performance Requirements

This chapter provides information that addresses the following job performance requirements (JPRs) of NFPA® 1001, *Standard for Fire Fighter Professional Qualifications* (2008).

5.3.8(A)   **5.3.11(A)**   **5.3.16(A)**

5.3.10(A)   **5.3.12(A)**

Learning Objectives

After reading this chapter, students will be able to:

1. Explain the three main aspects of the science of fire.

2. Describe why understanding the fire tetrahedron is crucial to fire prevention and safety efforts.

3. List the stages of fire development.

4. Explain special considerations that occur during a fire's growth.

5. Discuss the four aspects of fire extinguishment theory.

6. Define the five main classifications of fires.

Chapter 5
Scientific Terminology

Courtesy of NIST.

Case History

Rookie firefighter Carlos Mendoza just finished responding to his first residential fire. Now that his work was done, he was thinking about how closely the actual fire reflected what he learned in fire behavior class. He recognized the burning upholstered chair in the corner as a Class A fire and knew that the walls had kept the plume temperature high. He had been aware that the air was cooler closer to the floor was due to thermal layering. He had been alert to conditions that might have led to flashover, rollover, or backdraft.

The rookie also knew that his residential fire was in some ways similar to that fire at the Dupont Plaza Hotel and Casino in Puerto Rico back in 1986. Both fires had involved furniture in a corner that ultimately led to flashover. Of course, the stack of boxed furniture in the corner of a ballroom was a much bigger fuel package, and the earlier fire caused 96 deaths. Fortunately, today's fire did not injure or kill any firefighters or civilians.

This chapter introduces several basic concepts from physical science that describe the ignition and development of a fire. Firefighters can use the information in this chapter to interpret what they see on the fireground and develop methods to prevent, extinguish, and investigate fires. An understanding of fire behavior and the phases a fire passes through as it grows will help firefighters select the proper tactics to attack and extinguish fires. This knowledge also helps firefighters recognize potential hazards to themselves and others while they work on the fireground.

Firefighters responding to a fire may have to cope rapidly with a variety of conditions. The fire may be *exposing* (endangering) another structure or groups of structures, as in wildland/urban interface fires. The smoke and flames may be creating a *life hazard* (danger to survival) to occupants. The room of fire origin may be close to *flashover* (simultaneous ignition of room contents). If a building is not ventilated, there may be a *backdraft* (fire explosion) potential. All of these conditions result from fire and the way it behaves and will be described in this chapter. To perform safely and effectively in any fire fighting function, firefighters should have a basic understanding of the science of fire and the factors that affect its ignition, growth, and spread (fire behavior).

NOTE: Many of the concepts discussed in this chapter hold true for wildland fires, but a number of additional factors must be addressed in those incidents. Wildland fires are discussed in detail in the IFSTA **Wildland Fire Fighting for Structural Firefighters** manual.

Properties of Matter

Physical materials are called **matter**. It is said that matter is the "stuff" that makes up the universe. Matter is anything that occupies space and has mass (weight). Matter can undergo many types of physical and chemical changes. This section focuses on these changes as they are related to how matter reacts to fire.

Matter — Anything that occupies space and has mass.

Physical States of Matter

Matter possesses properties that can be observed, such as its physical state (solid, liquid, or gas), color, or smell. An easily understandable example of the three states of matter are the observable states of water. At normal **atmospheric pressure** (the pressure exerted by our atmosphere on all objects) and temperatures above 32°F (0°C), water is found as a liquid. At sea level, atmospheric pressure is approximately 14.7 psi (101 kpa). When the temperature of water falls below 32°F (0°C) and the pressure remains the same, water changes its state and becomes a solid called *ice*. At temperatures above its boiling point, water changes state to a gas called *steam*.

Atmospheric Pressure — Force exerted by the atmosphere at the surface of the earth due to the weight of air. Atmospheric pressure at sea level is about 14.7 psi (101 kPa) and is measured as 760 mm of mercury on a barometer. Atmospheric pressure increases as elevation decreases, and decreases as elevation increases.

Temperature, however, is not the only factor that determines when a change of state occurs. The other factor is pressure. As the pressure on the surface of a substance decreases, so does the temperature at which it boils. The opposite is also true. If the pressure on the surface increases, so will the boiling point. This principle is how pressure cookers heat water beyond the boiling point. The boiling point of the liquid increases as the pressure inside the vessel increases. Thus, foods cook faster in the device because the temperature of the boiling water is greater than 212°F (100°C).

Specific Gravity and Vapor Density

Matter can also be described using terms derived from its physical properties of mass and volume. **Density** is a measure of how tightly the molecules of a solid substance are packed together (**Figure 5.1**).

Density — Mass per unit of volume of a substance. The density of any substance is obtained by dividing the mass by the volume.

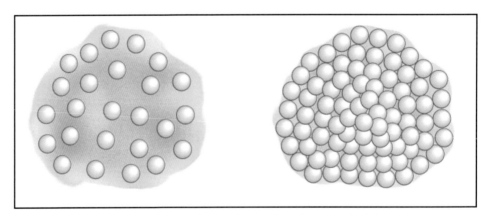

Figure 5.1 The molecules on the right are denser than those on the left.

Mass and Weight

Mass and weight are sometimes confused. The mass of a block of wood is a measure of its amount of matter.

The weight of a block of wood is a measure of the force on the wood exerted by gravity. If that block of wood were on the moon (where gravity is one-sixth of gravity on earth), its mass would be the same as on earth, but would weigh about one-sixth as much.

A common descriptive ratio of the weight of a liquid is its specific gravity. **Specific gravity** is the ratio of the mass of a given volume of a liquid compared with the mass of an equal volume of water. Thus, water has a specific gravity of 1. Liquids with a specific gravity less than 1 are lighter than water, while those with a specific gravity greater than 1 are heavier than water.

The specific gravity for vehicle gasoline is .739. Like other liquids with a specific gravity of less than 1, gasoline floats on water. Ethylene glycol (antifreeze), on the other hand, has a specific gravity of 1.1. Like other liquids with a specific gravity greater than 1, ethylene glycol sinks in water.

Vapor density is defined as the density of gas or vapor in relation to air. Since air is used for the comparison, it has a vapor density of 1. Gases with a vapor density of less than 1 will rise, and those with vapor densities greater than 1 will sink.

Physical and Chemical Changes

A **physical change** occurs when a substance remains chemically the same but changes in size, shape, or appearance, one of these observable properties. Examples of physical change are water freezing (liquid to solid) or boiling (liquid to gas).

A **chemical change** occurs when a substance changes from one type of matter into another. A chemical change often involves the reaction of two or more substances to form other types of compounds. **Oxidation** is a **chemical reaction** involving the combination of oxygen (or similar types of substances) with other materials. Oxidation can be slow, such as the combination of oxygen with iron to form rust, or rapid, as in combustion of methane (natural gas). Oxygen is one of the more common elements on earth (our atmosphere is composed of 21 percent oxygen), and it reacts with many other elements found on the planet.

Chemical and physical changes almost always involve an exchange of energy. A fuel's potential energy is released during combustion and converted to kinetic energy. Reactions that give off energy as they occur are called **exothermic**. Fire is an exothermic chemical reaction called *combustion* that releases energy in the form of heat and sometimes light. Reactions that absorb energy as they occur are called **endothermic**. Converting water from a liquid to a gas (steam) requires the input of energy and is an endothermic physical reaction. Converting water to steam is an important part of controlling and extinguishing fires.

Specific Gravity — Weight of a substance compared to the weight of an equal volume of water at a given temperature. A specific gravity less than1 indicates a substance lighter than water; a specific gravity greater than 1 indicates a substance heavier than water.

Vapor Density — Weight of a given volume of pure vapor or gas compared to the weight of an equal volume of dry air at the same temperature and pressure. A vapor density less than 1 indicates a vapor lighter than air; a vapor density greater than 1 indicates a vapor density heavier than air.

Physical Change — When a substance remains chemically the same but changes in size, shape, or appearance.

Chemical Change — When a substance changes from one type of matter into another.

Oxidation — Chemical process that occurs when a substance combines with oxygen; a common example is the formation of rust on metal.

Chemical Reaction — Any change in the composition of matter that involves a conversion of one substance into another.

Exothermic Heat Reaction— Chemical reaction between two or more materials that changes the materials and produces heat.

Endothermic Heat Reaction — Chemical reaction in which a substance absorbs heat energy.

Conservation of Mass and Energy

As fire consumes a fuel, its mass is reduced. What happens to this material? Where does it go? Because mass and energy can neither be created nor destroyed, the reduction in the mass of a fuel results in the release of energy in the form of light and heat.

The firefighter should be aware of this concept during pre-incident planning and size-up (initial evaluation of a situation) at fires. The more fuel available to burn, the more potential there is for greater amounts of energy being released as heat during a fire. The more heat that is released, the more extinguishing agent is needed to control a fire.

Combustion

Combustion — An exothermic chemical reaction that is a self-sustaining process of rapid oxidation of a fuel, that produces heat and light.

Fire — Rapid oxidation of combustible materials accompanied by a release of energy in the form of heat and light.

Combustion is a rapid and self-sustaining chemical reaction that releases energy in the form of heat, light, and byproducts that can cause further reactions. **Fire** is a form of combustion that requires fuel, oxygen, and heat to occur. Combustion is, using the term discussed earlier, an exothermic reaction.

Modes of combustion are differentiated based on where the reaction is occurring. In flaming combustion, oxidation involves fuel in the gas phase. Heat is required to convert liquid or solid fuels into gases. When heated, both liquid and solid fuels will give off vapors that mix with oxygen and can burn, producing flames. Some solid fuels, particularly those that are porous and can char, can undergo oxidation at the surface of the fuel. This form of oxidation is called nonflaming or smoldering combustion. Examples of nonflaming combustion include burning charcoal or smoldering fabric and upholstery.

The time it takes for a chemical reaction to occur determines the type of reaction that is observed. At the very slow end of the time spectrum is rust, where the reaction is too gradual to be observed. At the faster end of the spectrum are explosions that result from the very rapid reaction of a fuel and an oxidizer. These reactions release a large amount of energy over a very short time (**Figure 5.2**).

While fire can take a variety of forms, all fires involve a heat-producing chemical reaction between some type of fuel and oxygen or a similar substance. When anything burns, heat is generated faster than it can be dissipated, causing a significant increase in temperature. The sections that follow describe a number of important topics that are important for understanding of fire and the combustion process.

Fire Tetrahedron

For combustion to occur, four components are necessary:

- Heat
- Fuel (reducing agent)
- Oxygen (oxidizing agent)
- Self-sustained chemical chain reaction

These components can be graphically described as the *fire tetrahedron* (**Figure 5.3**). The fire tetrahedron represents the flaming mode of combustion. In the past, the fire triangle was used to describe the first three of these components (**see Info Box**).

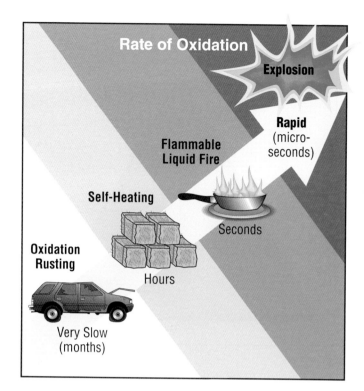

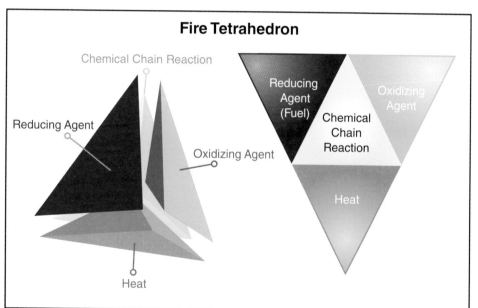

Figure 5.2 Combustion, a self-sustaining chemical reaction, may be very slow (rusting), or very fast (explosion).

Figure 5.3 The four components of combustion are shown.

Fire Triangle

For many years, firefighters were taught that three components were needed for a fire to occur: oxygen, fuel, and heat. This was represented by the *fire triangle* (**Figure 5.4, p. 174**). Remove any one of the three components and a fire cannot start — if burning, it will be extinguished. While this simple model is useful, it does not always provide a complete picture of the combustion process. The fire triangle provides a reasonable explanation of nonflaming or smoldering combustion.

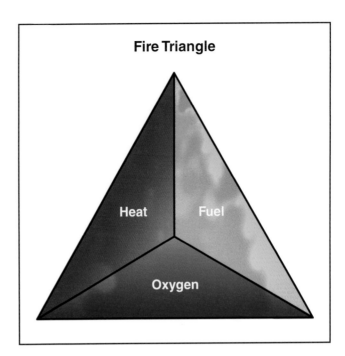

Figure 5.4 The fire triangle represented only three components of combustion.

Fire Triangle

Heat

Fuel

Oxygen

Each component of the tetrahedron must be in place in the right proportion for combustion to occur. Understanding the tetrahedron is extremely important to students of fire suppression, prevention, and investigation. Remove any one of the four components and combustion will not occur. If ignition has already occurred, the fire is extinguished when one of the components is removed from the reaction. To better explain fire and its behavior, each of the components of the tetrahedron is discussed in the sections that follow.

Heat and Temperature

Having a working knowledge of fire behavior requires an understanding of heat and temperature. Despite the fact that most people have a basic understanding of heat and temperature, these terms are often used interchangeably because the difference is not clearly understood.

Heat is a form of energy, and energy exists in two states: potential and kinetic. **Potential energy** is the energy possessed by an object that may be released in the future. **Kinetic energy** is the energy possessed by a moving object. Heat is kinetic energy associated with the movement of the atoms and molecules that comprise matter. Before ignition, a fuel has potential chemical energy. When that fuel burns, the chemical energy is converted to kinetic energy in the form of heat and light. Temperature is a *measurement* of kinetic energy. Heat energy will move from objects of higher temperature to those of lower temperature. This movement of heat energy is particularly important in understanding both fire development and fire control tactics.

Energy is the capacity to perform work. Work occurs when a force is applied to an object over a distance or when a chemical, biological, or physical transformation is made in a substance.

Although it is not possible to measure energy directly, it is necessary to measure the work that it does. In the case of heat, work means increasing the temperature of the substance. The measure for heat energy is *joules* in the International System of Units (SI). A joule is equal to one newton over a distance of one meter.

Potential Energy — Stored energy possessed by an object that can be released in the future to perform work.

Kinetic Energy — Energy possessed by a moving object.

In the customary system, the unit of measure for heat is the British thermal unit (Btu). The British thermal unit is the amount of heat required to raise the temperature of 1 pound of water 1 degree Fahrenheit. While not used in scientific and engineering texts, the Btu is still frequently used in the fire service.

There are several different scales used to measure temperature; the most common are the *Celsius* and *Fahrenheit* scales. The Celsius temperature scale is used in the SI system while the Fahrenheit scale is used in the customary system. The freezing and boiling points of water provide a simple way to compare these two scales **(Figure 5.5)**.

Energy exists in many forms and can change from one form to another. In the study of fire behavior, the conversion of energy into heat is particularly important because heat is the energy component of the fire tetrahedron. When a fuel is heated, its temperature increases. Applying additional heat causes *pyrolysis* (the chemical decomposition of a substance through the action of heat) in solid fuels and *vaporization* of liquid fuels, releasing ignitable vapors or gases. A spark or other external source can provide the energy necessary for ignition, or the fuel can be heated until it ignites without a spark or other source. Once ignited, the process continues the production and ignition of fuel vapors or gases so that the combustion reaction is sustained.

There are two forms of ignition: *piloted ignition* and *autoignition*. Piloted ignition occurs when a mixture of fuel and oxygen encounter an external heat (ignition) source with sufficient heat energy to start the combustion reaction. Autoignition occurs without any external flame or spark to ignite the fuel gases or vapors. In this case, the fuel surface is chemically heated to the point at which the combustion reaction occurs. **Autoignition temperature (AIT)** is the temperature to which the surface of a substance must be heated for ignition and self-sustained combustion to occur. The autoignition temperature of a substance is always higher than its piloted ignition temperature. While both piloted ignition and autoignition occur under fire conditions, piloted ignition is the most common.

Sources of Heat Energy

Chemical, mechanical, electrical, light, nuclear, and sound energy can all cause a substance to heat by increasing the speed with which molecules are moving. Chemical, electrical, and mechanical energy are common sources of heat that result in the ignition of a fuel. Each of these sources is discussed in depth in this section.

Chemical heat energy is the most common source of heat in combustion reactions. When any combustible is in contact with oxygen, oxidation occurs. This process almost always results in the production of heat.

Self-heating, also known as spontaneous heating, is a form of chemical heat energy that occurs when a material increases in temperature without the addition of external heat. Normally, oxidation produces heat slowly, and the heat is lost to the surroundings almost as fast as it is generated. An external heat source such as sunshine can initiate or accelerate this process. In order for self-heating to progress to spontaneous ignition, the material must be heated to its autoignition temperature. For spontaneous ignition to occur, the following factors are required:

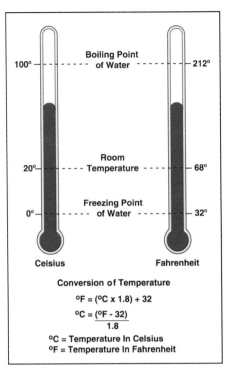

Figure 5.5 A comparison of the Celsius and Fahrenheit scales.

Autoignition Temperature (AIT) — Minimum temperature to which a fuel (other than a liquid) in the air must be heated in order to start self-sustained combustion; no external ignition source is required.

- The insulation properties of the material immediately surrounding the fuel must be such that the heat cannot dissipate as fast as it is being generated.

- The rate of heat production must be great enough to raise the temperature of the material to its ignition temperature.

- The available air supply (ventilation) in and around the material being heated must be adequate to support combustion.

An example of a situation that could lead to spontaneous ignition would be one or more oil-soaked rags rolled into a ball and thrown into a corner. If the heat generated by the natural oxidation of the oil and cloth is not allowed to dissipate, either by movement of air around the rags or some other method of heat transfer, the temperature of the cloth could eventually increase enough to cause ignition.

The rate of the oxidation reaction, and thus the heat production, increases as more heat is generated and held by the materials insulating the fuel. In fact, the rate at which most chemical reactions occur doubles with each 18°F (10°C) increase in the temperature of the reacting materials. The more heat generated and absorbed by the fuel, the faster the reaction causing the heat generation. When the heat generated by a self-heating reaction exceeds the heat being lost, the material may reach its ignition temperature and ignite spontaneously.

Electrical heat energy can generate temperatures high enough to ignite any combustible materials near the heated area. Electrical heating can occur in several ways, including the following:

- *Resistance heating* — When electric current flows though a conductor, heat is produced. Some electrical appliances, such as incandescent lamps, ranges, ovens, or portable heaters, are designed to make use of resistance heating. Other electrical equipment is designed to limit resistance heating under normal operating conditions.

- *Overcurrent or overload* — When the current flowing through a conductor exceeds its design limits, it may overheat and present an ignition hazard. Overcurrent or overload is unintended resistance heating.

- *Arcing* — In general, an arc is a high-temperature luminous electrical discharge across a gap or though a medium such as charred insulation. Arcs may be generated when a conductor is separated (such as in an electric motor or switch) or by high voltage, static electricity, or lightning.

- *Sparking* — When an electrical arc occurs, luminous (glowing) particles can be formed and spatter away from the point of arcing. In electrical terms, sparking refers to this spatter, while an arc is the luminous electric discharge.

Friction or compression generates *mechanical heat energy*. The movement of two surfaces against each other creates *heat of friction*. This movement results in heat and/or sparks being generated. *Heat of compression* is generated when a gas is compressed. Diesel engines use this principle to ignite fuel vapor without a spark plug. The principle is also the reason that self-contained breathing apparatus (SCBA) cylinders feel warm to the touch after they have been filled.

Transmission of Heat

The transfer of heat from one point or object to another is a basic concept in the study of fire. The transfer of heat from the initial fuel package to other fuels in and beyond the area of fire origin controls the growth of any fire. Firefighters use their knowledge of heat transfer to estimate the size of a fire before attacking it and to evaluate the effectiveness of an attack. In order for heat to be transferred from one object to another, the two objects must be at different temperatures. Heat moves from warmer objects to those that are cooler. The greater the difference in temperature between the objects, the greater the transfer rate. This principle is known as the **Law of Heat Flow**.

Heat can be transferred from one body to another by three mechanisms: **conduction**, **convection**, and **radiation**. Each of these is discussed in some detail in the sections that follow.

Conduction. When a piece of metal rod is heated at one end with a flame, the heat travels throughout the rod (**Figure 5.6**). This transfer of energy is due to the increased activity of atoms within the object. As heat is applied to one end of the rod, atoms in that area begin to move faster than their neighbors. This activity causes an increase in the collisions between the atoms. Each collision transfers energy to the atom being hit. The energy, in the form of heat, is transferred throughout the rod.

This type of heat transfer is called conduction. *Conduction* is the point-to-point transmission of heat energy. Conduction occurs when a body is heated as a result of direct contact with a heat source. Heat cannot be conducted through a vacuum because there is no medium for point-to-point contact.

In general, heat transfer early in the development of all fires is due almost entirely to conduction. Later, as the fire grows, hot gases begin to flow over objects some distance away from the point of ignition, and conduction again becomes a factor. Conduction transfers the heat from the gases in direct contact with structural components or other fuel packages to the object.

Law of Heat Flow — Natural law that specifies that heat tends to flow from hot substances to cold substances. This phenomenon is based on the supposition that one substance can absorb heat from another.

Conduction — Physical flow or transfer of heat energy from one body to another, through direct contact or an intervening medium, from the point where the heat is produced to another location, or from a region of high temperature to a region of low temperature.

Convection — Transfer of heat by the movement of heated fluids or gases, usually in an upward direction.

Radiation — (1) Transmission or transfer of heat energy from one body to another body at a lower temperature through intervening space by electromagnetic waves, such as infrared thermal waves, radio waves, or X-rays. *Also known as* Radiated Heat. (2) Energy from a radioactive source emitted in the form of waves or particles, as a result of the decay of an atomic nucleus; process known as *radioactivity. Also known as* Nuclear Radiation.

Figure 5.6 Direct contact with pipes or ducts can conduct heat through walls.

Figure 5.7 Convection is the transfer of heat energy by the movement of heated liquids or gases.

Heat insulation is closely related to conduction. Insulating materials do their jobs primarily by slowing the conduction of heat between two bodies. The best commercial insulators used in building construction are those made of fine particles or fibers with void spaces between them filled with a gas such as air.

Convection. As a fire begins to grow, the air around it is heated by convection. The hot air and products of combustion rise. If you hold your hand over a flame, you are able to feel the heat even though your hand is not in direct contact with the flame. The heat is being transferred to your hand by convection. *Convection* is the transfer of heat energy by the movement of heated liquids or gases. When heat is transferred by convection, there is movement or circulation of a fluid (any substance — liquid or gas — that will flow) from one place to another. As with all heat transfer, the flow of heat is from the warmer area to the cooler area (**Figure 5.7**).

Radiation. Radiation is the transmission of energy as an electromagnetic wave (such as light waves, radio waves, or X rays) without an intervening medium. Because it is an electromagnetic wave, the energy travels in a straight line at the speed of light. All warm objects will radiate heat.

Figure 5.8 Radiated heat is one of the major causes of fire spread to exposures.

The best example of heat transfer by radiation is the sun's heat. The energy travels at the speed of light from the sun through space (a vacuum) and warms the earth's surface. Radiation is the cause of most exposure fires (fires ignited in fuel packages or buildings that are remote from the fuel package or building of origin) (**Figure 5.8**).

As a fire grows, it radiates more and more energy in the form of heat. In large fires, it is possible for the radiated heat to ignite buildings or other fuel packages some distance away. Heat energy being transmitted by radiation travels through vacuums and substantial air spaces that would normally disrupt conduction and convection. Materials that reflect radiated energy will disrupt the transmission of heat.

The above information will help firefighters understand how fire will grow and spread – vital information for the development of strategy and tactics and for firefighter safety. For example, the company officer can direct the protection of exposure (radiation), cooling of fuel by applying water (conduction), and ventilation (convection).

NOTE: One, two, or even all three methods of heat transfer can occur simultaneously, such as a kitchen stove fire spreading to cabinets (radiation and conduction) and vertically through the exhaust hood (convection).

Fuel

Fuel is the material or substance being oxidized or burned in the combustion process. Fuel is also known as a *reducing agent* because it is the component whose mass is being reduced as it is consumed.

Most common fuels contain carbon along with combinations of hydrogen and oxygen. These fuels can be further subdivided into hydrocarbon-based fuels (such as gasoline, fuel oil, and plastics) and cellulose-based materials (such as wood and paper). Other fuels that are less complex in their chemical makeup include hydrogen gas and combustible metals such as magnesium and sodium. The combustion process involves two key fuel-related factors: the physical state of the fuel and its orientation (horizontal or vertical).

A fuel may be found in any of three physical states of matter: solid, liquid, or gas. To burn, however, fuels must be in the gaseous state. Heat energy is needed to change solids and liquids into gas.

Fuel gases are evolved from solid fuels by pyrolysis. **Pyrolysis** is the chemical decomposition of a substance through the action of heat (**Figure 5.9**). Simply stated, as solid fuels are heated, combustible materials (gases or vapors) are driven from the substance. If there is sufficient fuel and heat, the process of pyrolysis generates sufficient quantities of burnable gases which can ignite and sustain combustion if the other elements of the fire tetrahedron are present.

Because of their nature, solid fuels have a definite shape and size. This property significantly affects their ease of ignition. Of primary consideration is the surface-to-mass ratio of the fuel. The **surface-to-mass ratio** is the surface area of the fuel in proportion to the mass.

One of the best examples of the surface-to-mass ratio is the cutting of wood. To produce usable materials, a tree must be cut into a log. The mass of this log is very high, but the surface area is relatively low, thus the surface-to-mass ratio is low. The log is then milled into boards. The result of this process is to reduce the mass of the individual boards as compared to the log, but the resulting surface area is increased, thus increasing the surface-to-mass ratio. The sawdust that is produced as the lumber is milled has an even higher surface-to-mass ratio. If the boards are sanded, the resulting dust has the highest surface-to-mass ratio of any of the examples. As this ratio increases, the fuel particles become smaller (more finely divided — for example, sawdust as opposed to logs), and their ignitability increases tremendously. As the surface area increases, more of the material is exposed to the heat and thus generates more burnable gases due to pyrolysis.

A solid fuel's orientation also affects the way it burns. If the solid fuel is in a vertical position, fire spread will be more rapid than if it is in a horizontal position. For example, if a sheet of ⅛-inch (3 mm) plywood paneling that was resting horizontally on two sawhorses were to ignite, the fire would consume the fuel at a relatively slow rate. The same type of paneling in the vertical position burns much more rapidly. The rapidity of fire spread is due to increased heat transfer through convection as well as conduction and radiation (**Figure 5.10**).

Fuel — Flammable and combustible substances available for a fire to consume.

Pyrolysis — Thermal or chemical decomposition of fuel (matter) because of heat, generally resulting in the lowered ignition temperature of the material; the pre-ignition combustion phase of burning during which heat energy is absorbed by the fuel, which in turn gives off flammable tars, pitches, and gases. Pyrolysis of wood releases combustible gases and leaves a charred surface. *Also known as* Pyrolysis Process or Sublimation.

Surface-To-Mass Ratio — Ratio of the surface area of the fuel to the mass of the fuel.

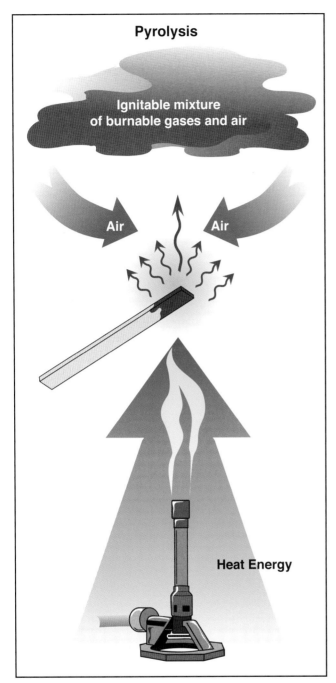

Pyrolysis

Ignitable mixture
of burnable gases and air

Air　Air

Heat Energy

Figure 5.9 Heat causes the pyrolysis of solid fuels and the production of ignitable vapors or gases.

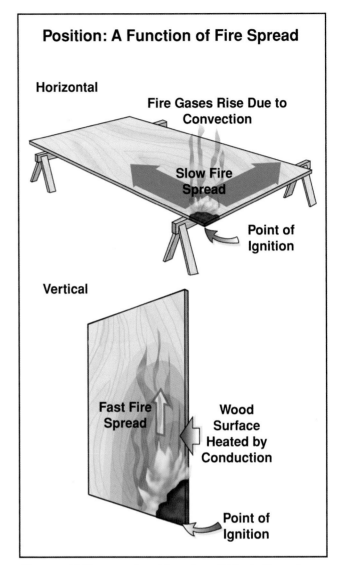

Position: A Function of Fire Spread

Horizontal

Fire Gases Rise Due to Convection

Slow Fire Spread

Point of Ignition

Vertical

Fast Fire Spread

Wood Surface Heated by Conduction

Point of Ignition

Figure 5.10 The actual position of a solid fuel affects the way it burns. Fuel in a vertical position will burn much more quickly due to increased heat transfer.

Vaporization — Physical process that changes a liquid into a gaseous state. The rate of vaporization depends on the substance involved, heat, pressure, and exposed surface area.

Liquid fuels have mass and volume, but no fixed shape except for a flat surface. Liquids assume the shape of their container. For liquids, fuel gases are generated by a process called vaporization. In scientific terms, **vaporization** is the transformation of a liquid to its vapor or gaseous state.

The transformation from liquid to vapor or gas occurs as molecules of the substance escape from the liquid's surface into the surrounding atmosphere. In order for the molecules to break free of the liquid's surface, there must be some energy input. In most cases, this energy is provided in the form of heat. For example, water left in a pan eventually evaporates. The energy required for this process comes from the sun or surrounding environment. Water in the same pan placed on a stove and heated to boiling vaporizes more rapidly because there is more energy being applied to the system. The rate of vaporization is determined by the substance, the amount of heat energy applied to it, and its exposed surface area.

Volatility — Ability of a substance to vaporize easily at a relatively low temperature.

Vaporization of liquid fuels generally requires less energy input than does pyrolysis for solid fuels. This is primarily caused by the different densities of substances in solid and liquid states and by the fact that molecules of a substance in the liquid state have more energy than when they are in the solid state. Solids also absorb more of the energy because of their mass. The **volatility** or ease with which a liquid gives off vapor influences its ignitability. All liquids give off vapors to a greater or lesser degree in the form of simple evaporation. Liquids that easily give off quantities of flammable or combustible vapors can be dangerous.

Like the surface-to-mass ratio for solid fuels, the surface-to-volume ratio of liquids is an important factor in their ignitability. A liquid assumes the shape of its container. Thus, when a spill or release occurs, the liquid assumes the shape of the ground (flat), flows, and accumulates in low areas. When contained, the specific volume of a liquid has a relatively low surface-to-volume ratio. When it is released, this ratio increases significantly as does the amount of fuel vaporized from the surface.

Flammable/Explosive Range — Percentage of a gas vapor concentration in the air that will burn if ignited.

Lower Flammable (Explosive) Limit (LFL) — Lower limit at which a flammable gas or vapor will ignite and support combustion; below this limit the gas or vapor is too *lean* or *thin* to burn (too much oxygen and not enough gas). *Also known as* Lower Explosive Limit (LEL).

Gases have mass, but no definite shape or volume. Gas placed in a container will completely fill the available space. Gases are ready to ignite **(see Safety Box)**. For combustion to occur after a fuel has been converted into a gaseous state, the fuel must be mixed with air (oxidizer) in the proper ratio. The range of concentrations of the fuel vapor and air (oxidizer) is called the **flammable/explosive range**. The flammable range of a fuel is reported using the percent by volume of gas or vapor in air for the **lower flammable limit (LFL)** and for the **upper flammable limit (UFL)**. The LFL is the minimum concentration of fuel vapor and air that supports combustion. Concentrations that are below the LFL are said to be *too lean* to burn. The UFL is the concentration above which combustion cannot take place. Concentrations that are above the UFL are said to be *too rich* to burn.

Upper Flammable Limit (UFL) — Upper limit at which a flammable gas or vapor will ignite. Above this limit the gas of vapor is too rich to burn (lacks the proper quantity of oxygen). *Also known as* Upper Explosive Limit (UEL).

Gaseous Fuels

Gaseous fuels can be the most dangerous of all fuel types because they are already in the natural state required for ignition. No pyrolysis or vaporization is needed to ready the fuel, and less energy is required for ignition.

Oxygen (Oxidizing Agent)

Oxidizing agents are those materials that release oxygen or other oxidizing gases during the course of a chemical reaction. **Oxidizers** are not themselves combustible, but they support combustion when combined with a fuel. While oxygen is the most common oxidizer, other substances also fall into the category. Common oxidizers include but are not limited to:

- Bromates
- Chlorates
- Nitrates
- Peroxides

For the purposes of this discussion, the oxygen in the air is considered the primary oxidizing agent. Normally, air consists of about 21 percent oxygen. At room temperature (70° F or 21° C), combustion is supported at oxygen concentrations as low as 14 percent. However, as temperatures in a compartment fire increase, lower concentrations of oxygen are sufficient to support flaming combustion.

NOTE: Air is composed of 78 percent nitrogen, 21 percent oxygen, and small amounts of other gases such as argon, carbon dioxide, neon, and helium.

When oxygen concentrations exceed 21 percent, the atmosphere is said to be an **oxygen enriched atmosphere**. Materials that burn at normal oxygen levels burn more rapidly in oxygen-enriched atmospheres and may ignite much more easily than normal. Oxygen-enriched conditions can be found in health care facilities, industrial occupancies, and even private homes where occupants use oxygen breathing equipment.

Some petroleum-based materials will autoignite in oxygen-enriched atmospheres. Many materials that do not burn at normal oxygen levels burn readily in oxygen-enriched atmospheres. One such material is Nomex® fire-resistant material, which is used to construct much of the protective clothing worn by firefighters.

At normal oxygen levels, Nomex® does not burn. When placed in an oxygen-enriched atmosphere of approximately 31 percent oxygen, however, Nomex® ignites and burns vigorously. Fires in oxygen-enriched atmospheres are more difficult to extinguish and present a potential safety hazard to firefighters operating in them.

Self-Sustained Chemical Reaction

The self-sustained chemical reaction involved in flaming combustion is complex. Combustion of a simple fuel such as methane (natural gas) and oxygen provides a good example. Complete oxidation of methane results in production of carbon dioxide and water as well as release of energy in the form of heat and light. While this process seems to be quite simple, it is actually quite complex. As combustion occurs, the molecules of methane and oxygen break apart to form free radicals (electrically charged, highly reactive parts of molecules). Free radicals combine with oxygen or with the elements that form the fuel material (in the case of methane, carbon and hydrogen) producing intermediate combustion products (new substances), even more radicals and increasing the speed of the oxidation reaction **(Figure 5.11, p. 184)**. At

Oxidizing Agent — Substance that oxidizes another substance; can cause other materials to combust more readily or make fires burn more strongly. *Also known as* Oxidizer.

Oxidizer — Any substance or material that yields oxygen readily and may stimulate the combustion of organic and inorganic matter.

Oxygen-Enriched Atmosphere — Area in which the concentration of oxygen is in excess of 21 percent by volume or 21.3 kPa; typically 23.5 percent for confined spaces, as defined by the Occupational Safety and Health Administration (OSHA).

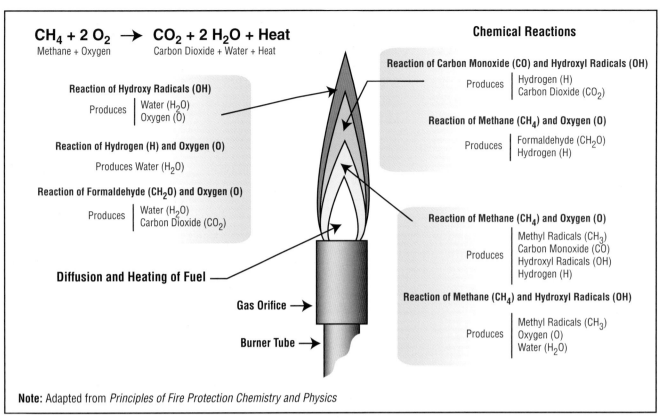

Note: Adapted from *Principles of Fire Protection Chemistry and Physics*

Figure 5.11 Combustion produces a variety of new substances.

various points in the combustion of methane, this process results in production of carbon monoxide and formaldehyde, which are both flammable and toxic. When more chemically complex fuels burn, this process involves many different types of radicals and intermediate combustion products, many of which are also flammable and toxic.

Flaming combustion is one example of a chemical chain reaction. Sufficient heat will cause fuel and oxygen to form free radicals and initiate the self-sustained chemical reaction. The fire will continue to burn until the fuel or oxygen is exhausted or an extinguishing agent is applied in sufficient quantity to interfere with the ongoing reaction. In some cases, extinguishing agents deprive the combustion process of fuel, oxygen, or sufficient heat to sustain the reaction. *Chemical flame inhibition* is when a Halon-replacement extinguishing agent interferes with this chemical reaction, forms a stable product, and terminates the combustion reaction.

The self-sustained chemical reaction and the related rapid growth are the factors that separate flaming combustion from slower oxidation reactions. Slow oxidation reactions, such as the rusting of steel or the yellowing of paper, do not produce heat fast enough to reach ignition, and they never generate sufficient heat to become self-sustained.

Surface combustion also involves oxidation at the surface of a fuel material without initiation or continuation of the chemical chain reaction found in flaming combustion. Glowing charcoal briquettes is one example of this type of combustion. This distinction is important in that a surface combustion cannot be extinguished by chemical flame inhibition (because there are no flames and related chemical chain reaction). These fires must be extinguished by working on one of the sides of the fire triangle (heat, fuel, and oxygen).

Figure 5.12 Wind and terrain affect outdoor fire spread.

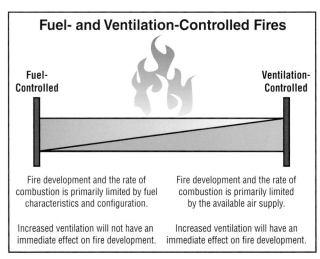

Fuel- and Ventilation-Controlled Fires

Fuel-Controlled

Ventilation-Controlled

Fire development and the rate of combustion is primarily limited by fuel characteristics and configuration.

Fire development and the rate of combustion is primarily limited by the available air supply.

Increased ventilation will not have an immediate effect on fire development.

Increased ventilation will have an immediate effect on fire development.

Figure 5.13 Fuel characteristics or the availability of an air supply may limit fire development.

Fire Development

When the four components of the fire tetrahedron come together in the correct proportions, ignition occurs and combustion is sustained. For a fire to grow beyond the first material ignited, heat must be transmitted beyond the first material ignited to additional fuel packages. In the early development of a fire, heat rises and forms a plume of hot gas. If a fire is in the open, the fire plume rises unobstructed, and air is drawn into it as it rises. This action has a cooling effect on the gases above the fire because the air being pulled into the plume is cooler than the fire gases. The spread of fire in an open area is primarily because heat energy is transmitted from the plume to nearby fuels. Fire spread in outside fires can be increased by wind and sloping terrain that allow exposed fuels to be preheated **(Figure 5.12)**.

The development of fires in a compartment is more complex than those in the open. For the purposes of this discussion, a *compartment* is an enclosed room or space within a building. The term *compartment fire* is defined as a fire that occurs within such a space. The growth and development of a compartment fire is usually controlled by the availability of fuel and oxygen. When the amount of fuel available to burn is limited, the fire is said to be **fuel-controlled**. When the amount of available oxygen is limited, the condition is said to be **ventilation-controlled (Figure 5.13)**.

Compartment fires are often described in terms of stages or phases that occur as the fire develops. These stages are as follows:

● Incipient

● Growth

● Flashover

● Fully developed

● Decay

Figure 5.14, p. 186 shows the development of a compartment fire in terms of time and temperature. It should be noted that the stages are an attempt to describe the complex reaction that occurs as a fire develops in a space with no suppression action taken. The ignition and development of a compartment

Fuel-controlled — Describes fire in which fire development is controlled by the characteristics and configuration of the fuel.

Ventilation-controlled — Describes fire in which fire development is limited by the air supply.

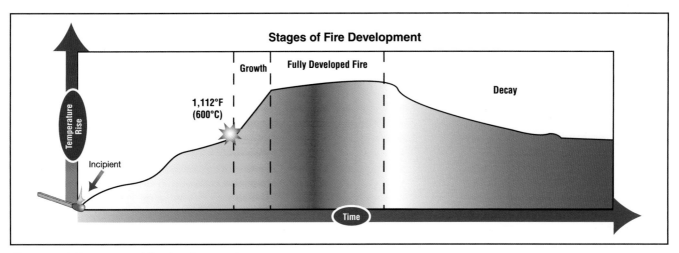

Figure 5.14 The stages of fire development in a compartment.

fire is very complex and influenced by many variables, such as the burning rate of the fuel(s), fuel type(s) and orientation(s), and available oxygen supply. As a result, all fires may not develop through each of the stages described.

Incipient

The incipient stage starts with *ignition*. Ignition describes the point when the three elements of the fire triangle come together and combustion occurs. All fires occur as a result of some type of ignition. Ignition can be *piloted* (caused by a spark or flame) or *nonpiloted* (caused when a material reaches its autoignition temperature as the result of self-heating) such as spontaneous ignition. At this point, the fire is small and confined to the material (fuel) first ignited — and it may self-extinguish (go out on its own).

Growth

Shortly after ignition, a fire plume begins to form above the burning fuel. As the plume develops, it begins to draw (entrain) air from the surrounding space into the column. The initial growth is similar to that of an outside unconfined fire, with the growth a function of the fuel first ignited. Unlike an unconfined fire, however, the plume in a compartment is rapidly affected by the ceiling and walls of the space. The first impact is the amount of air that is entrained into the plume. Because the air is cooler than the hot gases generated by the fire, the air has a cooling effect on the *temperatures within the plume.* The location of the fuel package in relation to the compartment walls determines the amount of air that is entrained and thus the amount of cooling that takes place **(see Info Box)**.

Fuel Package Location and Air Entrainment

Fuel packages near walls entrain less air and thus have higher plume temperatures. Fuel packages in corners entrain even less air and have the highest plume temperatures **(Figure 5.15)**.

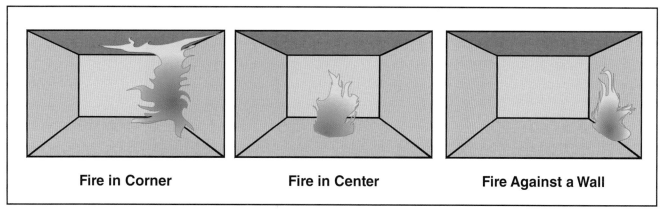

| Fire in Corner | Fire in Center | Fire Against a Wall |

Figure 5.15 The location of a fire inside a compartment can affect its rate of growth.

The location of the fuel package in relation to the compartment walls significantly affects the temperatures in the developing hot-gas layer above the fire. As the hot gases rise, they begin to spread outward when they hit the ceiling. The gases continue to spread until they reach the walls of the compartment. The depth of the gas layer then begins to increase.

The temperatures in the compartment during this period depend on the amount of heat conducted into the compartment ceiling and walls as the gases flow over them and on the location of the initial fuel package and the resulting air entrainment. Research shows that the gas temperatures decrease as the distance from the centerline of the plume increases.

The growth stage will continue if enough fuel and oxygen are available. Compartment fires in the growth stage are generally fuel controlled. As the fire grows, the overall temperature in the compartment increases.

Flashover

Flashover is the transition between the growth and the fully developed fire stages, rather than a specific event such as ignition. During flashover, conditions in the compartment change very rapidly as the fire changes from one that is dominated by the burning of the materials first ignited to one that involves all of the *exposed combustible surfaces* within the compartment. The hot-gas layer that develops at the ceiling level during the growth stage causes radiant heating of combustible materials remote from the origin of the fire (**Figure 5.16, p. 188**). This radiant heating causes pyrolysis in the combustible materials in the compartment. The gases generated during this time are heated to their ignition temperature by the radiant energy from the gas layer at the ceiling.

While scientists define flashover in many ways, most base their definition on the temperature in a compartment that results in the simultaneous ignition of all of the combustible contents in the space. While no exact temperature is associated with flashover, a range from approximately 900° F to 1,200° F (483° C to 649° C) is widely used. This range correlates with the ignition temperature of carbon monoxide (CO) (1,128° F or 609° C), one of the most common gases given off from pyrolysis.

Flashover — Stage of a fire at which all surfaces and objects within a space have been heated to their ignition temperature and flame breaks out almost at once over the surface of all objects in the space.

Figure 5.16 Flashover can happen almost instantaneously. *Courtesy of NIST.*

Just before flashover, several events happen within the burning compartment. These events include:

- The temperatures rapidly increase.

- Additional fuel packages become involved.

- Fuel packages give off combustible gases as a result of pyrolysis.

As flashover occurs, the combustible materials in the compartment and the gases given off from pyrolysis ignite. The result is full-room involvement, which releases a tremendous amount of heat **(see Safety Box)**. The heat release from a fully developed room at flashover can be on the order of 10,000 kW or more. (A wastepaper basket fire, by contrast, produces heat release of 40-50 kW.)

Signs of a Flashover

Occupants who have not escaped from a compartment before flashover occurs are unlikely to survive. Firefighters who find themselves in a compartment at flashover are at extreme risk even while wearing their personal protective equipment. For this reason, it is very important to recognize the events leading to flashover. Signs of potential flashover include:

- Turbulent black smoke

- Extremely high heat

- Free-burning fire

- Heavy rollover

Fully Developed

The fully developed fire stage occurs when all combustible materials in the compartment are burning. During this time, the burning fuels in the compartment are releasing the maximum amount of heat possible for the available fuel packages and producing large volumes of fire gases. In the fully developed stage, the fire is ventilation controlled because heat release is dependent on the compartment openings which are providing oxygen to support the ongoing combustion reaction and releasing products of combustion. Increases in the available air supply will result in higher heat release. During this stage, hot unburned fire gases are likely to flow from the compartment of origin into adjacent compartments or out through openings to the exterior of the building. These hot gases may ignite (fire gas ignition) as they enter a space where air is more abundant.

Decay

As the fire consumes the available fuel in the compartment, the rate of heat release begins to decline. Once again the fire becomes fuel controlled, the amount of fire diminishes, and the temperatures within the compartment begin to decline. The remaining mass of glowing embers can, however, result in moderately high temperatures in the compartment for some time.

Special Considerations

Several conditions or situations can occur during a fire's growth and development that have particular implications for firefighter safety. These considerations include rollover/flameover, thermal layering of gases, backdraft, and products of combustion.

Rollover/Flameover

The terms **rollover** (and less commonly *flameover*) describe a condition where the unburned fire gases accumulated at the top of a compartment ignite and flames propagate through the hot gas layer or across the ceiling. Rollover is a fire gas ignition and is also a significant indicator of impending flashover. Rollover is distinguished from flashover because it involves only the fire gases at the upper levels of the compartment and not the other fuel packages within a compartment. Rollover may occur during the growth stage as the hot-gas layer forms at the ceiling of the compartment. Flames may be observed in the layer when the combustible gases reach their ignition temperature. While the flames add to the total heat generated in the compartment, this condition is not flashover. Rollover will generally precede flashover, but it may not always result in flashover.

Thermal Layering of Gases

The **thermal layering of gases** is the tendency of gases to form into layers according to temperature. Other terms sometimes used to describe this tendency are *heat stratification* and *thermal balance*. The hottest gases tend to be in the top layer, while the cooler gases form the lower layers **(Figure 5.17, p. 190)**. Smoke, a heated mixture of air, gases, and particles, rises. If a hole is made in a roof, smoke will rise from the building or room to the outside. Understanding and taking advantage of thermal layering is critical to fire fighting activities. As long as the hottest air and gases are allowed to rise, the lower levels will be safer for firefighters.

Rollover — (1) Condition in which unburned combustible gases are released in a confined space (such as a room or aircraft cabin) during the incipient or early steady-state phase and accumulate at the ceiling level. These superheated gases are pushed, under pressure, away from the fire area and into uninvolved areas where they mix with oxygen. When their flammable range is reached and additional oxygen is supplied by opening doors and/or applying fog streams, they ignite and a fire front develops, expanding very rapidly in a rolling action across the ceiling. (2) Involves a vehicle rolling sideways onto its side and possibly continuing onto its top, then the opposite side.

Thermal Layering (of Gases) — Outcome of combustion in a confined space; gases tend to form into layers according to temperature, with the hottest gases found on the ceiling and the coolest gases at floor level. *Also known as* Heat Stratification or Thermal Balance.

Figure 5.17 Thermal layering is also described as thermal balance because the fire gases form into layers according to their temperatures. *Courtesy of NIST.*

This normal layering of the hottest gases to the top and out the ventilation opening can be disrupted if water is applied directly into the layer. When water is applied to the upper level of the layer, where the temperatures are highest, the rapid conversion to steam can cause the gases to mix rapidly. This swirling mixture of smoke and steam disrupts normal thermal layering, and hot gases mix throughout the compartment. This process is sometimes referred to as *disrupting the thermal balance* or *creating a thermal imbalance*. Many firefighters and civilians have been burned when thermal layering was disrupted. Once the normal layering is disrupted, forced ventilation procedures (such as using fans) must be used to clear the area. The proper procedure under these conditions is to ventilate the compartment, allow the hot gases to escape, and direct the fire stream at the base of the fire, keeping it out of the hot upper layers of gases.

Backdraft

Firefighters operating at fires in buildings must use care when opening a building to gain entry or to provide horizontal ventilation (opening doors or windows). As the fire grows in a compartment, large volumes of hot, unburned fire gases can collect in unventilated spaces. These gases may be at or above their ignition temperature but have insufficient oxygen available to actually

- Low oxygen
- High heat
- Smoldering fire
- High fuel vapor concentrations

AIR

AIR

Prebackdraft

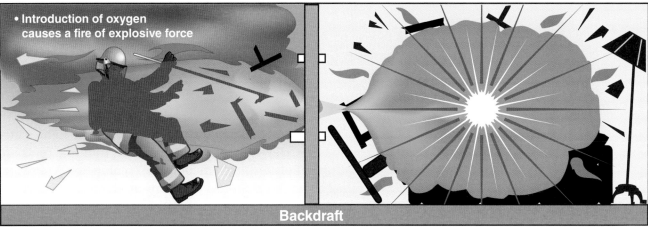

- Introduction of oxygen causes a fire of explosive force

Backdraft

Figure 5.18 Improper ventilation during fire fighting operations may result in a backdraft.

ignite. Any action during fire fighting operations that allows air to mix with these hot gases can result in an explosive ignition called **backdraft (Figure 5.18)**. A backdraft is sometimes confused with a **smoke explosion**.

Many firefighters have been killed or injured as a result of backdrafts; therefore, recognizing the conditions that indicate a potential backdraft is key to firefighter safety **(see Safety Box)**. The potential for backdraft can be reduced with proper vertical or "top side" ventilation (opening at highest point) because the unburned gases rise. Proper ventilation allows the gases to escape before firefighters enter.

Indicators of a Potential Backdraft

The following conditions may indicate the potential for a backdraft:

- Pressurized smoke exiting small openings
- Black smoke becoming a dense gray yellow
- Confinement and excessive heat
- Little or no visible flame
- Smoke leaving the building in puffs or at intervals (appearance of breathing)
- Smoke-stained windows

Backdraft — Instantaneous explosion or rapid burning of superheated gases that occurs when oxygen is introduced into an oxygen-depleted confined space. The stalled combustion resumes with explosive force; may occur because of inadequate or improper ventilation procedures.

Smoke explosion — Form of fire gas ignition; the ignition of accumulated flammable products of combustion.

Table 5.1
Flammable Ranges of Common Flammable Gases and Liquids (Vapor)

Substance	Flammable Range
Methane	5%–15%
Propane	2.1%–9.5%
Carbon Monoxide	12%–75%
Gasoline	1.4%–7.4%
Diesel	1.3%–6%
Ethanol	3.3%–19%
Methanol	6%–35.5%

Source: *Computer Aided Management of Emergency Operations* (CAMEO)

Products of Combustion

As any fuel burns, its chemical composition changes. This change results in the production of new substances and the release of energy. In a fire, this energy is in the form of light and heat. At a very simple level, complete combustion of methane (natural gas) in air results in the production of heat, light, water vapor, and carbon dioxide. However, in a structure fire, multiple fuels are involved and limited air supply results in incomplete combustion. These factors result in extremely complex chemical reactions producing a wide range of **products of combustion** including toxic and flammable gases, vapors, and particulates **(Table 5.1)**.

Products of Combustion — Materials produced and released during burning.

While the heat energy from a fire is a danger to anyone directly exposed to it, smoke and fire gases cause most deaths in fires. The materials that make up smoke vary from fuel to fuel, but generally all smoke can be considered toxic. The smoke generated in a fire contains narcotic (asphyxiant) gases and irritants. Narcotic or asphyxiant gases are those products of combustion that cause central nervous system depression, which results in reduced awareness, intoxication, and can lead to loss of consciousness and death. The most common narcotic gases found in smoke are carbon monoxide (CO), hydrogen cyanide (HCN), and carbon dioxide (CO_2). The reduction in oxygen levels as a result of a fire in a compartment will also cause a narcotic effect in humans. Irritants in smoke are those substances that cause breathing discomfort (pulmonary irritants) and inflammation of the eyes, respiratory tract, and skin (sensory irritants). Depending on the fuels involved, smoke contains numerous substances that can be considered irritants.

The most common of the hazardous substances contained in smoke is CO. While CO is not the most dangerous of the materials found in smoke, it is almost always present when combustion occurs. While someone may be killed or injured by breathing a variety of toxic substances in smoke, CO is the toxin that is most easily detected in the blood of fire victims and thus most often reported. CO displaces oxygen in the blood, creating carboxyhemoglobin (COHb), which starves the cells of oxygen.

NOTE: Because the substances in smoke from compartment fires are deadly (either alone or in combination), firefighters must **always** use SCBA for protection when operating in smoke.

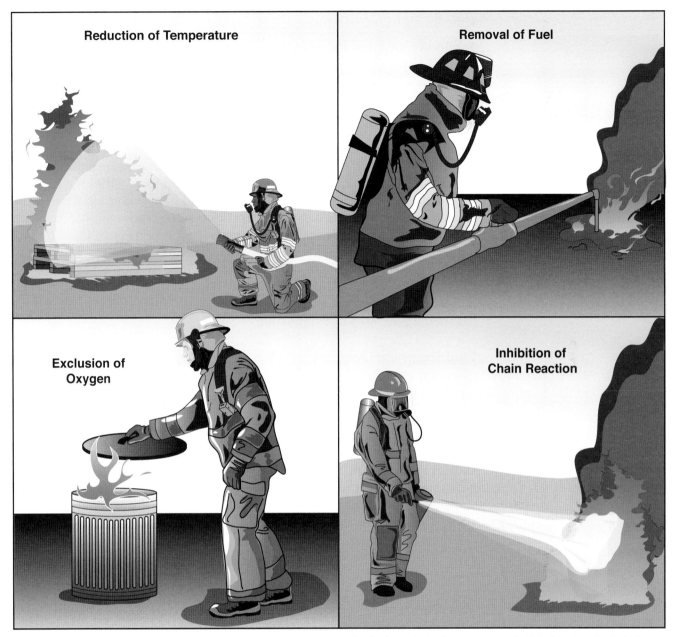

Figure 5.19 To extinguish a fire, reduce its temperature, remove the fuel, exclude the oxygen, or inhibit the chemical chain reaction.

Flame is the visible, luminous body of a burning gas. When a burning gas is mixed with the proper amounts of oxygen, the flame becomes hotter and less luminous. The loss of luminosity is caused by a more complete combustion of the carbon. For these reasons, flame is considered to be a product of combustion. Of course, it is not present in those types of combustion that do not produce a flame, such as smoldering fires.

Fire Extinguishment Theory

Fire is extinguished by limiting or interrupting one or more of the essential elements in the combustion process (fire tetrahedron) **(Figure 5.19)**. A fire may be extinguished in the following ways:

- Reducing its temperature
- Eliminating available fuel
- Eliminating available oxygen
- Stopping the self-sustained chemical chain reaction

Temperature Reduction

One of the most common methods of extinguishment is cooling with water. This process depends on reducing the temperature of a fuel to a point where it does not produce sufficient vapor to burn. Solid fuels with high ignition temperatures (such as heavy timber) and liquid fuels with high flashpoints (such as motor oil) can be extinguished by cooling. However, cooling with water cannot sufficiently reduce vapor production to extinguish fires involving low flash point liquids and flammable gases (such as gasoline, or acetone). The use of water for cooling is also the most effective method available for the extinguishment of smoldering fires. To extinguish a fire by reducing its temperature, enough water must be applied to the burning fuel to absorb the heat being generated by combustion.

Fuel Removal

Removing the fuel source effectively extinguishes some fires. The fuel source may be removed by stopping the flow of liquid or gaseous fuel or by removing solid fuel in the path of a fire. Another method of fuel removal is to allow a fire to burn until all fuel is consumed.

Oxygen Exclusion

Reducing the oxygen available to the combustion process reduces a fire's growth and may totally extinguish it over time. In its simplest form, the oxygen exclusion method is used to extinguish cooking stove fires when a cover is placed over a pan of burning food. The oxygen content can be reduced by flooding an area with an inert gas such as carbon dioxide. This action displaces the oxygen and disrupts the combustion process. Oxygen can also be separated from fuel by blanketing the fuel with fire suppressant foam. Of course, neither method (inert gas flooding or fire suppressant foam application) works on those rare fuels that are self-oxidizing.

Chemical Flame Inhibition

Extinguishing agents, Such as some dry chemicals and halogenated agents (halons) interrupt the combustion reaction and stop flaming. This method of extinguishment is effective on gas and liquid fuels because they must flame to burn. Smoldering fires are not easily extinguished by these agents. The very high agent concentrations and extended periods of time necessary to extinguish smoldering fires make the use of these (water is an exception) extinguishing agents impractical in smoldering fires.

Classification of Fires

The classification of a fire is important to the firefighter when discussing extinguishment. Each class of fire has its own requirements for extinguishment. The five classes of fire are discussed below, along with normal extinguishment methods and problems.

Class A Fires

Class A fires involve ordinary combustible materials such as wood, cloth, paper, rubber, and many plastics. Water is used to cool or quench the burning material below its ignition temperature. The addition of Class A foams may enhance water's ability to extinguish Class A fires, particularly those that are deep seated in bulk materials (such as piles of hay bales, sawdust piles, etc.). The Class A foam agent reduces the water's surface tension, allowing it to penetrate more easily into piles of the material. Class A fires are difficult to extinguish using oxygen-exclusion methods like CO_2 flooding or coating with foam because those methods do not provide the cooling effect needed for total extinguishment.

Class B Fires

Class B fires involve flammable and combustible liquids and gases such as gasoline, oil, lacquer, paint, mineral spirits, and alcohol. The smothering or blanketing effect of oxygen exclusion is most effective for extinguishment and also helps reduce the production of additional vapors. Other extinguishing methods include removal of fuel, temperature reduction when possible, and the interruption of the chain reaction with dry chemical agents such as Purple K®.

Class C Fires

Fires involving energized electrical equipment are **Class C fires**. Household appliances, computers, transformers, and overhead transmission lines are examples. These fires can sometimes be controlled by a nonconducting extinguishing agent such as carbon dioxide, dry chemical, or halon. The fastest extinguishment procedure for Class C fires is to first de-energize high-voltage circuits and then fight the fire appropriately depending upon the fuel involved.

Class D Fires

Class D fires involve combustible metals such as aluminum, magnesium, titanium, zirconium, sodium, and potassium. These materials are particularly hazardous in their powdered form. Proper airborne concentrations of metal dusts can cause powerful explosions, given a suitable ignition source. The extremely high temperature of some burning metals makes water and other common extinguishing agents ineffective. In addition, many Class D materials such as magnesium will violently react when exposed to water.

No single agent effectively controls fires in all combustible metals. Special extinguishing agents are marked for the metal fire they can extinguish. These agents are used to cover and exclude oxygen from the burning material.

Firefighters may find these materials in a variety of industrial or storage facilities. It is essential to use caution in a Class D materials fire. Information regarding a material and its characteristics should be reviewed prior to attempting to extinguish a Class D fire. The burning material should be isolated and treated as recommended in its Material Safety Data Sheet (MSDS) or in the *Emergency Response Guidebook* (*ERG*). All personnel operating in the area of the material should be in full protective equipment, and those exposed should be limited to only the people necessary to contain or extinguish the fire.

Class A Fire — Fires involving ordinary combustibles such as wood, paper, cloth, and similar materials.

Class B Fire — Fires of flammable and combustible liquids and gases such as gasoline, kerosene, and propane.

Class C Fire — Fires involving energized electrical equipment.

Class D Fire — Fires of combustible metals such as magnesium, sodium, and titanium.

Class K Fires

Class K fires specifically involve combustible cooking media such as vegetable or animal oils and fats. The use of high-efficiency cooking equipment, which is highly insulated and slow to cool, has prompted the fire service to take a look at the traditional commercial kitchen exhaust hoods and the dry chemical and liquid agent fire suppression systems. Because these newer cooking oils have a wide range of autoignition temperatures, the entire mass of oil must be cooled below its autoignition temperature in order for any fire to be extinguished. To combat Class K fires, wet-chemical extinguishers that contain a special potassium acetate based, low-pH agent are used. The extinguishing agent is dispensed in a fine mist. For more information about these types of fires, consult NFPA® 96, *Standard for Ventilation Control and Fire Protection of Commercial Cooking Operations*. This standard discusses the requirements for kitchen ventilation control and fire protection of commercial cooking operations.

Chapter Summary

It is crucial that all firefighters understand the science of fire if they are to operate safely and efficiently on the fireground. By developing a basic understanding of fire behavior, the firefighter will be able to better anticipate the ways in which fire develops and spreads. This knowledge is of the utmost importance on the fireground as emergency responders continually evaluate the fire and determine how to attack the fire itself, protect exposures, and ensure the safety of everyone at the scene.

Review Questions

1. What three elements does the chemical reaction of fire require?

2. How do conduction, convection, and radiation influence the development of fire?

3. What are the four elements of the fire tetrahedron?

4. What is the result when one of the four elements of the fire tetrahedron is removed?

5. What chemical reaction do oxidizers support when combined with a fuel?

6. What are the three physical states of matter in which fuel can be found?

7. What are the five major phases of fire?

8. What is the difference between a rollover and a flashover?

9. What effect does thermal layering have on fire suppression activities?

10. What are four main fire extinguishment techniques?

Endnotes

1 Raymond Friedman, *Principles of Fire Protection Chemistry and Physics,* 3rd edition, National Fire Protection Association®, 1998; also Richard L. Tuve, *Principles of Fire Protection Chemistry,* 1st edition, 1976.

2 Ibid.

3 Jerry S. Faughn, Raymond Chang, and Jonathon Turk, *Physical Science,* 2nd edition, Ft. Worth: Saunders College Publishers, 1995.

Other References:

Flammable Ranges, NFPA® 325, *Fire Hazard Properties of Flammable Liquids, Gases, and Volatile Solids,* found in NFPA®'s *Fire Protection Guide to Hazardous Materials,* 2001 edition.

Chapter 5, "Basic Fire Science," NFPA® 921, *Guide for Fire and Explosion Investigations,* 2008.

Building Construction

Chapter Contents

chapter 6

Key Terms

FESHE Outcomes

This chapter provides information that addresses the outcomes for the Fire and Emergency Services Higher Education (FESHE) *Principles of Emergency Services* course.

10. Identify and explain the components of fire prevention including code enforcement, public information, and public and private fire protection systems.

NFPA® Job Performance Requirements

This chapter provides information that addresses the following job performance requirements (JPRs) of NFPA® 1001, *Standard for Fire Fighter Professional Qualifications* (2008).

5.3.10(A)   5.3.12(A)   6.3.2(A)

Building Construction

Learning Objectives

After reading this chapter, students will be able to:

1. Distinguish the main differences between the five types of building construction.

2. Explain how common building materials effect fire prevention and code enforcement.

3. Describe how building construction and materials relate to fire fighting operations.

Chapter 6
Building Construction

Case History

Mac worked as a carpenter's helper in a housing development during two summers, so he had a solid practical understanding of how buildings were constructed. And he knew that drywall, shingles, and siding sometimes covered "shortcuts" in the framing.

At the rookie academy, Mac learned more about how buildings are made and how they function in a fire. He worked on three or four of the five types of building construction and now could identify their characteristics. He had known about wood and now knew about how several other materials were used in buildings – and how they behaved in fire. As a former carpenter's helper, Mac was very interested in the hazards that happened during construction, renovation, and demolition. Like any firefighter, he was eager to learn about how building construction affected his safety.

From a safety standpoint, all firefighters should have a basic knowledge of the principles of building construction. Knowledge of the various types of building construction and how each building will react to fire gives the firefighter and fire officer an advantage in planning for a safe and effective fire attack. Failure to recognize the potential dangers and possible effects during a fire that a particular type of construction presents can lead to deadly results.

New technologies and designs are being used for building construction every day. Therefore, it is impossible to highlight every situation in this chapter. The purpose of this chapter is to introduce the firefighter to some of the most basic types of building construction and their fire protection characteristics. The chapter also introduces the firefighter to common building construction terms and components. In addition, the chapter discusses some of the indicators that signify danger during fire fighting operations. This subject is one of extreme importance for the fire service, and it is expected that any career or volunteer firefighter will undertake a more in-depth study of this subject.

NOTE: Additional information can be found in the IFSTA **Building Construction Related to the Fire Service** manual.

Types of Building Construction

Each of the model **building codes** classifies building construction in different terms. In general, construction classifications are based on the type of materials used in the construction and on the **fire-resistance rating** requirements

Building Code — Body of local law, adopted by states/provinces, counties, cities, or other governmental bodies to regulate the construction, renovation, and maintenance of buildings.

Fire Resistance — Ability of a structural assembly to maintain its load-bearing ability under fire conditions.

Fire Resistance Rating — Rating assigned to a material or assembly after standardized testing by an independent testing organization; identifies the amount of time a material or assembly will resist a typical fire, as measured on a standard time-temperature curve.

of certain structural components. Most building codes have the same five construction classifications, but use different terms to name the classifications.

The five types of building construction are as follows:

- Type I construction (formerly known as fire-resistive)
- Type II construction (formerly known as noncombustible or limited combustible)
- Type III construction (formerly known as ordinary)
- Type IV construction (formerly known as heavy timber)
- Type V construction (formerly known as wood-frame)

Construction Classifications and Subclassifications

NFPA® 220, *Standard on Types of Building Construction,* details the requirements for each of the classifications and subclassifications. In NFPA® 220, each classification is designated by a three-digit number code. For example, Type I construction can be either 4-4-2 or 3-3-2. The digits are explained as follows:

- The first digit refers to the fire-resistance rating (in hours) of exterior bearing walls.
- The second digit refers to the fire-resistance rating of structural frames or columns and girders that support loads of more than one floor.
- The third digit indicates the fire-resistance rating of the floor construction.

In Type IV construction the designation 2HH is used. The structural members so indicated are of heavy timber with minimum dimensions greater than those used in Type III or Type V construction. The highest requirements for fire resistance are for Type I construction, with lesser requirements for other types of construction.

The International Building Code (IBC) makes use of construction classifications similar to NFPA® 220, although the requirements for individual structural members differ. **Table 6.1** shows the basic fire-resistance rating requirements for the five construction types and subclassifications in the IBC. Note that the basic requirements in Table 6.1 are permitted to be reduced.

Type I Construction

Fire resistance provides structural integrity during a fire. **Type I construction** has structural members, including walls, columns, beams, floors, and roofs, made of noncombustible or limited combustible materials (**Figure 6.1, p. 204**).

The fire-resistive compartmentation that partitions and floors provide tends to retard the spread of fire through the building. These features allow time for occupant evacuation and interior fire fighting. Because of the limited combustibility of the materials of construction, the primary fire hazards are the contents of the structure. In a Type I structure, firefighters are able to launch an interior attack with greater confidence than they can in a building that is not fire resistant. Openings made in partitions and improperly designed and dampered heating and air-conditioning systems can compromise the ability of Type I construction to confine the fire to a certain area.

Type I Construction — Construction type in which structural members, including walls, columns, beams, floors, and roofs, that are made of noncombustible materials or limited combustible materials and have a specified degree of fire resistance. *Formerly known as* Fire Resistive Construction.

Building Element	Type I		Type II		Type III		Type IV	Type V	
	A	B	A[e]	B	A[e]	B	HT	A[e]	B
Structural Frame[a]	3[b]	2[b]	1	0	1	0	HT	1	0
Bearing Walls 　Exterior[g] 　Interior	 3 3[b]	 2 2[b]	 1 1	 0 0	 2 1	 2 0	 2 1/HT	 1 1	 0 0
Nonbearing Walls and Partitions 　Interior[f]	0	0	0	0	0	0	See Section 602.4.6*	0	0
Floor Construction 　Including Supporting Beams and 　Joists	2	2	1	0	1	0	HT	1	0
Floor Construction 　Including Supporting Beams and 　Joists	1½[c]	1[c, d]	1[c, d]	0[c, d]	1[c, d]	0[c, d]	HT	1[c, d]	0

For SI: 1 foot = 304.8 mm
HT = Heavy Timber

a. The structural frame shall be considered to be the columns and the girders, beams, trusses, and spandrels having direct connections to the columns and bracing members designed to carry gravity loads. The members of the floor panel or roof panels which have no connection to the columns shall be considered secondary members and not a part of the structural frame.

b. Roof supports: Fire-resistance ratings of structural frame bearing walls are permitted to be reduced by 1 hour where supporting a roof only.

c. Except in Group F-1, H, M, and S-1 occupancies, fire protection of structural members shall not be required, including protection of a roof framing and decking where every part of the roof construction is 20 feet or more above any floor immediately below. Fire-retardant-treated wood members shall be allowed to be used for such unprotected members.

d. In all occupancies, heavy timber shall be allowed where a 1-hour or less fire-resistance rating is required.

e. An approved automatic sprinkler system in accordance with Section 903.3.1.1* shall be allowed to be substituted for 1-hour fire-resistance-rated construction, provided such system is not otherwise required by other provisions of the code or used for an allowable area increase in accordance with Section 504.2*. The 1-hour substitution for the fire-resistance exterior of walls shall not be permitted.

f. Not less than the fire-resistance rating required by other sections* of this code.

g. Not less than the fire-resistance rating based on fire separation distance.

* Section numbers refer to sections in the *2006 International Building Code*®.

Courtesy of the International Code Council®, *International Building Code*®, *2006, Table 601.*

Figure 6.1 Type I construction has structural members made of noncombustible or limited combustible materials. *Courtesy of McKinney (TX) Fire Department.*

Common Types of Openings in a Structure

Openings in partitions, floors, and ceilings are very common and include those for:

- Electrical service
- Plumbing
- Television, cable, or data lines
- HVAC
- Laundry chutes
- Crawl spaces/attics

Type II Construction — Construction Type that is similar to Type I except that the degree of fire resistance is lower. *Formerly known as* Noncombustible or Noncombustible/Limited Combustible Construction.

Type III Construction — Construction type in which exterior walls and structural members are made of noncombustible or limited combustible materials, but interior structural members, including walls, columns, beams, floors, and roofs, are completely or partially constructed of wood. *Formerly known as* Ordinary Construction.

Type II Construction

Type II construction is similar to Type I construction, but has lower fire resistance. Materials with no fire-resistance ratings, such as untreated wood, may be used in limited quantities in noncombustible, Type II, construction (**Figure 6.2**). Again, one of the primary fire protection concerns is the contents of a building. The heat buildup from a fire in the building can cause structural supports – even those made of steel — to fail. In addition, the type of roof on the building can cause another potential problem. Buildings of Type II construction often have flat, built-up roofs. These roofs contain combustible felt, insulation, and roofing tar (**Figure 6.3**). Fire extension to the roof can eventually cause the entire roof to become involved and fail.

Type III Construction

Type III construction features exterior walls and structural members constructed of noncombustible or limited combustible materials. In Type III construction, interior structural members, including walls, columns, beams, floors, and roofs, are completely or partially constructed of wood (**Figure 6.4**). The wood used in these members is of smaller dimensions than that required

Figure 6.2 Buildings of Type II construction are permitted to have materials that are slightly less fire-resistive than buildings of Type I construction. *Courtesy of McKinney (TX) Fire Department.*

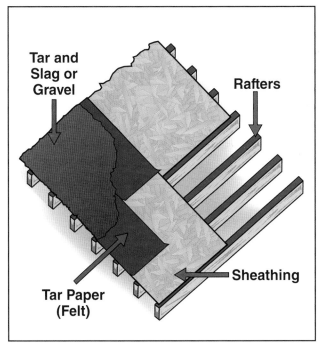

Figure 6.3 The materials used in built-up roofs are combustible.

Figure 6.4 Type III construction features interior structural members constructed completely or partially of wood while exterior walls and structural members are noncombustible or limited combustible materials. *Courtesy of McKinney (TX) Fire Department.*

for heavy timber construction (see the Type IV Construction). The primary fire concern specific to Type III construction is the fire and smoke spreading through concealed spaces and voids. These spaces are between the walls, floors, ceiling, and cocklofts. Heat from a fire may be conducted to these concealed spaces through finish materials such as drywall, gypsum board, or plaster. The heat can also enter the concealed spaces through holes in the finish materials. From there the heat, smoke, and gases may spread to other parts of the structure. If enough heat is present, the fire may actually burn within the concealed spaces and feed on the combustible construction materials in the space. Placing fire-stops inside these spaces to limit the spread of the combustion by-products (heat, smoke, etc.) can considerably reduce these hazards.

Figure 6.5 An example of heavy timber construction.

Type IV Construction

Type IV construction features exterior and interior walls and their associated structural members made of noncombustible or limited combustible materials. Other interior structural members, including beams, columns, arches, floors, and roofs, are made of solid or laminated wood with no concealed spaces (**Figure 6.5**). This wood must have dimensions large enough to be considered heavy timber (8 inches [203 mm] for a column and 6 inches [150 mm] for a horizontal beam), according to NFPA® 220, *Standard on Types of Building Construction*. These dimensions vary depending on the particular code being used.

Type IV (formerly heavy timber) construction was used extensively in old factories, mills, and warehouses. It is rarely used today, other than occasionally in churches. The primary fire hazard associated with heavy timber construction is the massive amount of combustible contents presented by the structural timbers, in addition to the contents of the building. Though the heavy timbers remain stable for a long period under fire conditions, they give off tremendous amounts of heat and pose serious exposure protection problems for firefighters.

Type V Construction

Type V construction has exterior walls, bearing walls, floors, roofs, and supports made completely or partially of wood or other approved materials of smaller dimensions than those used for Type IV construction. Type V (formerly wood-frame) construction is the type most commonly used to construct the typical single-family residence. This type of construction presents almost unlimited potential for fire extension within the building of origin and to nearby exposures, particularly if the nearby structures are also wood-frame construction (**Figure 6.6**). Firefighters must be alert for fire coming from doors or windows extending to the exterior of the structure. In addition, firefighters should anticipate the possibility of lightweight elements in floors and attic spaces.

Type IV Construction — Heavy timber construction in which interior and exterior walls and their associated structural members are made of noncombustible or limited combustible material; interior structural framing consists of heavy timber with minimum dimensions larger than those used in Type III construction. *Formerly known as* Heavy Timber Construction.

Type V Construction — Construction type in which exterior walls, bearing walls, floors, roofs, and supports are made completely or partially of wood or other approved materials of smaller dimensions than those used Type IV construction. *Formerly known as* Wood Frame Construction.

Figure 6.6 This single-family residence under construction is a typical example of Type V construction.

Balloon-Frame Construction

In **balloon-frame construction**, the exterior wall studs are continuous from the foundation to the roof. Ribbon boards that are recessed into the vertical stud are used to support the joists which, in turn, support the second floor. The term *balloon- frame* came from the fragile appearance of the thin, closely spaced studs compared to the more massive members used in earlier timber construction. They were said to be as fragile as a balloon.

The vertical combustible spaces between the studs in balloon-frame construction provide a channel for the rapid communication of fire from floor to floor. Unlike timber framing, light-wood framing is usually not left exposed. The framing is usually covered with an interior finish of plaster or drywall. The interior finish will act to retard the spread of fire into the stud spaces; however, a fire may penetrate the interior finish through penetrations for electrical fixtures, plumbing, or heating.

Once the fire spreads, originates in, or spreads into the stud space, it can readily spread from the vertical cavity into the floor joists and into the attic space. Therefore, a fire in a balloon-frame building can be difficult to control. For example, fire issuing from an attic may give arriving firefighters the impression that the fire originated in the attic when it may have originated in the basement and communicated through the stud wall.

Balloon framing has the advantage of minimizing the effects of lumber shrinkage that can occur over time as the lumber dries and loses its moisture content. Shrinkage in lumber occurs to a greater degree in the cross-sectional dimensions than in its length. Therefore, less pronounced shrinkage effects occur with the use of the continuous studs of balloon framing. With the increased use of dried lumber, however, the advantages of balloon framing have diminished. Balloon framing has not been widely used since the 1920s, although many balloon-frame buildings remain.

Balloon-Frame Construction — Type of structural framing used in some single-story and multistory wood frame buildings; studs are continuous from the foundation to the roof and there may be no fire stops between the studs.

Effects of Fire on Common Building Materials

All materials react differently when exposed to heat or fire. Knowing how these materials will react gives fire suppression personnel an idea of what to expect during fire fighting operations at a particular occupancy. This section of the chapter reviews the common materials found in building construction and explains how they react to fire involvement.

Figure 6.7 A party wall that supports two adjacent structures is a load-bearing wall.

Figure 6.8 A partition wall that simply divides two areas is a non-load-bearing wall.

Load-Bearing Wall — Wall that supports itself, the weight of the roof, and/ or other internal structural framing components, such as the floor beams and trusses above it. *Also known as* Bearing Wall.

Non-Load-Bearing Wall — Wall, usually interior, that supports only its own weight. These walls can be breached or removed without compromising the structural integrity of the building. *Also known as* Nonbearing Wall.

Nonbearing Wall — *See* Non-Load-Bearing Wall.

Party Wall — Dividing wall that stands between two adjoining buildings or units, often on the property line, and is common to both buildings. A party wall is almost always a load-bearing wall and usually serves as a fire wall.

Partition Wall — Interior non-load-bearing wall that separates a space into rooms.

Wood

Wood is used in various structural support systems. It may be used in **load-bearing walls** (those that support structural weight) or **nonload-bearing walls** (those that do not support structural weight). Most exterior walls are load-bearing walls. A **party wall** that supports two adjacent structures is a load-bearing wall (**Figure 6.7**). A **partition wall** that simply divides two areas within a structure is an example of a non load-bearing wall (**Figure 6.8**). Some interior walls may also be load bearing. It is often difficult to tell whether or not a wall is load-bearing just by looking at it. This information should be obtained during pre-incident planning trips so firefighters lessen their chances of being surprised at the fire scene.

The reaction of wood to fire conditions depends mainly on two factors: dimensions and moisture content. The smaller the wood size, the more likely it is to lose structural integrity. Large pieces of wood, such as those used in Type IV construction, retain much of their original structural integrity even after extensive fire exposure. Smaller pieces of wood can be protected by drywall or gypsum to increase their resistance to heat or fire.

The moisture content of the wood affects the rate at which it burns. Wood that has a high moisture content (sometimes referred to as *green* wood) does not burn as fast as wood that has been cured or dried. In some cases, fire retardants may be added to wood to reduce the speed at which it ignites or burns; however, they are not always totally effective in reducing fire spread.

Wood's moisture content also affects its strength. Wood in a living tree contains a large amount of water. When the tree is cut, the water begins to evaporate. As the water leaves the wood, either naturally or through drying, the wood begins to shrink in size and increase in strength. It is possible to dry lumber to any moisture content, but most structural lumber has a moisture content of 19 percent or less.

Wood can be treated to greatly reduce its combustibility. Building codes permit the use of fire-retardant-treated wood for certain applications in fire-resistive and noncombustible construction (Type I and II). For example, the International Building Code allows **fire-retardant** treated wood in non-load bearing partitions where the required fire resistance is two hours or less.

Fire-retardant-treated-wood resists ignition and has increased fire endurance when compared with nontreated wood. However, wood that has received a fire-retardant treatment is not completely noncombustible and should not be confused with materials that are fire-resistive.

The two main methods of fire-retardant treatment are pressure impregnation and surface coating. Surface coating is used primarily to reduce the surface burning of wood i.e., the flame spread rating.

Pressure impregnation of wood is performed by placing the wood to be treated in a large cylinder in which a vacuum is created. The vacuum draws air out of the cells of the wood. A solution containing the fire-retardant chemical is introduced into the cylinder and the cylinder is pressurized. The pressure forces the fire-retardant chemicals into the cells of the wood. Pressure impregnation has the advantage of producing a treatment that is permanent when used under proper conditions.

Water used during extinguishing operations does not have a substantial negative effect on the structural strength of wood construction materials. Applying water to burning wood minimizes damage by stopping the charring process, which reduces wood's strength. Firefighters should check wood studs and structural members for charring to ascertain their structural integrity.

Newer construction often contains lightweight composite building components and materials that are made of wood fibers, plastics, and other substances joined by glue or resin binders. Such materials include plywood, particleboard, fiberboard, and paneling. While these materials can be stronger than wood, some of these products may be highly combustible, can produce significant toxic gases, or can deteriorate rapidly under fire conditions.

NOTE: Visiting building sites and even home improvement stores is a practical way to learn about building construction.

Masonry

Masonry includes bricks, stones, and concrete products such as concrete masonry units (CMUs or cinder blocks) and paver-style bricks (**Figure 6.9 a and b, p. 210**). Masonry in a variety of wall types is commonly used for **fire wall assemblies**, which consist of all the components needed to provide a separating **fire wall** that meets the requirements of a specified fire-resistance rating. The assembly components include the wall structure, doors, windows, and any other opening protection meeting the required protection-rating criteria.

Firewall assemblies may be used to separate two connected structures (such as townhouses or a strip mall) and prevent the spread of fire from one structure to the next. Firewall assemblies can also divide large structures into smaller portions and confine a fire to a particular portion of the structure. **Cantilever fire walls** are freestanding firewalls commonly found in large churches and shopping centers (**Figure 6.10, p. 210**). While block walls may be load-bearing walls, most brick and stone walls are **veneered walls**, which are decorative and usually attached to the outside of some type of load-bearing frame structure.

Fire Retardant — Any substance, except plain water, that when applied to another material or substance will reduce the flammability of fuels or slow their rate of combustion by chemical or physical action.

Masonry — Bricks, blocks, stones, and unreinforced and reinforced concrete products.

Fire Wall Assembly — All of the components needed to provide a separating fire wall that meets the requirements of a specified fire-resistance rating.

Fire Wall — (1) Fire rated wall with a specified degree of fire resistance, built of fire-resistive materials and usually extending from the foundation up to and through the roof of a building, that is designed to limit the spread of a fire within a structure or between adjacent structures. (2) Bulkhead separating an aircraft engine from the aircraft fuselage or wing. (3) The partition between the engine compartment and the passenger compartment of a vehicle. It is designed to protect vehicle occupants from the engine and its associated hazards.

Cantilever Fire Wall — Free standing fire wall, commonly found on large churches and shopping malls.

Veneered Wall — Wall with a surface layer of attractive material laid over a base of a common material.

Figure 6.9a A structure with a masonry exterior of brick and concrete.

Figure 6.9b A structure with a masonry exterior of composite masonry units (cinder blocks) and concrete.

Figure 6.10 A cantilever fire wall is a freestanding firewall.

Fire and exposure to high temperatures have minimal affect on masonry. Bricks rarely show any signs of loss of integrity or serious deterioration. Stones may spall or lose small portions of their surface when heated. Blocks may crack, but they usually retain most of their strength and basic structural stability. The mortar between the bricks, blocks, and stone, however, may be subject to more deterioration and should be checked for signs of weakening (**Figure 6.11**).

Rapid cooling, which can occur when water is used to extinguish fire, sometimes causes bricks, blocks, or stone to spall and crack. Spalling is a common problem when water is used to extinguish chimney flue fires. The water causes the flue liner or firebricks to crack. Masonry products should be inspected for signs of this damage after extinguishment has been completed.

Cast Iron

Cast iron is rarely used in modern construction and is usually found only in older buildings (**Figure 6.12**). It was commonly used as an exterior surface covering (veneer wall) and for columns. These large veneer walls were fastened to the masonry on the front of the building. Cast iron stands up well to fire

Figure 6.11 The mortar between bricks, blocks, or stone should be checked for signs of weakness.

Figure 6.12 The darker components of this structure are made of cast iron.

Figure 6.13 Steel serves as a structural component in this building. *Courtesy of McKinney (TX) Fire Department.*

and intense heat situations, but it may crack or shatter when rapidly cooled with water. A primary concern from a fire fighting standpoint is that the bolts or other connections that hold the cast iron to the building can fail, causing these large, heavy sections of metal to come crashing down.

Steel

Steel is the primary material used for structural support in modern building construction (**Figure 6.13**). Of primary importance to firefighters is the fact that steel structural members elongate when heated. If an unrestrained steel beam 20 feet (6.1 m) long were heated from 70°F (21°C) to a uniform temperature of 1,000°F (538°C), it would expand 1.4 inches (35 mm). If the steel is restrained

Figure 6.14a Examples of lightweight steel trusses. *Courtesy of McKinney (TX) Fire Department.*

Figure 6.14b Examples of steel I-beams used in constructing a high-rise structure.

from movement at the ends, it buckles and fails somewhere in the middle. For all practical purposes, the failure of steel structural members can be anticipated at temperatures near or above 1,000° F (538° C). The temperature at which a specific steel member fails depends on many variables, including the size of the member, the load it is under, the composition of the steel, the geometry of the member, and whether or not the steel member is protected. For example, a lightweight, open-web truss will fail much quicker than a large, heavy I-beam (**Figure 6.14 a and b**).

From a fire fighting perspective, firefighters must be aware of the type of steel members (such as lightweight trusses and heavy I-beams) used in a particular structure, based on information from the pre-incident survey. Firefighters also need to determine how long the steel members have been exposed to heat in order to calculate when the members might fail. Another possibility for firefighters to consider is that elongating steel can actually push out load-bearing walls and cause a collapse (**Figure 6.15**). Water can cool steel structural members and reduce the risk of failure, which in turn reduces the risk of a structural collapse.

Reinforced Concrete

Reinforced concrete is concrete that is internally fortified with steel reinforcement bars or mesh (**Figure 6.16**). This reinforcement gives the material the tensile strength of steel in addition to the compressive strength of concrete. Reinforced concrete does not perform particularly well under fire conditions; it loses strength and spalls. Heating may cause a failure of the bond between the concrete and the steel reinforcement. Firefighters should look for cracks and spalls in reinforced concrete surfaces. Such damage is an indication that the strength of the concrete may be reduced.

Gypsum

Gypsum is an inorganic product from which plaster and plasterboards are constructed and is used in making **gypsum board** (**Figure 6.17**). It is unique because it has high water content, and the evaporation of this water requires

Gypsum — Hydrated calcium sulfate used for gypsum plaster and wallboard.

Gypsum Board — Widely used interior finish material; consists of a core of calcined gypsum, starch, water, and other additives that are sandwiched between two paper faces. *Also known as* Gypsum Drywall, Plasterboard, Sheetrock®, and Drywall.

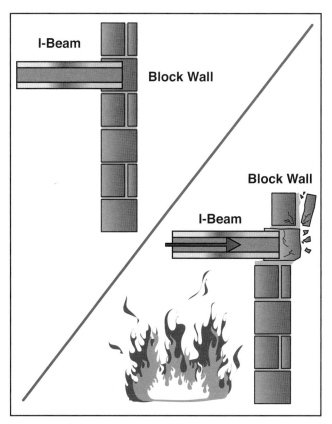

Figure 6.15 Steel beams expand when heated and can push a wall outward causing a collapse.

Figure 6.16 Reinforcing rods increase structural integrity.

Figure 6.17 Gypsum board is used to cover interior walls.

Figure 6.18 A modern high-rise building with a glass exterior.

a great deal of heat. The water content gives gypsum excellent heat-resistant and fire-retardant properties. Gypsum is commonly used to provide insulation to steel and wood structural members that are less adapted to high-heat situations because it deteriorates gradually under fire conditions. In areas where the gypsum has failed or has holes, the structural members behind it will be subjected to higher temperatures and could fail as a result.

Glass/Fiberglass

Glass is not typically used for structural support; it is used in sheet form for doors and windows (**Figure 6.18**). Wire-reinforced glass may provide some thermal protection as a separation, but for the most part conventional glass is not an effective barrier to fire extension. Furthermore, heated glass may crack and shatter when struck by a cold fire stream.

Fiberglass is typically used for insulation purposes. The glass component of fiberglass is not a significant fuel, but the materials used to bind the fiberglass may be combustible and can be difficult to extinguish.

Firefighter Hazards Related to Building Construction

The primary reason that firefighters need to understand building construction and materials is to be able to apply that information to the fireground. Firefighters should use their knowledge of these principles to monitor building conditions for signs of structural instability.

Even though a safety officer may be designated at the scene, it is the obligation of all personnel to constantly monitor the scene for unsafe conditions. The following sections highlight some of the more critical issues related to building construction that effect firefighter safety.

Dangerous Building Conditions

Firefighters must be aware of the dangerous conditions created by a fire as well as dangerous conditions that may be created as firefighters try to extinguish the fire. A potentially serious situation can be compounded if firefighters fail to recognize the seriousness of the situation and take actions that only make the situation worse. There are two primary types of dangerous conditions that may be posed by a particular building:

1. Conditions that contribute to the spread and intensity of the fire, such as large quantities of combustible materials

2. Conditions that make the building susceptible to collapse, such as type of construction, renovation, and demolitions hazards , or poor maintenance

These two conditions are obviously related — conditions that contribute to the spread and intensity of the fire increase the likelihood of structural collapse. The following sections describe some of these conditions.

Fire Loading

Fire load is the maximum heat that can be produced if all the combustible materials in a given area burn, expressed in BTUs. Heavy *fire loading* is the presence of large amounts of combustible materials in an area of a building. The arrangement of materials in a building directly affects fire development and severity and must be considered when determining the possible duration and intensity of a fire.

Heavy content fire loading is perhaps one of the most critical hazards in commercial and storage facilities because the fire may quickly override the capabilities of a fire sprinkler system (if present) and cause access problems for fire fighting personnel during fire fighting operations (**Figure 6.19**). Proper inspection and code enforcement procedures in pre-incident surveys are the best ways to be aware of these hazards.

Fire Load — (1) The amount of fuel within a compartment; expressed in pounds per square foot, and obtained by dividing the amount of fuel present by the floor area. Fire load is used as a measure of the potential heat release of a fire within a compartment. (2) Maximum amount of heat that can be produced if all the combustible materials in a given area burn. *Also known as* Fuel Load.

Figure 6.19 Heavy content fire loading can pose a problem during fire fighting operations because a large amount of fuel will lead to a hotter, larger fire.

Figure 6.20 Combustible furnishings burn readily and emit many toxic gases.

Combustible Furnishings and Finishes

Combustible furnishings and finishes contribute to fire spread and smoke production (**Figure 6.20**). Fire spread and smoke production have been identified as major factors in the loss of many lives in fires. Proper inspection and code enforcement procedures are the most effective defense against these hazards. Some codes regulate the furnishings found in occupancies such as hospitals, theatres, and detention facilities.

Roof Coverings

Roof coverings are the final outside layer that is placed on top of a roof assembly. Common roof coverings include wood and composite shingles, tile, slate, tin, asphaltic tar paper, and newer rubberized, pour-on roof coatings. The combustibility of a roof's surface is a basic concern to the fire safety of an entire community. Some of the earliest fire regulations ever imposed in the United States hundreds of years ago related to combustible roof-covering because these roof coverings caused several conflagrations from flaming embers flying from roof to roof.

History has shown time and time again that wood shake shingles, even when treated with fire retardant, can contribute significantly to fire spread particularly in wildland/urban interface fire situations where wood shake shingle roofs have contributed to large fires (**Figure 6.21**). Firefighters must use aggressive exposure protection tactics when faced with fires involving wood shake shingles.

Wooden Floors and Ceilings

Combustible structural components such as framing, floors, and ceilings made of wood also contribute to the fire loading in a building. Prolonged exposure to fire may weaken them and increase the risk of collapse.

Figure 6.21 Shake shingle roofs are vulnerable to ignition from burning embers, radiated heat, and direct flame impingement.

Figures 6.22 The large open space in this structure could contribute to rapid fire spread.

Large, Open Spaces

Large, open spaces in buildings contribute to fire spread. Such spaces may be found in "big box" stores, enclosed malls, warehouses, churches, large atriums, common attics or cocklofts, and theaters (**Figures 6.22**). In these facilities, proper vertical ventilation (channeling smoke from a building at its highest point) is essential for slowing the spread of fire. Recognition of advanced fire conditions near the ceiling is critical in large open spaces since visibility and conditions at floor level may not be drastically affected until late in the progression of a fire.

Building Collapse

Structural collapses during fire fighting operations have killed, disabled, or injured many firefighters. Collapse often results from damage to the structural system of the building caused by the fire or by fire fighting operations. Some buildings, because of their construction and age, are more inclined to collapse than others. For example, buildings featuring lightweight or truss construction will succumb to the effects of fire much more quickly than a heavy timber building. Older buildings that have been exposed to weather or that have been poorly maintained are more likely to collapse than newer, well-maintained buildings (**Figure 6.23**). Information on building age and construction type should be obtained when conducting inspections and documented in pre-incident plans.

Fire immediately begins to weaken the structural support system until it becomes incapable of holding the weight of the building. The longer a fire burns in a building, the more likely the building will collapse. The time it takes for this to happen varies with the fire severity, fire loading, the type of construction, the presence or absence of heavy industrial machinery on upper floors or on the roof, and the general condition of the building.

Figure 6.23 Older, poorly maintained buildings are likely to collapse more quickly than newer buildings.

Indicators of Building Collapse

Firefighters should be aware of the following indicators of building collapse:

- Cracks or separations in walls, floors, ceilings, and roof structures (**Figure 6.24**)

- Evidence of existing structural instability such as the presence of tie rods and stars that hold walls together

- Loose bricks, blocks, or stones falling from buildings (**Figure 6.25**)

- Deteriorated mortar between the masonry

- Walls that appear to be leaning

- Structural members that appear to be distorted

- Fires beneath floors or roofs that support heavy machinery, HVAC units, or other extreme weight loads

- Prolonged fire exposure to the structural members

- Unusual creaks and cracking noises

- Structural members pulling away from walls

- Excessive weight of building contents

Figure 6.24 Cracks in walls are a warning of building instability.

Figures 6.25 Loose or missing bricks indicate a potentially dangerous situation.

Fire fighting operations also increase the risk of building collapse. Improper vertical ventilation techniques can result in the cutting of structural supports that could weaken the structure. The water used to extinguish a fire adds extra weight to the structure and can weaken it. Water only a few inches (millimeters) deep over a large area can add many tons (tonnes) of weight to an already weakened structure. A basic guideline for the amount of water added during fire fighter operations is that hoselines flowing 250 gpm (946 Lpm) can add one ton of water per minute inside a structure. If the building is already weakened and if the water cannot drain from the building adequately, it may collapse from the additional water alone.

Immediate safety precautions must be taken if fire personnel believe that the collapse of a building is imminent or even possible. All personnel who are operating within the building should immediately evacuate. Ensure the collapse zone has been established around the perimeter of the building (**Figure 6.26, p. 220**). The minimum collapse zone should be equal to one and a half times the height of the building. No personnel or apparatus should be allowed to operate in the collapse zone except to place unmanned master stream devices. Once these devices have been placed, personnel should immediately retreat to an area outside the collapse zone.

CAUTION
Firefighters must always be aware of any evacuation or emergency signals used by their department.

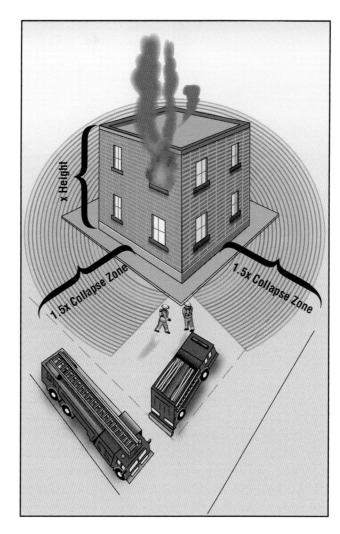

Figure 6.26 A collapse zone should be equal to one and one half times the height of a building.

Truss — (1) Structural member used to form a roof or floor framework; trusses form triangles or combinations of triangles to provide maximum load-bearing capacity with a minimum amount of material. Often rendered dangerous by exposure to intense heat, which weakens gusset plate attachment. (2) Beams consisting of one tensile chord, one compression chord, and truss blocks or spaces between the two.

Lightweight Steel Truss — Structural support made from a long steel bar that is bent at a 90-degree angle with flat or angular pieces welded to the top and bottom.

Lightweight Wood Truss — Structural supports constructed of 2- 3-inch or 2- 4-inch (51 mm by 76 mm or 51 mm by 102 mm) members that are connected by gusset plates.

Lightweight and Truss Construction Hazards

One of the most serious building construction hazards facing firefighters is the increased use of lightweight and trussed support systems. Lightweight construction is most commonly found in houses, apartments, and small commercial buildings (Types II and V construction). The two most common types are lightweight metal and lightweight wood trusses. **Lightweight steel trusses** are made from a long steel bar that is bent at a 90-degree angle with flat or angular pieces welded to the top and bottom (**Figure 6.27**). **Lightweight wood trusses** are constructed of 2- × 3- or 2- × 4-inch (51 mm x 76 mm or 51 mm x 102 mm) boards that are connected by gusset plates (**Figure 6.28**). Gusset plates used for wood truss construction are small metal plates (usually 18 to 22 gauge metal) with prongs that penetrate about 3/8-inch (10 mm) into the wood.

Experience has shown that lightweight metal and wood trusses will fail after only 5 to 10 minutes of exposure to fire. For steel trusses, 1,000°F (538°C) is the critical temperature. Gusset plates in wood trusses will fail early when exposed to heat. Although the trusses may be protected with fire-retardant treatments to give longer protection, most are not protected at all.

Figure 6.27 Lightweight steel trusses are especially vulnerable to collapse during a fire.

Figure 6.28 Lightweight wood trusses are also vulnerable to collapse.

Truss Construction Evolution

Truss construction continues to evolve. New developments include:

1. Lightweight wood trusses manufactured using finger-joint bonding (glue) without metal gusset plates.
2. Knock-out panels built into the trusses to allow HVAC, plumbing, and electrical components to pass through trusses.

Wooden I-beams are also used in lightweight construction. They have fire characteristics similar to wood trusses and similar precautions should be used when they are found in a structure (**Figure 6.29**).

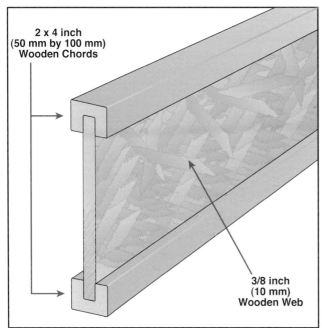

2 x 4 inch
(50 mm by 100 mm)
Wooden Chords

3/8 inch
(10 mm)
Wooden Web

Figure 6.29 Wooden I-beams have a large surface area for combustion, so they can burn through and weaken quickly.

Figure 6.30 Bowstring trusses are used in buildings that have large open spaces. Their weakness is that they fail quickly during a fire. *Courtesy of McKinney (TX) Fire Department.*

Other types of trusses, such as bowstring trusses, are found in virtually every community. They are used in buildings that have large open spaces, such as car dealerships, bowling alleys, factories, and supermarkets. Bowstrings are often easily denoted by their rounded appearance, though many appear otherwise (**Figure 6.30**).

The arch of a bowstring truss roof may be hidden by a rectangular parapet wall and a suspended ceiling. It may only be possible to see the curvature by ascending to the roof.

All trusses are designed to work as an integral unit. Some members are in *tension* (vertical and horizontal stresses that tend to pull things apart), and others are in *compression* (vertical and horizontal stresses that tend to press things together).

Identifying Truss Roof and Floor Construction within the District

It is *extremely* important that firefighters know which buildings in their district have truss roofs or floors. One thing common to all types of trusses is that if one member fails, the entire truss is likely to fail. Once an entire truss fails, usually the truss next to it fails, and the domino principle takes over until a total collapse occurs.

Truss-containing buildings exposed to fire conditions for 5 to 10 minutes (which is usually how long they have been exposed before the fire department arrives) should not be entered, and crews should not go onto the roofs. When in doubt, it is better to assume that a structure is of lightweight construction. Vital information like this can be obtained from thorough pre-incident planning that identifies types of construction and life and safety hazards.

New Building Construction Technologies

The latter 20th and early 21st centuries have witnessed the introduction of many new building construction technologies that firefighters must be knowledgeable. These include items such as:

- Alternative energy sources such as solar panels mounted to the roof or heat pumps **(Figure 6.31)**
- Styrofoam foundation forms
- Energy efficient windows

Figure 6.31 These solar panels add a significant amount of weight to this roof.

Figure 6.32 A building in this early stage of construction does not yet have any fire resistant structural elements in place. *Courtesy of McKinney (TX) Fire Department.*

- Reinforced drywall sheets
- Tornado and hurricane impact resistant windows
- Building access and security systems, such as electronic magnetic locking door and window security bar systems, which limit or prevent occupant evacuation and firefighter access

Each of these can create a hazard or an obstacle to firefighters during emergency operations. Solar panels mounted to the roof add additional weight to the roof which could be weakened during a fire and result in an increased chance of roof collapse. These panels can also impair vertical ventilation operations by obstructing part of the roof where ventilation holes must be cut. Additionally, these panels and the wiring leading to the building's electrical panel are energized as long as the panels are receiving sunlight. Obstacles to forcible entry operations include energy efficient windows, Lexan® reinforced drywall sheets and tornado and hurricane impact resistant windows, as well as building access and security systems.

Construction, Renovation, and Demolition Hazards

The risk of fire rises sharply for a number of reasons when construction, renovation, or demolition is being performed on a structure. Building contractors and their associated equipment can create contributing factors such as additional fire load and ignition sources (such as hotwork operations like open flames from welding torches and sparks from grinding or cutting processes). Unapproved flammable liquid storage also poses a serious hazard.

Buildings under construction or demolition are subject to rapid fire spread when they are partially completed because many of the protective features such as drywall are not yet in place (**Figure 6.32**). The exposed wood framing can be likened to a vertical lumberyard. The lack of doors or other measures that would normally slow fire spread are also contributing factors to rapid fire growth.

Buildings that are being renovated, demolished, or abandoned are also subject to faster-than-normal fire growth. Breached walls, open stairwells, missing doors, and disabled fire protection systems are all potential problems. The potential for a sudden building collapse during fire conditions is also a serious consideration. Arson is also a factor at construction or demolition sites because of easy access into the building.

Due to the rising costs of new construction, renovating old buildings is becoming more popular. Hazardous situations may arise during renovation construction because occupants and their belongings may remain in the building while construction continues. With the accumulation of debris, new construction materials, and equipment, exits can easily be blocked if good housekeeping is not maintained, preventing the egress of persons from the building in an emergency.

Chapter Summary

Whenever firefighters enter a burning structure, conduct an exterior fire attack, or provide exposure protection, factors of building construction directly affect their safety. Just as firefighters learn to "read" fires for signs of flashover or backdraft, they must also know how to "read" buildings for signs of dangerous conditions. At a minimum, firefighters should recognize the five types of building construction, know how building materials react to fire, be able to identify dangerous building conditions and the hazards of lightweight truss construction, and be aware of hazards during construction, renovation, and demolition.

Review Questions

1. How does the type of building construction affect fire suppression activities?

2. What classification is assigned to a building based on the type of materials used in construction?

3. Compare and contrast the differences in the various levels of building construction ratings.

4. Why is it important to understand the basic effects of fire on common building materials?

5. Name six commonly used building materials and describe the basic effect of fire on each of these materials.

6. How does a fire load in a building affect the spread of fire?

7. What are six basic dangerous building conditions a firefighter can face during fire suppression?

8. What difficulties can construction, renovation, and demolition sites present during a fire?

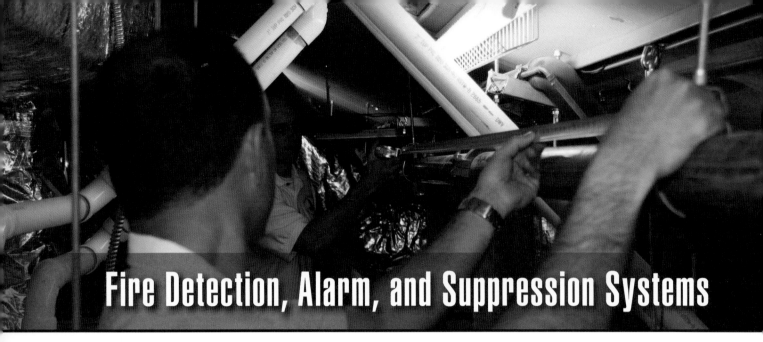

Fire Detection, Alarm, and Suppression Systems

Chapter Contents

Key Terms

FESHE Outcomes

This chapter provides information that addresses the outcomes for the Fire and Emergency Services Higher Education (FESHE) *Principles of Emergency Services* course.

10. Identify and explain the components of fire prevention including code enforcement, public information, and public and private fire protection systems.

NFPA® Job Performance Requirements

This chapter provides information that addresses the following job performance requirements (JPRs) of NFPA® 1001, *Standard for Fire Fighter Professional Qualifications* (2008).

5.3.14(A)

6.5.3(A)

Learning Objectives

After reading this chapter, students will be able to:

1. Identify common fire detection, alarm, and suppression systems.

2. Describe the impact of automatic sprinkler systems on fire prevention and safety.

3. Identify how various standpipe systems impact fire fighting operations.

Chapter 7
Fire Detection, Alarm, and Suppression Systems

Case History

Jeff O'Leary remembers when he decided to become a firefighter. He was seven the night the smoke alarm woke his family from a deep sleep. He was very scared while his parents hurried everybody outside and woke the neighbors so that they could use their phone to call 9-1-1. The fire captain said that the smoke alarm saved them that night, but Jeff thought the firefighters were the real heroes.

Before starting rookie academy, Jeff had no idea that there were so many kinds of detection, alarm, and suppression systems. He's fascinated at how the systems and the fire service work together to protect people – including firefighters – and property. Now when he goes into a building, Jeff usually looks up to check for detectors and sprinklers.

The first part of this chapter discusses the most common types of fire detection and alarm systems and devices in use in North America. The second part of the chapter describes automatic sprinkler systems. Firefighters should learn about and understand the different types of systems within their jurisdictions and become familiar with how these systems impact emergency response and fire suppression activities at various facilities.

Reasons for Installing Fire Detection, Alarm, and Suppression Systems

There are a number of reasons for installing fire detection, alarm, and suppression systems in residential buildings and other properties. In some jurisdictions, codes require such systems. Each of these systems is designed to fulfill specific needs. The following are recognized functions:

- To notify occupants of a facility to take necessary evasive action to escape the dangers of a hostile fire

- To summon organized assistance to initiate or to assist in fire control activities

- To initiate automatic fire control and **automatic suppression systems**

- To supervise fire control and suppression systems to ensure that operational status is maintained

- To initiate a wide variety of auxiliary functions involving environmental, utility, and process controls (including control of elevators)

Automatic Suppression Systems — Fire suppression systems that sense heat, smoke, or gas, and activate automatically. These include sprinkler, standpipe, carbon dioxide, and halogenated systems, as well as fire pumps, dry chemical agents and their systems, foam extinguishers, and combustible metal agents.

Individual fire detection, alarm, and suppression systems may incorporate one or all of these features. Such systems may include components that operate mechanically, hydraulically, pneumatically, or electrically, but most state-of-the-art systems operate electronically.

Despite advances in other forms of fixed fire suppression systems, **automatic sprinkler systems** remain the most reliable form of fire suppression for commercial, industrial, institutional, residential, and other occupancies. It is clear that many fires controlled by **sprinklers** result in less business interruption and less water damage than those that have to be extinguished by traditional fire-attack methods. In fact, some data indicates that about 70-90 percent of all fires in sprinklered buildings are controlled by the activation of five or fewer sprinklers.

Figure 7.1 An example of a manual pull station.

Types of Alarm Systems

The most basic alarm system is designed to only be initiated manually by pulling a handle **(Figure 7.1)**. While these systems are properly termed **protected premises fire alarm systems**, they are more commonly called *local alarm systems*. These systems are installed in some small school buildings and other public properties. In these systems, the signal only alerts building occupants of the need to evacuate the premises; it does *not* notify the fire department. Therefore, when a local alarm system is activated, it is still necessary for someone to dial 9-1-1 to alert the fire department.

There are five basic types of automatic alarm-initiating devices. They are designed to detect heat, carbon monoxide (CO), smoke, fire gases, or flame. The sections that follow describe the most common types of devices in use.

Heat Detectors

Heat detectors initiate alarms when the ambient tempearature near the detector reaches a predetermined level. While there are several different designs of heat detection devices, there are just two basic types: fixed-temperature devices and rate-of-rise detectors.

Fixed-Temperature Heat Detectors

Systems using **fixed-temperature heat detectors** are relatively inexpensive compared to other types of systems. They are also least prone to false activations. Depending on where they are installed, however, fixed-temperature heat detectors can also be the slowest to activate of all the various types of alarm-initiating devices.

Fixed-temperature heat detectors activate when they are heated to the temperature for which they are rated. If the **ambient temperature** in the room where they are installed is relatively low – below freezing, for example – a fire in the room would burn undetected until it raised the temperature of a heat detector to its rated activation temperature. Depending upon the size of the room, a fire could burn for quite some time before activating a fixed-temperature heat detector.

Fixed-Temperature Heat Detector — Temperature-sensitive device that senses temperature changes and sounds an alarm at a specific point, usually 135°F (57°C) or higher.

Ambient Temperature — Temperature of the surrounding environment.

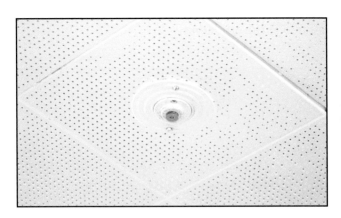

Figure 7.2 Heat detectors should have an activation temperature slightly above the normally expected ceiling temperature.

Because heat rises, heat detectors are installed in the highest portions of a room, usually on the ceiling **(Figure 7.2)**. The heat detectors installed should have an activation temperature rating slightly above the highest ceiling temperatures normally expected in that space. Heat detectors rated at 165°F (74°C) are common for living spaces. Attics and other areas subject to elevated temperatures and may have detectors rated at 200°F (93°C) or more.

The various types of fixed-temperature devices discussed in this section activate by one or more of three mechanisms:

- Expansion of heated material

- Melting of heated material

- Changes in electrical resistance of heated material

Rate-of-Rise Heat Detectors

A **rate-of-rise heat detector** operates on the assumption that the temperature in a room will increase faster from a fire than from normal atmospheric heating. Typically, rate-of-rise heat detectors are designed to initiate a signal when the rise in temperature exceeds 12 to 15°F (7 to 8°C) in one minute. Because a sudden rise in temperature intiates the alarm regardless of the initial temperature, an alarm can be initiated at a room temperature far below what is required for initiating a fixed-temperature device.

Most rate-of-rise heat detectors are reliable and not subject to false activations. If they are not properly installed, however, they can be activated under nonfire conditions. For example, if a rate-of-rise heat detector is installed just

Rate-of-Rise Heat Detector — Temperature-sensitive device that sounds an alarm when the temperature rises at a preset value, such as 12-15°F (7 to 8°C) increase per minute.

inside an exterior door in an air-conditioned building, opening the door on a hot day can initiate an alarm because of the influx of heated air. Relocating the detector farther from the doorway should alleviate the problem.

There are several different types of rate-of-rise heat detectors in use; all automatically reset if they are undamaged. The different types of rate-of-rise heat detectors include:

- Pneumatic rate-of-rise spot detector, which monitors a small area surrounding it

- Pneumatic rate-of-rise line detector, which can monitor large areas

- Rate-compensated detector for use in areas normally subject to regular temperature changes which are slower than those under fire conditions

- Thermoelectric detector, which operates on the principle that when two wires of dissimilar metals are twisted together and heated at one end, an electrical current is generated at the other end

Figure 7.3 An example of a smoke detector in an industrial facility.

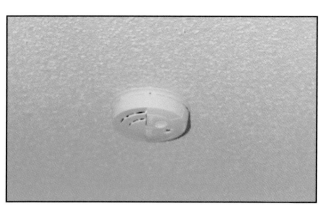

Figure 7.4 An example of a residential smoke alarm.

Smoke Detectors and Smoke Alarms

Smoke Detector — Alarm-initiating device designed to actuate when visible or invisible products of combustion (other than fire gases) are present in the room or space where the unit is installed.

Smoke Alarm — Device designed to sound an alarm when the products of combustion are present in the room where the device is installed. The alarm is built into the device rather than being a separate system.

Before discussing the various types of smoke detectors, a distinction must be made between devices that merely detect the presence of smoke or other products of combustion and those that both detect and sound an alarm. In most cases, the devices installed in nonresidential and large multifamily residential occupancies are only capable of detecting the presence of smoke and must transmit a signal to another device that sounds the alarm. These units are called **smoke detectors (Figure 7.3)**. The devices that are installed in single-family residences and smaller multifamily residential occupancies are self-contained units capable of both detecting the presence of smoke and sounding an alarm. These units are called **smoke alarms (Figure 7.4)**. The sections that follow describe a variety of smoke detectors and alarms.

Photoelectric Smoke Detectors

A **photoelectric smoke detector**, sometimes called a *visible products-of-combustion detector*, uses a photoelectric cell coupled with a tiny light source. The photoelectric cell functions in two ways to detect smoke: beam application and refractory application.

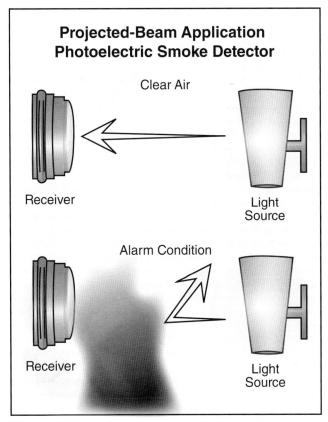

Projected-Beam Application Photoelectric Smoke Detector

Clear Air

Receiver

Light Source

Alarm Condition

Receiver

Light Source

Refractory Application Photoelectric Smoke Detector

Housing

Photo Cell

Reflected Light

Light Rays

Lamp

Baffles

Openings

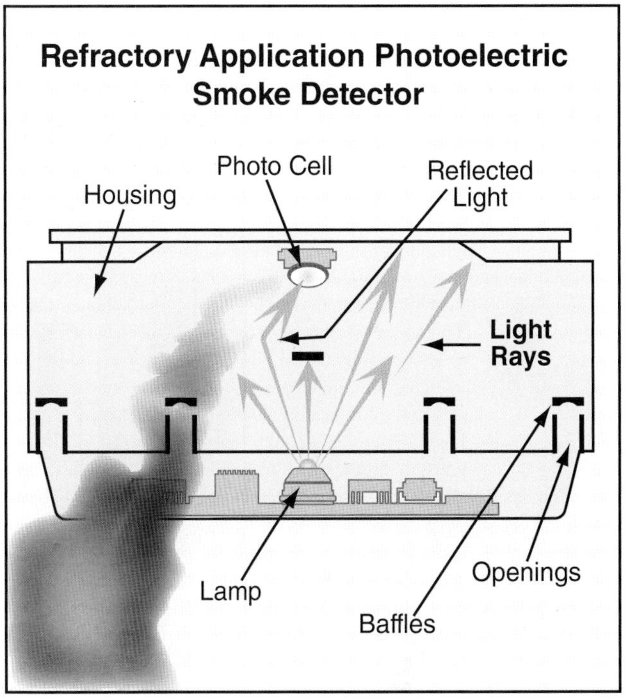

Figure 7.6 When smoke causes the light beam in a refractory application photoelectric smoke detector to scatter, light reflects onto the photosensitive device and an alarm sounds.

Figure 7.5 The projected-beam application photoelectric smoke detector is activated when smoke enters the light beam.

The *beam application* type of smoke detector uses a beam of light that focuses across the area being monitored and onto a photoelectric cell. The cell constantly converts the beam into electrical current, which keeps a switch open. When smoke obscures the path of the light beam, the required amount of current is no longer produced, the switch closes, and an alarm signal is initiated **(Figure 7.5)**. A photoelectric smoke alarm works satisfactorily on all types of fires and automatically resets when the atmosphere is clear. Photoelectric smoke alarms are generally more sensitive to smoldering fires than are ionization alarms.

The *refractory application photocell* uses a light beam that passes through a small chamber at a point away from the light source. Normally, the light does not strike the photocell and no current is produced allowing the switch to remain open. When smoke enters the chamber, it causes the light beam to be refracted (scattered) in all directions. A portion of the scattered light strikes the photocell, causing current to flow. This current causes the switch to close and transmits the alarm-initiation signal **(Figure 7.6)**.

Ionization Smoke Alarms

During combustion, minute particles and aerosols too small for the naked eye to see are produced. **Ionization smoke alarms** use a tiny amount of radioactive material (usually americium) to ionize air molecules as they enter a chamber within the detector and detect these invisible products of combustion. These ionized particles allow an electrical current to flow between negative and

Photoelectric Smoke Detector — Type of smoke detector that uses a small light source, either an incandescent bulb or a light-emitting diode (LED), to detect smoke by shining light through the detector's chamber. Smoke particles reflect the light into a light-sensitive device called a photocell.

Ionization Smoke Alarm — Type of smoke detector that uses a small amount of radioactive material to ionize air particles as they enter a sensing chamber; the ionized air particles then combine with products of combustion that enter the chamber, reducing the number of ionized particles. When the number of ionized particles falls below a given threshold, an alarm is initiated.

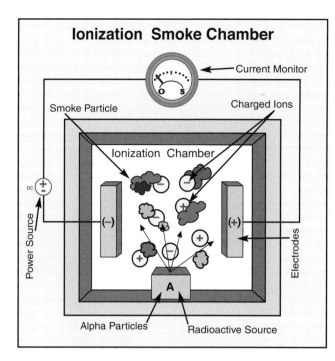

Ionization Smoke Chamber

Current Monitor

Smoke Particle

Charged Ions

Ionization Chamber

Power Source

(−)

(+)

Electrodes

Alpha Particles

Radioactive Source

Figure 7.7 In an ionization detector, the alarm sounds when products of combustion reduce the normal current between the charged plates. This type of detector usually responds best to flaming fires.

positive plates within the chamber. When the particulate products of combustion (smoke) enter the chamber, they attach themselves to electrically charged molecules of air (ions), making the air within the chamber less conductive. The decrease in current flowing between the plates transmits an alarm-initiating signal **(Figure 7.7)**. Ionization detectors respond satisfactorily to most fires but these types of detectors generally respond faster to flaming fires than to smoldering ones. They automatically reset when the atmosphere has cleared.

Flame Detector — Detection and alarm devices used in some fire detection systems, generally in high-hazard areas that detect light/ flames in the ultraviolet wave spectrum (UV detectors) or detect light in the infrared wave spectrum (IR detectors). *Also known as* Light Detector.

Smoke Alarm Legislation

Firefighters should be aware of any state/province or local laws that deal with smoke alarms. Such legislation, in addition to specifying minimum installation requirements for given occupancies (including homes), may designate the power source (battery or hard-wired) to be used.

Other Detectors

Other types of detectors of interest to the entry-level firefighter include **flame detectors**, combination detectors, carbon monoxide detectors, and indicating devices. Basic information on these types of detectors is presented below.

There are three basic types of flame detectors (sometimes called *light detectors*):

1. Those that detect light in the ultraviolet wave spectrum (UV detectors)

2. Those that detect light in the infrared wave spectrum (IR detectors)

3. Those that detect both types of light **(Figure 7.8)**

While these types of detectors are among the most sensitive used to detect fires, nonfire conditions such as welding, sunlight, and other sources of bright light may activate the detectors as well. To combat this problem, flame detectors are usually positioned in areas where these other light sources are unlikely.

Figure 7.8 An example of a combination ultraviolet (UV) and infrared (IR) detector.

Depending on the design of the system, various combinations of the previously described means of detection may be used in a single device called a **combination detector**. These combinations include fixed temperature/rate-of-rise heat detectors, combination heat/smoke detectors, and combination smoke/fire-gas detectors. The different combinations make these detectors more versatile and more responsive to fire conditions.

Carbon monoxide (CO) detectors, while not fire detectors, are often the subject of fire department response **(Figure 7.9)**. In addition, some CO detectors are combined with smoke detectors into a single unit.

CO detectors detect the colorless, odorless, dangerous gas (both toxic and combustible) formed by the incomplete combustion of carbon. Sources of incomplete combustion include poorly designed or maintained heating systems (furnaces, boilers, chimneys and vents, and swimming pool heaters), generators or grills used indoors, and idling automobiles.

Increasingly, jurisdictions are requiring the installation of CO detectors, along with smoke alarms, in residential occupancies. When a CO detector alerts, residents typically contact the emergency services. Individual fire departments have their own policies and procedures for responding to a CO signal. Response to a CO alert usually includes evacuating residents, opening doors and windows, and contacting utility company personnel.

> ## CAUTION
> Always follow the department's established procedures for responding to a carbon monoxide alert, including the use of SCBA.

Figure 7.9 An example of a carbon monoxide (CO) detector.

A variety of audible and visible alarm-indicating devices are also in use. Some produce a loud signal to attract attention in high-noise areas; some generate an electronic tone that can be heard in almost any type of environment. Some systems employ bells, horns, or chimes; others use speakers that broadcast prerecorded evacuation instructions **(Figures 7.10 a-c, p. 236)**. To accommodate special circumstances or populations, such as those who must wear hearing protection because of very high noise levels in their work areas or people with hearing impairments, visual alarm indicators that employ a high-intensity clear strobe may be used.

Tamper-proof Smoke Alarms
Some municipalities are starting to require smoke alarms that have a tamper-proof, non-removable battery. This type of alarm presumably prevents occupants from removing the battery during a false alarm or when the television remote needs a new battery.

Figure 7.10a A fire alarm bell.

Figure 7.10b A fire alarm speaker.

Figure 7.10c A combination fire alarm speaker and strobe light unit.

Automatic Alarm Systems

Under some circumstances, insurance carriers may require occupancies to have a system that will transmit a signal to an off-site location for the purpose of summoning organized assistance in fighting a fire. This signal produces an automatic response upon activation of the local alarm at the protected premises. Various brands of alarm systems do this signaling with dedicated wire pairs, leased telephone lines, fiberoptic cable, or wireless communication links. Types of **automatic alarm** systems include auxiliary systems, remote receiving station systems, proprietary systems, and central station systems, as described below.

Auxiliary alarm systems connect the protected property with the fire department alarm communications center using a municipal master fire alarm box or over a dedicated telephone line. *Remote receiving station systems* are similar to auxiliary systems but are connected to the fire department telecommunication center directly or through an answering service using some means other than the municipal fire alarm box system (such as through a leased telephone line or, where permitted, by a radio signal on a dedicated frequency).

Proprietary systems are complex fire protection systems that the property owner both owns and operates. These systems are used to protect large commercial and industrial buildings, high-rise buildings, and groups of commonly owned buildings in a single location such as a college campus or industrial complex **(Figure 7.11)**. Each building or area has its own system that is wired into a common receiving point somewhere on the facility. Trained representatives constantly staff the receiving station.

Central station systems are very similar to proprietary systems. The primary difference is that instead of having the occupant's reprsentative monitor the alarm-receiving point on the protected premises, the receiving point is at an off-site, contracted service point called a *central station* **(Figure 7.12)**. Typically, the central station is an alarm company that contracts with individual customers. When an alarm is initiated at a contracting occupancy, central station employees initiate an emergency response, which usually includes calling the fire department and representatives of the protected occupancy.

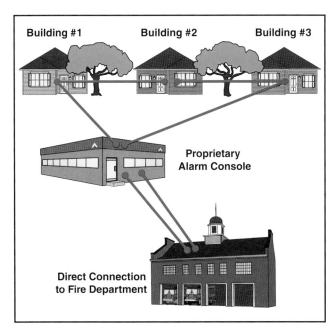

Figure 7.11 A proprietary system is used to protect commonly owned buildings that are close together.

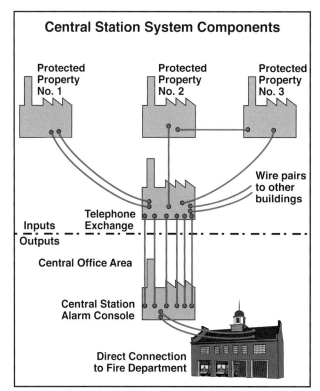

Figure 7.12 In a central station system, the receiving point for the alarm is located at an outside, contracted service point.

Auxiliary Services

Contemporary emergency signaling systems that integrate process and environmental controls, security, and personnel-access controls are now common. Examples of auxiliary services include shutting down or altering airflow in heating, ventilating, and air-conditioning (HVAC) systems for smoke control, closing smoke or fire-rated doors and dampers, facilitating evacuation by increasing air pressure in stairwells to exclude smoke, controlling elevators, and controlling personnel access to hazardous process or storage areas.

Other Alert Systems

In recent years, several subscription alert systems have been developed and widely marketed. Such systems respond to a trouble signal and contact the subscriber to verify the problem and then contact an emergency service telecommunication (dispatch) center. Other alert systems include the OnStar® system for General Motors vehicles and the Life Alert® wearable pendant.

Automatic Sprinkler Systems

Automatic sprinkler protection consists of a series of sprinklers (also called *sprinkler heads*) arranged so that the system will automatically distribute sufficient quantities of water directly onto a fire. Their purpose is to either extinguish or control the fire until firefighters arrive **(Figure 7.13, p. 238)**. Water is supplied to the sprinklers through a system of piping. The sprinklers can extend from exposed pipes or protrude through the ceiling or walls from hidden pipes.

Figure 7.13 A sprinkler system is designed to extinguish a fire or to keep it under control until firefighters can arrive.

Early Sprinkler Systems

The first sprinkler system probably dates to one installed in a London theater in 1812. During the Industrial Revolution in the United States, various forms of sprinkler systems protected mills and factories in New England. Eventually, due to incidents involving a large loss of life, automatic sprinklers began to be required in North America in public occupancies, such as hotels and hospitals. Over time, sprinkler systems have become required in almost all types of occupancies. Gradually, codes also are mandating the installation of automatic sprinkler systems in all types of residences, including single-family homes.

There are two general types of sprinkler coverage: complete sprinkler coverage and partial sprinkler coverage. A *complete sprinkler system* protects the entire building. A *partial sprinkler system* protects only certain areas such as high-hazard areas, exit routes, or places designated by code or by the authority having jurisdiction (AHJ).

In order to assure system reliability, a nationally recognized testing laboratory such as Underwriters' Laboratories Inc. (UL), Underwriters' Laboratories of Canada (ULC), or FM Global (formerly Factory Mutual) should list the automatic sprinkler and all component parts of the system. Automatic sprinkler systems are recognized as the most reliable of all fire protection devices, and it is essential for the firefighter to understand the basic system and the operation of pipes and valves. The various applications of sprinkler systems should also be understood by firefighters along with sprinkler system effects on life safety.

Sprinkler Systems and Their Effects on Life Safety

The life safety of building occupants is enhanced by the presence of a sprinkler system because it discharges water directly on a fire while it is relatively small. Because the fire is extinguished or controlled in the early growth stage, combustion products are limited. Sprinklers are also effective in the following situations:

- Preventing fire spread upwards in multiple-story buildings
- Protecting the lives of occupants in other parts of the building
- Protecting the means of egress

Sprinklers

Sprinklers discharge water after the release of a cap or plug that is activated by some heat-responsive element **(Figure 7.14, p. 240)**. This sprinkler may be thought of as a fixed-spray nozzle that is operated individually by a thermal detector. There are numerous types and designs of sprinklers. An exterior connection (called a fire department connection) is used to pump water into the sprinkler system with the fire department pumper. The pumper supplements the system with additional pressure and water supply for effective sprinkler system operations.

The temperature at which a sprinkler is designed to operate is how sprinklers are commonly identified. Color-coding the sprinkler frame arms, using different colored liquid in bulb-type sprinklers, or stamping the temperature into the sprinkler itself **(see Table 7.1, p. 240)** are ways for identifying the sprinkler's designated temperature. Three of the most commonly used release mechanisms to activate sprinklers are fusible links, frangible bulbs, and chemical pellets. All of these sprinkler mechanisms fuse (melt) or open in response to heat **(Figures 7.15 a through c, p. 241)**.

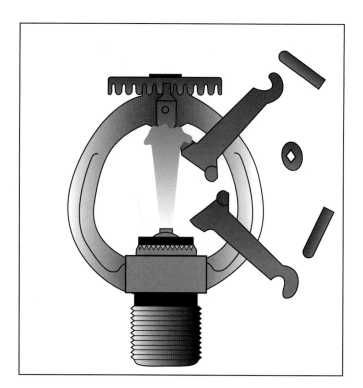

Figure 7.14 Sprinklers discharge water after the release of a cap or plug that is activated by a heat-response element.

	Table 7.1				
Sprinkler Temperature Ratings, Classifications, and Color Codings					

Max. Ceiling Temp.		Temperature Rating		Temperature Classification	Color Code	Glass Bulb Colors
°F	°C	°F	°C			
100	38	135 to 170	57 to 77	Ordinary	Uncolored or black	Orange or red
150	66	175 to 225	79 to 107	Intermediate	White	Yellow or green
225	107	250 to 300	121 to 149	High	Blue	Blue
300	149	325 to 375	163 to 191	Extra high	Red	Purple
375	191	400 to 475	204 to 246	Very extra high	Green	Black
475	246	500 to 575	260 to 302	Ultra high	Orange	Black
625	329	650	343	Ultra high	Orange	Black

Sprinkler Position

There are three basic positions for sprinklers: pendant, upright, and sidewall. Sprinklers designed for one type of application cannot be interchanged with those designed for another type because they are not designed to provide the proper spray pattern and coverage in a different position. There are also various special-purpose sprinklers used in other applications.

Control Valves

Every sprinkler system is equipped with a main water control valve. *Control valves* are used to turn off the water supply to the system in order to replace sprinklers, perform maintenance, or interrupt operations. These valves are located between the source of the water supply and the sprinkler system (**Figure 7.16, p. 242**). The control valve is usually located immediately under the sprinkler alarm valve, the dry-pipe or deluge valve (see Dry-Pipe System and Deluge System sections in this chapter), or outside the building near the sprinkler system that it controls. The main control valve should always be returned to the open position after maintenance is complete. The valves should be secured in the open position or supervised to ensure that they are not inadvertently closed.

Figures 7.15 a, b, and c All of these sprinklers activate in response to heat: **(a)** fusible link sprinkler, **(b)** frangible bulb sprinkler, and **(c)** chemical pellet sprinkler

Main water control valves are indicating and manually operated. An *indicating control valve* is one that shows at a glance whether it is open or closed. There are four common types of indicator control valves used in sprinkler systems: outside stem and yoke (OS&Y), post indicator, wall post indicator (WPIV), and post indicator valve (PIV) assembly (PIVA). Details are as follows:

- *Outside stem and yoke (OS&Y) valve* — Has a yoke on the outside with a threaded stem that controls the opening and closing of the gate. The threaded portion of the stem is out of the yoke when the valve is open and inside the yoke when the valve is closed (**Figure 7.17 p. 242**).

- *Post indicator valve (PIV)* — Hollow metal post that is attached to the valve housing. The valve stem is inside this post, and a movable target is located on the stem with the words *OPEN* and *SHUT* at the opening (**Figure 7.18 p. 242**).

- *Wall post indicator valve (WPIV)* — Similar to a PIV except that it extends through the wall with the target and valve operating nut on the outside of the building (**Figure 7.19 p. 242**).

- *Post indicator valve assembly (PIVA)* — Does not use a target with words *OPEN* and *SHUT*, but has a sight area that is open when the valve is open and closed when the valve is closed (**Figure 7.20 p. 243**).

Waterflow Alarms

When waterflows through the sprinkler system, **waterflow alarms** operate. Sprinkler waterflow alarms are normally operated either hydraulically or electrically. The hydraulic alarm is a local alarm used to alert the personnel in a sprinklered building or a passerby that water is flowing in the system (**Figure 7.21 p. 243**).

Waterflow Alarm — Alarm-initiating device actuated by the movement (flow) of water within a pipe or chamber; most common installation is in the main water supply pipe of a sprinkler system. *Also known as* Waterflow Detector and Sprinkler System Supervision System.

Figure 7.16 Sprinkler system control valves are located between the source of the water supply and the sprinkler system.

Figure 7.17 The outside stem and yoke valve (OS&Y) is a type of indicating valve.

Figure 7.18 On a post indicator valve (PIV), the words OPEN and SHUT indicate the position of the valve.

Figure 7.19 A wall post indicator valve (WPIV) extends through the wall with the target and valve operating nut on the outside of the building.

NOTE: These waterflow alarms are sometimes referred to as a water motor gong, because of their distinctive sound. This type of alarm uses the water in the system to branch off to a water motor that drives a local alarm gong. The electric waterflow alarm is also employed to alert building occupants. The alarm can also be set up to notify the fire department.

Applications of Sprinkler Systems

The following sections highlight the major applications of sprinkler systems. Firefighters should have a basic understanding of the operation of each type of system:

- Wet-pipe
- Dry-pipe
- Preaction
- Deluge
- Residential

Wet-Pipe System

A **wet-pipe sprinkler system** is used in locations that will not be subjected to temperatures below 40°F (4°C). It is the simplest type of automatic fire sprinkler system and generally requires little maintenance. This system contains water under pressure at all times and is connected to the public or private water supply. When a sprinkler head is activated (opens), water is discharged and an alarm is actuated.

Figure 7.20 The post indicator valve assembly PIVA has a sight area that is open when the valve is open and closed when the valve is closed.

Wet-Pipe Sprinkler System — Fire-suppression system that is built into a structure or site. The system's piping contains either water or foam solution continuously; activation of a sprinkler causes the extinguishing agent to flow from the open sprinkler.

Water Motor Gong

Test Drain

Figure 7.21 Waterflow alarms alert building occupants that water is flowing in the sprinkler system. In this picture, the alarm at the top is ringing while the system is tested.

Dry-Pipe System

A **dry-pipe sprinkler system** is used in locations where the piping may be subjected to temperatures below 40°F (4°C). All pipes in dry-pipe systems are pitched to help drain the water in the system back toward the main drain. In this system, air under pressure replaces water in the sprinkler piping above the *dry-pipe valve* (device that keeps water out of the sprinkler piping until a fire actuates a sprinkler). When a sprinkler fuses, the pressurized air escapes first, and then the dry-pipe valve automatically opens to permit water into the piping system (**Figures 7.22 a and b**).

Preaction System

A **preaction sprinkler system** is a dry system that employs a deluge-type valve (see the next section), fire detection devices, and closed sprinklers. This type of system is used when it is especially important to prevent water damage, even if pipes are broken. The system will not discharge water into the sprinkler piping except in response to either smoke- or heat-detection system actuation. A preaction system is essentially a closed head deluge system

Deluge System

A **deluge sprinkler system** discharges water from all sprinklers in a designated area where a fire has activated the system. Along with open sprinklers, this system is ordinarily equipped with a deluge valve. When the deluge valve is activated, water is discharged from every open sprinkler that is connected to the system controlled by that specific deluge valve. A deluge is usually used to protect extra-hazardous occupancies. Many aircraft hangars are equipped with an automatic deluge system.

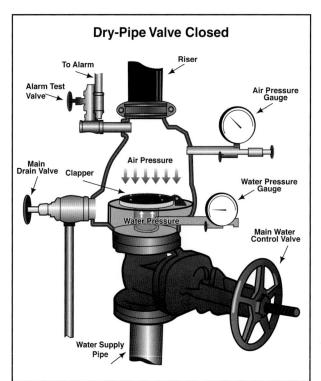

Figure 7.22a A dry-pipe system is pressurized with air to prevent water from filling the system piping until it is needed.

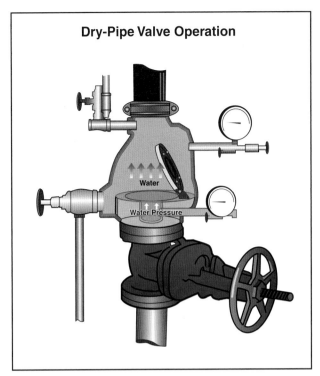

Dry-Pipe Valve Operation

Water

Water Pressure

Figure 7.22b Once a sprinkler is opened, the air escapes from the piping, the valve opens, water enters the piping, and water is sprayed from the open sprinkler.

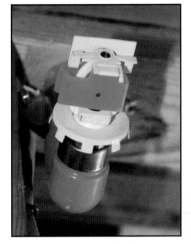

Figure 7.23 A residential sprinkler during construction of a house.

Residential Systems

Residential sprinkler systems are installed in one- and two-family dwellings (**Figure 7.23**). This type of sprinkler system is designed to prevent total fire involvement in the room of origin and to give occupants of the dwelling a chance to escape. These systems are covered by NFPA® 13D, *Standard for the Installation of Sprinkler Systems in One-and Two-family dwellings and Manufactured Homes*, and may be either wet- or dry-pipe systems.

Standpipe Systems

The third type of fire detection and suppression systems is a standpipe system. A **standpipe system** is a wet or dry system of pipes used in large single-story or multistory buildings to provide a water supply for firefighting. An exterior connection (called a **fire department connection [FDC]**) is used to pump water into the standpipe system, while hose connections are located within the building. These hose connections are located within the interior of a building in a hose station, hose cabinet, or in the stairwell and sometimes on the roof. To simplify, water is pumped into a fire department connection, and is discharged through a hose connection.

A standpipe system can be a very simple system consisting of only a vertical pipe (called a riser) with hose connections and a fire department connection (**Figure 7.24, p. 246**). A standpipe can also be a very complex building system consisting of multiple pumps and risers, valves, and reservoirs located on the upper floors. Standpipes can be designed to supply small-diameter hose for use by building occupants, to supply fire department hose, or both.

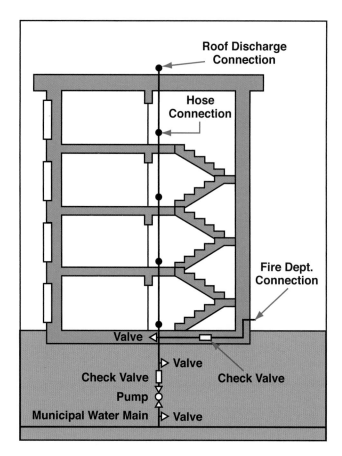

Roof Discharge
Connection

Hose
Connection

Fire Dept.
Connection

Valve

Valve

Check Valve

Check Valve

Pump

Municipal Water Main   Valve

Figure 7.24 A standpipe system is designed to enable building occupants or firefighters to put water on a fire from different levels in a building.

CAUTION

Although standpipe systems are a necessity in high-rise buildings, they neither take the place of nor lessen the need for automatic sprinkler systems. Automatic sprinklers are still the most effective method of fire control in high-rise or other hazardous occupancies.

Classes of Standpipe Systems

NFPA® 14, *Standard for the Installation of Standpipes and Hose Systems* is frequently used for the design and installation of standpipes. The standard recognizes three classes of standpipe systems: Class I, Class II, and Class III.

Class I Standpipe Systems

Fire fighting personnel trained in handling large handlines (2½-inch [64 mm] hose) are the primary users of Class I standpipe systems. Class I systems must be capable of supplying effective fire streams during the more advanced stages of fire within a building or for fighting a fire in an adjacent building. Class I systems have 2½-inch (64 mm) hose connections or hose stations attached to the standpipe riser (**Figure 7.25**).

Figure 7.26 Class II standpipe systems are designed for use by building occupants.

Figure 7.25 Class I standpipe systems are designed to be used by firefighters to supply water for large hoselines.

Class II Standpipe Systems

Building occupants who have no specialized fire training are the intended users of Class II standpipe systems. These systems are limited to 1½-inch (38 mm) hose (**Figure 7.26**). This hose is typically the single-jacket variety and is equipped with a lightweight, twist-type shutoff nozzle. Sometimes it is referred to as a *house line*. Firefighters should follow their department's standard operating procedures (SOPs) when operating standpipes. The Class II system is less prevalent now than in the past, but firefighters can still encounter them.

Class III Standpipe Systems

Class III standpipes combine the features of Class I and Class II systems. Class III systems have both 2½-inch (64 mm) connections for fire department personnel and 1½-inch (38 mm) hose stations and connections for use by the building occupants (**Figure 7.27**). The design of the system must allow both the Class I and Class II services to be used simultaneously.

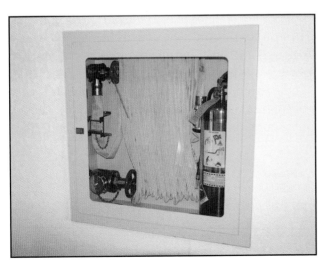

Figure 7.27 Class III systems have connections for both small and large hoselines.

Types of Standpipe Systems

In addition to the classes of standpipes, the two basic types of standpipe systems are as follows:

1. A wet standpipe system is maintained wet at all times. The water supply is capable of supplying the system demand automatically. When a hose valve is opened, water is immediately available.

2. A dry standpipe system does not have a permanent water supply and is supplied only through a fire department connection.

A wet standpipe with an automatic water supply is the most desirable type of standpipe. With this type of system, water is constantly available at the hose station. Wet standpipe systems cannot be used in cold environments; a dry system may have to be used in these situations. Automatic wet systems have the disadvantages of greater cost and maintenance requirements. The main advantage of a dry standpipe with no permanent water supply is the reduction in cost.

Pressure-Regulating Devices

When the discharge pressure at a hose outlet exceeds 100 psi (689 kPa), the use of a pressure-regulating device prevents pressures that make hose difficult or dangerous to handle.

There are several different types of pressure-regulating devices. One type consists of a simple restricting orifice inserted in the waterway. Another type of pressure-regulating device may consist of vanes in the waterway that can be rotated to change the cross-sectional area through which the waterflows. A pressure-regulating device may also take the form of a pressure-reducing valve.

A pressure-regulating device should be specified and/or adjusted to meet the pressure and flow requirements of the individual installation. If a pressure-regulating device is not properly installed or is not properly adjusted for the required inlet pressure, outlet pressure, and flow, the available flow may be greatly reduced and fire fighting capabilities seriously impaired.

Chapter Summary

Fire detection, alarm, and suppression systems play a vital part in recognizing the early signs of a fire and in summoning aid. The alarms initiated by these systems are vital for quick evacuation of building occupants. The presence of fixed detection systems not only saves lives, but damage to property can also be limited if trained help can be summoned as quickly as possible. It is very important that firefighters be familiar with the basic operation of the various types of detection, alarm, and suppression systems used in their communities.

Review Questions

1. What are the three basic types of alarm systems?

2. Compare and contrast the differences between a smoke detector and a smoke alarm.

3. How is a photoelectric smoke detector different from an ionization smoke alarm?

4. Describe the three basic types of flame detectors that are sometimes known as light detectors.

5. How are the four types of automatic alarm systems different when notifying in the event of a fire?

6. What are the three most commonly used release mechanisms that activate sprinklers and what do these open in response to?

7. Why can sprinklers designed for one basic position not be interchanged for another?

8. What are the four types of indicating control valves used in sprinkler systems?

9. What are the five main types of sprinkler system applications?

10. Explain the different classifications for each of the three classes of standpipe systems.

Roles of Public and Private Support Organizations

Chapter Contents

Key Terms

FESHE Outcomes

This chapter provides information that addresses the outcomes for the Fire and Emergency Services Higher Education (FESHE) *Principles of Emergency Services* course.

6. Define the role of national, state, and local support organizations in fire and emergency services.

NFPA® Job Performance Requirements

This chapter provides information that addresses the following job performance requirements (JPRs) of NFPA® 1001, *Standard for Fire Fighter Professional Qualifications* (2008).

5.1.1

Roles of Public and Private Support Organizations

Learning Objectives

After reading this chapter, students will be able to:

1. Describe the various agencies and organizations that make up the fire and emergency services field locally.

2. Identify the various agencies and organizations that make up the fire and emergency services field on the state level.

3. Recognize the various federal fire and emergency services organizations in the United States and Canada.

4. Identify trade, professional, and membership organizations in the United States and Canada.

Chapter 8
Roles of Public and Private Support Organizations

Case History

Preparing to follow in his Grandpa Jack's footsteps, Jed Andrews conducted extensive research into the Fire Service. After searching the Internet, he sat down to talk with his grandfather. Grandpa Jack explained that a wide variety of organizations and agencies at the local, state, and federal levels are related to the Fire Service. For example, the fire commissions of different states and provinces in North America establish entry level firefighter training requirements. Most often these requirements are adopted from standards developed by the National Fire Protection Association® such as NFPA® 1001, *Standard for Fire Fighter Professional Qualifications*. Modern firefighters, Jed's grandfather explained, can get certified to different levels of qualification by agencies accredited by the National Board on Fire Service Professional Qualifications (Pro Board), the International Fire Service Accreditation Congress (IFSAC), or the Center for Public Safety Excellence.

Grandpa Jack told Jed how fire departments and firefighters closely work with other local agencies such as law enforcement, building departments, planning and zoning commissions, water departments, and many other departments to protect the citizens of the community. He also told Jed about the roles of state level agencies such as the fire training academy, the fire marshal's office, state police, environmental protection agency, and office of emergency management.

Jed asked his grandfather, "How do federal organizations such as the Department of Homeland Security, Federal Emergency Management Agency, United States Fire Administration, and the National Fire Academy support local fire departments?" Grandpa Jack explained the role of each organization and the roles of many others, including professional organizations such as the International Association of Fire Fighters, the International Association of Fire Chiefs, the International Fire Service Training Association, Underwriters Laboratories, and numerous others.

Figures 8.1 a and b
Both city and county organizations may have authority over the fire department and the delivery of emergency services.

During the course of his or her career, a firefighter will be affected by, and exposed to, many different organizations that are a part of, or related to, the fire service. The purpose of this chapter is to acquaint the reader with local, state, federal agencies, and trade and professional organizations.

Local Agencies and Organizations

Much of a firefighter's interaction with outside agencies will be at the local level. Local agencies and nongovernmental organizations such as civic groups and businesses will be familiar because firefighters will have day-to-day interactions with them. In this section, some of these groups will be reviewed to provide firefighters an overview of their functions.

Local Government

Local government at the town, village, borough, township, city, parish, or county level consists of elected officials responsible for enacting legislation to govern the people under their jurisdiction **(Figures 8.1 a and b)**. These officials may also establish the fire department if it is within their power. Depending on the local structure, the governing body may have control over hiring practices and other matters involving the fire department.

Local government may also finance the fire department. Funds come from taxes and are budgeted to various departments, including the fire department. The chief, who is ultimately responsible for fire department finances, must have a good working relationship with local government so that the fire department can get its fair share of financing. Some municipalities are divided further into geographical fire "districts" where taxpayers pay a "fire tax" or fee to that district in addition to local taxes.

Districts

The term "district" is used differently in different areas. In some areas, a district may include several villages, townships, other municipalities, or unincorporated areas. In those cases, each municipality may contribute tax monies to the budget of the district or the district may be entirely volunteer.

Figure 8.2 Fire departments depend on law enforcement personnel to help keep the emergency scene under control.

Local Law Enforcement

Because fire and law enforcement personnel share the goal of protecting the public, the two must work together successfully. The fire department depends on local police for such things as traffic control, crowd control, and personal protection during civil unrest **(Figure 8.2)**. Cooperation between the two agencies will undoubtedly make their job easier to accomplish. Law enforcement officers often arrive on the scene of an emergency prior to fire department personnel. In some parts of the world, they can provide medical or rescue assistance prior to the arrival of fire department units.

Building Department (Code Enforcement)

The local **building department** is responsible for enforcing various codes and regulations that the local government adopts. The department may review and approve plans for new buildings and renovation before construction begins **(Figure 8.3, p. 256)**. The department may inspect structures and facilities for compliance with its own standards as well as fire prevention codes. An effective building department program is an asset to the local fire department. It provides a medium through which the fire department can get fire prevention code requirements integrated into local construction. Involving the building department provides safer structures and reduces injuries and damage from fire. It is extremely important for the fire department fire prevention staff and building officials to have an excellent working relationship.

Building Department — Local governmental agency responsible for enforcing various codes and regulations.

Figure 8.3 A plans examiner reviewing construction documents to ensure compliance with local building codes.

Water Department/Water Authority

Water for fire protection can come from a **water department**, water authority, private company, natural sources, or even swimming pools. The quality of the water supply system often means the difference between a successful extinguishment and a total loss. Therefore, the water department must provide enough water at proper pressure to satisfy the fire protection needs of a community. The fire department must work with the water department to determine such things as water main size and location, fire flow determination, hydrant locations, and pumping and storage capacity. The fire department must also be notified when parts of the system are closed so that firefighters can arrange for alternate water supplies.

Zoning Commission/Planning Commission

The **zoning commission** and planning commission, whether one agency or two, are responsible for planning community growth. Among other activities, these commissions determine the divisions between residential and commercial districts, allowed density of structures, and layout of city streets. In the simplest terms, the zoning commission determines what type of occupancies may be located in an area, and the planning commission determines how these occupancies shall be developed. These activities are important because the fire protection needs of residential and commercial districts may be different. The difference dictates where the fire department locates fire stations and places apparatus.

Department of Public Works

The department of public works (or street department) is responsible for building and maintaining public throughways. The fire department must know when roads will be closed so that it can establish alternate routes. The fire department may want to help design roadways and bridges to make sure that they are accessible for large apparatus. In some cities, the street department also provides equipment, such as automatic traffic signal changers, that allow firefighters on the apparatus to change signal lights from red to green **(Figure 8.4)**. As with state highway departments, the local street department may also be able to provide equipment and services to abate hazardous materials or

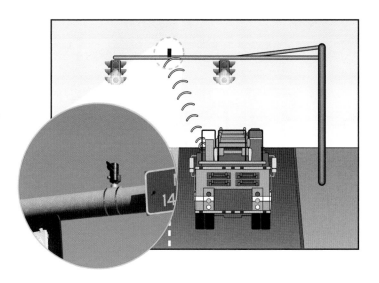

Figure 8.4 The Opticom™ emitter on the apparatus sends a signal to the detector on the traffic light support, which converts the optical signal to an electronic impulse. The system processes the signal then manipulates the controller to provide a green signal for the emergency vehicle(s) and red signals in all other directions.

other emergencies. Many of these systems are available through Geographical Information Systems (GIS) and can be incorporated into automated dispatching through Computer Aided Dispatch (CAD).

Utilities

Uncontrolled **utilities** at structure fires and other emergency incidents can result in fatalities, injuries, and property damage. To prevent or reduce these traumatic injuries and excessive property losses, utility services must be controlled in a safe and timely manner. Flammable gases, electrical systems, downed electrical power lines, and leaking water are some of the major utility hazards that fire departments face on a regular basis. While the fire department can control some utilities, other situations require the assistance of trained technicians or public or private utility service personnel. It is critical that fire departments work with these departments to reduce hazards, injuries, and damage.

Utilities — Services such as gas, electricity, and water that are provided to the public.

Telephone and Cable Utility Lines

Telephone and cable companies are technically utilities. In most cases, cable and phone utility lines do not pose a hazard, but most responders are not trained to differentiate between high-voltage or low-voltage lines. For that reason, all utility lines should be treated with caution.

Judicial System

The fire department's primary contact with the **judicial system** often involves two situations: fire department personnel testifying in court and court orders. Fire department personnel are called to testify in arson and insurance claim cases, and firefighters are often called as witnesses to incidents that occurred on the fireground. In order to force the correction of code violations, the fire department often needs a judge to issue a court order. When fire marshals carry the power of the law, they deal directly with the court system to perform their duties.

Judicial System — System of courts set up to interpret and administer laws and regulations.

Figure 8.5 Fire department and emergency management personnel working together during an incident.

Figure 8.6 An example of a local health department.

Office of Emergency Management

Fire departments collaborate with local emergency management agencies, known as the office of emergency management or similar designation, during large-scale disasters and provide personnel and equipment **(Figure 8.5)**. They are also instrumental in the pre-incident planning and stockpiling of supplies for large-scale disasters.

Local Health Department

The local **health department** will be called on after fire incidents to inspect occupancies involving food preparation and storage, such as schools, hospitals, nursing homes, etc. The health department will make a determination about whether the establishment can safely remain open. Local health departments are also a key component in planning for and managing health-related emergencies, such as epidemics and pandemics **(Figure 8.6)**.

Civic Groups and Businesses

Community civic groups are nongovernmental organizations and an excellent resource for departments to use when trying to spread their fire and life safety messages. The groups can provide a core of interested citizens who are willing and able to assist the department in becoming an integral part of the community. Scouting organizations, such as the Boy Scouts of America, may assist fire departments with community service and fire and life safety education activities. Through cooperative and effective working relationships with organizations, such as the local Chamber of Commerce, fire departments may also gain political support for their needs. Some of the more common local civic groups include the Lions, Rotary, Kiwanis, and Jaycee clubs as well as American Legion and Veterans of Foreign Wars (VFW).

State/Provincial Agencies and Organizations

The concern about the fire problem at the state/provincial level has helped to establish state fire protection agencies. State governments operate and maintain the majority of fire protection agencies, although some agencies are independent. Brief descriptions of the most common agencies are presented in this section to make firefighters aware of the organizations that may exist in their states. These agencies include the following:

- State fire marshal or fire commissioner
- State/provincial fire training
- Fire commission
- State police
- State Highway Department of Turnpike Commission
- State Environmental Protection Agency
- State Occupational Safety and Health Administration
- State Health Department
- State Forestry Department
- Office of Emergency Management
- Special Task Forces

A state agency may have the same name as a similar agency in another state; however, the agency may have different responsibilities. In addition, some of these agencies may not exist in all states. These descriptions are only general in nature.

A number of nongovernmental organizations exist on the state or provincial level to promote fire safety and fire service professional development. Examples of such organizations are discussed in the sections that follow and include the following:

- State Fire Chiefs Association
- State Firefighter Association
- State Fire Instructors Association
- State Fire Officers Association

State Fire Marshal or Fire Commissioner

The state fire marshal's office is the principal authority on fire protection in nearly all states in the United States. In Canada, a fire commissioner performs fire prevention activities.

The state legislative body usually delegates the powers of the State Fire Marshall's office. These delegations carry the effect of law. The responsibilities of the fire marshal vary from state to state because of different opinions on what the office should do. In some states, the fire marshal's office is an independent government office. In other states, the fire marshal's office is a function of the state police. The following is a list of the typical responsibilities of the state fire marshal's office:

- Review and approve construction plans for fire safety
- Conduct fire prevention activities
- Investigate and determine fire causes
- Actively fight arson
- Regulate the storage and use of combustibles, hazardous materials, and explosives

- Provide specifications for required exits, detection systems, alarm systems, and extinguishing systems
- Develop and deliver fire service training programs (in some states)

State Fire Marshals may also inspect hospitals, day care facilities, assisted living and nursing homes, prisons, and state colleges or universities. Additionally, they may perform background checks on firefighters, inspect fair rides, and collect fire data or incident reports from fire departments around the state. Many state fire marshals belong to the National Association of State Fire Marshals or the Council of Canadian Fire Marshals and Fire Commissioners.

State/Provincial Fire Training

Most states and provinces have a training agency for firefighters and officers. These programs have full-time staff as instructors and administrators. They also have a part-time staff of instructors spread across the state or province to conduct classes at local fire departments. These state-level organizations are associated with state universities, fire marshal offices, and vocational-technical programs **(Figure 8.7)**. In some cases, state or provincial fire training agencies provide technical assistance as well as training programs to fire departments.

Members of state and provincial fire training agencies, like their peers on the local level, often belong to national organizations such as the International Society of Fire Service Instructors (ISFSI) or the North American Fire Training Directors (NAFTD), which are discussed later in this chapter.

Figure 8.7 Fire service trainees and an instructor at a state fire training academy.

Fire Commission

Several states have appointed fire commissions to establish professional qualifications standards for firefighters, fire officers, fire service instructors, and other fire department positions. These commissions are state funded and use their money to assist in training, testing, and administering the state certification program for the fire service. Most fire commissions have a director who works directly with the training delivery mechanisms of the area whether they are state, county, or local agencies.

State Police

Many state police forces provide a fire investigation unit that utilizes highly technical equipment used to uncover hard-to-find evidence. State police often work with fire department arson squads to solve difficult cases. State police may also help firefighters with hazardous materials, explosives disposal, traffic control, and personal protection during riots **(Figure 8.8)**. In some states, the state fire marshal's office is a division of the state police.

Figure 8.8 State police agencies can provide specialized personnel and equipment such as this bomb squad unit.

State Highway Department/Department of Transportation/Turnpike Commission

The primary relationship that highway departments and turnpike commissions may have with fire departments involves road, bridge, and route design. Fire departments must have unobstructed access to all areas under their jurisdiction. The fire department should also be notified anytime a highway or bridge is closed for repairs to eliminate surprises during emergencies. In some cases where specialized or heavy equipment is required, pre-incident planning may include the cooperation of the highway department or turnpike commission. The department or commission may also provide materials, such as sand, for hazardous materials incidents.

State Environmental Protection Agency

State environmental agencies usually become involved with local fire departments when a fire or disaster might contaminate the environment with hazardous materials. The agency usually sends a representative to monitor and report on the situation.

Figure 8.9 State forestry organizations can provide personnel and heavy equipment for wildland fire fighting incidents.

State Occupational Safety and Health Administration

States become involved in firefighter safety through their occupational safety and health agencies. When the legislature requires it, the agencies write specifications for the equipment that firefighters use. States that manage their own occupational safety and health programs are required to have regulations that are equal to or greater than the requirements of the federal OSHA regulations. Some state OSHA agencies also investigate firefighter deaths and injuries.

State Health Department

After a fire, the health department may inspect a facility to see whether any potential hazards to the public exist as a result of the fire and extinguishing operations, especially for establishments that provide food or lodging. The fire department may interact with the health department and assist in the investigation.

State Forestry Department/Department of Natural Resources

In wildland fires, fire departments often have to work with the state forestry department to contain and control the blaze. The forestry department has heavy equipment, such as bulldozers, and also has the equipment and expertise to conduct operations such as backfiring **(Figure 8.9)**.

Office of Emergency Management

The Office of Emergency Management (often formerly called Civil Defense) interacts with the fire department during natural disasters, large wildland fires, civil unrest, and other larger emergency situations. The office can provide personnel, vehicles, and communication equipment and is always available to help.

Special Task Forces

Special groups are often formed to address specific problems that arise within a state. An example could be an arson task force that would combine law enforcement, fire service, insurance, and state agencies in a joint effort against arson. Another example would be a haz mat group formed to address the hazardous materials problem.

State Firefighter Association

These organizations are formed by the members of departments across the state to bring firefighters together to work toward common goals. The association may lobby, develop insurance plans, work on pension legislation or administration, promote fire and life safety activities, or assist in training. Many state firefighter associations hold an annual conference with training opportunities, contests, guest speakers, and social activities.

State Fire Chiefs Association

In some states, fire chiefs have organized a state association. At meetings, they can discuss common problems and suggest solutions. They can also present an organized force to lobby for legislation to benefit the state's fire protection efforts. Many state associations hold an annual conference with educational activities for professional development.

Other State Agencies and Organizations

Each state has its own public agencies that interact with the fire service. Firefighters should become familiar with the agencies in their state such as water resources, natural resources, transportation, and parks and recreation.

In addition, many fire service membership organizations exist on the state or regional level. These organizations include state or regional fire instructors associations and state or regional fire officers associations.

Federal Organizations in the United States and Canada

Because of the national government's concern over public safety, numerous federal agencies have been formed to help decrease the number of fire-related deaths and injuries. Public funds and public officials support and administer these agencies. Many agencies operate a series of regional offices.

Some of the more important agencies and their functions will be described in this section. While this section focuses on agencies within the government of the United States, there are often equivalent agencies in Canada. Agencies discussed below are:

- Bureau of Alcohol, Tobacco, Firearms, and Explosives (ATF)
- Chemical Safety and Hazard Investigation Board (CSB)
- Congressional Fire Services Caucus
- Congressional Fire Services Institute (CFSI)
- Consumer Product Safety Commission (CPSC)
- Emergency Management Institute (EMI)

- Environmental Protection Agency (EPA)
- Federal Aviation Administration (FAA)
- Federal Emergency Management Agency (FEMA)
- National Fire Academy (NFA)
- National Highway Traffic Safety Administration (NHTSA)
- National Institute for Occupational Safety and Health (NIOSH)
- National Institute of Standards and Technology (NIST)
- National Transportation Safety Board (NTSB)
- Nuclear Regulatory Commission (NRC)
- Occupational Safety and Health Administration (OSHA)
- Public Safety Canada (PS)
- Transport Canada
- United States Coast Guard (USCG) **(Figure 8.10)**
- United States Department of Energy (DOE)
- United States Department of Homeland Security (DHS)
- United States Department of the Interior (DOI)
- United States Department of Labor (DOL)
- United States Department of Transportation (US DOT)
- United States Fire Administration (USFA)
- United States Forest Service (USFS)

Figure 8.10 The U.S. Coast Guard is equipped to perform marine rescue and fire fighting. *U.S. Navy photo by Chief Mass Communication Specialist Bill Mesta.*

Bureau of Alcohol, Tobacco, Firearms, and Explosives (ATF)

The Bureau of Alcohol, Tobacco, Firearms, and Explosives (ATF), a division of the Department of Justice, assists local agencies in major arson investigations and regulates the storage and transportation of explosives. ATF has an Arson and Explosives Program, operates a fire research laboratory, and deploys a National Response Team for large-scale or selected other fire investigations.

Address: 99 New York Ave. NE, Room 5S144, Washington, DC 20226

Web site: www.atf.gov

Chemical Safety and Hazard Investigation Board (CSB)

The CSB is an independent federal agency charged with investigating industrial chemical accidents, including fires and explosions. The Clean Air Act Amendments of 1990 authorized and established the Board which began operating in 1998.

Address: 2175 K. Street, NW, Suite 400, Washington, DC 20037-1809

Web site: www.csb.gov

Congressional Fire Services Caucus

Pennsylvania Congressman Curt Weldon founded The Congressional Fire Services Caucus as a not-for-profit organization in November 1987. The constituency includes everyone from volunteers in small fire departments to major international industries. Advancing the concerns of the entire fire safety constituency, the Caucus marks the first attempt within Congress to comprehensively address America's fire problem.

Members of the Congress are made aware of major fire safety issues and legislation through educational seminars, legislative updates, and policy analyses. The Fire Services Caucus has become the largest caucus on Capitol Hill.

Address: 900 Second Street, NE, Suite 303, Washington, DC 20002

Web site: www.cfsi.org

Congressional Fire Services Institute (CFSI)

In 1989, the Congressional Fire Services Institute was formed to educate members of Congress about fire and life safety issues. This Institute enables the Congressional Fire Services Caucus to expand its membership within Congress and reach out into the fire service community. The Institute tracks legislation, monitors hearings, develops policy, identifies consensus priorities of the fire service, and reports these findings to the Caucus and the public. The Institute educates members of the Congress about the fire problem and at the same time instructs the fire service on how to make government more responsive. Its annual fundraising dinner attracts more than 2,000 attendees and guest speakers including Presidents and Vice Presidents of the United States.

Address: 900 Second Street N.E., Suite 303, Washington, DC 20002.

Web site: www.cfsi.org

Consumer Product Safety Commission (CPSC)

CPSC is an independent agency that recalls unsafe products and conducts research on the safety of consumer goods and on injury and loss patterns. CPSC regulates products such as cigarette lighters and enforces standards for flammability of clothing, carpets and rugs, upholstered furniture, and mattresses.

Address: 4330 East-West Highway, Bethesda, Maryland 20814-4408.

Web site: www.cpsc.gov

Emergency Management Institute (EMI)

The Emergency Management Institute (EMI) is authorized under the Civil Defense Act of 1950 to provide training to public sector managers to prepare for, mitigate, respond to, and recover from all types of emergencies. EMI is now part of the Federal Emergency Management Agency within the U.S. Department of Homeland Security.

EMI provides programs in emergency management, technical development, and professional development at the National Emergency Training Center (NETC) and state emergency management agencies. NETC also operates a Resource Center and Community Emergency Response Teams (CERT)

Address: 16825 S. Seton Avenue, Emmitsburg, MD 21727

Web site: http://training.fema.gov

CERT (Community Emergency Response Team)

Citizens can be trained to be better prepared to respond to emergency situations in their communities through local Community Emergency Response Teams. Each CERT member completes 20 hours of training on disaster preparedness, basic disaster medical operations, fire safety, light search and rescue, and other essential topics.

CERT training also includes a disaster simulation in which participants practice skills they learned throughout the course. In the event of an emergency, CERT members can provide immediate assistance to victims, assist in organizing spontaneous volunteers at a disaster site and provide critical support to first responders.

For additional information about CERT, visit www.fema.gov and www.citizencorps.gov.

Environmental Protection Agency (EPA)

The Environmental Protection Agency (EPA) is an independent federal agency with the mission of protecting human health and the environment.

As part of this mission, EPA provides an "on-scene coordinator" at oil or hazardous substances spills that threaten or reach inland waters. The coordinator has the authority to ensure that the spill is contained and cleaned up to minimize environmental damage.

Address: Ariel Rios Building, 1200 Pennsylvania Avenue, N.W., Washington, DC 20004.

Web site: www.epa.gov

Federal Aviation Administration (FAA)

The Federal Aviation Administration (FAA) is the agency within the U.S. Department of Transportation concerned with fire protection in all aspects of civil aviation, including aircraft and airports. It also controls the transportation of hazardous materials by air.

Address: 800 Independence Avenue S.W., Washington, DC 20591

Web site: www.faa.gov

Figure 8.11 Federal Emergency Management Agency (FEMA) personnel respond to and help mitigate large scale disaster incidents. *Courtesy of FEMA News Photos, photo by Dianna Gee.*

Federal Emergency Management Agency (FEMA)

This agency was formed in 1978 as a part of President Jimmy Carter's third reorganization plan. FEMA gives the President the capability, within a single federal agency, to provide for national needs in preparing for, mitigating, and responding to all types of emergencies **(Figure 8.11)**. FEMA is now part of the Department of Homeland Security.

FEMA's mission is to support citizens and first responders to build, sustain, and improve the capability to prepare for, protect against, respond to, recover from, and mitigate all hazards. Programs include the following:

- Fire prevention and control
- Continuity of government
- Strategic stockpiles
- Civil defense
- Federal insurance plans
- Flood plain management
- Dam safety
- Hurricane preparedness
- Earthquake preparedness
- Radiological emergency preparedness

These programs form the foundation on which the continuity of civilian government is built and on which authority is exercised in the aftermath of emergencies. The overriding objective is the maximum preservation of life and property in peacetime disasters and in national security emergencies, including attack.

Address: 500 C Street, S.W., Washington, DC 20472

Web site: www.fema.gov

National Fire Academy (NFA)

The Federal Fire Prevention and Control Act of 1974 (Public Law 93-498) established the NFA. Since its establishment, the NFA has become part of the Federal Emergency Management Agency within the U.S. Department of Homeland Security. The Academy's purpose is to advance the professional development of fire service personnel and other people engaged in fire prevention and control.

The Academy provides programs at the resident facility and in the field through state and local fire training agencies. The NFA offers programs in the following areas:

- Organizational and executive development
- Fire service education and public fire education
- Management technology
- Arson mitigation
- Hazardous materials
- Incident command
- Fire prevention

Resident courses are typically one to two weeks and are held on campus at the National Emergency Training Center in Emmitsburg, Maryland. Field courses are typically two-day weekend courses **(Figure 8.12)**, online courses, and state weekends are also available. NFA courses meet or exceed the appropriate NFPA® professional qualification standards and are accredited by the American Council on Education.

Address: 16825 S. Seton Avenue, Emmitsburg, MD 21727

Web site: www.usfa.dhs.gov/nfa

Figure 8.12 The National Fire Academy presents intensive courses on fire and emergency services topics at its Emmitsburg campus. *Courtesy of the National Fire Academy.*

Training Resources and Data Exchange (TRADE)

The Training Resources and Data Exchange (TRADE) program is a regionally based network designed to foster the exchange of fire-related training information and resources among Federal, State, and local levels of governments. The TRADE network consists of the directors of the 50 state fire service training systems and senior training officers from the national's largest fire departments. The objectives of TRADE are to:

- Identify fire, rescue, and emergency medical services training needs at the regional level

- Identify and exchange training programs and resources within regions

- Provide to the National Fire Academy an annual assessment of fire training resources needs within the region

- Identify national trends with an impact on fire-related training and education

The TRADENET LISTSERV is sponsored by the National Fire Academy.

Web site: www.usfa.dhs.gov/nfa/trade/

National Highway Traffic Safety Administration (NHTSA)

The National Highway Traffic Safety Administration (NHTSA) is the agency within the U.S. Department of Transportation whose mission is to save lives, prevent injuries and reduce economic costs due to road traffic crashes, through education, research, safety standards and enforcement activity. NHTSA is the federal focal point for EMS.

Office of EMS Mission

The mission of the Office of EMS within the U.S. Department of Transportation's National Highway Traffic Safety Administration (NHTSA) is to reduce death and disability by providing leadership and coordination to the EMS community. Programs include:

- National standard curricula for various levels of EMS providers

- National registration of EMT-Paramedics

- National EMS Advisory Council to provide NHTSA with advice and recommendations related to EMS

- Federal Interagency Committee on EMS to assure coordination among federal agencies involved with EMS and 911 services

- National EMS Information Systems

- In Canada, EMS is under control of Canadian Medical Association (CMA)

    Address: 1200 New Jersey Avenue, S.E., West Building,
             Washington, DC 20590

    Web site: www.ems.gov

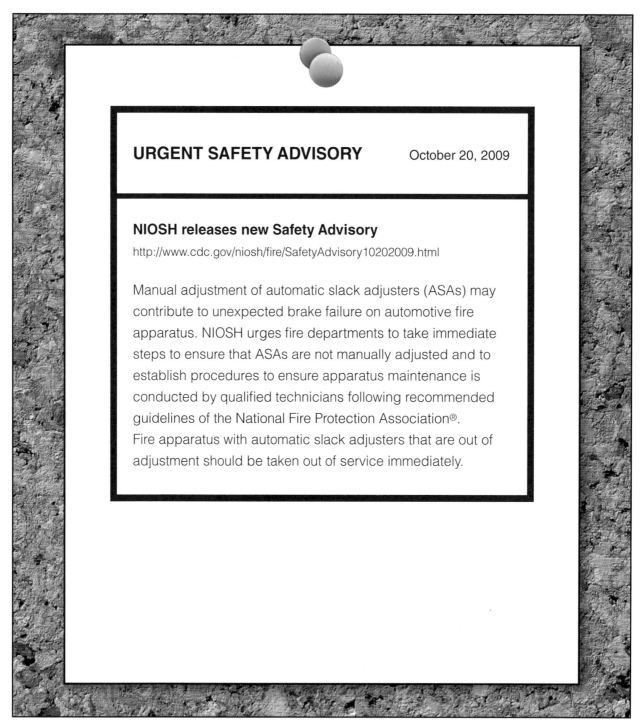

URGENT SAFETY ADVISORY   October 20, 2009

NIOSH releases new Safety Advisory

http://www.cdc.gov/niosh/fire/SafetyAdvisory10202009.html

Manual adjustment of automatic slack adjusters (ASAs) may contribute to unexpected brake failure on automotive fire apparatus. NIOSH urges fire departments to take immediate steps to ensure that ASAs are not manually adjusted and to establish procedures to ensure apparatus maintenance is conducted by qualified technicians following recommended guidelines of the National Fire Protection Association®. Fire apparatus with automatic slack adjusters that are out of adjustment should be taken out of service immediately.

Figure 8.13 An example of an Urgent Safety Advisory issued by the National Institute for Occupational Safety and Health (NIOSH). *Courtesy of NIOSH.*

National Institute for Occupational Safety and Health (NIOSH)

NIOSH was established by the Occupational Safety and Health Act within the Department of Health, Education, and Welfare (now the Department of Health and Human Services) to conduct research and provide educational functions to support OSHA. Now part of the Centers for Disease Control and Prevention (CDC), NIOSH also recommends occupational safety and health standards that affect workers. NIOSH operates the Fire Fighter Fatality Investigation and Prevention Program and issues emergency advisories **(Figure 8.13)**.

Address: 395 E Street S.W., Suite 9200
Patriots Plaza Building
Washington, DC 20201

Web site: www.cdc.gov/niosh

Figure 8.14 The National Institute of Standards and Technology (NIST) campus in Gaithersburg, Maryland. *Courtesy of NIST.*

National Institute of Standards and Technology (NIST)

Established in 1901, NIST was formerly known as the National Bureau of Standards (NBS). NIST is part of the U.S. Department of Commerce and, through its Building and Fire Research Laboratory (BFRL), is engaged in fire research and tests involving building technology, as well as advancing fire technology **(Figure 8.14)**.

Address: Building and Fire Research Laboratory, National Institute of Standards and Technology, 100 Bureau Drive, Stop 8600, Gaithersburg, MD 20899-3460

Web site: www.nist.gov

National Transportation Safety Board (NTSB)

The National Transportation Safety Board was established in 1967 to investigate all civil aviation accidents and significant accidents in the other modes of transportation (railroad, highway, marine and pipeline) in the United States and to issue safety recommendations aimed at preventing future accidents.

The Safety Board determines the probable cause of other incidents of interest to the fire service, including releases of hazardous materials in all forms of transportation.

Address: 490 L'Enfant Plaza, S.W., Washington, DC 20594

Web site: www.ntsb.gov

Nuclear Regulatory Commission (NRC)

The NRC's primary responsibilities are to develop and enforce guidelines on building and operating nuclear facilities. It is also heavily involved in fire protection relating to the nuclear industry through programs such as fire protection for operating reactors, fire protection for nuclear fuel cycle facilities, and fire research.

Address: Office of Public Affairs, Washington, D.C. 20555-0001

Web site: www.nrc.gov

Occupational Safety and Health Administration (OSHA)

OSHA was established in 1970 when the Occupational Safety and Health Act became federal law. OSHA's role is to assure safe and healthy working conditions for working men and women. OSHA accomplishes this goal through the following:

- Authorizing enforcement of the standards developed under the Act
- Assisting and encouraging the States in their efforts to assure safe and healthful working conditions
- Providing for research, information, education, and training in the field of occupational safety and health

OSHA is part of the Department of Labor, which enforces its regulations.

Address: Department of Labor Building, 200 Constitution Ave. N.W., Washington, DC 20210

Web site: www.osha.gov

Public Safety Canada (PS)

Public Safety Canada was created in 2003 to ensure coordination across all federal departments and agencies responsible for national security and the safety of Canadians. From natural disasters to crime and terrorism, the PS mandate is to keep Canadians safe. PS develops national policy, response systems and standards.

Public Safety Canada issues timely alerts and similar products to help protect Canada's critical infrastructure. They also work closely with emergency management organizations across Canada and support their regional partners and first responders with funds, tools and training.

Address: 269 Laurier Avenue West, Ottawa, Canada K1A 0P8

Web site: www.publicsafety.gc.ca

Transport Canada

Transport Canada is responsible for developing regulations, policies, and some services related to safety and security for road, rail, marine, and aviation systems in Canada. Of particular interest to the fire service is Transport Canada's role in railways include regulations, standards, and services for safe transport of dangerous goods and operation of the Canadian Transport Emergency Centre to assist emergency response and handling of emergencies involving dangerous goods.

Address: Transport Canada, 330 Sparks Street, Ottawa, ON, K1A 0N5

website: www.tc.gc.ca/eng/menu.htm

Figure 8.15 A U.S. Coast Guard vessel during an oil skimming training exercise. *U.S. Coast Guard photo by Petty Officer 3rd Class Lauren Downs.*

United States Coast Guard (USCG)

The Coast Guard provides on-scene coordinators for spills or emergencies that threaten or reach coastal or navigable waterways or other waterways under Coast Guard jurisdiction **(Figure 8.15)**. The coordinators' authority is similar to that of EPA coordinators. They perform marine rescue and fire fighting operations, although their fire fighting capabilities are limited.

Address: 2100 Second Street S.W., Washington, DC 20593

Web site: www.uscg.mil

United States Department of Energy (DOE)

The Department of Energy was created on August 4, 1977 through the unification of the Nuclear Regulatory Commission and the Energy Research and Development Administration. Its mission deals with the U.S. policies on energy production, research, and conservation, and safety in handling nuclear materials. The DOE sponsors basic and applied scientific energy research.

Address: U.S. Department of Energy 1000 Independence Ave., SW
Washington, D.C. 20585

Web site: www.energy.gov

United States Department of Homeland Security (DHS)

Created in the aftermath of the September 11, 2001, terrorist attacks upon the United States, the DHS was the result of the most significant government transformation in the U.S. government in over 50 years. Twenty-two federal agencies were transferred under the control of the DHS in 2003. While the DHS was created to secure the United States against terrorist attacks, the department's charter also includes preparation for and response to all hazards and disasters.

DHS has seven major divisions:

- The Transportation Security Administration
- U.S. Customs and Border Protection
- U.S. Citizenship and Immigration Services
- U.S. Immigration Customs Enforcement
- U.S. Secret Service
- Federal Emergency Management Agency (FEMA), which includes the U.S. Fire Administration, National Fire Academy, and Emergency Management Institute.
- U.S. Coast Guard

  Address: U.S. Department of Homeland Security, Washington, D.C. 20528

  Web site: www.dhs.gov

United States Department of the Interior (DOI)

DOI has several internal agencies that provide important fire protection services. The Bureau of Land Management (BLM) provides protection against wildland fires on 545 million acres (220,553,675 hectares) of public land. The BLM also supports the Interagency Fire Center in Boise, Idaho. The National Park Service (NPS) also has major operations in the area of fire prevention, management, and suppression in the national park system.

Addresses:

DOI - 1849 C Street, Washington, DC 20240

BLM - U.S. Dept. of Interior/BLM, Room 406-LS, 1849 C Street, Washington, DC 20240

NPS - U.S. Dept. of Interior/NPS, 1849 C Street, Washington, DC 20240

Web site: www.doi.gov

United States Department of Labor (DOL)

The Department of Labor is responsible for administering and enforcing the Occupational Safety and Health Act. The DOL compiles national occupational injury and illness data through the Bureau of Labor Statistics. DOL establishes national and regional programs in addition to administration programs.

Address: Frances Perkins Building, 200 Constitution Avenue N.W., Washington, DC 20210

Web site: www.dol.gov

United States Department of Transportation (US DOT)

The DOT is concerned with public safety on the nation's highways, airways, railways, and coastal waters and also controls interstate petroleum pipelines. The DOT has developed a variety of regulations that control such things as hazardous materials and their shipping containers. DOT subdivisions include the Federal Aviation Administration, Federal Highway Administration, Federal Railroad Administration, Materials Transportation Bureau, and National Highway Traffic Safety Administration.

Address: 1200 New Jersey Avenue, S.E., Washington, DC 20590

Web site: www.dot.gov

United States Fire Administration (USFA)

The United States Fire Administration (USFA) was established by the Federal Fire Prevention and Control Act of 1974 (Public Law 93-498) and is now part of the Federal Emergency Management Agency within the U.S. Department of Homeland Security. Its purposes are:

- Reduce the nation's losses from fire through better fire prevention and control

- Supplement existing programs of research, training, and education

- Encourage new, improved programs and activities by state and local governments

The USFA also administers an extensive fire data and analysis program. The USFA and the National Institute of Occupational Safety and Health administer a program concerned with firefighter health and safety. The USFA is headquartered on campus at the National Emergency Training Center in Emmitsburg, Maryland.

Address: 16825 S. Seton Avenue, Emmitsburg, MD 21727

Web site: www.usfa.fema.gov

United States Forest Service (USFS)

An arm of the Department of Agriculture, the Forest Service provides fire protection to national forests, grasslands, and nearby private lands across the United States. The USFS has equipment, aircraft, personnel, and communications systems to combat large-scale wildland fires. It also has research facilities and provides technical and financial assistance to the states. The Forest Service also delivers training, pays the cost of fire fighting, and provides surplus federal equipment.

Address: U.S. Forest Service, 1400 Independence Ave. S.W., Washington, D.C. 20250-0003

Web site: www.fs.fed.us

Trade, Professional, and Membership Organizations in the United States and Canada

Historically, trade, professional, and membership organizations have arisen from individuals with similar interests that band together to further unite their cause. Today, such organizations serve vital roles in the overall fire protection field. The following section describes some of the trade, professional, and membership organizations that firefighters are likely to encounter in the United States and Canada. These organizations include:

- American National Standards Institute (ANSI)

- Canadian Association of Fire Chiefs (CAFC)

- The Canadian Centre for Emergency Preparedness (CCEP)

- Canadian Fallen Firefighters Foundation (CFFF)

- Canadian Fire Alarm Association (CFAA)
- Canadian Fire Safety Association (CFSA)
- Canadian Standards Association
- The Canadian Volunteer Fire Services Association (CVFSA)
- Council of Canadian Fire Marshals and Fire Commissioners
- FM Global (Formerly Factory Mutual Research Corporation) (FM)
- Fire Prevention Canada
- Insurance Services Office Inc. (ISO)
- International Association of Arson Investigators (IAAI)
- International Association of Black Professional Fire Fighters
- International Association of Fire Chiefs (IAFC)
- International Association of Fire Fighters (IAFF)
- International Association of Women in the Fire and Emergency Service (IWOMEN)
- International City/County Management Association (ICMA)
- International Code Council (ICC)
- International Fire Marshals Association (IFMA)
- International Fire Service Training Association (IFSTA)
- International Municipal Signal Association (IMSA)
- International Society of Fire Service Instructors (ISFSI)
- The Joint Council of National Fire Service Organizations (JCNFSO)
- National Association of Hispanic Firefighters
- National Association of State Fire Marshals
- National Fallen Firefighters Foundation
- National Fire Protection Association® (NFPA®)
- National Volunteer Fire Council (NVFC)
- North American Fire Training Directors (NAFTD) (Formerly the National Association of State Directors of Fire Training and Education (NASDFTE)
- Society of Fire Protection Engineers (SFPE)
- Underwriters Laboratories Inc. (UL)
- Underwriters Laboratories of Canada (ULC)

American National Standards Institute (ANSI)

ANSI identifies public requirements for national standards and coordinates voluntary standardization activities of concerned organizations. An example is *ANSI Z88.5, Practices for Respiratory Protection for the Fire Service.*

Address: 1819 L Street NW, Suite 600, Washington, DC 20036

Web site: www.ansi.org

Canadian Association of Fire Chiefs (CAFC)

The Canadian Association of Fire Chiefs (CAFC) is an independent, non-profit organization with a voluntary membership; its head office is in Ottawa, Ontario. Membership in the CAFC totals more than 1,200 individuals and organizations. These CAFC members are drawn from fire departments, health care facilities, federal, provincial and municipal levels of government, universities and colleges, and the fire and emergency service industry at large. The CAFC is financed primarily by sales of fire-service related publications and materials, and its membership dues.

Address: 280 Albert Street, Suite 702
Ottawa, ON K1P 5G8
Web site: www.cafc.ca

The Canadian Centre for Emergency Preparedness (CCEP)

The Canadian Centre for Emergency Preparedness (CCEP) is a federally incorporated, not-for-profit organization based in Burlington, Ontario. Its vision is to foster the development of a disaster resilient Canada through individuals, communities, and businesses. The CCEP mandate is to increase community resiliency through emergency preparedness programs that drive individuals, small enterprises and non-profit organizations from awareness to action.

Address: 860 Harrington Court, Suite 210, Burlington, Ontario L7N 3N4
Web site: www.ccep.ca

Canadian Fallen Firefighters Foundation (CFFF)

The Canadian Fallen Firefighters Foundation (Fondation canadienne des pompiers morts en service) was created to honor and remember firefighters who have been killed in the line of duty and support their families. The CFFF is a registered charity and operates by fundraising.

Address: 440 Laurier Ave. W, Suite 200 Ottawa, ON, K1R 7X6
Web site: www.cfff.ca

Canadian Fire Alarm Association (CFAA)

The mission of the Canadian Fire Alarm Association (CFAA) is to "Maximize the Use and Effectiveness of Fire Alarm Systems in the Protection of Life and Property." CFAA began in 1973 when a small group of Canadian fire alarm professionals met with representatives of the U.S.-based Automatic Fire Alarm Association (AFAA) to explore the feasibility of establishing an AFAA chapter in Canada.

Address: 85 Citizen Court, Unit 5, Markham, Ontrio L6G IA8

Web site: www.cfaa.ca

Canadian Fire Safety Association

The Canadian Fire Safety Association is a non-profit organization established in 1971 to promote fire safety through the use of seminars, safety training courses, informative newsletters, scholarships, and regular meetings.

Address: 2175 Sheppard Avenue East, Suite 310, North York, Ontario,
M2J 1W8, Canada

Web site: www.canadianfiresafety.com

Canadian Standards Association (CSA)

CSA marked products are used and sold in the U.S. everyday. The CSA is accredited by ANSI and NES and is also a Nationally Recognized Testing Laboratory (NRTL) accredited by OSHA. CSA International can test and certify products following standardized test protocols in laboratories across the U.S.

> **Address:** 178 Rexdale Boulevard, Toronto, Ontario, CANADA, M9W 1R3
>
> **Web site:** www.csa-international.org

The Canadian Volunteer Fire Services Association (CVFSA)

CVFSA is a national organization created to benefit the community by maintaining and strengthening Canadian volunteer fire services through the provision of education and training, administration and organizational standards for volunteer firefighter units.

> **Address:** 187 Avondale Ave., North York, Ontario M2N 2V4
> **Web site:** http://cvfsa.ca

Council of Canadian Fire Marshals and Fire Commissioners

The Council of Canadian Fire Marshals and Fire Commissioners was formed to:

- Advise on and promote legislation, policies, and procedures pertinent to fire protection

- Participate in the development of codes and standards relating to fire safety

- Promote fire safety awareness

- Support the professional development of the Canadian fire service

- Arrange for the compilation and dissemination of national fire loss statistics

- Identify trends relative to the causes and the severity of fire

- Provide advice to accredited agencies involved in the certification and testing of fire protection equipment, materials, and services relating to fire safety

- Provide a forum for the exchange of information on fire safety matters

> **Address:** 65 Brunswick Street, 2nd Floor
> Fredericton, New Brunswick E3B 1G5
>
> **Web site:** www.ccfmfc.ca

FM Global (Formerly Factory Mutual Research Corporation) (FM)

FM conducts research in property loss control, primarily to meet the needs of the Factory Mutual System. The information, however, is available for use by others. Data is gathered by testing, conducting surveys, and studies. The FM Global labs test and approve fire protection equipment such as sprinklers and sprinkler valves **(Figure 8.16)**.

> **Address:** FM Global Corporate Offices, 270 Central Ave.
> Johnston, RI 02919-4949
>
> **Web site:** www.fmglobal.com

Figure 8.16 The FM label on this fire extinguisher shows that the extinguisher has been tested and approved by FM Global.

Fire Prevention Canada

Incorporated in 1976 as a registered charity, FIPRECAN is a non-profit organization. Its primary mission is to increase visibility and awareness of fire prevention nationally, through educating the public directly and through the Fire Service. Fire Prevention Canada always has the Governor General of Canada as its patron.

    Address: P.O. Box 47037, Ottawa, ON K1B 5P9

    Web site: www.firecan.ca

Insurance Services Office Inc. (ISO)

Insurance Services Office (ISO) was formed in 1971 by the consolidation of several other insurance services organizations. ISO is an association of insurers that evaluates and rates the fire protection in communities throughout the United States. (Fire department ratings are related to taxpayers' insurance premium costs.) The *Commercial Fire Rating Schedule* and the *Fire Suppression Rating Schedule* are important documents available from this organization.

    Address: 545 Washington Boulevard, Jersey City, NJ 07310-1686

    Web site: www.iso.com

International Association of Arson Investigators (IAAI)

Individuals may join the IAAI as active members if they are currently engaged in suppressing arson for a government or private organization. Others may join as associate members if they meet IAAI requirements. The primary function of the association is attacking the problem of arson.

    Address: 2111 Baldwin Ave., Suite 203, Crofton, MD 21114

    Web site: www.firearson.com

International Association of Black Professional Fire Fighters (IABPFF)

Since 1970, the International Association of Black Professional Fire Fighters (IABPFF) has been dedicated to assisting black career firefighters in areas such as working conditions, advancement, and interracial programs. The association also serves as a liaison among black firefighters throughout the country and includes the Black Chief Officers Committee.

Address: 1020 North Taylor Avenue, St. Louis, MO 63113

Web site: www.iabpff.org/index2.htm

International Association of Fire Chiefs (IAFC)

Active membership in the International Association of Fire Chiefs (IAFC) is open to all chief officers of organized public, industrial, or government fire departments. Fire marshals, commissioners, and directors are also included if they are involved in active fire fighting and administrative duties. The association, formed in 1873, is designed to further the professional advancement of the fire service. The IAFC holds an annual conference for the purpose of technical and educational advancement. This conference is held in a different city in North America each year.

IAFC has sections focused on particular interest groups. IAFC sections are:

- Emergency Medical Services (EMS)
- Emergency Vehicle Management
- Federal and Military Fire Service
- Fire and Life Safety
- Industrial Fire and Safety
- Metro Chiefs
- Safety, Health, and Survival
- Volunteer and Combination Officers

Address: 4025 Fair Ridge Drive, Suite 300, Fairfax, VA 22033-2868

Web site: www.iafc.org

International Association of Fire Fighters (IAFF)

The International Association of Fire Fighters (IAFF) is a labor organization (union) of more than 240,000 permanent, paid firefighters and emergency medical service personnel in the United States and Canada. The IAFF was formed in 1918 and is affiliated with the AFL-CIO. Membership exists through joint councils, state associations, and chartered locals. Among other issues, IAFF is concerned with firefighter health and safety and operates the National Fire Fighter Near Miss Reporting System.

Address: 1750 New York Avenue N.W., Suite 300,
Washington, DC 20006-5395

Web site: www.iaff.org

International Association of Women in Fire and Emergency Services

The outcome of a joint meeting sponsored by the National Fire Academy between the boards of trustees of Women in the Fire Service (WFS) and Women Chief Fire Officers (WCFO) was the merger of the two organizations to form the International Association of Women in Fire and Emergency Services (IWOMEN). IWOMEN has a membership of approximately 1,000, while an estimated 6,200 women in the U.S. currently work as full-time, career firefighters and officers **(Figure 8.17)**. WFS was incorporated in 1982 as a nonprofit support network for fire service women and for women looking for careers in the fire service.

Figure 8.17 Female firefighters during a training conference sponsored by IWOMEN.

Address: 4025 Fair Ridge Drive, Suite 300, Fairfax, VA 22033,

Phone: 703.896.4858

Web site: www.i-women.org

International City/County Management Association (ICMA)

ICMA is a 9,000 member professional and educational association of appointed local government administrators worldwide. Its purposes are to strengthen urban government through quality professional management and to develop and disseminate new approaches by training programs, information services, and publications. ICMA is the publisher of the text, *Managing Fire and Rescue Services*.

Address: 777 North Capitol Street, NE, Suite 500, Washington, DC 20002

Web site: www.icma.org

International Code Council (ICC)

Established in 1994 as a nonprofit organization, the International Code Council has developed a single set of comprehensive and coordinated national model construction codes. Prior to establishing the ICC, its founders (the Building Officials and Code Administrators International, Inc. [BOCA], International Conference of Building Officials [ICBO], and Southern Building Code Congress International, Inc. [SBCCI]) developed the three separate sets of model codes used throughout the United States. The offices of the founding agencies now serve as regional offices for the ICC.

Address: 500 New Jersey Ave. N.W., 6th Floor, Washington, DC 20001

Web site: www.iccsafe.org

International Fire Marshals Association (IFMA)

IFMA was organized as a section of the NFPA® in 1906 and unites those involved in fire prevention and arson investigation and helps its members by correlating activities and exchanging information.

Address: 1 Batterymarch Park, P.O. Box 9101, Quincy, MA 02169-7471

Web site: www.nfpa.org/MemberSections/IFMA/IFMA.asp

Figure 8.18 The International Fire Service Training Association (IFSTA) reviews and validates fire service training materials which are then published by Fire Protection Publications.

International Fire Service Training Association (IFSTA)

The International Fire Service Training Association was formed in 1934 to develop training manuals and materials for the fire service. The committees of IFSTA meet each July and January to revise and validate selected manuals. After validation, the texts are published by Fire Protection Publications, an extension of Oklahoma State University **(Figure 8.18)**. Among other manuals, IFSTA publishes *Essentials of Fire Fighting.* IFSTA publications are used throughout the United States, Canada and in several countries beyond North America.

Address: Oklahoma State University, Fire Protection Publications, Headquarters for the International Fire Service Training Association (IFSTA), 930 N. Willis, Stillwater, Oklahoma 74078

Web site: www.ifsta.org

International Municipal Signal Association (IMSA)

IMSA's mission is to provide quality certification programs for the safe installation, operation, and maintenance of public safety systems. The association was organized in 1896 and has 10,000 members. Its members are municipal signal and communication department heads. IMSA was organized to assist its members with technical knowledge and information on fire and police alarms and traffic controls. IMSA offers such training programs as Fire Alarm Interior Levels I and II and Fire Alarm Municipal Levels I and II.

Address: P.O. Box 539, 165 East Union Street, Newark, NY 14513-0539

Web site: www.imsasafety.org

International Society of Fire Service Instructors (ISFSI)

The primary function of the International Society of Fire Service Instructors is to provide a medium for the exchange of educational ideas and training techniques for the fire service. ISFSI has done much to assist fire service instructors in their quest for improvement such as starting and, for many years, operating the Fire Department Instructors Conference (FDIC). The society was formed in 1960.

Address: 2425 Highway 49 East, Pleasant View, TN 37146

Web site: www.isfsi.org

The Joint Council of National Fire Service Organizations (JCNFSO)

The original intent and purpose of the Joint Council of National Fire Service Organizations (JCNFSO) was to provide a means whereby national fire service organizations could cooperate in defining and achieving the national goals of the fire service. The Council held its first meeting on August 31 and September 1, 1970, in Williamsburg, Virginia. Originally, the Council was composed of the chief executive officers of several fire service organizations **(see Info Box)**.

Members of the Joint Council of National Fire Service Organizations

Organizations represented on the Joint Council of National Fire Service Organizations were:

- Fire Marshals Association of North America
- International Association of Arson Investigators
- International Association of Black Professional Firefighters
- International Association of Fire Chiefs
- International Fire Service Training Association
- International Municipal Signal Association
- International Society of Fire Service Instructors
- Metropolitan Chiefs Committee of the International Association of Fire Chiefs
- National Fire Protection Association®
- National Volunteer Fire Council

The Council's most outstanding achievement was the establishment of the National Professional Qualifications Board. After nearly 20 years of operation, the Joint Council of National Fire Service Organizations voted to disband in August 1989. There were two principal reasons for its disbandment. One reason was due to a rule change that allowed subordinates to attend meetings in place of the chief executive officers. Another factor was the requirement of a unanimous vote on policy matters. A standing committee of several of the remaining members was formed to handle closing business and to provide assistance in continuing the work of the NPQB. See Chapter One for more information about the National Professional Qualifications Board.

National Association of Hispanic Firefighters (NAHF)

National Association of Hispanic Firefighters was established in 1995 and is dedicated to promoting firefighters through recruitment, professional development, community advocacy, and building fellowship among all firefighters.

Among other programs, NAHF offers Spanish-language training through *Tactical Spanish for Firefighters and EMS*, a self-study Spanish language program for firefighters and EMS personnel.

Address: 1220 L St. NW, Suite 100-199, Washington D.C. 2000

Phone: 202 487-9071

Website: www.nahf.org

National Association of State Fire Marshals

The National Association of State Fire Marshals (NASFM) represents the most senior fire official of each of the 50 states and District of Columbia. State Fire Marshals' responsibilities vary from state to state, but they are usually responsible for fire safety code adoption and enforcement, fire and arson investigation, fire incident data reporting and analysis, public education, and advising governors and state legislatures on fire protection. Some state fire marshals are responsible for firefighter training, hazardous materials incident responses, wildland fires, and the regulation of natural gas and other pipelines.

Web site: www.firemarshals.org

Figure 8.19 The National Fallen Firefighters Memorial located on the campus of the National Fire Academy. *Courtesy of NFFF/USFA.*

National Fallen Firefighters Foundation (NFFF)

The United States Congress created the National Fallen Firefighters Foundation to lead a nationwide effort to remember America's fallen firefighters. Since 1992, the NFFF has developed and expanded programs to honor fallen fire heroes and assist their families and coworkers **(Figure 8.19)**. The NFFF is a nonprofit organization that receives funding through private donations from individuals, organizations, corporations, and foundations.

Each October, the NFFF sponsors the official national tribute to all firefighters who died in the line of duty during the previous year and provides travel, lodging, and meals for immediate survivors of fallen firefighters being honored. The NFFF conducts support programs for survivors, award scholarships to spouses, children, and stepchildren of fallen firefighters for education and job training costs, offers training and other resources to departments that have experienced a line of duty death, and conducts the Everyone Goes Home program to prevent line-of-duty deaths. **Appendix D** lists the 16 Firefighter Life Safety Initiatives of the Everyone Goes Home program.

Address: PO Drawer 498, Emmitsburg, MD 21727,

Phone: 301-447-1365.

Website: http://firehero.org

National Fire Protection Association® (NFPA®)

Organized in 1896, the NFPA® is an organization concerned with fire safety standards development, technical advisory services, education, research, and other related services. Its members come from all segments of the fire protection field, both private and public.

The NFPA®'s primary service to the fire protection field is the development of more than 300 technical consensus standards (including those for fire service professional qualifications, fire service occupational safety and health, and personal protective ensembles). The codes and standards are developed by Technical Committees appointed by a Standards Council and are open for public comment, review, and appeal. The 7,453 committee members include 559 with a fire service affiliation.

The NFPA® publishes the *Fire Protection Handbook* and other materials, sponsors Fire Prevention Week, and conducts seminars. NFPA®'s 16 members sections include the following:

- Fire Service
- Building Fire Safety Systems
- Industrial Fire Protection
- Electrical
- Architects, Engineers, and Building Officials (AEBO)
- Wildland Fire Management
- Education
- Research
- Latin American
- Health Care
- Lodging Industry
- Fire Science and Technology Educators
- Aviation
- Rail Transportation
- International Fire Marshals Association
- Metropolitan Fire Chiefs

NFPA® codes and standards of particular interest to incoming members of the fire service include:

- NFPA® 472, *Standard for Competence of Responders to Hazardous Materials/ Weapons of Mass Destruction Incidents*
- NFPA® 1001, *Standard for Fire Fighter Professional Qualifications*
- NFPA® 1002, *Standard for Fire Apparatus Driver/Operator Professional Qualifications*
- NFPA® 1403, *Standard on Live Fire Training Evolutions*

- NFPA® 1500, *Standard on Fire Department Occupational Safety and Health Program*
- NFPA® 1583, *Standard on Health-Related Fitness Programs for Fire Department Members*
- NFPA® 1901, *Standard for Automotive Fire Apparatus*

  Address: 1 Batterymarch Park, P.O. Box 9101, Quincy, MA 02169-7471

  Web site: www.nfpa.org

National Volunteer Fire Council (NVFC)

The mission of the National Volunteer Fire Council is to provide a unified voice for volunteer fire and EMS organizations. Organized in 1976, the NVFC is composed of representatives of 49 state fire associations and provides information resources for volunteer departments and personnel.

Address: 7852 Walker Drive, Greenbelt, MD 20770

Web site: www.nvfc.org

North American Fire Training Directors (NAFTD) (Formerly the National Association of State Directors of Fire Training and Education (NASDFTE)

NAFTD was organized as the National Association of State Directors of Fire Training and Education in 1981 for two purposes: (1) to serve as a representative for state fire training programs at various organizations and agencies whose policies, programs, and decisions have some impact on state programs; and (2) to serve as a forum for the enhancement and enrichment of state fire training programs and their managers.

Address: Changes each time a new association president is elected.

Web site: www.naftd.org

Society of Fire Protection Engineers (SFPE)

The Society of **Fire Protection Engineers** was established in 1950 as a section of the NFPA® and incorporated as an independent organization in 1971. It is the professional society representing those practicing the field of fire protection engineering, including those employed by fire departments. The Society has over 4000 members in the United States and abroad, and over 60 regional chapters. Among other activities, the SFPE supports the professional engineering (licensing) exam for fire protection engineers and has a fire service committee.

Address: 7315 Wisconsin Avenue, Suite 620E, Bethesda, MD 20814

Web site: www.sfpe.org

Underwriters Laboratories Inc. (UL)

The goal of Underwriters Laboratories is to promote public safety through its scientific investigation of various materials to determine how hazardous the materials are. After testing an item of equipment or a material, the organization then lists and marks the material as having passed its rigorous tests (**Figure 8.20**). In addition, UL offers online fire service training. The nonprofit UL was founded in 1894.

Figure 8.20 The UL label on this microwave oven shows that the product has been tested and listed by Underwriters Laboratories Inc.

Address: 333 Pfingsten Road, Northbrook, IL 60062-2096

Web site: www.ul.com

Underwriters Laboratories of Canada (ULC)

An affiliate of the Underwriters Laboratory, ULC's goal is to promote public safety through its scientific investigation of various materials to determine how hazardous the materials are. After testing, the organization then lists and marks the material as having passed its rigorous tests.

The nonprofit ULC was founded in 1920.

Address: 7 Underwriters Road, Toronto, ON, M1R 3A9

Web site: www.ulc.ca

Other Organizations

The following organizations also provide helpful information:

- **Association of American Railroads Bureau of Explosives**

    Address: P.O. Box 11130, Pueblo, Colorado 81001

    Web site: www.boe.aar.com

- **American Trucking Associations (ATA) and the National Tank Truck Carriers, Inc. (NTTC)**

    Address: 2200 Mill Road, Alexandria, VA 22314-4677

    ATA web site: www.truckline.org

    NTTC website: www.tanktruck.org

- **American Red Cross**

    Address: National Headquarters, 2025 E. St. NW, Washington, DC 20006

    Web site: www.redcross.org

- **American Heart Association**

    Address: 7272 Greenville Avenue, Dallas, TX 75231

    Web site: www.heart.org

- **Center for Public Safety Excellence**

    Address: 4501 Singer Court, Ste. 180, Chantilly, VA 20151, (866) 866-2324

    Web Site: publicsafetyexcellence.org

- **Salvation Army National Headquarters**

  Address: 615 Slaters Lane, P.O. Box 269, Alexandria, VA 22313

  Web site: www.salvationarmyusa.org

Chapter Summary

Fire departments do not operate alone. They depend on other public agencies to provide services during planning and response to emergency scenes. They use the services of provincial and state training agencies to acquire or refresh skills. Various private and public organizations provide information and bargaining power on safety legislation and on wage and staffing issues. State and local law enforcement agencies help control emergency scenes and investigate suspicious fires. Government agencies help to provide support following natural disasters or terrorist attacks. It is very important that firefighters understand and appreciate the ways in which different organizations provide support to help ensure public safety.

Review Questions

1. Compare and contrast how a firefighter's interaction with local civic and business groups, like the Girl Scouts, differs from interaction with a local government agency, like a code enforcement department.

2. Why does the role of the state fire marshal or commissioner vary from state to state?

3. Why is it necessary to have such a wide variety of state and national agencies that work toward fire prevention and safety?

4. How can state and local agencies work to support the efforts of national organizations?

5. Why are trade, professional, and membership organizations usually formed?

6. What are the benefits of belonging to a trade, professional, and membership organization?

Fire and Emergency Services Apparatus, Equipment, and Facilities

Chapter Contents

Key Terms

FESHE Outcomes

This chapter provides information that addresses the outcomes for the Fire and Emergency Services Higher Education (FESHE) *Principles of Emergency Services* course.

8. Describe the common types of fire and emergency service facilities, equipment, and apparatus.

NFPA® Job Performance Requirements

This chapter provides information that addresses the following job performance requirements (JPRs) of NFPA® 1001, *Standard for Fire Fighter Professional Qualifications* (2008).

5.3.1(A)   5.3.2(A)   5.3.6(A)

Fire and Emergency Services Apparatus, Equipment, and Facilities

Learning Objectives

After reading this chapter, students will be able to:

1. Identify fire department apparatus.

2. Recognize the uses for uniforms and personal protective clothing.

3. Explain the three basic types of breathing apparatus.

4. Describe how powered and non powered tools and equipment can be used in the fire and emergency services.

5. Recognize ropes, webbing, related hardware, and harnesses as used in the fire and emergency services.

6. Describe why ground ladders are key to fire suppression activities.

7. Explain the basic functions of fire hose, nozzles, and hose appliances and tools.

8. Recognize uses for various fire department facilities.

Chapter 9
Fire and Emergency Services Apparatus, Equipment, and Facilities

Case History

Juan Sanchez had been interested in tools since he was a kid watching his dad in his shop in the basement. He came to the rookie academy with a wide knowledge of tools, but he was still amazed at the variety of tools that firefighters use. The longer he was in the academy, the more he realized that his safety and success as a firefighter would depend on how well he understood and could use dozens of specialized tools. At the same time, he learned that the fire department also relied on unique apparatus and facilities to meet its mission.

The operating functions of a fire department are centered on its personnel, facilities, apparatus, and equipment. As a firefighter begins his or her career, there are various types of fire department apparatus, tools and equipment, personal protective clothing, self-contained breathing apparatus (SCBA), facilities, and other apparatus with which he or she must become familiar. Depending on its size, setting, and environment, a department may not have all of the types of resources described in this chapter. However, the knowledge and information gained from other organizations can sometimes lead to creative solutions to problems that other departments have faced.

National Fire Protection Association® (NFPA®) Standards

The NFPA® produces a number of standards which provide the minimum requirements for the manufacturing or construction of fire and emergency services apparatus, tools, equipment, and facilities. When an NFPA® standard is updated it does not render the old equipment useless or illegal. It means that manufacturers and fire and emergency services organizations should no longer manufacture or purchase apparatus, equipment, and facilities that do not comply with the current standard. Thus, newly purchased apparatus, tools, equipment, and facilities should meet the appropriate NFPA® standard requirements at the time of purchase.

Figure 9.1a Fire engines such as this one transport fire fighting personnel and equipment to emergency scenes and pump water to combat fires. *Courtesy of Ron Jeffers.*

Figure 9.1b Firefighters using hose lines from a fire engine to extinguish a fire during a training exercise.

Apparatus — Motor-driven vehicle or group of vehicles designed and constructed for the purpose of fighting fires; may be of different types such as engines, water tenders, and ladder trucks.

Engine — Ground vehicle providing specified levels of pumping, water, hose capacity and staffed with a minimum number of personnel. *Also known as* Fire Department Pumper.

Fire Department Apparatus

Fire departments have an array of **apparatus** to help firefighters perform their duties. Each type of apparatus is designed for a specific function. All departments do not have all the types of apparatus listed in the sections that follow, but these types of apparatus are commonly used throughout North America.

The Engine (Pumper)

The **engine** (sometimes called the pumper) is the most basic of all fire department apparatus. The name *engine* or *pumper* is derived from the function of the apparatus and from the pump, which is the main feature of the apparatus. The primary purpose of the pumper or engine company is to confine and extinguish fires with water delivered through hoselines under pump pressure **(Figures 9.1 a and b)**. As described in Chapter 2, engine company personnel usually consist of a company officer, a driver/operator or engineer, and typically two or more firefighters.

Pumpers are designed to meet the requirements set forth in NFPA®1901, *Standard for Automotive Fire Apparatus.* Standard pumpers are equipped with fire pumps that have the following rated capacities:

- 750 gpm (gallons per minute) (3 000 L/min)
- 1,000 gpm (4 000 L/min)
- 1,250 gpm (5 000 L/min)
- 1,500 gpm (6 000 L/min)
- 1,750 gpm (7 000 L/min)
- 2,000 gpm (8 000 L/min)

Common Types of Fire Pumps

Centrifugal and positive displacement pumps are the primary types of pumps that the fire service uses. See IFSTA's **Pumping Apparatus Driver/ Operator Handbook** for more information.

Gauges and other instruments are provided for the pump operator. Controls regulate the speed of the pump, which in turn affects the pressure and volume of the water **(Figure 9.2)**. A pumper usually has a water tank, sometimes referred to as a booster tank, with capacities ranging from 500 to 1,500 gallons (2 000 L to 6 000 L). This water is used to start a fire attack before the pumper is connected to an external water supply, usually a fire hydrant. There may also be a smaller tank for special extinguishing agents such as foam concentrate. A proportioning device on the main fire pump mixes the foam concentrate with water to produce a foam fire stream for use on structural or flammable and combustible liquids fires.

Most pumpers have bins or compartments, called hose beds, located around the apparatus for carrying the various sizes of fire hose. Most of the hose used for water supply to the apparatus is kept in the main hose bed of the apparatus; some attack lines may also be carried in the same location **(Figure 9.3)**. Other attack lines may be carried in hose beds on different portions of the apparatus, such as the front bumper or above the pump panel area. In many cases, these attack lines are preconnected to a discharge for rapid deployment. NFPA® 1901 requires each pumper to carry a minimum of 400 feet (122 m) of small attack hose (1 1/2-inch [38 mm], 1 3/4-inch [45 mm], or 2-inch [50 mm]) and 800 feet (244 m) of supply hose larger than 2 1/2 inches (65 mm) in diameter. Apparatus may also be equipped with a booster reel, but standards no longer require booster reels **(Figure 9.4)**. A booster reel is a reel of small (1-inch [25 mm] diameter or less), noncollapsible hose used for extinguishing small exterior fires or for overhaul operations.

Figure 9.2 The driver/operator controls the pump and flow of water at the pump panel.

Figure 9.3 Supply and attack hose lines should be loaded into the hose beds according to department policies.

Figure 9.4 Booster hose is used on smaller fires.

In addition to hose, pumpers carry a variety of equipment for fire and rescue operations. Most pumpers carry the following:

- Ladders
- Forcible entry tools
- Nozzles
- Hose adapters and appliances
- Hose tools
- Self-contained breathing apparatus (SCBA)
- Portable fire extinguishers
- Pike poles
- Salvage covers and other loss control tools
- Other tools the company uses

Depending on the functions of the engine company in a particular municipality, the pumper may carry specialized equipment such as the following:

- Rescue and extrication tools
- Emergency medical equipment
- Ventilation equipment
- Portable water tanks for water shuttle and drafting operations

Commercial and Custom Fire Apparatus

A *Commercial Fire Apparatus* is a fire apparatus body (compartments, pump, tank, hose bed, etc.) designed and configured by a fire apparatus manufacturer to be placed on a cab and chassis that has been built by and acquired from a commercial truck builder (Kenworth, International, Ford, Sterling, etc.). That particular cab and chassis is similar to one used for milk trucks, concrete mixer trucks, delivery trucks, over the road trucks, school buses, etc. Generally, the largest advantage that a commercial apparatus has is that it typically has a lower initial cost. In addition, parts and service can usually be found locally. One disadvantage of commercial apparatus can be the limited seating capacity.

A *Custom Fire Apparatus* is a fire apparatus completely engineered and manufactured by a fire apparatus manufacturer, including the cab and chassis, compartments, pump, tank, aerial ladder, etc. These apparatus are engineered and built specifically for the fire service. The advantage of a custom apparatus is that it is usually built with a chassis and components that are more heavy-duty which gives it a longer operational expectancy. A custom apparatus also includes a more comfortable travel environment designed for firefighters.

One common misconception is that the purchaser has no say in the options or layout of a commercial apparatus while only custom apparatus can be built to the purchasers' exact specifications. In fact, manufacturers of custom as well as commercial apparatus will design an apparatus to the department's exact specifications.

Figure 9.5 An example of a mini-pumper.

Smaller Fire Apparatus

The apparatus dispatched depends on the type and size of fire. The quick response fire apparatus is typically a small, pumping apparatus that is known by many different names throughout the fire service. Different names used include the following:

- Mini-pumper **(Figure 9.5)**
- Midi-pumper
- Quick attack apparatus
- Rapid intervention vehicle
- Attack pumper
- Squad
- Quick response vehicle

An initial attack fire apparatus is designed to handle small fires that do not require the capacity and personnel of a larger pumper. This unit also enables a fire department to save money on fuel and apparatus replacement costs while still having larger pumpers ready for action.

An initial attack fire apparatus is most often mounted on a pickup chassis with a custom-made body. Its fire pump must have a capacity of at least 250 gpm (946 L/min). Initial attack fire apparatus should be equipped with water tanks that carry no less than 200 gallons (800 L) of water. Much of the equipment carried on a larger pumper is also carried on an initial attack fire apparatus, although there are fewer pieces of equipment. Some of these vehicles also carry medical equipment, which enables them to serve as a rescue unit as well as a fire fighting unit. Some initial attack fire apparatus are also equipped with a turret gun that can be supplied directly from another pumper. The small size and maneuverability of this pumper allows it to get into small spaces and set up a master stream where a larger pumper would not be able to fit.

An initial attack apparatus operates with a crew of two to five people. A crew of more than three people requires a four-door cab to carry all the crew members. Some fire departments use the initial attack apparatus as part of a "mini-maxi" concept. They use the initial attack apparatus as a "first-in" quick attack unit. The full-sized pumper can then lay supply hoselines and provide additional support.

Mobile Water Supply Apparatus

The **mobile water supply apparatus** or **tender**, is widely used to transport water to areas beyond a water system or to areas where water supply is inadequate **(Figures 9.6, p. 298)**. Most attack pumpers carry water, but not in large enough

Mobile Water Supply Apparatus — Fire apparatus with a water tank of 1,000 gallons (3 785 L) or larger whose primary purpose is transporting water; may also carry a pump, some hose, and other equipment. *Also known as* Tanker or Tender.

Tender — Term used within the incident command system for a mobile piece of apparatus that has the primary function of supporting another operation; examples include a water tender that supplies water to pumpers, or a fuel tender that supplies fuel to other vehicles.

Figure 9.6 Mobile water supply apparatus may be equipped to transport water to other vehicles or to make independent fire attacks.

Figure 9.7 Areas with severe water problems often use large semitrailers for water supply. *Courtesy of Ron Jeffers.*

quantities to sustain an extended attack. A mobile water supply apparatus has water tanks that are larger than those generally found on a standard pumper, with the smallest carrying at least 1,000 gallons (4 000 L) of water.

NOTE: In some areas the term *tanker* refers to aircraft that deliver water to fight fire.

The size of a water tank on a mobile water supply apparatus depends upon a number of the following variables:

- *Terrain* — The mobile water supply apparatus may be required to climb steep hills or to operate on winding roads. Very large, heavy apparatus may not be able to negotiate steep hills or may be very difficult to maneuver on winding roads.

- *Bridge weight limits* — Bridges in the protected area may be too old or may not be designed to bear the weight of heavy mobile water supply apparatus. This presents a danger to firefighters when alternate routes are not available.

- *Monetary constraints* — The fire department may not have enough money to purchase a large mobile water supply apparatus.

- *Size of other mobile water supply apparatus in the area* — Mobile water supply apparatus shuttle operations flow more easily when mobile water supply apparatus of the same or similar size are used.

If an approved mobile water supply apparatus is desired, the requirements of NFPA® 1901 should be met. The road tests and weight distribution requirements generally limit tank capacity to 1,500 gallons (6 000 L) or less for single rear-axle vehicles. When tanks of capacities greater than 1,500 gallons (6 000 L) are desired, either tandem rear axles or a tractor-trailer design should be considered. Straight-chassis apparatus have tanks up to 4,000 gallons (16 000 L). Anything larger than that requires a tractor-trailer arrangement (**Figure 9.7**). Some mobile water supply apparatus are equipped with full-sized fire pumps and equipment similar to that described for pumpers. This apparatus is called a *pumper-tanker* or a *tanker-pumper*, and it can operate as either a pumper or a mobile water supply apparatus depending on the requirements of the call.

Figure 9.8 Wildland apparatus are designed to operate in rough terrain.

Wildland Fire Apparatus

Because it can go places that are inaccessible to larger apparatus, a lightweight, highly maneuverable vehicle is needed to control wildland fires. The fire apparatus specifically adapted for fighting wildland fires is designed to fulfill these needs and should meet the requirements of NFPA® 1906, *Standard for Wildland Fire Apparatus*. This unit is usually built on a utility-type vehicle chassis, and most have all-wheel drive **(Figure 9.8)**. Booster tanks for wildland fire apparatus vary from approximately 50 gallons (200 L) on smaller chassis vehicles to around 1,000 gallons (4 000 L) on larger apparatus.

Wildland apparatus (also known as brush engines) are usually equipped with a portable pump, auxiliary-engine-driven pump, or a *power take-off (PTO)* powered pump. These "pump and roll" vehicles have the ability to pump water while moving. Fire pumps for wildland fire apparatus range from 10 to 500 gpm (40 L/min to 2 000 L/min). A PTO-powered pump on wildland apparatus normally has a larger gpm (L/min) capacity than a portable pump, but it has a smaller capacity than an auxiliary pump. The PTO-powered pump is easily put into operation and requires little maintenance of the power source other than normal apparatus engine service. An auxiliary-powered pump delivers a constant flow regardless of the apparatus engine speed. A portable pump may serve as the main pump for wildland apparatus or may be carried as a backup unit for PTO-driven or auxiliary-driven pumps. Some apparatus have pre-piped water spray nozzles mounted on the vehicle; other apparatus can have pre-piped air systems.

WARNING!
Riding on the exterior of wildland fire apparatus is extremely dangerous and specifically prohibited by most applicable codes or standards.

Figure 9.9 Wildland apparatus carry a wide variety of tools in compartments built into the apparatus.

Most wildland fire vehicles use non-collapsible hard rubber booster hose (sometimes called a red line or hose reel) as attack lines. A wildland fire apparatus may also carry small diameter, single-jacket forestry hose that allows for handlines to be stretched far from the apparatus. Using short sections of 1 1/2-inch (38 mm) hose and adjustable flow nozzles, however, reduces friction loss and gives the nozzle operator a choice of flows to combat the volume and intensity of fire. A ground sweep nozzle may be useful if the number of personnel is limited and the fuel is short and slow burning. In addition to hose, a brush fire apparatus carries a variety of related equipment such as rakes, axes, backpack water tanks, backfire torches, and shovels **(Figure 9.9)**.

Aerial Apparatus

An **aerial apparatus** is a large vehicle with a powered aerial device that provides firefighters access to the upper levels of a structure. At fireground operations, the company of firefighters assigned to the aerial apparatus is most commonly charged with search and rescue operations, forcible entry, and ventilation. The members assigned to the aerial apparatus are called the truck or ladder company. The truck or ladder companies usually consist of a company officer, a driver/operator or engineer, and two or more firefighters. All aerial apparatus fall under the requirements set forth by NFPA® 1901.

Aerial apparatus can be divided into the following, three distinct categories:

1. Aerial ladder apparatus

2. Elevating platform apparatus including three subcategories: aerial ladder platforms, telescoping aerial platforms, and articulating aerial platforms.

3. Water towers

Aerial Ladder Apparatus

An aerial ladder is a power-operated ladder mounted on a special truck chassis. The working height for aerial ladders is measured from the ground to the highest ladder rung with the ladder at maximum elevation and extension.

Aerial Apparatus — Fire fighting vehicle equipped with a hydraulically operated ladder, elevating platform, or other similar device for the purpose of placing personnel and/or water streams in elevated positions.

Figures 9.10 An example of an aerial ladder apparatus with the ladder raised.

The full-extended length (also referred to as the working height) of North American-made aerial ladders is 50 to 135 feet (15 m to 41 m) **(Figure 9.10)**. Models manufactured in other countries may exceed these heights. The main uses of aerial ladders are as follows:

• Rescue

• Ventilation

• Elevated master stream application

• Gaining access to upper levels

To accomplish these uses, the aerial ladder apparatus carries a complement of ground ladders, tools, and other equipment. Most aerial ladders are power operated with hydraulic pumps, cylinders, and motors. An electric or mechanical backup system must be provided for the truck to meet the specifications of NFPA® 1901.

The aerial ladder may be mounted on either a two- or three-axle, single-chassis vehicle or on a three-axle tractor-trailer vehicle. The single-chassis vehicle is usually equipped with dual rear wheels and is shorter than the tractor-trailer vehicle.

A tractor-drawn aerial apparatus (also known as a tiller truck) is equipped with steerable rear wheels on the trailer. A tiller operator is required to steer the rear wheels of this type of vehicle and continuously communicates with the driver/operator **(Figure 9.11)**. A tractor-drawn aerial is more maneuver-

Figure 9.11 This tillered apparatus has a cab at the rear that can be steered separately. *Courtesy of Ron Jeffers.*

Figures 9.12 An example of an aerial ladder platform apparatus.

able than a single-chassis vehicle. This maneuverability is an asset when the apparatus must negotiate narrow streets or heavy traffic.

Aerial Ladder Platform Apparatus

An aerial ladder platform apparatus is similar to an aerial ladder apparatus except that a work platform is attached to the end of the aerial ladder **(Figure 9.12)**. This vehicle is always single chassis and is usually of three-axle design. Aerial ladder platform apparatus have a rear-mounted or mid-mounted aerial device. The aerial ladder platform combines the safe work area of a platform with a safe, climbable aerial ladder. NFPA® 1901 requires that platforms be constructed of metal, usually steel or aluminum alloy. A heat protective shield that offers protection to occupants of the platform usually encases the platform. The working height of all types of elevating platforms is measured from the ground to the top surface of the highest platform handrail with the aerial device at maximum extension and elevation. Aerial ladder platforms range in height from 85 to 110 feet (26 m to 34 m).

Fire fighting equipment on the platform typically includes a permanently mounted turret nozzle supplied by a water system incorporated with the booms or the ladder. A shower spray nozzle is also located beneath the platform to provide extra protection to the platform and its occupants during high heat situations **(Figure 9.13)**. A foot pedal located on the platform operates the shower nozzle. Electrical, breathing air, and hydraulic outlets are usually provided in the platform, and floodlighting and forcible entry equipment may

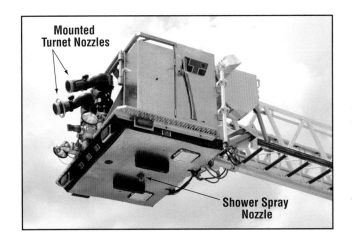

Figure 9.13 This elevating platform is equipped with two turret nozzles and an under platform shower spray nozzle.

Figure 9.14 A firefighter wearing a breathing mask that is connected to the aerial device's built-in breathing air system.

also be in or attached to the platform. A backup hydraulic system is required. Two operating control stations are also required – typically one at the turntable and one in the platform. A communication system between the two control stations is always necessary. Many platforms are provided with outlets to provide handlines and a mobile standpipe to upper floors.

Some aerial devices are equipped with fixed breathing air systems (**Figure 9.14**). These systems provide a source of clean air, which must meet the requirements of NFPA® 1500, *Standard on Fire Department Occupational Safety and Health Program*. Breathing air systems allow for a firefighter to breathe from a special supplied air hose that is attached to a fitted facepiece. This supply hose is connected to an air outlet fitting on the aerial device. The air outlet is connected to compressed breathing air cylinders mounted at the bottom of the aerial device through a system of hoses and/or tubing. In some cases, the facepiece air hose may be long enough to enable the firefighter to leave the aerial device and work remotely from it while still connected to the breathing air system. See IFSTA's **Aerial Apparatus Driver/Operator Handbook** for additional information on aerial apparatus.

Telescoping Aerial Platform Apparatus

NFPA® places the aerial ladder platform and the telescoping aerial platform under the same definition, but each type of apparatus has different capabilities. The primary difference between the two is that an aerial ladder platform is designed with a large ladder that allows firefighters to climb up to and down from the same platform. A telescoping aerial platform, on the other hand, is equipped with a small ladder attached to the boom, which is designed primarily as an escape ladder for firefighters to use during an emergency (**Figure 9.15**). The equipment carried on this type of apparatus is typical of all aerial apparatus.

A telescoping aerial platform device has two or more sections and is made of either box-beam construction or tubular truss-beam construction. Box-beam construction consists of four sides welded together to form a box shape with a hollow center (**Figures 9.16 a and b, p. 304**). Hydraulic lines, airlines, electrical cords, and waterways may be encased within the center or

Figure 9.15 The escape ladder extends up the backside of this telescoping aerial platform.

Figure 9.16a A telescoping aerial platform device with box-beam construction. *Courtesy of Ron Jeffers.*

Figure 9.16b A telescoping aerial platform device with tubular truss-beam construction. *Courtesy of Ted Boothroyd.*

on the outside of the box beam. Tubular truss-beam construction is similar in design to the truss construction of aerial ladders. Tubular steel is welded to form a box shape using cantilever or triangular truss design.

Articulating Aerial Platform Apparatus

The articulating aerial platform apparatus is similar to the telescoping aerial platform apparatus. The primary difference is in the operation of the aerial device. Instead of telescoping into each other, the boom sections of an articulating aerial platform apparatus are connected by a hinge and fold like an elbow **(Figure 9.17)**. The boom is constructed in basically the same manner as the telescoping platform. This unit is often used along with or in place of aerial ladder apparatus. It is used to perform many of the same functions such as rescue, ventilation, master stream application, and accessing upper floors.

Figure 9.17 The articulating aerial platform has hinged sections.

Figure 9.18 This apparatus is equipped with an articulating water tower. *Courtesy of Las Vegas (NV) Fire and Rescue.*

Figure 9.19 A quint can be operated as both an aerial device and a pumper. *Courtesy of Steve Loftin.*

NFPA® 1901 requires that articulating aerial platform apparatus and all other platform apparatus have at least one permanently installed monitor nozzle and supply system. Air, water, and electric power are piped or wired to the platform to facilitate fire fighting and rescue operations. These may be either inside the booms or attached to the outside.

Water Towers

Many fire departments choose to outfit their pumpers with water towers. These are telescoping or articulating aerial devices whose primary function is to deploy elevated master streams above the apparatus **(Figures 9.18).** The water tower is hydraulically operated and is equipped with a waterway to the tip of the device. At the end of the waterway is a nozzle capable of flowing large volumes of water at high pressure. The movement of the water tower and control of the fire stream are remotely controlled by the driver/operator from ground level. These controls are located either at the rear of the apparatus or on the midship pump panel. Most water towers are designed so that their fire streams may be deployed at a range of elevations starting from a few degrees below horizontal to nearly 90° from the ground. Common sizes for these devices range from 35 to 130 feet (11 m to 40 m). They are capable of maximum flows ranging from 1,000 to 5,000 gpm (3 785 L/min to 18 927 L/min).

Historically, some manufacturers of telescoping water towers have equipped them with ladders. In order for them to be truly considered an aerial ladder, the ladder affixed to the water tower must meet the same requirements as those listed in NFPA® 1901 for the aerial ladder. Otherwise, it is recommended that these devices be used only as emergency escape routes.

Quintuple Aerial Apparatus (Quint)

A properly equipped aerial apparatus can also be operated as a **quint**. In addition to the aerial device, a quint is equipped with a fire pump, water tank, ground ladders, and hose bed **(Figure 9.19)**. Many fire departments have used quints to replace traditional engine and ladder companies.

Many departments are also starting to use a standard fire pumper that is equipped with a 65- to 75-foot (20 m to 23 m) aerial ladder or platform. This

Quintuple Combination Pumper (Quint) — Apparatus that serves as an engine and as a ladder truck; equipped with a fire pump, water tank, ground ladders, hose bed, and aerial device.

Figure 9.20 A light rescue vehicle carries only basic hand tools and small equipment

Figure 9.21 An example of a medium rescue vehicle. *Courtesy of Ron Jeffers.*

pumper lacks the space to carry a full complement of ground ladders or other truck company equipment, but it can perform many of the same functions as an aerial apparatus.

Rescue Apparatus

A rescue apparatus is used to transport specially trained firefighters and their equipment. As the name implies, its primary function is to carry the rescue tools and equipment necessary to rescue people from positions of danger such as fires, motor vehicle accidents, trench cave-ins, structural collapses, and many other emergencies. The number of personnel assigned to a rescue company depends on the type of service provided, the type of apparatus, and local needs. There are three general types of rescue apparatus: light, medium, and heavy rescue vehicles. The requirements for each type can vary from region to region.

Light Rescue Vehicle

A light rescue vehicle is designed to handle only basic extrication and life-support functions, so it is equipped with basic hand tools and power equipment. Often, a light rescue unit functions as a first responder; the crew functions to stabilize the situation until heavier equipment arrives. The standard equipment carried on ladder and engine companies also gives them light rescue capabilities.

A light rescue vehicle is usually built on a 1-ton or a 1 1/2-ton chassis **(Figure 9.20)**. The rescue unit's body resembles a multiple-compartment utility truck. The size of this vehicle limits the amount of equipment it can carry. A light rescue vehicle can carry a variety of small hand tools, such as saws, jacks, and pry bars, as well as smaller hydraulic rescue equipment and small quantities of emergency medical supplies.

//////////////////////

CAUTION
A vehicle carrying more than three people requires either a four-door cab or an enclosed crew compartment in the body of the vehicle.

Medium Rescue Vehicle

The medium rescue vehicle has more capabilities than the light rescue vehicle **(Figure 9.21)**. In addition to basic hand tools, this vehicle may carry the following equipment:

- Powered hydraulic spreading tools and cutters
- Air bag lifting systems
- Power saws
- Acetylene cutting equipment
- Ropes and rigging equipment

A medium rescue unit is capable of handling the majority of rescue incidents. It may also carry a variety of fire fighting equipment, which makes it a dual-purpose unit.

Figure 9.22 A heavy rescue vehicle is equipped to deal with a wide variety of emergencies. *Courtesy of Ron Jeffers.*

Heavy Rescue Vehicle

A heavy rescue vehicle must be capable of providing the support necessary to extricate victims from almost any entrapment. As its name implies, the heavy rescue vehicle has larger and more specialized equipment than smaller rescue units **(Figure 9.22)**. Additional types of equipment carried by the heavy rescue unit include the following:

- A-frames or gin poles **(Figure 9.23)**
- Cascade systems
- Larger power plants
- Trenching and shoring equipment
- Small pumps and foam equipment
- Large winches
- Hydraulic booms
- Large quantities of rope and rigging equipment
- Air compressors
- Ladders
- Scene lighting equipment

Figure 9.23 An A-frame rig attached to a rescue vehicle. *Courtesy of Lake Ozark (MO) Fire District.*

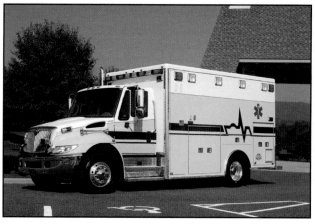

Figure 9.24a An example of a Type I ambulance. *Courtesy of American Emergency Vehicles (AEV).*

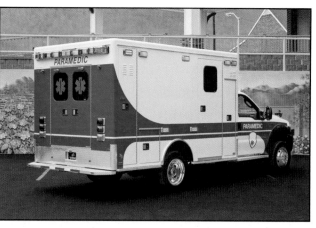

Figure 9.24b An example of a Type I-AD ambulance. *Courtesy of American Emergency Vehicles (AEV).*

Figure 9.24c An example of a Type II ambulance. *Courtesy of American Emergency Vehicles (AEV).*

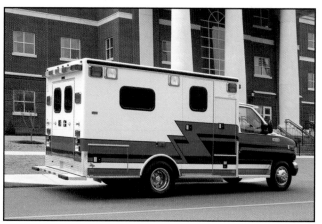

Figure 9.24d An example of a Type III ambulance. *Courtesy of American Emergency Vehicles (AEV).*

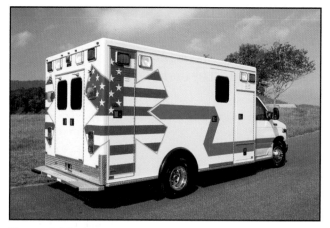

Figure 9.24e An example of a Type III-D ambulance. *Courtesy of American Emergency Vehicles (AEV).*

Other specialized equipment may be carried according to the responsibilities of the rescue unit and the special needs of the department. The heavy rescue unit is oriented more toward fire fighting than the smaller unit because it has more space available for fire fighting equipment.

Fire Service Ambulances

Many fire departments have assumed the responsibility of transporting patients to medical facilities for treatment and have added ambulances to their vehicle fleets. Ambulances are classified by their gross vehicle weight rating (GVWR) and their construction. The five classifications are as follows **(Figures 9.24 a – e)**:

- *Type I Ambulance (10,001 TO 14,000 GVWR)* — Type I vehicles have a cab chassis furnished with a modular ambulance body.

- *Type I-AD (Additional Duty) Ambulance (14,001 GVWR or more)* — Type I-AD vehicles have a cab chassis with modular ambulance body and increased GVWR, storage, and payload.

- *Type II Ambulance (9,201 to 10,000 GVWR)* — Type II ambulances are long wheelbase vans with an integral cab-body.

- *Type III Ambulance (10,001 to 14,000 GVWR)* — Type III ambulances are cutaway vans with integrated modular ambulance body.

- *Type III-D (Additional Duty) Ambulance (14,001 GVWR or more)* — Type III-AD vehicles are cutaway vans with integrated modular body and increased GVWR, storage, and payload.

Aircraft Rescue and Fire Fighting Apparatus (ARFF)

Aircraft rescue and fire fighting (ARFF) apparatus are specifically designed and built to combat aircraft fires. There are several types of ARFF apparatus. NFPA® 414, *Standard for Aircraft Rescue and Fire-Fighting Vehicles,* categorizes ARFF vehicles into three groups based on vehicle water tank capacities:

- 120 to 528 gal (454 L to 1 999 L)

- Less than 528 and greater than or equal to 1,585 gal (less than 1 999 L to greater than or equal to 6 000 L) **(Figure 9.25)**

- >1,585 gal (>6 000 L)

Figure 9.25 A mid-size aircraft and rescue fire fighting (ARFF) apparatus.

Figure 9.26 An ARFF apparatus demonstrating pump-and-roll capability. *Courtesy of Edwin A. Jones, USAFR.*

Because of the large volumes of fuel involved in aircraft fires, mass application of extinguishing agents may be required very quickly in order to protect the occupants of the aircraft. ARFF personnel use specialized aircraft fire fighting vehicles equipped with turrets, handlines, ground sweeps, undertruck nozzles, and extendable turrets to apply the extinguishing agents. Additionally, ARFF vehicles carry medical equipment, ladders, extrication tools, and rescue tools and equipment. Foam concentrate tanks vary in size up to about 1,000 gallons (4 000 L). Fire pumps have a capacity of up to 2,000 gpm (8 000 L/min).

ARFF apparatus have the ability to discharge fire streams while the vehicle is moving, often called pump-and-roll capability **(Figure 9.26)**. This capability is crucial when combating aircraft fires. The large master stream nozzles on the roof of the apparatus are operated from within the cab. Many of the ARFF apparatus also carry foam-compatible fire extinguishing agents, such as carbon dioxide, dry chemical and clean agents, and the equipment needed to deliver them simultaneously with or separate from the foam.

Because not all work is performed on paved or hard surfaces, the ARFF apparatus is built on a special chassis with power to all the wheels. ARFF apparatus are usually supported by a tanker or fed by supply lines from a pumper for a continuous fire fighting operation.

Modern ARFF vehicle features and options include:

- Antilock brake systems
- Central inflation/deflation tire systems
- Driver's enhanced vision systems (DEVS) **(Figure 9.27 a and b)**
- High-mobility suspension systems (independent suspension systems)

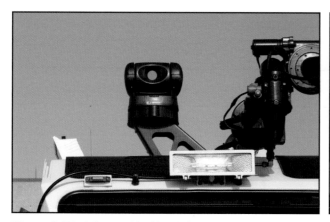

Figure 9.27a A forward looking infrared camera mounted on the roof of an ARFF apparatus.

Figure 9.27b The in-cab DEVs display helps driver/operators drive ARFF apparatus at night or during limited visibility conditions.

Figure 9.28 An apparatus designed and equipped to support hazardous materials operations. *Courtesy of Ron Jeffers.*

Some airports may also have structural fire fighting apparatus that have been modified to assist on aircraft emergencies. These units serve the dual role of providing protection to the terminal area and responding to aircraft emergencies.

Hazardous Materials Response Unit

Many fire departments now assume the responsibility for stabilizing hazardous materials incidents. This job requires additional training and specialized tools and equipment as well as specially designed apparatus to carry the hazardous materials crew members and their equipment **(Figure 9.28)**. Personnel who are thoroughly trained to identify and deal with hazardous materials comprise the personnel on a hazardous materials response unit. This unit carries the usual array of standard hand tools such as screwdrivers, wrenches, hammers, and saws, although many departments use nonsparking copper-beryllium alloy tools. This unit can also carry the following items:

- All types of common patches and plugs from sheet metal screws to wooden plugs and duct tape
- Special kits designed to patch, seal, or contain specific cylinders and containers
- A variety of special protective clothing
- SCBA
- Variety of monitors to test unknown substances
- Radiological detectors and various gas monitors
- Variety of reference material in the form of books and documents
- Onboard computers and modems that allow response personnel to access databases and other sources of information on the hazardous material
- Cellular telephones and facsimile (fax) machines that allow for direct communications with other individuals or companies
- A variety of radio equipment that allows the members to communicate with anyone on the emergency scene
- Weather monitoring equipment so that conditions that may affect the incident can be anticipated and managed
- MSDS (Material Safety Data Sheets) of known materials in area and the current *North American Emergency Response Guide (ERG)*
- Decontamination equipment **(Figure 9.29, p.312)**

Figure 9.29 Hazardous materials apparatus carry decontamination equipment such as shown here.

Mobile Air Supply Unit

Many fire departments and county organizations are placing the mobile air supply unit in service. Its primary purpose is to refill exhausted SCBA cylinders at the scene of an emergency **(Figure 9.30)**. This unit may simply carry a large number of air cylinders for replacement, may be a single or multiple cascade of three to five or more large cylinders, or may include an air compressor to refill a series of storage cylinders. The compressor is fitted with a purification system and various controls to ensure safe operation. Tools and parts are carried on the unit to make field repairs, adjustments, and replacements to damaged SCBA. The types of vehicles used range from pickup trucks with trailers to larger vans or custom-designed apparatus. These units may be combined with other operations such as light apparatus and rescue.

Mobile Command Post

A mobile command post, which is used by the Incident Commander (IC) and the command staff to run an incident, brings needed communication and reference materials directly to the emergency scene **(Figure 9.31)**. For most incidents, a staff vehicle, sports utility vehicle (SUV), or pickup truck has sufficient space to carry radio equipment, area and water system maps, pre-incident plans, hazardous materials references, and unit status boards. During lengthy incidents or at major emergencies employing many pieces of equipment, the unit must serve as a combination field dispatch center and temporary headquarters.

The larger mobile command post may be a step-van, converted bus, trailer, motor home, or custom-designed unit. This unit is equipped with a wide variety of radio and telephone communications equipment, computers, television and video equipment, and other resources needed in that locale. It generally has an electrical generator that allows it to operate independent of outside utilities.

Figure 9.30 An example of a mobile air supply apparatus. *Courtesy of McKinney (TX) Fire Department.*

Figure 9.31 Mobile command units respond to large-scale operations that involve many agencies or jurisdictions and may last a long period of time.

Figure 9.32 Some fire departments along waterways and sea ports employ fire boats for marine fire fighting operations. *Courtesy of Ron Jeffers.*

Fireboats and Search and Rescue Boats

Cities on a waterfront usually have fireboats to protect docks, wharves, piers, and boats. A **fireboat** may be a small, high-speed, shallow-draft vessel, or may be the size of a river, harbor, or ocean-going tug depending on its duties and the area to be covered **(Figures 9.32)**. The number of personnel varies with the size of the vessel.

The fireboat can also be used to relay water to land-based companies. The two phases of fire fighting to which fireboats are particularly adapted are pumping through large master stream devices and providing additional water for onshore fire fighting operations. Fireboats have been built to deliver as much as 26,000 gpm (104 000 L/min). Individual master stream turrets that discharge 2,000 to 3,000 gpm (8 000 L/min to 12 000 L/min) are common.

Fire and emergency service organizations also use **search and rescue boats** **(Figure 9.33)**. These vessels are used to provide search and rescue capability in the marine environment. These rescue boats also serve as a floating platform for dive team and underwater search operations.

Fireboat — Vessel or watercraft designed and constructed for the purpose of fighting fires; provides specified level of pumping capacity and personnel for the extinguishment of fires in the marine environment. *Also known as* Marine Unit.

Search and Rescue Boat — Watercraft designed and equipped to carry personnel during search and rescue operations such as boating accidents, flood evacuations, and dive rescues.

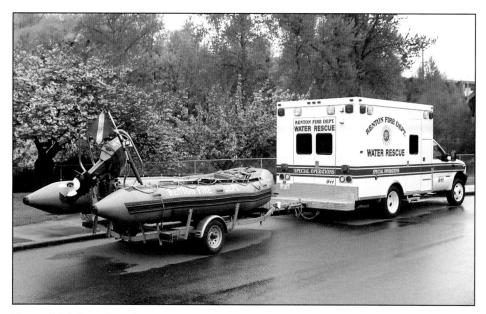

Figure 9.33 Search and rescue boats serve as mobile platforms for searches and rescues on lakes and rivers.

Figure 9.34 An example of a lighting and power apparatus. *Courtesy of McKinney (TX) Fire Department.*

Figure 9.35 A fixed-wing air tanker conducting a slurry drop on a wildland fire.

Power and Light Unit

Some fire departments have special apparatus to furnish lights and power at the scene of an incident **(Figure 9.34)**. Large-capacity generators are used to power electric tools, provide standby power to buildings, and light the emergency scene. An auxiliary motor powers the trailer- or truck-mounted generator. Banks of floodlights and telescoping towers are provided, as well as an ample supply of extension cords, adapters, and portable lights. Personnel may be specially assigned to this company and used only on special calls. In many cases, power and light units are combined with air supply units onto one vehicle. These are called air/power/light units.

Mobile Fire Investigation Unit

The mobile fire investigation unit carries materials and equipment necessary to determine fire origin and cause and to detect arson. These resources include supplies for the collection, preservation, and preliminary evaluation of physical evidence. Equipment carried on this unit includes the following:

* Flammable liquids detectors
* Gas chromatographs
* Magnifying lenses
* Common hand tools
* Lighting equipment
* Cameras
* Tape recorders
* Fingerprint kits
* Sifting screens
* Materials for making plaster casts and fire scene sketches
* Containers such as plastic bags, steel cans with lids, and boxes for storing evidence

Fire Fighting Aircraft

Fixed-wing aircraft (airplanes) and helicopters are usually used to supplement wildland fire fighting units **(Figure 9.35)**. The use of airplanes is usually limited to dropping fire-retardant materials and parachute deployment

Figure 9.36 A rotary-wing air tanker conducting a slurry drop.

Figure 9.37 A large positive-pressure fan mounted on a large vehicle.

of hand-tool crews (smoke jumpers) on natural cover fires. A wide variety of aircraft are used to fight wildland fires depending upon regionally available aircraft. These planes can carry from 120 to 29,000 gallons (480 L to 116 000 L) of retardant material or water. The aircraft pilot can choose the amount of product released by using multiple bay doors, giving the drop different characteristics of penetrating power, length, and width. While extremely useful at fires, aircraft do not replace wildland fire fighting forces.

Like fixed-wing aircraft, a helicopter can be used to drop retardant or water on natural cover fires from a suspended bucket or a tank attached underneath **(Figure 9.36)**. While a helicopter is limited in the amount of retardant material it can carry, its ability to hover adds the advantage of pinpoint accuracy. In addition, it does not have to land in order to procure water.

Other Uses for Fire Service Helicopters

The helicopter is also used for airborne command posts, aerial photography, and fire area mapping. A helicopter is useful for water or rough terrain rescues; an outside winch can be used to lower rescuers and retrieve victims. Specially equipped helicopters are also used to transport critically injured persons from an accident to a medical facility. Helicopters used for medical transport are usually not owned by fire departments; they come from private or state medical services.

Other Special Units

Other special companies can be designed to fulfill local needs. Some special fire fighting companies include high-expansion foam units, dry chemical units, hose monitor or deluge units, smoke ejector companies, and large positive-pressure fans **(Figure 9.37)**. Some special units that do not have fire fighting functions but are necessary for efficient operations include the following:

- Gasoline or diesel service trucks **(Figure 9.38 a, p. 316)**
- Mechanical service trucks
- Wreckers/tow trucks

Figure 9.38a A fire department refueling truck can deliver fuel to several fire apparatus at long duration incidents.

Figure 9.38b Many fire departments use rehabilitation (rehab) units to allow firefighters to rest and rehydrate during fire and emergency operations.

- Thawing apparatus

- Maintenance vehicles

- Rehabilitation (rehab) units (**Figures 9.38 b**)

    NOTE: Variations and combinations of all the previously discussed companies may be necessary, particularly in smaller departments where one piece of apparatus may be required to perform several functions.

Uniforms and Personal Protective Clothing

Firefighters wear a variety of uniforms and personal protective clothing in the performance of their duties. As mentioned in Chapter 1, uniforms serve to identify the member as part of a fire and emergency services organization. The different types of personal protective clothing are designed to protect the wearer from a variety of hazardous environments and conditions. This section will describe the common types of uniforms and personal protective clothing and their uses.

Uniforms

Most fire and emergency services organizations require their personnel to wear some type of uniform while on duty. These may range from casual uniforms to station/work uniforms to full dress uniforms. Casual uniforms usually consist of polo shirts, pocketed trousers, and steel-toed shoes or boots. Station/work uniforms often consist of button down shirts, work trousers, and steel-toed shoes or boots. Full dress or Class A uniforms include a department cap, formal coat, and dress shirt, tie, pants, and shoes. Some departments also specify a standardized work-out uniform for firefighters when they are performing physical fitness activities. These usually consist of a t-shirt, gym shorts or sweat pants, and tennis shoes.

Personal Protective Clothing — Garments emergency responders must wear to protect themselves while fighting fires, mitigating hazardous materials incidents, performing rescues, and delivering emergency medical services.

All station/work uniforms must meet the requirements of NFPA® 1975, *Standard on Station/Work Uniforms for Emergency Services*. The purpose of the standard is to provide minimum requirements for work wear that is functional, will not contribute to firefighter injury, and will not reduce the effectiveness of outer protective clothing. **Figure 9.39** shows the common types of uniforms used in the fire and emergency services.

Figure 9.39 Common examples of fire and emergency services uniforms.

Personal Protective Clothing

Fire and emergency services personnel rely on **personal protective clothing** and **personal protective equipment (PPE)** to protect them from a wide variety of hazardous environments and conditions. Together, these items form personal protective ensembles. The most common types of personal protective clothing are:

- Structural
- Wildland
- Proximity
- Hazardous Materials

Each of these ensembles are composed of the correct components and materials to provide protection to the wearer against the hazards for which the ensemble was designed. The ensemble should also meet any applicable NFPA® requirements for that type of PPE. **Table 9.1, p. 332-334** provides information for each type of personal protection clothing, the environments/conditions for which they are designed, and the common components of each.

Personal Protective Equipment (PPE) — General term for the equipment worn by fire and emergency services responders; includes helmets, coats, pants, boots, eye protection, hearing protection, gloves, protective hoods, self-contained breathing apparatus (SCBA), personal alert safety system (PASS) devices, and chemical protective clothing. When working with hazardous materials, bands or tape are added around the legs, arms, and waist. *Also known as* Bunker Clothes, Chemical Protective Clothing, Full Structural Protective Clothing, Protective Clothing, Turnout Clothing, or Turnout Gear.

Breathing Apparatus

Because fire and emergency services personnel frequently encounter hazardous atmospheric conditions, ranging from oxygen deficient (less than 19 percent oxygen) to those contaminated by a wide range of chemicals to highly heated atmospheres, emergency personnel use a variety of breathing apparatus to protect their respiratory systems and to allow them to perform their duties. The most common types of breathing apparatus are as follows:

- Air purifying respirators (APRs)
- Supplied air respirators (SARs)
- **Self-contained breathing apparatus** (SCBA)

Each type of breathing apparatus is designed to perform a specific function under adverse conditions. Air purifying respirators filter out harmful particles, vapors, or gases by using filters attached to the masks being used. An APR mask may be partial-face covering or full-face covering. Some APRs use powered fans to create a positive pressure within the facepiece.

SARs consist of a source of breathing air (air cylinders or compressor), a facepiece with regulator, up to 300 feet (91 m) of air hose, and an emergency breathing air system or cylinder. These respirators allow emergency responders to operate in hazardous atmospheres without carrying a breathing air source.

SCBAs are atmosphere-supplying respirators for which the user carries the breathing air supply. There are two basic types of SCBA, open-circuit and closed-circuit. **Open-circuit SCBAs**, which are more common in the fire and emergency services, expel the exhaled air into the outside atmosphere. **Closed-circuit SCBAs** reutilize exhaled air by filtering out carbon dioxide and then supplementing the air with oxygen from an oxygen source within the unit.

Breathing apparatus used in the fire and emergency services must meet stringent NFPA® standards and, in the United States, must be tested and approved by the National Institute for Occupational Safety and Health (NIOSH). **Table 9.2, p. 335-338** describes each type of breathing apparatus, its usage, and the components that make up that type.

Tools and Equipment

Fire department operations, including vehicle extrication, depend on the safe and effective use of a wide variety of specialized tools and equipment. While some of these tools and equipment – such as the saws used for ventilation or extrication – are used in "civilian life," many others are unique to the fire service.

The tools and equipment that the fire and emergency services use generally fall into one of two categories: hand tools (nonpowered) or power tools and equipment. Hand tools can be further identified by their specific purpose such as striking, cutting, prying, stabilizing, and lifting. Power tools are often described by their source of power and their purpose.

Emergency responders need to learn the purpose and operation of each type of tool and each piece of equipment they may have to use. Safety is always a priority when operating tools and equipment. Tools and equipment must be properly maintained to ensure their operability during emergency operations.

Tables 9.3 a through e, p. 339-347 list commonly used hand tools and their uses. **Tables 9.4a through d, 348-351** list power tools and equipment used by fire and emergency personnel and their uses.

NOTE: This section will not describe the skills required to use, inspect, or maintain the tools and equipment described. For more detailed descriptions of tools and equipment and particularly for information on use, inspection, and maintenance skills, see IFSTA's **Essentials of Fire Fighting**, **Principles of Vehicle Extrication**, and **Aircraft Rescue and Firefighting** manuals.

Ropes, Webbing, Related Hardware, and Harnesses

Fire and emergency responders use ropes to raise or lower tools, equipment, and/or personnel. Some ropes may be used as guide lines to prevent responders from becoming lost during structural search operations.

There are two classifications of rope: life-safety and utility rope. Ropes can be made of natural (hemp or cotton) or synthetic fibers. Natural fiber rope is no longer used for life-safety purposes.

Webbing is often used in conjunction with ropes. There are two types of webbing, flat and tubular. Most webbing is made from the same materials as synthetic rope.

Emergency responders use a wide range of hardware in conjunction with ropes and webbing. Each piece of hardware serves a specific purpose during rope and webbing operations. Rescue harnesses are designed to help protect rescuers and victims as they move and/or work in elevated positions during rope rescue operations. **Table 9.5, p. 352-354** lists common types of ropes, webbing, hardware, and rescue harnesses and their uses.

Ground Ladders

Not all fire fighting, rescue, and ventilation operations take place on ground level. Emergency responders use ground ladders to reach places above and below grade. Ground ladders are ladders that are not permanently mounted on an apparatus and are carried from an apparatus to the location where they will be raised. These ground ladders are raised into position manually and provide relatively quick and easy access to windows, balconies, rooftops, and other above and below grade places.

Ground ladders may be constructed out of aluminum, fiber glass, or wood. A number of types of ground ladders exist to perform specific tasks **(Figure 9.40, p. 320)**. Fire and emergency services personnel must become familiar with all components of single and extension ground ladders **(Figures 9.41 a and b, p. 321-322)**.

Fire Hose, Nozzles, and Hose Appliances and Tools

Fire hose is produced in a variety of sizes, each for a specific purpose. It is commonly cut and coupled into 50 or 100 feet (15 m or 30 m) long sections for ease of handling but longer pieces are available. The two basic types of fire hose are intake hose and attack hose. Intake hose is used to connect a

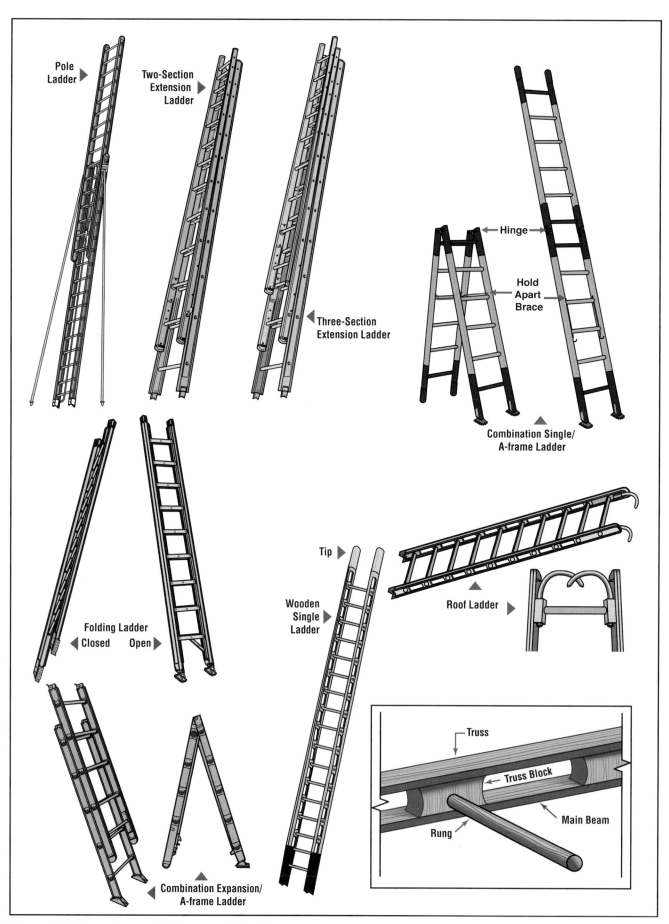

Figure 9.40 Types of ground ladders used in the fire and emergency services.

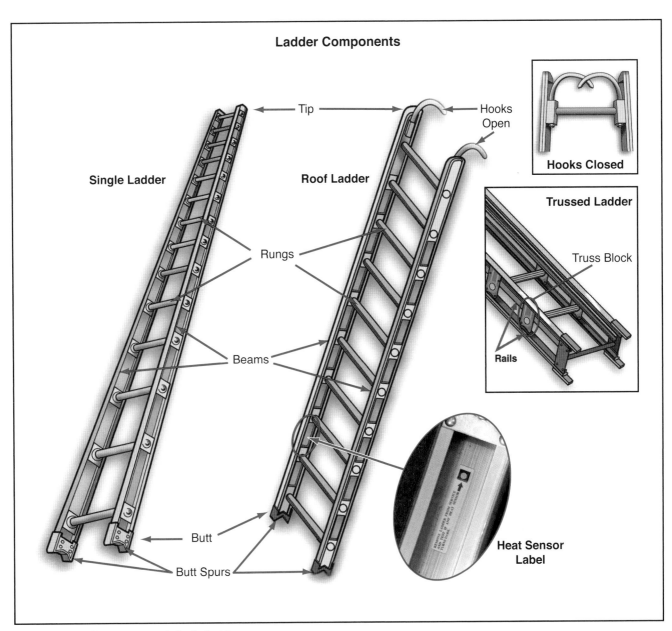

Figure 9.41a Components of single ladders.

Ladder Components

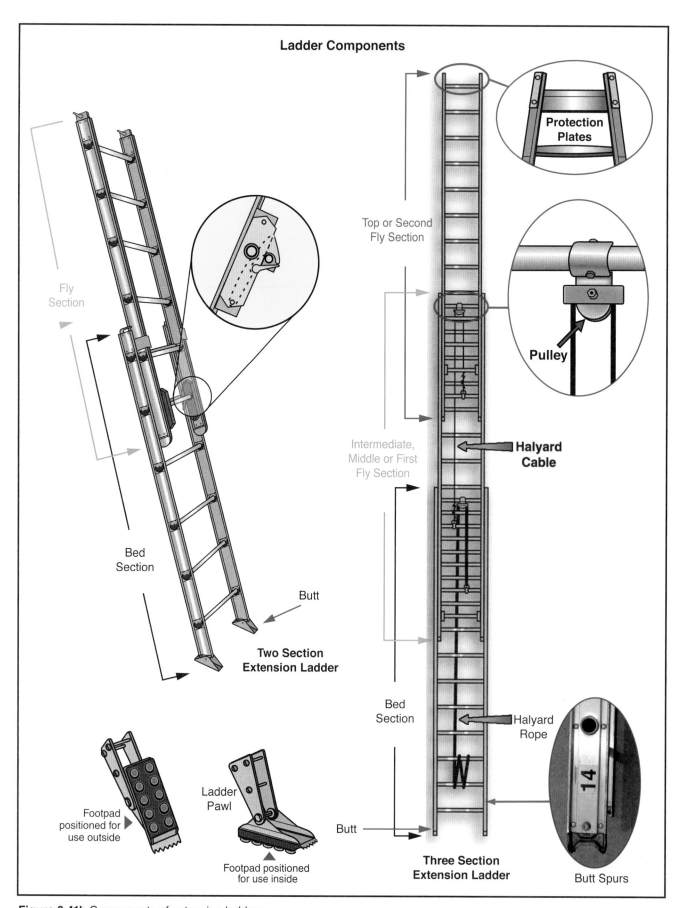

Protection Plates

Fly Section

Two Section Extension Ladder

Bed Section

Butt

Top or Second Fly Section

Intermediate, Middle or First Fly Section

Pulley

Halyard Cable

Bed Section

Halyard Rope

Butt

Three Section Extension Ladder

Footpad positioned for use outside

Ladder Pawl

Footpad positioned for use inside

14

Butt Spurs

Figure 9.41b Components of extension ladders.

Intake Hose

Attack Hoses

Figure 9.42 Supply hose carries water from a water source to the pump while attack hose carries water from the pump to the fire.

fire pumper or a portable pump to a water source while attack hose is used to carry water from a pumper or pump to attack a fire **(Figure 9.42)**. Fire hose is manufactured in a variety of sizes from ¾ inch (20 mm) to 6-inches (150 mm). It is commonly composed of a rubber interior hose line with rubber or woven fiber covering(s) **(Figure 9.43, p. 324)**. Couplings are attached to each end of a section of fire hose to allow it to be connected to other sections of hose, pump fittings, nozzles, and hose appliances. Couplings may be threaded or non-threaded **(Figure 9.44, p. 324)**.

Nozzles are used to create fire streams that are appropriate to the fire being fought. Solid-bore nozzles are used to create a solid stream. Fog nozzles are used to create straight streams and narrow and wide fog patterns **(Figure 9.45, p. 325)**.

Hose appliances are those pieces of hardware such as valves, valve devices, and fittings that are coupled to sections of hose and through which water flows. They can serve to split or connect hoselines, shut water flow on or off, connect hoses with dissimilar threads, or connect a smaller hose to a larger one.

Firefighters use hose tools to tighten and loosen hose couplings, to secure fire hose to an object, or to protect the hose during fire fighting operations.

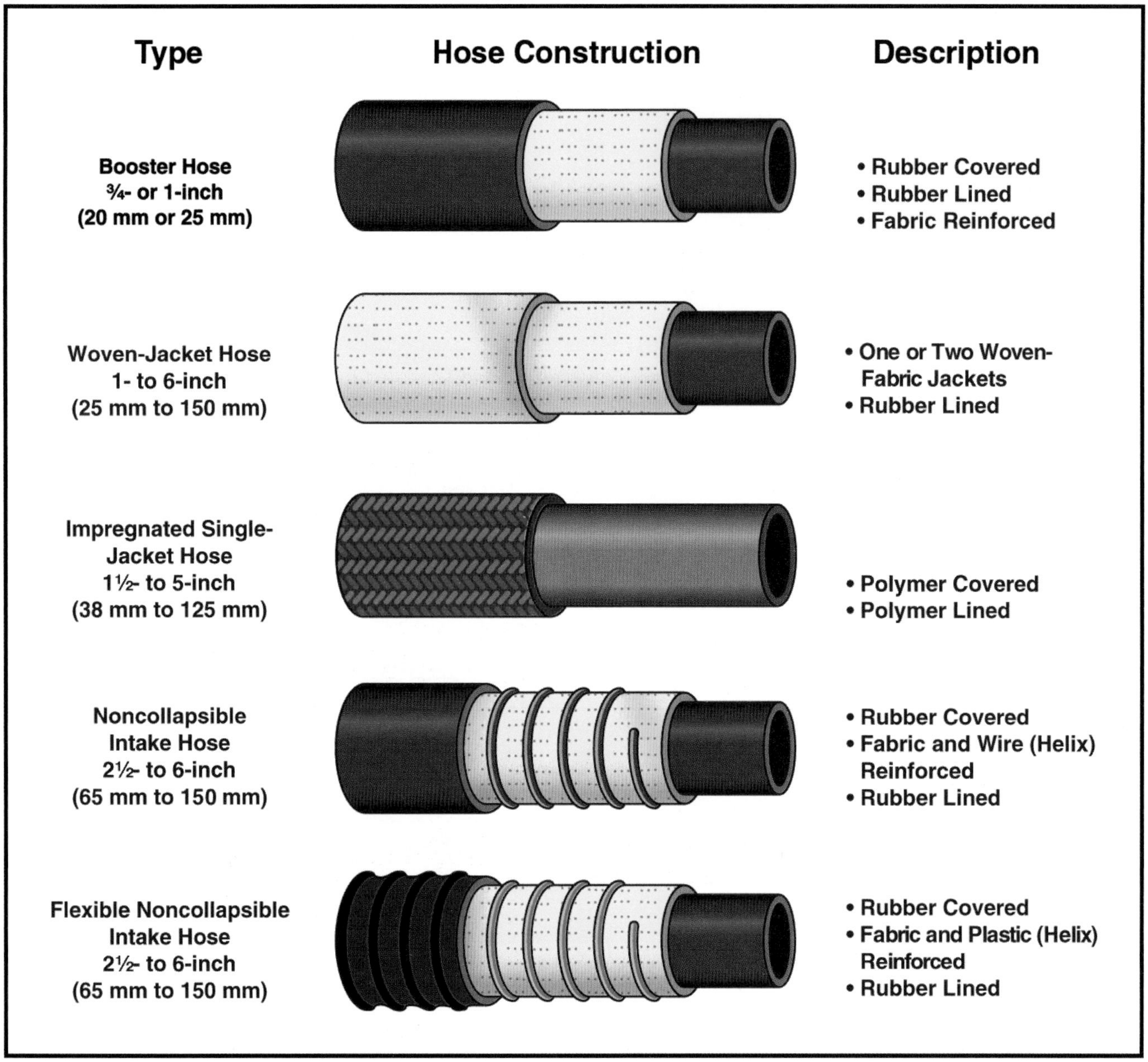
Type
Hose Construction
Description
Booster Hose
¾- or 1-inch
(20 mm or 25 mm)
• Rubber Covered
• Rubber Lined
• Fabric Reinforced
Woven-Jacket Hose
1- to 6-inch
(25 mm to 150 mm)
• One or Two Woven-Fabric Jackets
• Rubber Lined
Impregnated Single-Jacket Hose
1½- to 5-inch
(38 mm to 125 mm)
• Polymer Covered
• Polymer Lined
Noncollapsible Intake Hose
2½- to 6-inch
(65 mm to 150 mm)
• Rubber Covered
• Fabric and Wire (Helix) Reinforced
• Rubber Lined
Flexible Noncollapsible Intake Hose
2½- to 6-inch
(65 mm to 150 mm)
• Rubber Covered
• Fabric and Plastic (Helix) Reinforced
• Rubber Lined

Figure 9.43 Examples of the most common types of fire hose construction.

Male Coupling
Female Coupling
Non-threaded Coupling
Threaded Coupling

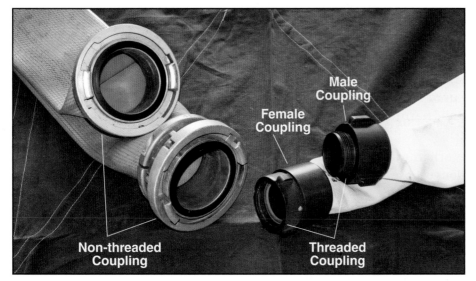

Figure 9.44 Examples of non-threaded hose couplings (left) and threaded hose couplings (right).

Water does not flow through hose tools. **Table 9.6, p. 355-356** lists commonly used hose appliances and tools and their uses.

Fire Department Facilities

Various types of facilities are required for the operation of a fire department. Depending on the size of the department, some or all of these facilities may be found at one location, or the facilities may be separate structures located throughout the jurisdiction. Fire department facilities include:

- Fire stations
- Administrative offices and buildings
- Telecommunications centers
- Training centers
- Maintenance shops

Fire Stations

Fire stations, known in some jurisdictions as firehouses or fire halls, are used to shelter fire apparatus, personnel, and equipment. The required number and size of fire stations vary with the size of the department. A small community may have a fire department with only a small building to house its apparatus. Larger cities may have many fire stations to house multiple pieces of apparatus as well as the firefighters on duty **(Figures 9.46 a and b, p. 326)**.

The layout and contents of fire stations also vary widely. While each fire department has its own requirements for its stations, some components are present in all stations. The most obvious component, of course, is the apparatus bay or garage area. This portion of the station is where the apparatus is parked. The apparatus bay may contain the following equipment and utilities for servicing the apparatus:

- Water piping and outlets for refilling the apparatus water tank
- Sufficient drains and plumbing under apparatus
- An electrical shore line system for supplying power to the apparatus mounted battery charger
- Compressed air for filling tires or keeping air brake systems ready during periods of inactivity
- Apparatus exhaust removal systems to help maintain air quality throughout the entire station

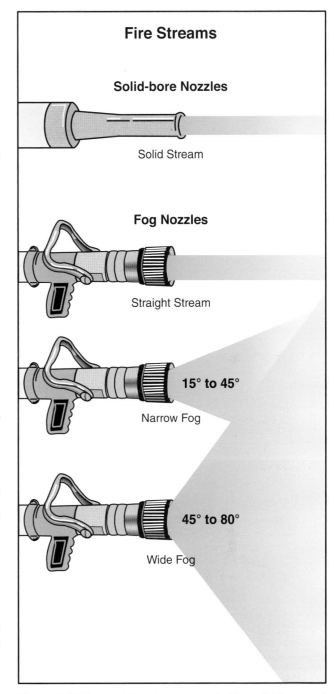

Figure 9.45 Types of fire streams created by solid-bore and fog nozzles.

Fire Station — (1) Building in which fire suppression forces are housed. *Also known as* Fire Hall or Fire House. (2) Location on a vessel with fire fighting water outlet (fire hydrant), valve, fire hose, nozzles, and associated equipment.

Figure 9.46a A small fire station with two bays for apparatus.

Figure 9.46b A larger fire station with six bays for apparatus.

All fire stations must have an area in which to keep tools and equipment for station, apparatus, and equipment maintenance **(Figure 9.47)**. The size of this area and the tools provided depend on how much maintenance work the firefighters actually perform.

Each station should be equipped with an appropriate area for the storage of personal protective equipment (PPE). This area may be include racks, lockers, or cubicles **(Figure 9.48)**. The storage arrangement must provide for adequate ventilation, which allows for proper drying of the equipment. The fire station may be equipped with an air cascade system or breathing-air compressor from which SCBA cylinders can be filled. Also important are hose racks and hose dryers to keep hose dry and free of mildew.

Figure 9.47 A section in a fire station for storing and maintaining tools and equipment.

Figure 9.48 The personal protective equipment (PPE) storage area in a fire station.

Beyond these basics, the features of the fire station vary widely. Stations that are used to house shift firefighters need living accommodations, which include dining, sleeping, bathing, and recreational spaces. Both volunteer and career departments often have training or meeting rooms built into the station. These rooms allow large groups to hold meetings or classroom instructional sessions. Smaller career and volunteer departments may have office facilities in the station for their officers. Volunteer stations may also be equipped with facilities that are used for fund-raising purposes, including banquet facilities, club rooms, and meeting rooms.

Administrative Offices and Buildings

Larger fire departments require office space for administrative purposes. This office space may be attached to a fire station – typically a headquarters fire station – or it may be in a separate building **(Figure 9.49)**. These offices house the administrative chief officers of the department; the staff for research and planning, safety, and personnel; and other related entities. Administrative buildings must have appropriate office space for all professional and clerical staff.

These buildings may also contain record storage sections, meeting rooms, pressrooms, and other special-function rooms as required by the department. Depending on the size and organization of the department, the telecommunications, investigation, inspection, and training staffs may also be located in the main administrative building.

Telecommunication Centers

The telecommunications center is the focal point for all fire department communications. It is considered the "brain" of the fire department's central nervous system. Depending on local requirements, the telecommunications center may be located at fire department headquarters, in a fire station, or at a separate facility. In some cases, the telecommunications center is a joint facility that dispatches various services, such as police, fire, and emergency medical services, for the same municipality **(Figure 9.50)**. In other cases, it may be a facility that dispatches many different fire departments or agencies within the same county or region.

Figure 9.49 Fire apparatus are not stationed at this fire department administration building.

Figure 9.50 An example of a telecommunications center.

The telecommunications center monitors the companies that are in the field and serves as an information center during emergency operations. The center is equipped with a multitude of telephone and radio equipment, including recording devices to record telephone calls and radio transmissions. Modern telecommunications centers are equipped with computer-aided-dispatch (CAD) systems that streamline the dispatch operation by providing exact information on locations and assigned emergency responses. Enhanced 911 systems, which display the caller's address, are becoming more prevalent in telecommunications centers. Emergency vehicles that are equipped with mobile data terminals or laptops can quickly retrieve such information as building construction type, pre-incident plans, street maps, and occupant information pertaining to firefighter safety such as guns, drugs, and the like.

Training Centers

Some fire and emergency services agencies have dedicated facilities for formal educational and training activities. In some cases, two or more agencies may jointly own the training center. The training administration building may contain any of the following:

- Administrative offices
- Classrooms and laboratories
- Auditorium
- Cafeteria
- Exercise equipment
- Locker, shower, and dressing areas
- Storage for equipment, supplies, and apparatus

The training center also has buildings and facilities designed for specific educational purposes. These buildings and facilities are discussed in the following sections.

Burn Building

A **burn building** is designed to have fires set in it repeatedly. Its purpose is to allow firefighters the opportunity to practice interior structural fire attacks under controlled conditions **(Figure 9.51)**.

Burn Building — Training structure specially designed to contain live fires for the purpose of fire suppression training.

Figure 9.51 This burn building is designed for repeated live fire training evolutions.

Typically, a burn building is constructed of masonry, using special firebricks and mortar. Burning straw or wood products such as excelsior provides the fire in many of these buildings, while more modern buildings use piped-in natural gas or propane to build the fire. This situation allows for more control over the conditions in the building because the fire can be extinguished immediately if a problem arises. Burn buildings and live burn training exercises need to comply with the standards set forth in NFPA® 1403, *Standard on Live Fire Training Evolutions.*

Drill Tower

A **drill tower** is used for ladder, rope, aerial device, and other types of training that require a tall structure – usually three to seven stories **(Figure 9.52)**. It is equipped with interior stairways that allow access to the upper floors of the structure, which can also be used for high-rise training. If the tower is used frequently for rope rescue and rappelling, it may also be equipped with safety nets around the outside. These nets are designed to catch a firefighter in case of a fall from the rope or structure.

Drill Tower — Tall fire training structure, normally more than three stories high, used by training personnel to develop realistic fire service situations, especially for ladder and rope evolutions.

Smoke House

A smoke house is designed to provide simulated smoke conditions for firefighters. Simulated smoke conditions help the firefighters develop their confidence and skills when performing interior searches under poor visibility, but nonetheless, controlled conditions **(Figure 9.53)**. Some smokehouses may be designed with an interior similar to that of a house, while others are

Figure 9.52 An example of a drill tower used for ladder, rope, and high-angle rescue training.

Figure 9.53 Smoke houses are used to familiarize firefighters with operating in obscured visibility conditions

Figure 9.54 An example of a training pad used for specialized fire service training evolutions. *Courtesy of Pat McAuliff.*

designed with obstacle courses that can be changed by moving partitions or dividers. The smoke for these structures is nontoxic. A special machine that uses a water-based or vegetable oil-type fluid is used to produce the smoke. The smokehouse should have adequate access points so that panicky students can be removed. It should also have a venting system that can quickly clear the structure if necessary.

Training Pads

Training centers may be equipped with a variety of training pads, or areas, that are designed for a specific purpose **(Figures 9.54)**. These include the following:

- Flammable and combustible liquids and gas fire fighting

- Driver/operator training, including pump operator and pump testing facilities and drafting

- Vehicle extrication

- Hazardous materials abatement props

- Trench and confined space rescue props

- Other specialized props

Maintenance Facilities

The apparatus and equipment the firefighters use greatly affect their ability to perform their duties. The maintenance of this equipment requires special facilities and personnel. Small fire departments may have maintenance areas built into the fire station where apparatus and equipment can be repaired. Larger fire departments, on the other hand, often have separate facilities for

Figure 9.55 Specially trained mechanics conduct apparatus repairs in a fire department apparatus maintenance facilities such as this one.

these activities. Apparatus maintenance shops look like and are equipped much like any commercial truck repair facility **(Figure 9.55)**.

Maintenance facilities are also needed for the upkeep of fire department equipment, including the repair of self-contained breathing apparatus, fire hose, electrical equipment, ladders, and hand tools. Each type of equipment requires special tools and machines in order to be repaired or maintained. Most fire departments prefer to keep all tools and machines in a central location.

Other Maintenance Providers

Some fire and emergency services organizations utilize city motor pools, city yards, or commercial garages for maintenance of their apparatus. Likewise, they may contract commercial equipment and tool vendors to maintain the tools and equipment used by the organization.

Table 9.1
Personal Protective Clothing
Structural, Wildland, and Proximity Protective Clothing

Type	Uses	
Structural (also called *turnouts*, *bunker gear*, or *bunkers*)	To protect emergency responders from: - Excessive heat and thermal injury encountered during structural fire fighting operations. - Physical injury during structural fire fighting, vehicle extrication, and search and rescue operations.	
Wildland (also called *brush gear*)	To protect emergency responders from excessive heat and thermal injury encountered during wildland/urban interface fire fighting operations.	
Proximity (also called *silvers*)	To protect emergency responders from: - Excessive heat and thermal injury encountered during aircraft rescue and fire fighting and industrial fire fighting operations. - Physical injury aircraft rescue and fire fighting and industrial fire fighting operations.	

Table 9.1
Personal Protective Clothing (continued)

Hazardous Materials Protective Clothing
(Based upon U.S. Environmental Protection Agency [EPA] Levels of Protection)

Type	Uses
Level A (also called *vapor-protective*)	To protect emergency responders at hazardous materials incidents when: - Unknown or unidentified chemical hazards. - Identified chemical(s) are highly hazardous to respiratory system, skin and eyes. - A high potential for splash, immersion, or exposure to unexpected vapors, gases, or particulates of material that are harmful to skin or capable of being absorbed through the intact skin. - Substances are present with known or suspected skin toxicity or carcinogenicity. - Operations are conducted in confined or poorly ventilated areas.

Type	Uses
Level B (also called *liquid-splash protective*)	To protect emergency responders at hazardous materials incidents when: - Substances identified and require a high level of respiratory protection but less skin protection. - Atmosphere contains less than 19.5 percent oxygen or more than 23.5 percent oxygen. - Presence of incompletely identified vapors or gases is indicated by a direct-reading organic vapor detection instrument, but the vapors and gases are known not to contain high levels of chemicals harmful to skin or capable of being absorbed through intact skin. - Presence of liquids or particulates is indicated, but they are known not to contain high levels of chemicals harmful to skin or capable of being absorbed through intact skin.

Table 9.1
Personal Protective Clothing (continued)

Hazardous Materials Protective Clothing
(Based upon U.S. Environmental Protection Agency [EPA] Levels of Protection)

Type	Uses
Level C	To protect emergency responders at hazardous materials incidents when: - Atmospheric contaminants, liquid splashes, or other direct contact will not adversely affect exposed skin or be absorbed through any exposed skin. - Types of air contaminants have been identified, concentrations have been measured, and an APR is available that can remove the contaminants. - All criteria for the use of APRs are met. - Atmospheric concentration of chemicals does not exceed IDLH levels. The atmosphere must contain between 19.5 and 23.5 percent oxygen.

Type	Uses
Level D (work uniforms, street clothing, coveralls, or firefighter structural protective clothing)	To protect emergency responders at hazardous materials incidents when: - Atmosphere contains no hazard. - Work functions preclude splashes, immersion, or the potential for unexpected inhalation of or contact with hazardous levels of any chemicals. **NOTE:** May not be worn in the hot zone and are not acceptable for haz mat emergency response above the Awareness Level.

Table 9.2
Breathing Apparatus
Air Purifying Respirators (APRs)

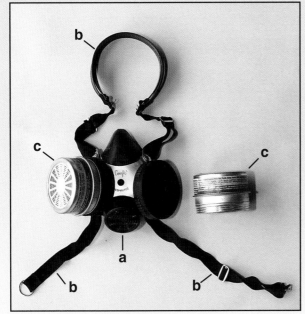

Partial-face Covering APR

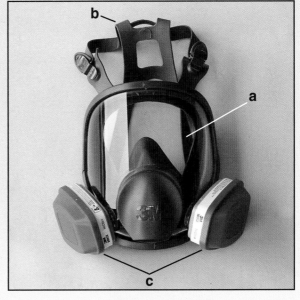

Full-face Covering APR

Type	Uses	Components
Partial-face covering APR	Protects firefighters and other emergency response personnel by filtering out hazardous particles, hazardous or toxic chemical vapors and gases, or a combination of particles and vapors and gases. The level and type of protection provided is dependent upon the types of filters used with the APR.	**a.** Partial facepiece **b.** Straps **c.** Filters
Full-face covering APR		**a.** Full Facepiece **b.** Straps **c.** Filters

Table 9.2 (*continued*)
Breathing Apparatus
Supplied Air Respirators (SARs)

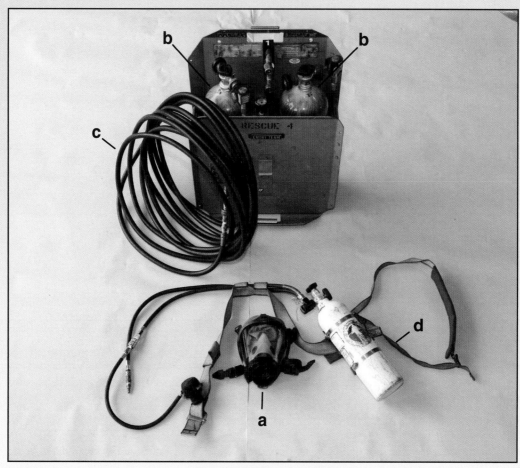

Supplied Air Respirators (SARs)

Type	Uses	Components
Supplied Air Respirators (SARs)	To protect firefighters and other emergency response personnel during operations involving toxic, potentially toxic, or oxygen deficient atmospheres. The unit is designed to vent exhaled air to the outside atmosphere.	a. Facepiece b. Air supply c. Air hose d. Emergency breathing system

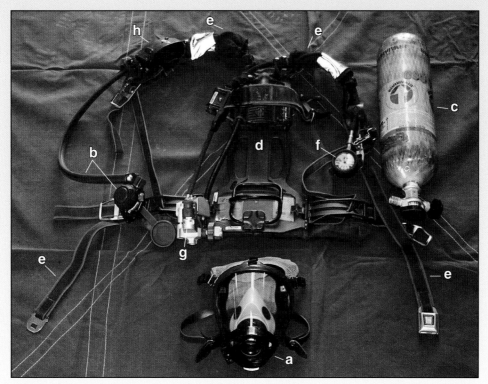

Open Circuit SCBAs

Type	Uses	Components
Open Circuit SCBAs	To protect firefighters and other emergency response personnel during operations involving toxic, potentially toxic, or oxygen deficient atmospheres. The unit is designed to vent exhaled air to the outside atmosphere.	**a.** Facepiece **b.** Hose and regulator **c.** Air cylinder **d.** Backplate **e.** Straps **f.** Pressure gauge **g.** Low pressure alarm **h.** Personal Alert Safety System (PASS) device

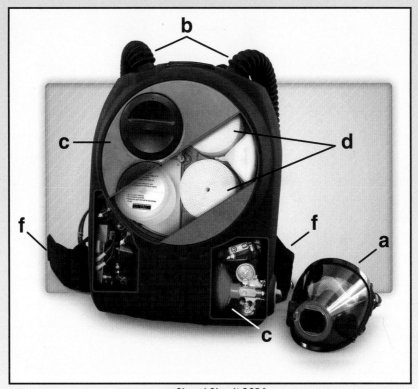

Closed Circuit SCBAs

Type	Uses	Components
Closed Circuit SCBAs	To protect firefighters and other emergency response personnel during operations involving toxic, potentially toxic, or oxygen deficient atmospheres by providing a greater duration of breathable air. The unit is designed to re-use exhaled air by scrubbing out carbon dioxide and adding fresh oxygen from a cylinder to the breathing mixture.	**a.** Facepiece **b.** Hoses **c.** Oxygen cylinder **d.** CO2 filtration system **e.** Housing assembly **f.** Waist straps ***Not Shown:*** • Shoulder straps Pressure gauge • Low pressure alarm • Personal Alert Safety System (PASS) device

Courtesy of Biomarine, Incorporated.

Table 9.3a
Hand Tools
Striking Tools

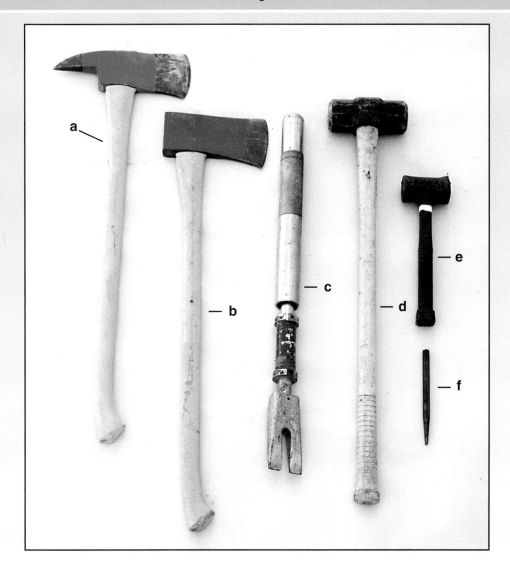

Function	Examples
Used to strike or penetrate an object (wall, roof, floor, etc...) or to force another tool to do so.	**a.** Pick head axe **b.** Flat head axe **c.** Ram bar **d.** Sledge hammer **e.** Mallet **f.** Punch

Table 9.3b
Hand Tools
Prying Tools

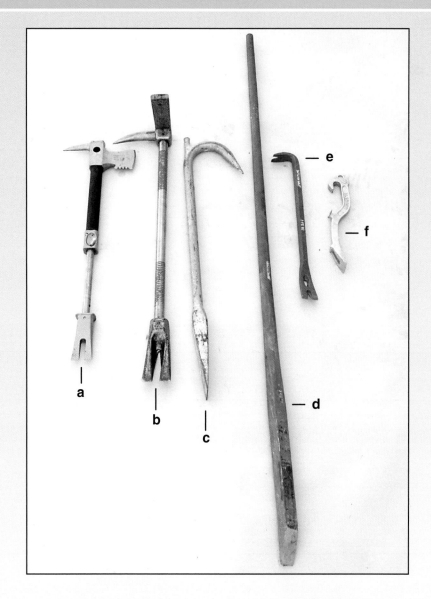

Function	Examples
Used to gain a mechanical advantage or leverage in order to move or remove an object.	**a.** Pry-axe **b.** Halligan bar **c.** Claw tool **d.** Pry bar **e.** Crowbar **f.** Spanner wrench

Table 9.3c
Hand Tools
Cutting Tools

Chopping

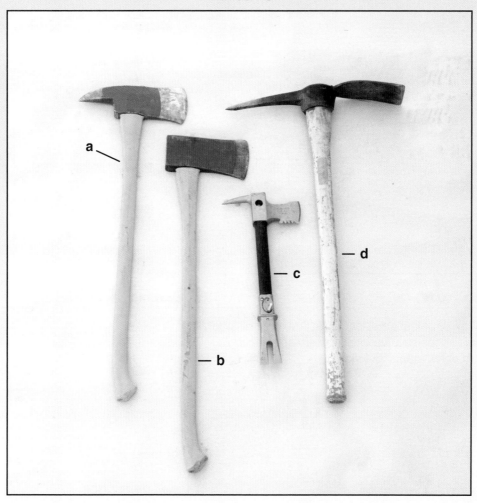

Function

Used to cut away or into an object, structure, or vehicle in order to gain access such as forcible entry or extrication, to remove an object trapping a victim, or to provide an avenue for smoke, heated products of combustion, or hazardous atmospheres to ventilate. Subdivided into Chopping Tools, Snipping Tools, Handsaws, and Knives

* May also belong in another category of tools.

Examples

a. Flat-head axe*
b. Pick-head axe*
c. Pry-axe
d. Pick

Table 9.3c
Hand Tools
Cutting Tools

Snipping

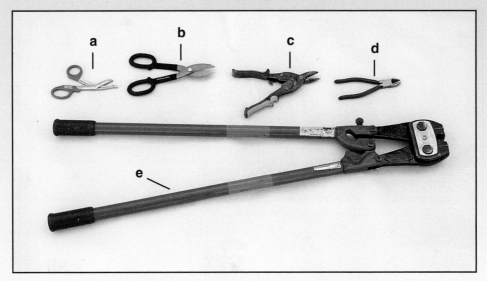

Function	Examples
Used to cut away or into an object, structure, or vehicle in order to gain access such as forcible entry or extrication to remove an object trapping a victim.	**a.** Scissors **b.** Shears **c.** Tin snips **d.** Wire cutters **e.** Bolt cutters

Table 9.3c
Hand Tools
Cutting Tools

Knives

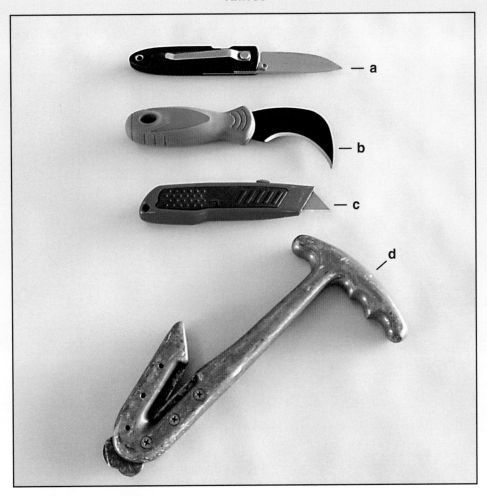

Function	Examples
Used to cut away or into an object, structure, or vehicle in order to gain access such as forcible entry or extrication, to remove an object trapping a victim, or to provide an avenue for smoke, heated products of combustion, or hazardous atmospheres to ventilate.	**a.** Pocket **b.** Linoleum **c.** Utility **d.** V-blade

Table 9.3d
Hand Tools
Lifting Tools

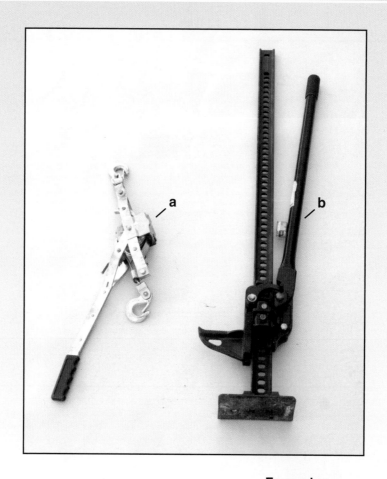

Function	Examples
Used to lift an object, part of a structure, or a vehicle.	**a.** Come-along **b.** Ratchet (Hi-Lift ®) jack

Table 9.3d
Hand Tools
Stabilizing Tools

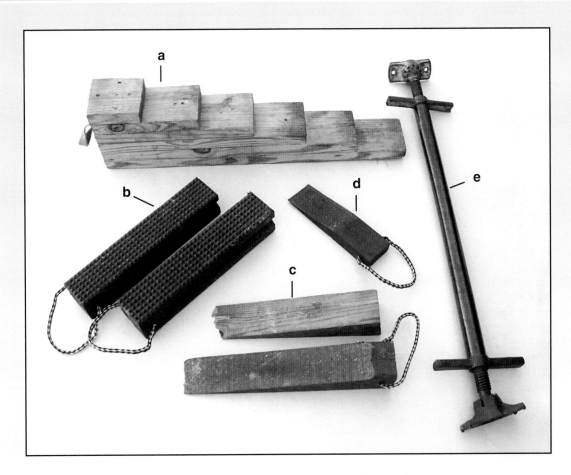

Function	Examples
Used to stabilize an object, part of a structure, or a vehicle during lifting operations.	**a.** Step chock **b.** Chocks **c.** Wedges **d.** Shim **e.** Strut

Table 9.3e
Other Hand Tools
Specialized Hand Tools

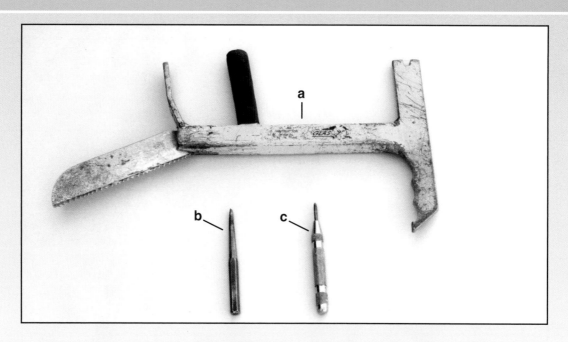

Function

Used to break or shatter glass during:
- Forcible entry into a structure
- Structural ventilation operations
- Vehicle extrication operations

* May also be classified under another type of tool.

Examples

a. Glass saw*
b. Standard center punch
c. Spring-loaded center punch

Table 9.3e
Other Hand Tools
Mechanic's Tools

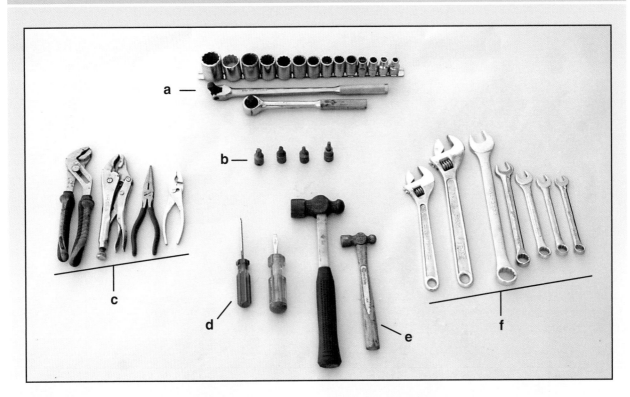

Function

Used to manipulate bolts, nuts, screws, and other fasteners during victim extrication from structures, vehicle, and industrial equipment.

Examples

a. Socket set
b. Torx® drivers (Star drivers)
c. Pliers
d. Screw drivers
e. Ball peen hammers
f. Wrenches

Table 9.4a
Power Tools

Electric Powered

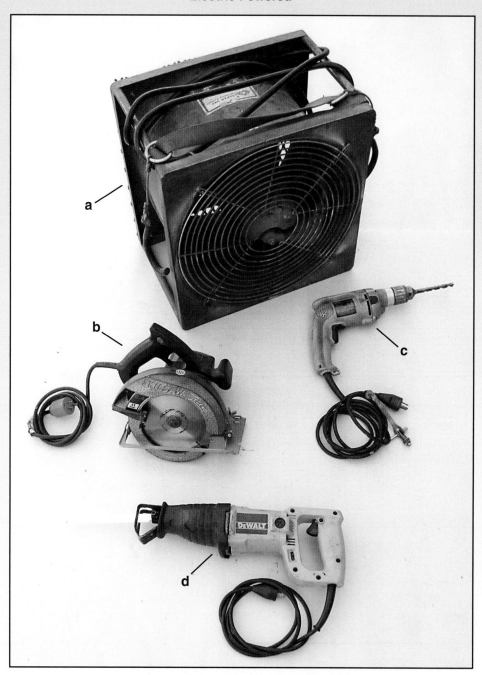

Function	Examples
Some power tools are used to cut or remove an object, part of a structure, or vehicle. Others are used to move air in order to ventilate a structure.	**a.** Smoke blower **b.** Rotary saw **c.** Drill or driver **d.** Reciprocating saw

Table 9.4b
Power Tools

Pneumatic Powered

Function

Some power tools are used to cut, spread, lift, move, or remove an object, part of a structure, or vehicle.

Examples

a. Low pressure hose and air bag
b. Low/medium pressure air manifold
c. High pressure air manifold
d. Air pressure regulator
e. Air cylinder
f. High pressure air bags and hose
g. Air chisel
h. Air wrench

Table 9.4c
Power Tools

Hydraulic – Manually Operated

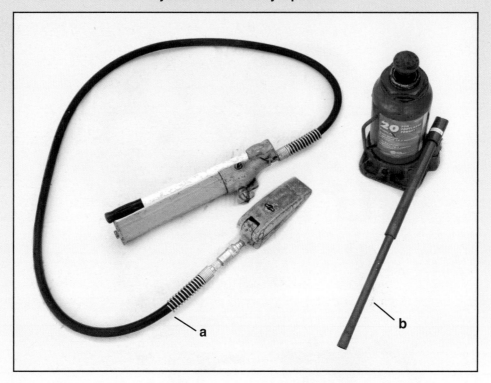

Function	Examples
Some power tools are used to spread, lift, move remove an object, part of a structure, or vehicle.	**a.** Porta-Power® **b.** Hydraulic jack

Table 9.4d
Power Tools

Hydraulic – Power Driven

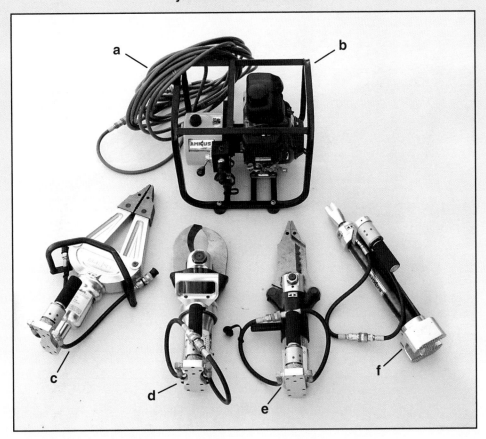

Function	Examples
Some power tools are used to cut, spread, lift, move, or remove an object, part of a structure, or vehicle.	**a.** Hydraulic hose lines **b.** Power unit **c.** Spreaders **d.** Sheers **e.** Combination spreaders/sheers **f.** Ram

Table 9.5
Ropes, Webbing, Hardware, and Harnesses

Natural and Synthetic Ropes

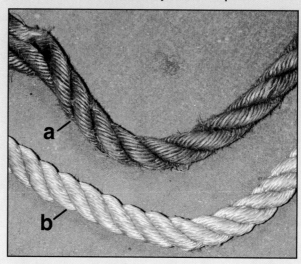

Uses	Types
To raise and lower tools, equipment, and personnel. May also serve as a guide line during structural search operations. **NOTE:** Natural fiber ropes are no longer used for life-safety purposes.	**a.** Natural fiber rope **b.** Synthetic rope

Webbing

Uses	Types
To raise and lower tools, equipment, and personnel. May also be used to anchor an item to prevent movement.	**a.** Flat webbing **b.** Tubular webbing

Table 9.5 (continued)
Ropes, Webbing, Hardware, and Harnesses

Hardware

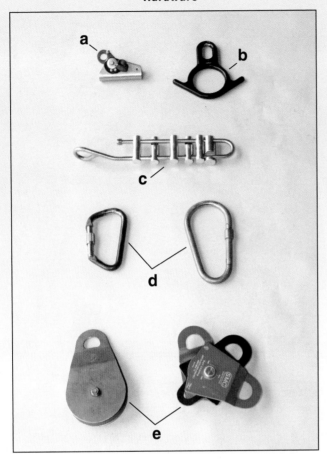

Uses	Types
To connect sections of a rope system together (carabiner), act as a brake during rappelling (figure-eight plate or brake-bar rack), to ascend a vertical rope (ascender), or change the direction of pull or create mechanical advantage (pulley).	**a.** Ascender **b.** Figure-eight plate **c.** Brake-bar rack (descender) **d.** Carabiner **e.** Pulley

Table 9.5 (continued)
Ropes, Webbing, Hardware, and Harnesses

Rescue Harnesses

a.

b.

Uses	Types
To help protect rescuers and victims as they move and/or work in elevated positions during rope rescue operations.	**a.** Class I (loads up to 300 lb [1.33 k/N]) and Class II (loads up to 600 lb [2.67 k/N]) **b.** Class III (full body harness)

Table 9.6
Hose Appliances and Tools

Hose Appliances

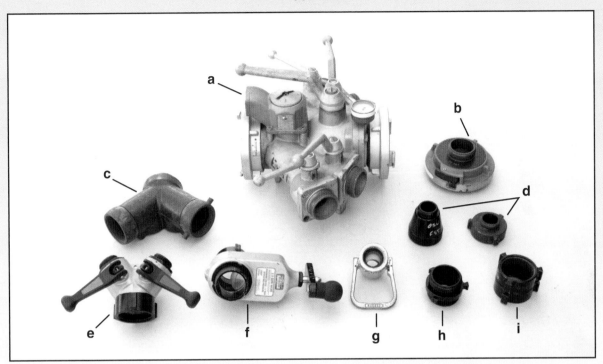

Function	Examples
Hose appliances are used to split or connect hoselines, shut water flow on or off, connect hoses with dissimilar threads, or connect a smaller hose to a larger one.	**a.** Large diameter hose (LDH) manifold **b.** Adapter **c.** Siamese **d.** Reducers **e.** Gated wye **f.** Gate valve **g.** Ball valve **h.** Double male **i.** Double female

Table 9.6
Hose Appliances and Tools

Hose Tools

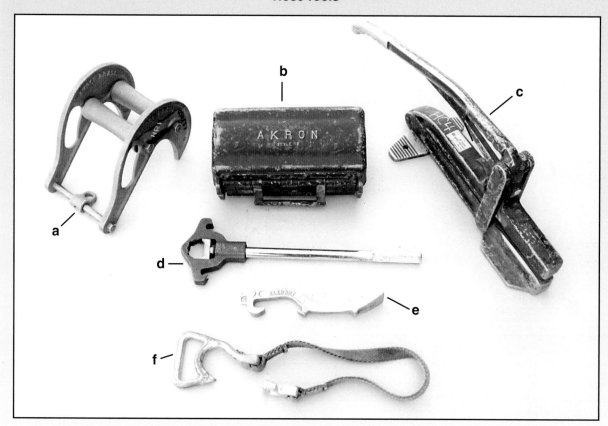

Function	Examples
Hose tools are used to tighten and loosen hose couplings, to secure fire hose to an object, to restrict the flow of water through a hose, or to protect the hose during fire fighting operations.	**a.** Hose roller **b.** Hose jacket **c.** Hose clamp **d.** Hydrant wrench **e.** Spanner wrench **f.** Hose strap

Chapter Summary

The job of responding to emergency medical calls, extricating victims from vehicle accidents, and fighting fires requires a great deal of specialized equipment and training in its use. From the telecommunications center to the central offices to the fire station, firefighters must become familiar with the many different types of apparatus and equipment that are needed to help victims and protect property. While many smaller departments do not have the demand or resources to equip specialized units, all firefighters will need to become familiar with basic fire fighting apparatus such as pumpers and ladder trucks. Nearly all will need to become familiar with emergency medical equipment. Fire departments must also work closely with other departments to share resources and to be prepared to provide mutual aid when necessary.

Review Questions

1. What determines the type of apparatus dispatched to an incident scene?

2. What is the main difference between an aerial ladder apparatus and an aerial ladder platform apparatus?

3. What are the main differences between a light, medium, and heavy rescue vehicle?

4. Describe the four general styles of fire service ambulances.

5. What equipment would a mobile fire investigation unit carry?

6. What are the four types of common personal protective clothing?

7. What are the three types of breathing apparatus commonly used in fire suppression?

8. What piece of equipment is used to create appropriate fire streams?

9. What are five common types of fire department facilities?

10. Describe the differences between a burn building and a smoke house.

Fire Department Organization and Management

Key Terms

FESHE Outcomes

This chapter provides information that addresses the outcomes for the Fire and Emergency Services Higher Education (FESHE) *Principles of Emergency Services* course.

4. List and describe the major organizations that provide emergency response service and illustrate how they interrelate.

7. Discuss and describe the scope, purpose, and organizational structure of fire and emergency services.

9. Compare and contrast effective management concepts for various emergency situations.

NFPA® Job Performance Requirements

This chapter provides information that addresses the following job performance requirements (JPRs) of NFPA® 1001, *Standard for Fire Fighter Professional Qualifications* (2008).

5.1.1   5.3.5(A)   6.1.1   6.1.2

Learning Objectives

After reading this chapter, students will be able to:

1. List the common purposes of fire protection agencies.

2. Describe the basic principles of organization.

3. Identify basic positions in the local government structure that can affect fire and emergency services.

4. Explain the different types of fire departments.

5. Describe automatic aid and mutual aid.

6. Explain the different ways a fire department can be funded.

7. Discriminate between a policy and procedure as used in the fire and emergency services.

8. Describe how the Incident Management System works in the fire and emergency services field.

Chapter 10
Fire Department Organization and Management

Case History

Like many people in her small town, Jean St. Clair usually ran to watch whenever the volunteer fire department responded to a call. The emergency scenes were busy places, and to an outsider it all looked very confusing. But Jean had to admit that everyone seemed to know their jobs. Now at the rookie academy, Jean is beginning to understand how the fireground is organized. She knows that concepts like chain of command, span of control, and division of labor were right in front of her every time she watched her small town department respond.

Before entering into any discussion on fire department organization, it is necessary to preface this chapter with a qualifying statement: Virtually no two fire departments in the world are organized in exactly the same manner. Therefore, any discussion on fire department organization must be made in a very general way. The purpose of this chapter is to introduce the reader to the following concepts:

- Purposes of fire protection agencies
- Principles of organization
- Local government structures
- Types of fire departments
- Response considerations
- Fire department funding
- Policies and procedures
- Incident management systems
- Fire department planning

Purposes of Fire Protection Agencies

Whether they are public fire departments, industrial fire brigades, military fire departments, or private services, all fire protection agencies share several common purposes. Some of the more important purposes include the following:

- Provide adequately equipped and trained fire suppression capabilities to meet public requirements and reasonable budgetary allocations.

- Conduct fire safety and fire prevention programs and make other efforts to improve customer awareness.

- Investigate fires to determine cause and to detect possible arson.

- Coordinate the customer's total fire protection system. This effort includes a review of new construction and development to ensure that materials and designs provide adequate suppression systems, hydrants, apparatus access, adequate separations, and means of egress.

- Provide other emergency services, such as emergency medical care, technical rescue, and hazardous materials response, as required.

- Advise local government in matters of fire protection and public safety, including resources needed and laws and ordinances required to support fire protection and life safety.

- Establish and maintain agreements with public and private entities for coordinated responses and mutual aid.

Fire and Rescue Services as Emergency Managers

In many communities, the emergency manager function is assigned to the fire and rescue services. In these cases, it is very important that the role of emergency manager as a coordinator is seen as involving the entire resources of the community and not just the fire and rescue services.

Principles of Organization

A fire department is composed of individuals with different backgrounds and different ideas about life. The success of the department depends on the willingness of its members to put aside their differences and work for the benefit of the public and the department. To ensure that department members cooperate effectively, the methods of cooperation are outlined in policies, job descriptions, and organizational charts.

An organizational chart shows the structure of the fire department and its chain of command. The complexity of a department is represented on its organizational chart. Small fire departments have a relatively simple chain of command, while large departments have a considerably more complex chart. **Figures 10.1, 10.2, and 10.3, p. 363-364** show sample organizational charts for small, medium, and large fire departments. These are meant only to serve as a reference. Charts for local municipalities vary.

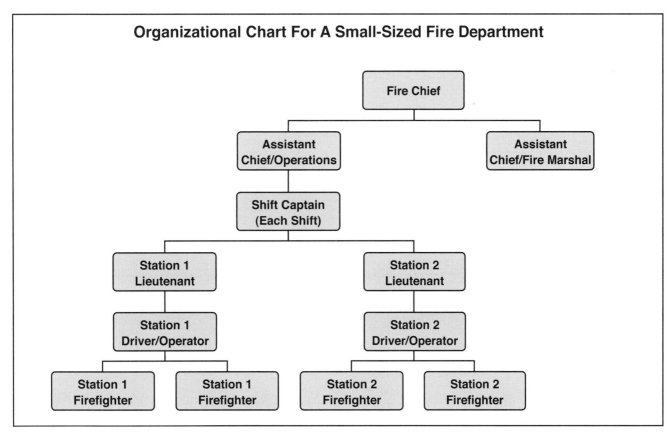

Figure 10.1 Small departments have relatively simple organizational charts.

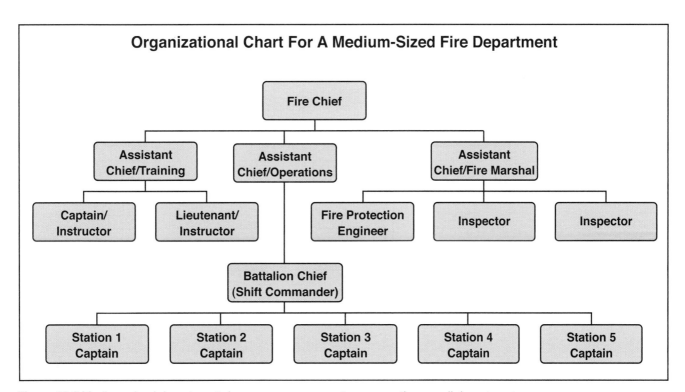

Figure 10.2 Medium-sized departments have more resources to manage than small departments.

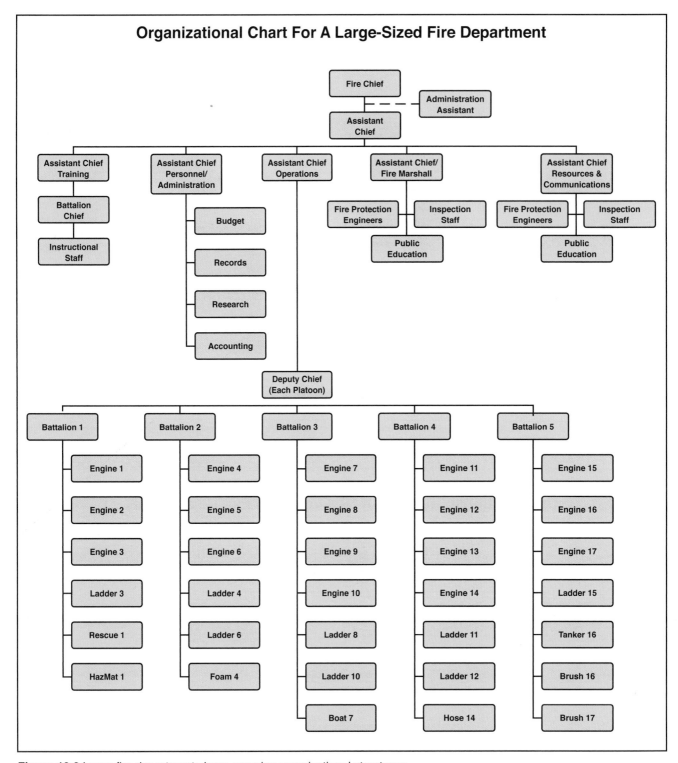

Organizational Chart For A Large-Sized Fire Department

Figure 10.3 Large fire departments have complex organizational structures.

There are four basic organizational principles that firefighters must remember if they are to operate effectively as a team members:

- Unity of command
- Span of control
- Division of labor
- Discipline

Unity of Command

Unity of command is an important concept to the fire department. The principle behind unity of command is that a person can only report to one supervisor. Directly, each subordinate reports to one superior; however, indirectly everyone reports to the fire chief through the chain of command **(Figure 10.4)**. The **chain of command** is the pathway of responsibility from the highest level of the department to the lowest level. The fire chief issues general orders that filter through the chain of command and turn into specific work assignments for the firefighter. Unity of command ensures that all fire department personnel are aware of and understand the chief's orders. In this way, work can be divided into specific job assignments without loss of control.

Chain of Command — (1) Order of rank and authority in the fire and emergency services. (2) The proper sequence of information and command flow as described in the Incident Management System-Incident command System (NIMS-ICS).

Unity of Command — Organizational principle in which workers report to only one supervisor in order to eliminate conflicting orders and the confusion that would result.

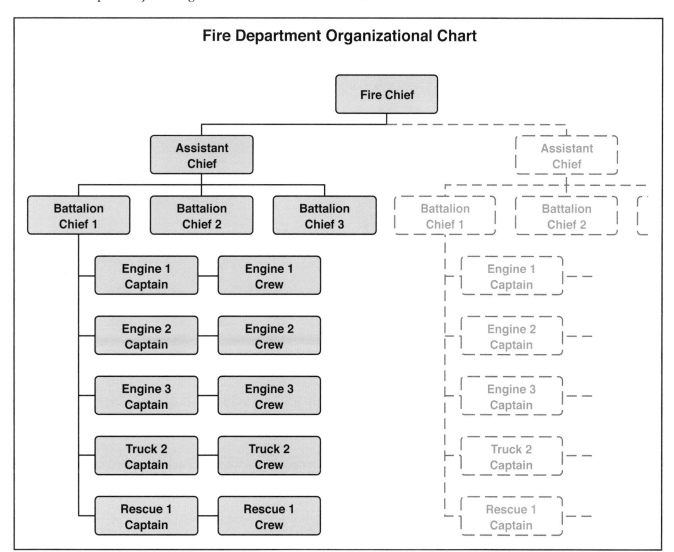

Figure 10.4 This simple organizational chart shows the department's chain of command.

If a firefighter is put into a situation that requires reporting to more than one supervisor, a number of difficult situations can result. For example, a firefighter at a fire scene may be given an order by a company officer and then given a conflicting order by a higher-ranking officer. Such circumstances represent an organizational problem, not a personnel problem. However, if a firefighter bypasses the company officer and takes a problem to a higher-ranking officer, this becomes a personnel problem. Bypassing company officers is a bad practice because often the company officer is the best qualified to solve the problem.

In reality, there are always situations that do not transpire according to the chain of command. Officers must realize that breaches in unity of command do occur. Therefore, fire department policies must outline procedures for handling these situations, and company officers must learn to deal with them in a positive manner.

Span of Control

Span of Control — Maximum number of subordinates that that one individual can effectively supervise; ranges from three to seven individuals or functions, with five generally established as optimum.

The term **span of control** refers to the number of personnel one individual can effectively manage. A general guideline in the fire service is that an officer can effectively supervise three to seven firefighters directly, but the actual number varies with the situation **(Figure 10.5)**.

Figure 10.5 A five-to-one span of control is desirable.

Division of Labor

Division of Labor — Subdividing an assignment into its constituent parts in order to equalize the workload and increase efficiency.

Division of labor is the practice of subdividing large jobs into small jobs. These small jobs are then assigned to specific individuals. The division of labor concept is necessary in the fire service for the following reasons:

- To assign responsibility
- To prevent duplication of effort
- To make specific and clear-cut assignments

Discipline

Traditionally, **discipline** has been understood to mean correction or punishment. In this instance, however, discipline refers to an organization's responsibility to provide the direction needed to satisfy the goals and objectives it has identified. In other words, it is setting the limits or boundaries for expected performance and enforcing them. This direction may come in the form of rules, regulations, or policies (often referred to as Standard Operating Procedures [SOPs]), but regardless of the term used, they must define how the department plans to operate. The rules of the organization must be clearly written and presented.

Discipline — To maintain order through training and/or the threat or imposition of sanctions; setting and enforcing the limits or boundaries for expected performance.

Local Government Structure

The structure of the local government varies from city to city. Firefighters should become familiar with the type of local government structure of which they are a part, because the political decisions of the governing body will affect the operations and services that the fire service agency offers. Regardless of the type of government structure, the voters remain at the top of the organizational chart. Funding for the department is derived through the voters of the community. Forms of local government include the following:

- Commission
- Council (Board) Manager
- Mayor/Council

Commission

In the Commission form of government, voters elect a board of commissioners who will carry out the legislative and executive functions. The board of commissioners then appoints officials and supervisors for various governmental needs. The commission may select one of the commissioners to serve as the chairman of the commission. Department heads are elected positions and are not appointed by the commissioners.

Council (Board) Manager

In the Council (Board) Manager form of government, voters elect a council or board of officials who carry out the legislative responsibilities. These elected officials appoint a professional manager to handle the administrative (executive) matters. This manager appoints the department heads to execute the needs of the council within their specific areas of responsibility.

Mayor/Council

In the Mayor/Council form of government, voters elect a mayor and a council to govern the community. The mayor plays the role of an elected independent executive who is both policy advocate and chief executive officer. The mayor, acting as a manager, appoints the department heads. In some communities, with a *weak mayor* form of government, the city hires a professional manager.

Types of Fire Departments

What is an adequate level of fire protection? What is a reasonable community cost? These are basic questions that every community must face. The acceptable level of risk that the local government assumes is a political and community decision. Every community must define the level of fire protection it desires once the extent of the problem has been determined. The community must also determine what it is willing to pay for emergency and nonemergency services. Values, trends, and community forces all play a part in determining the types and levels of services that the fire department provides.

Fire departments generally function under the local government, although some departments are independent. Some states furnish fire fighting and rescue services for state turnpikes or other large state roads, forests and parks, and state institutions. The federal government has little or no control over local fire protection, although there are some foreign countries in which fire protection is controlled and operated solely by the national government. The military branches of the United States maintain their own fire protection forces, and the personnel are military specialists or civil service employees. The federal government does, however, furnish fire protection for its national parks and forests. The National Park Service and the U.S. Forestry Service have extensive fire prevention and suppression activities and often contract for mutual aid with other local fire departments.

The term *fire department* has come to be applied to virtually any fire protection agency. However, a more precise meaning of the term refers to the fact that the organization is a departmental division of a larger body, such as a municipal government or county, parish, or borough commission. Other departments may include law enforcement, water and sanitation, utilities, and streets and highways **(Figures 10.6)**. There are more than 33,000 public fire departments in the United States. The two most common ways of classifying public fire departments are as follows:

1. By the type of jurisdiction in which the department operates
2. By whether personnel are paid and fire stations are normally staffed around the clock

Figures 10.6 Law enforcement personnel during a firefighter's funeral procession.

Jurisdiction

In this context, the term *jurisdiction* has two distinct connotations. First, it refers to the area that a fire protection agency serves. Jurisdiction also refers to the authority that gives the agency the legal right to provide such services and to take the actions necessary to ensure adequate protection. In some cases, the jurisdiction of a fire protection agency is clearly tied to a level of government, such as a municipal fire department operating within the boundaries of its city and with the authorization of its city government. Because fires and other emergencies do not recognize territorial and legal boundaries, and often require greater resources than a local government can provide on its own, fire protection agencies are frequently organized across jurisdictional boundaries.

Public Fire Departments

Some of the more common public jurisdictions that provide fire protection include the following:

- Municipal
- County/parish/borough
- Fire district
- Fire protection district

Municipal

As used here, the term *municipal fire department* refers to a functional division of the lowest level of local government, such as a city, town, township, village, or incorporated or unincorporated community, which is authorized at the state or provincial level to form a fire department. This is the most common jurisdiction for fire departments. The municipal fire department — whether full-time, part-time, career, volunteer, or a combination — operates as part of the local government and receives funding, authority, and oversight from that body. Typically, the personnel who staff career departments are municipal employees.

Virtually every city in the United States and Canada with a population of more than 100,000 and the majority of cities with populations between 50,000 and 100,000 maintain full-time fire departments. Of those cities and towns with populations of less than 50,000, nearly half maintain full-time fire departments.

As a departmental agency within municipal government, most full-time public fire departments exhibit an organizational structure that reflects the local governmental structure. The department head generally oversees the operation of the department and serves as the principal interface between the fire department and the rest of the municipal government. In most public fire departments in North America, this official carries the title of chief or, in some cases, commissioner. The chief must ensure that the department has an adequate organizational structure and management system, including required policies and procedures, to govern the operation of the department in support of its mission **(Figures 10.7)**.

The size of the public fire department depends primarily on the population, area of the municipality served, and other factors such as special fire protection requirements (heavy industry, use and transportation of hazardous materials, etc.), and level of services to be provided as determined by the local governing

Figure 10.7 A fire chief discussing budget issues with a department fire marshal.

body. All departments maintain one or more fire stations, sometimes called *houses* or *halls,* from which personnel and equipment respond, while larger departments may operate several stations throughout their service area as well as separate facilities for administration, training, and other functions. In smaller departments, personnel may be called upon to serve in multiple roles in order to provide a full range of services, such as hazardous materials response, technical rescue, emergency medical care, arson investigation, and fire safety/code enforcement inspections. Larger departments may have personnel who specialize in such areas as well as response personnel who are certified as driver/operators of the apparatus they drive.

NOTE: Regardless of departmental size, all personnel need to be trained or certified so that they can perform specific duties, such as driver/operator or haz-mat response, safely.

To provide this wide variety of services, larger departments may have administrative and functional subdivisions, such as districts, divisions, battalions, companies, and special squads or teams. These subdivisions may be under the supervision of officers with a variety of titles or ranks such as chief officers, captains, or lieutenants. A small percentage of fire departments use different military ranks/titles such as majors, sergeants, and so on.

Funding to support operation of a fire department is part of the municipal budget and is usually obtained through the collection of taxes. However, some communities also charge subscription fees for fire services or bill users for at least part of the cost of providing an emergency response, particularly for emergency medical responses and nonemergency transfers. The department's budget generally is set on an annual basis and must cover all department expenses, including equipment purchases and maintenance, operating expenses, and funding for personnel.

County/Parish/Borough

The second tier in local government is normally the county, parish, or borough. Fire departments at this level are becoming more common. Often these departments start as part of the mutual aid agreements of communities in the county and through the establishment of shared fire prevention, fire communications, and hazardous materials response plans and systems. Occasionally, departments are consolidated because of shared county facilities, such as county airports or industrial complexes. Such agreements and common facilities may lead to cooperation in the acquisition of specialized equipment, personnel, and other resources. For example, one community may acquire a hazardous materials response unit, while a neighboring community builds a regional training center and a third town invests in a new mobile command post. Hazardous materials specialists and emergency medical technicians may be strategically located in towns across the county, while a single arson investigator serves on the entire county. In this way, small towns and suburban areas benefit from the availability of sophisticated fire protection resources without each individual community having to bear the expense alone. The county fire department may exist to augment small town and rural fire departments, or it may consolidate them into a single response organization.

Fire Bureaus

Another type of municipal or county/borough fire protection agency is the public safety department. Sometimes called *fire bureaus*, these organizations are typically under the direction of a single department head that is responsible for both police and fire protection within the jurisdiction. Public safety departments consolidate police and fire services and resemble combination fire departments in that some of the personnel are full-time career firefighters whose numbers are supplemented by full-time career police officers when there is a fire. Public safety departments also usually cross-train and equip their police officers to function as firefighters under the supervision of fire department company officers and command officers who have no law enforcement duties or training.

Fire District

In some states, a fire district serves the same purpose as the county fire department but is not directly related to a single county, parish, or borough. Fire districts may be formed as a portion of a county or may overlap county lines to serve a special shared need, such as a large manufacturing plant on the border between two counties. In effect, the district is a special, state-authorized, governing body authorized to provide fire protection to an area. Generally, the district operates under a board of trustees or commissioners who represent the residents of the district.

The department itself may have a full-time, paid staff; a volunteer staff, or a combination staff. Some stations may function in one way while others function differently, especially when the district absorbs local fire protection organizations during its creation. In some cases, the fire protection organization truly is a department because the district board may be responsible for administering other services, such as rural water delivery and law enforcement. However, in most cases, the district deals almost exclusively with fire protection, fire suppression, hazardous materials incidents, emergency medical services, and related activities. Even so, it is customary to refer to the organization as a fire department although the district may not have other departments.

Unlike municipal fire departments, fire districts do not have the support services that a municipal services center can provide for apparatus maintenance, station maintenance, etc. Fire districts must provide these services themselves or contract with private providers.

Fire Protection District

Fire districts and fire protection districts are essentially the same. In some states, a fire protection district is less formal than a fire district in that it does not exist as a separate government entity; in others, they are virtually the same. Fire protection districts may be established when a group with shared interests petitions an established fire department to provide fire protection services. For example, the owners of a group of lakeside cabins may find it difficult to obtain fire protection service because they are not an incorporated community. In addition, a volunteer fire department would be impractical when the owners stay at their cabins only on weekends and during vacations. One option is for them to form a homeowners' association and request a nearby community to provide fire protection services for their cabins. If the community agrees, the town's government officials will sign a contract with the homeowners' association to establish the fire protection district and define the terms and conditions of the services. The town will collect money under the contract, which can then be used to buy additional apparatus or to meet other expenses. The state or province may formally recognize the district and may even provide some funding for the contract through earmarked taxes. In other instances, the only legal recognition will be through the contract itself, with the homeowners' association and community serving as legal entities.

Private Fire Departments

There are two major types of private fire departments. First, some industrial complexes and military installations may choose to maintain fire fighting resources to protect their property rather than rely solely or partially on the local public fire department for such protection. The second type of private fire protection is a business that owns fire fighting equipment and hires firefighters to provide fire protection for the public under contract with government agencies.

Industrial Fire Departments

In addition to the municipal fire department structure and organization, it is important for firefighters to realize the important role that industrial fire brigades play in the overall fire protection picture. The fire brigade is responsible for the primary response to emergencies at its facility. Depending on the organization of the brigade, fire brigade members may respond to fire, hazardous materials, and medical emergencies.

Many commercial facilities, such as oil refineries and airports (both public and private), maintain fire brigades or other emergency response teams **(Figure 10.8)**. There are many reasons for this, including the following:

- The inability or unwillingness of the local community to provide needed resources
- The need to have a more immediate response than the local public fire department can provide
- The need to protect special hazards that requires capabilities beyond those of the local public fire department
- Remoteness from any public fire department
- Reduced insurance rates
- Reduction of potential liabilities
- Compliance with Federal Aviation Administration regulations at airports

For these and other reasons, businesses may choose to maintain their own facilities, personnel, and equipment to respond to fires and other incidents. Often, such firms are willing to enter into mutual aid agreements and are generally willing to work with public fire officials to develop fire and haz mat protection plans involving their facilities. Consequently, company officers may be required to work with private departments and corporate organizations in

Figure 10.8 Industrial fire brigade members during a live-fire training evolution.

order to provide fire protection for these facilities and the surrounding area. Company officers should become acquainted with the facility personnel and procedures that might be involved in such a response.

Each industrial location determines the level of fire protection it desires and the capabilities of its fire brigade. Small facilities with few hazards may have a small group of people who are trained only in such incipient fire fighting procedures as the use of portable fire extinguishers and handlines. Large industrial facilities, such as petrochemical plants or multi-building manufacturing facilities, may have fully trained fire brigades with their own apparatus. Although most brigades are composed of employees from various disciplines within the facility, some large facilities have full-time fire fighting personnel.

Effective fire brigades help minimize emergency situations and reduce losses considerably. In many cases, they control the situation before the arrival of the municipal fire department. Larger brigades may respond to emergencies on their own and only call for the local fire department when additional aid is required.

An effective brigade has to be well planned, well organized, and well trained. Top management must provide extensive financial and administrative support. The chief and officers should be well qualified and knowledgeable about all operations within the plant. Fire brigade members should be trained to the level to which they are expected to perform, and they must be willing to take on extra work. It takes all of these things to have a successful fire brigade; any deficiency may result in failure.

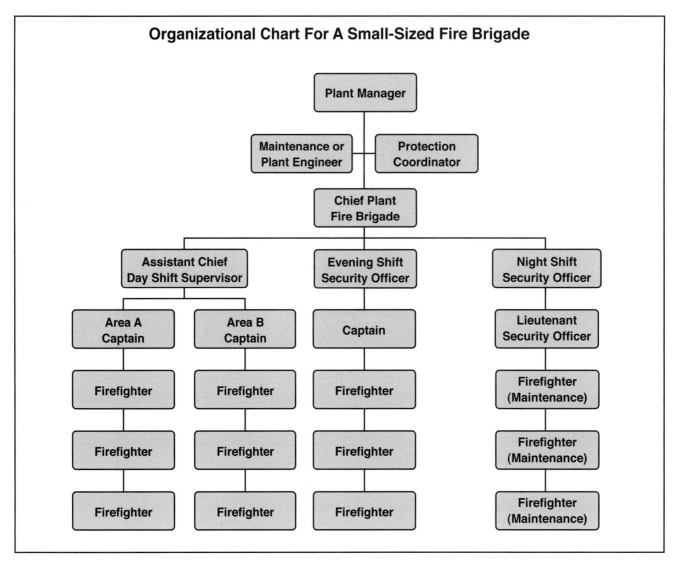

Organizational Chart For A Small-Sized Fire Brigade

Figures 10.9a Organizational charts for industrial fire brigades must reflect each organization's special needs. (a) An organization chart for a small fire brigade.

The following list contains examples of activities for which fire brigades are normally responsible:

- Preventing fires and eliminating hazards
- Seeing that all fire fighting and safety equipment is properly maintained and available for immediate use
- Assisting department managers in training employees in fire prevention, safety, and proper use of first aid fire equipment
- Responding to and handling all fire alarms and reports of fires
- Handling other emergency situations such as bomb threats, hazardous materials incidents, and medical emergencies
- Coordinating plant emergency operations with the local fire department

Developing a suitable fire brigade organizational structure is very important. The number of brigade members, assigned brigade responsibilities, and the plant's physical characteristics make each organizational plan unique **(Figures**

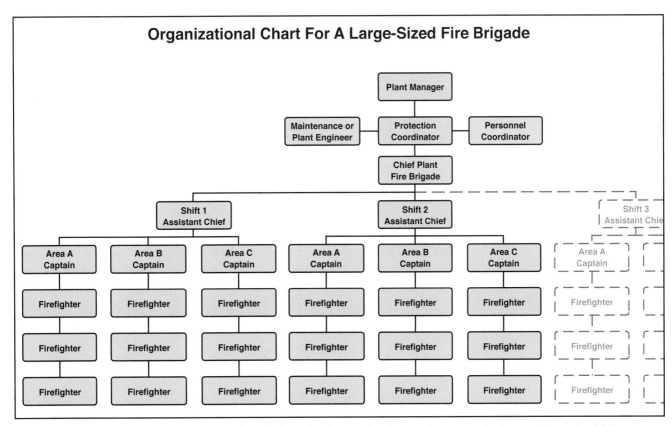

Organizational Chart For A Large-Sized Fire Brigade

Figures 10.9b Organizational charts for industrial fire brigades must reflect each organization's special needs. (b) An organizational chart for a large brigade.

10.9 a and b). Each plant must choose an organizational structure that will work best for its operation and accomplish its objectives and responsibilities. The organization must also provide protection during all shifts, weekends, and holidays. Coordination with the local fire department is essential.

Because the interface between the fire brigade and the local fire department is very important, each group should be familiar with the other's capabilities and standard operating procedures (SOPs). Joint training sessions should be held to acquaint line personnel with each other. These exercises invariably prove to be beneficial during emergency situations when both agencies will be working together. For more information on fire brigades, see IFSTA's **Industrial Emergency Services Training: Incipient Level** and **Industrial Exterior and Structural Fire Brigades** manuals.

Military Fire Departments

The U.S. Department of Defense operates hundreds of fire and emergency services departments on military installations worldwide. These departments provide structural fire protection on military installations, airfield rescue and fire fighting (ARFF) services, and specialized marine firefighting services for vessels, vessel maintenance facilities, and the like **(Figure 10.10, p. 376)**. In addition, these military fire departments may also provide fire protection off base under mutual aid agreements with local civilian fire departments.

The Canadian Defense Department oversees military and civilian fire service agencies operating in dozens of installations in and around North

Figure 10.10 Aircraft and rescue fire fighting (ARFF) apparatus parked in front of a military fire department.

America. These departments provide structural protection, ARFF, vehicle extrication, and hazardous materials response for land-based installations. They also provide fire fighting teams for maritime vessels that carry aircraft. These agencies operate with neighboring communities through mutual aid agreements.

Commercial Fire Protection Services

The private sector is providing more and more services to consumers — from delivering mail to collecting refuse to operating correctional facilities — that were once considered to be government functions. An increasing number of entities are finding it less expensive or more convenient to contract with private industry to provide these services, including emergency services. While still not the norm, it is not uncommon for cities to contract with private industry to provide some services that public fire departments provide elsewhere, such as fire, rescue, and emergency medical services. This trend is likely to continue, and public fire departments must realize that their very survival as an entity may depend on their ability to deliver their services to their customers more efficiently.

Airport Fire Departments

Some public, nonmilitary airports depend entirely or partially on the local municipal fire department for fire protection services. However, a significant number of airports have their own fire departments or contract with commercial fire departments for these services **(Figure 10.11)**. Regardless of how the departments are funded and organized, they must provide both ARFF services and structural protection for the buildings on the facility.

Response Considerations

Many factors affect the degree to which a fire department is able to provide all of the services that a community requires. A primary consideration for most departments is fiscal limitations. Because fire protection is just one of the many services that a local government's budget must support, government leaders have to determine the distribution of funds to satisfy these different requirements. Limited funds frequently result in compromises in individual services to provide a reasonable overall balance in meeting the community's various needs.

Figure 10.11 ARFF apparatus responding to an emergency from an airport fire department.

One of the roles of all fire department personnel, particularly the company officer and other fire department leaders, is to make the best possible use of available resources. This involves not only protecting personnel and equipment and conserving supplies but also formulating plans that will minimize the level of funding needed to fulfill the department's mission.

One of the most common techniques for extending the department budget has the following two parts:

1. Fund only the minimum number and types of resources needed to deal with those emergencies most likely to occur within the jurisdiction.

2. Use agreements with other agencies to supplement departmental resources for unusually large or exceptional incidents. These agreements are usually formal, written plans that define the roles of the participants and can be categorized as **automatic aid**, **mutual aid**, or **outside aid** agreements.

Automatic Aid

Automatic aid is a formal, written response agreement between fire departments and is initiated under predetermined conditions. For example, automatic mutual aid will be initiated whenever an emergency is reported in a predetermined response area or when specific equipment that the requesting department lacks is required for response. The agreement may provide for automatic aid in the event of any fire involving a given number of alarms.

Automatic aid agreements may also be required at specific facilities such as airports, oil refineries, or chemical manufacturing plants. A major incident at one of these facilities may virtually ensure that the resources of the primary jurisdiction will be exceeded so that any incident involving that facility will lead to an automatic response by other agencies. An adjoining department may automatically assume a backup response role if a company in a neighboring department is deployed.

Automatic Aid — Written agreement between two or more agencies to automatically dispatch predetermined resources to any fire or other emergency reported in the geographic area covered by the agreement. These areas are generally located near jurisdictional boundaries or in jurisdictional "islands".

Mutual Aid — Reciprocal assistance from one fire and emergency services agency to another during an emergency, based upon a prearranged agreements; generally made upon the request of the receiving agency.

Outside Aid — Assistance from agencies, industries, or fire departments that are not part of the agency having jurisdiction over the incident.

Mutual Aid

Mutual aid is a reciprocal agreement between two or more fire protection agencies. The agreements may be local, regional, statewide, or interstate so the agencies may or may not have shared boundaries. The agreement defines how the agencies will provide resources in various situations and how the actions of the shared resources will be monitored and controlled. Responses under a mutual aid agreement are usually provided only when an agency asks for assistance, such as when an unusually large incident or a number of simultaneous small incidents depletes its resources. Under these agreements, the requested agency may, at its option, dispatch the requested aid. But if the agency receiving the request has or is likely to have to commit its resources within its own boundaries, the request for mutual aid may be denied.

There are a number of reasons why fire departments enter into mutual aid agreements. The most common reasons are as follows:

- To allow sharing of limited or specialized resources between neighboring fire protection agencies

- To address the need for neighboring fire protection agencies to assist each other when a response requirement exceeds the primary jurisdiction's capabilities

- To allow departments to meet National Fire Protection Association® (NFPA®), Insurance Services Office (ISO), and other requirements for staffing, apparatus availability, response times, etc., shared resources

- To provide quicker responses when other departments are closer to the emergency site than the primary jurisdiction's resources

- To define responses for areas on the boundaries between adjacent jurisdictions

- To define response methods for fire protection agencies within a jurisdiction, such as a military base or corporate fire protection agency within a city's limits

- To define response methods for areas that lie between neighboring jurisdictions

As mentioned earlier, a fire department is likely to require the assistance of neighboring agencies for any of several reasons. Adjoining fire departments or districts sometimes work together to acquire selected apparatus or personnel resources that are required to support their overall mission but whose utilization is limited to the point that none of the individual cooperating departments could justify the expenditure. The departments may fund the resource jointly and share it, or they may agree that one or more of a number of such limited-need resources be acquired by each of the departments and shared with the others.

One department may also require assistance from another because of the size or nature of an emergency. Some fires involve such a large area or structure that they exceed the response capabilities of the responsible jurisdiction, or an emergency may result in more casualties than the primary jurisdiction can evacuate and treat.

Some occupancies within a jurisdiction may be considered such high-risk facilities that they warrant mutual aid agreements **(Figure 10.12)**. For example, the facility may store and use substances that could pose a serious health risk

Figure 10.12
Municipalities with large high-risk facilities such as this refinery often establish mutual aid agreements in the event of a serious incident.

to the public. If the facility is located near the boundary of another jurisdiction or if prevailing winds or waterways are likely to transport contaminants into an adjoining jurisdiction, the affected departments may choose to establish mutual aid agreements.

An agency may also require assistance if its resources are deployed at an incident when a second emergency occurs. In effect, a second agency may provide backup response for subsequent emergencies in the event that the primary jurisdiction's resources are already committed.

Company officers may be asked to assist in the development and maintenance of mutual aid agreements. At a minimum, these agreements should detail the following:

- Define roles of each agency, including incident management and chains of command.

- Establish standard operating guidelines.

- Define lines and methods of communications.

- Include common terminology, references, specifications, adapter requirements, and other factors that may directly affect the different agencies as they work with each other.

- Provide maps, identify evacuation routes, hydrant locations and data, provide details of potentially affected systems (sewers, railroads, waterways, etc.), and similar information useful in a response outside of one's jurisdiction.

- Address insurance and legal considerations (such as workers compensation, liabilities, and losses) that may affect the agreement.

- Establish additional nonemergency agreements, such as training and routine communications, as desired.

Mutual aid agreements should undergo periodic review to ensure that they remain current. Both the creation and maintenance of mutual aid agreements are likely to require department personnel to work with other agencies, including their own and other community governments. In some cases, implementation of new city policies or ordinances may be necessary to support the mutual aid agreements. To be most effective, all departments participating in these agreements should conduct joint training exercises so that differences in equipment and procedures may be identified and rectified prior to a major incident.

Fire Department Funding

In many respects, a fire department is like a business -- money is required for capital and personnel expenses. In order to remain operational, this flow of revenue must be continuous and well maintained. A fire department can be funded through its municipality, independently through alternative revenue sources, or through its fire district. Private sector departments may fall under any one of these funding strategies and are discussed later in this section.

A municipally-funded department relies on monies that are allocated in the local government's operating budget. The fire department receives a portion of the money that is collected through the local government's established tax system. This fire department income could come from earned income or sales or property taxes. In most cases, the local governing body, either a council or commission, has the ultimate approval control over the fire department's spending.

Most independently funded fire departments are volunteer organizations. These departments rely on alternative revenue sources, rather than taxes, for their income. Revenues are raised by fund drives, raffles, car washes, carnivals, dinners and dances, bingo, coin tosses, and subscription fees. In these fund-raising events, the fire department has autonomous control over expenditures.

Fire protection districts usually have separate governing bodies and are financed by taxes or membership fees, similar to a school or a water district. Fire protection districts may be either career or volunteer fire departments. The members of the fire district's board of directors have final approval over expenditures.

A private sector fire department is an organization that provides fire service to the public for profit. The department receives its funding from either subscription fees paid that individual property owners pay or from municipal funding through taxes. The department itself may be a corporation, a partnership, or a sole proprietorship. The private sector department both purchases or leases fire equipment (including trucks) and a building for housing the equipment.

Policies and Procedures

A firefighter who joins a department should become familiar with the department's regulations and procedures. Any questions should be discussed with a supervisor to eliminate any misunderstanding that could cause trouble later on. This section describes some of the rules and regulations that most departments follow.

First, it is important to understand the difference between policy and procedure. A policy is a guide to decision making within an organization. Policy originates mostly with top management in the fire department and points to the kinds of decisions that must be made by fire officers or other management personnel in specified situations.

A procedure is a kind of formal communication closely related to policy. Whereas a policy is a guide to thinking or decision-making, a procedure is a detailed guide to action. A procedure describes in writing the steps to be followed in carrying out organizational policy for some specific, recurring problem or situation.

Figure 10.13 A fire officer issuing an order to a firefighter at an emergency scene.

Orders and directives may be either written or verbal. An order is based upon the administrative policy or procedure, and directives are not based on policy or procedure. Yet both are essential for implementing the formal guidelines of the department. On the fireground, fire officers issue many instructions, directives, and requests **(Figure 10.13)**. However, because of the seriousness of the situation, all of these utterances are generally considered orders.

Standard Operating Procedures (SOPs)

Some fire departments have a predetermined plan or written policy for nearly every type of emergency that they can conceive of occurring. This plan or written policy is known as the department's **standard operating procedure** (SOP). The first fire company that reaches the scene usually initiates the SOP. The SOP may vary considerably in different localities, but the principle is usually the same. The procedure is primarily a means to get the fire attack started. Its use does not replace size-up, decisions based on professional judgment, evaluation, or command. In addition, there may be several SOPs from which to choose, depending on fire severity, location, and the ability of first-in units to achieve control. The SOP should be established to follow the most commonly accepted order of fireground priorities:

- Rescue
- Fire control
- Property conservation

Standard Operating Procedure (SOP) — Predetermined method or rule that an organization uses to perform routine functions, in addition to operating actions used to perform at every possible type of emergency incident. Usually these procedures are written in a policies and procedures handbook, and all firefighters should be well versed in their content. An SOP may specify the functional limitations of fire brigade members in performing emergency operations. *Also known as* Operating Instruction (OI), Predetermined Procedures, or Standard Operating Guideline (SOG).

The need to save lives is always the first consideration. Once all possible victims have been rescued, attention is turned to controlling the fire, which includes protecting the exposures as well. Last, firefighters should make all possible efforts to minimize damage to the structure. Minimizing damage can be accomplished through proper fire fighting tactics and good loss control (salvage and overhaul) techniques.

SOPs are used to standardize general activities at any emergency scene. Special SOPs can be implemented to make operations at target hazards more efficient. The use of SOPs reduces confusion and increases efficiency on the fireground.

SOPs are not limited to the emergency scene. Many departments prefer to carry out the administrative and personnel functions of the department through SOPs. SOPs may include regulations on dress, conduct, vacation and sick leave, station life and duties, and other departmental policies.

Disciplinary Procedures

Fire departments should have written discipline procedures for members who stray from the established rules or SOPs. Disciplinary measures taken against an individual may vary depending on several factors:

- The severity of the offense
- The number of occurrences for a specific offense
- The previous record of the individual
- Precedence on similar occurrences

The type of disciplinary action taken also depends on the type of department. Career departments have specified levels of action that start at a verbal warning and proceed through time off without pay or even termination. Volunteer departments may warn individuals, suspend them for a period of time, or terminate their membership.

Formal Communications

Communication is the exchange of ideas and information that conveys an intended meaning in a form that is understood. It involves messages being sent and understood. Yet, there are many barriers to effective communication.

The term used to describe the common organizational structure in the fire service is *scalar*. Scalar is defined as "having an uninterrupted series of steps" or a "chain of authority." The scalar organization is a paramilitary, pyramid-type of organization with authority centralized at the top. Decisions are directed down from the top of the structure through intermediate levels to the base. Information in turn is transmitted up from the bottom through the structure to the positions at the top.

Due to the scalar organizational structure, each level of the organization acts as an unintended filter that reduces the quality and quantity of information passed up or down. Many human factors affect the interpretation of the message, and subordinates are often reluctant to communicate upward with their superiors, especially if there is bad news to pass on. Verbal communication is not the most effective method for dissemination of information to the department on a large scale; therefore, there is a need for formal written

Incident Management System (IMS) — (1) System described in NFPA® 1561, *Standard on Emergency Services Incident Management System*, that defines the roles, responsibilities, and standard operating procedures used to manage emergency operations. Such systems may also be referred to as Incident Command Systems (ICS). (2) Management system developed by the National Fire Service Incident Management System Consortium, combining pre-existing command systems into one.

communication. Policies and procedures are examples of standing or repeat-use plans designed to deal with the recurring problems of an organization. Formal communication of these policies and procedures in writing helps to ensure that the organizational objectives are met throughout all divisions of the department.

Incident Management System

The **Incident Management System (IMS)** (sometimes called an **incident command system**) is designed to be applicable to incidents of all sizes and types. It applies to small, single-unit incidents that may last a few minutes as well as to complex, large-scale incidents involving several agencies and many mutual aid units that possibly can last for days or weeks.

Fire departments are required to adopt and utilize an incident management system for their strategic and tactical operations. Following several terrorist incidents the United States government mandated that all emergency services organizations use common terminology and command structures to improve their interoperability. After this mandate, Homeland Security Presidential Directive/HSPD-5 took the issue a step further stating that all state and local governments and tribal entities MUST adopt the **National Incident Management System (NIMS)** in order to be eligible for federal funds. Consequently, emergency organizations must ensure that their command structure will interface with "outside" organizations during an emergency, as these outside organizations will most certainly adopt NIMS.

In 2004, the U.S. government officially adopted ICS as part of NIMS, and all federal agencies or agencies receiving federal funding or subject to federal regulations must use the updated NIMS-ICS. Additional information on the NIMS-ICS model and its application may be found in the NIMS document itself and the *Model Procedures Guide* series developed by the National Fire Service Incident Management Consortium and published by Fire Protection Publications. NIMS-ICS is designed to be applicable to small, single-unit incidents that may last a few minutes and also to complex, large-scale incidents involving several agencies and many mutual aid units that possibly last for days or weeks. Information regarding NIMS-ICS can be found on the NIMS website at http://www.fema.gov/emergency/nims/.

Components of NIMS-ICS

NIMS-ICS combines command strategy with organizational procedures. It provides a functional, systematic command organizational structure and system. The ICS organizational structure clearly shows the lines of communication and chain of command. NIMS-ICS is designed for single-agency or multiagency use, and it increases the effectiveness of command and personnel safety. The organizational design is applicable to all types of emergency and nonemergency events.

NIMS-ICS is the basic operating system for all incidents within each facility or agency. Under NIMS-ICS, the transition from a small-scale to large-scale incident and/or multiagency operation requires minimal adjustment for any of the agencies involved. The following components work together interactively to provide the basis for clear communication and effective operations:

Incident Command System (ICS) — (1) System by which facilities, equipment, personnel, procedures, and communications are organized to operate within a common organizational structure designed to aid in the management of resources at emergency incidents. (2) Management system of procedures for controlling personnel, facilities, equipment, and communications so that different agencies can work together toward a common goal in an effective and efficient manner. (3) Recommended method of establishing and maintaining command and control of an incident. It is an organized approach to incident management, adaptable to any size of type of incident. (4) Management system of procedures for establishing and maintaining command and control of an incident; developed in California in the early 1970s to address the resource management needs associated with large-scale wildland fires. *Also known as the* California FIRESCOPE Incident Command System.

National Incident Management System - Incident Command System (NIMS-ICS) —The U.S. mandated incident management system that creates a unified structure for federal, state, and local lines of government for incident response. NIMS-ICS defines the roles, responsibilities, and standard operating procedures used to manage emergency operations.

- Common terminology
- Modular organization
- Integrated communications
- **Unified command** structure
- Consolidated action plans
- Manageable span of control
- Pre-designated incident facilities
- Comprehensible resource management

To understand the application of NIMS-ICS, firefighters should be aware of the major position **Section** descriptions within the NIMS-ICS structure **(Figure 10.14)**. NIMS-ICS involves the following five major organizational positions:

- Command
- Operations
- Planning
- Logistics
- Finance/Administration

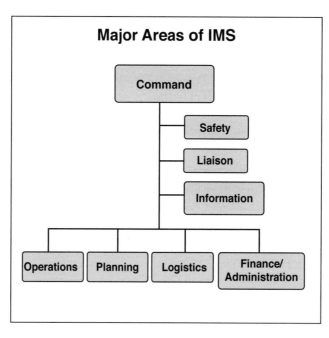

Figure 10.14 There are five major areas – command, operations, planning, logistics, and finance administration – within the Incident Management System (IMS).

NIMS-ICS also adds another position, Intelligence, which is responsible for gathering information related to an incident. In some instances, information gathering may actually be part of the Planning function. With the initial response one person will be responsible for establishing some of these functions. If the incident is large and complex these functions may be delegated to responding fire department personnel or other qualified personnel within the mutual/automatic aid organizational structure. All personnel within the airport organization need to ensure that they are familiar with the functions they could be assigned to perform. The Incident Commander (IC) retains the responsibility for these functions until they are delegated.

NOTE: Refer to **Appendix E** for a view of an expanded IMS structure.

Command

The person in overall **command** of an incident is the **Incident Commander (IC)**. The IC is ultimately responsible for all incident activities, including the development and implementation of a strategic plan. This process may include making a number of critical decisions and being responsible for the results of those decisions. The IC has the authority both to call resources to the incident and to release them from it. If the size and complexity of the incident require it, the IC may delegate authority to others, who together with the IC form the Command Staff. Positions within the Command Staff include the *Safety Officer, Liaison Officer,* and *Public Information Officer.*

Operations

The **Operations Section Chief** reports directly to the IC and is responsible for managing all operations that directly affect the primary mission of eliminating the problem. The Operations Section Chief directs the tactical operations to meet the strategic goals developed by the IC. Operations may be subdivided into as many as five branches if necessary.

Planning

The **Planning Section** is responsible for the collection, evaluation, dissemination, and use of information concerning the development of the incident. Planning is also responsible for tracking the status of all resources assigned to the incident. Command uses the information compiled by Planning to develop strategic goals and contingency plans. Specific units under Planning include the *Resource Unit, Situation Status Unit, Demobilization Unit,* and any technical specialists whose services are required.

Logistics

Logistics is responsible for providing the facilities, services, and materials necessary to support the incident. There are two branches within Logistics: the support branch and the service branch. The *support branch* includes medical, communications, and food services. The *service branch* includes supplies, facilities, and ground support (vehicle services).

Finance/Administration

Finance/Administration has the responsibility for tracking and documenting all costs and financial aspects of the incident. Generally, Finance/Administration will be activated only on large-scale, long-term incidents. Day-to-day mutual aid responses are usually considered to be reciprocal and do not require interagency reimbursement.

IMS Terms

The IMS uses several terms that all firefighters should understand. The terms defined in the sections that follow are widely used in incident management systems throughout the United States.

Division

Division is a geographic designation assigning responsibility for all operations within a defined area. Divisions are assigned clockwise around an outdoor

Command — (1) Act of directing, ordering, and/or controlling resources by virtue of explicit legal, agency, or delegated authority. (2) Term used on the radio to designate the incident commander (IC). (3) Function of NIMS-ICS that determines the overall strategy for the incident, with input from throughout the ICS structure.

Incident Commander (IC) — Person in charge of the incident command system and responsible for the management of all incident operations during an emergency.

Operations Section — Incident command system section responsible for all tactical operations at the incident. The Operations Section includes branches, divisions and/or groups, task forces, strike teams, single resources, and staging areas. Also *known as* Ops Section.

Operations Section Chief — Person responsible to the incident commander for managing all tactical operations directly applicable to accomplishing the incident objectives. *Also known as* Ops Chief or Ops Section Chief.

incident with Division A at the front (street address side) of the incident. In buildings, divisions are usually identified by the floor or area to which they are assigned: First floor is Division 1; second floor is Division 2, etc. In a one-story building, the entire interior may be assigned as a division (Interior Division) **(Figure 10.15)**. All groups or functional sectors operating within that specific geographic area report to that division supervisor. Organizationally, the division level is between a strike team or other operational unit and a branch.

Group

Groups are functional designations (forcible entry, salvage, ventilation, etc.). When their assigned function has been completed, they are available for reassignment.

Section

The organizational level having responsibility for a major functional area of incident management, e.g., Operations, Planning, Logistics, Finance/Administration, and Intelligence (if established). The section is organizationally situated between the branch and the Incident Command.

Figure 10.15 Examples of IMS divisions.

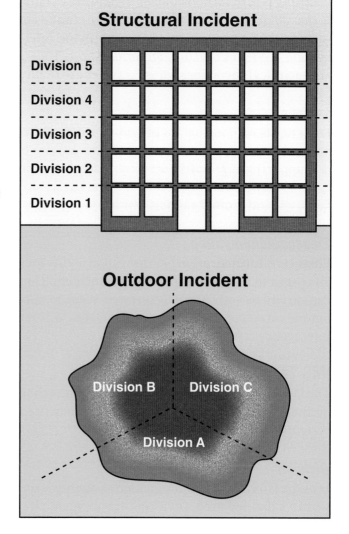

Supervisor

A *supervisor* is someone in command of a division, a group, or a sector. Supervisors play a key role in communications and relaying commands throughout the system.

Incident Action Plan (IAP)

The written or unwritten plan for managing the emergency is the *Incident Action Plan* (IAP). A plan should be formulated for *every* incident. Small, routine incidents usually do not require a written plan, but large, complex incidents do. The plan identifies the strategic goals and tactical objectives that must be achieved to eliminate the problem.

Incident Commander (IC)

The *Incident Commander (IC)* is the officer at the top of the incident chain of command and is in overall charge of the incident. The IC is ultimately responsible for everything that takes place at the emergency scene. The IC is primarily responsible for formulating the IAP and for coordinating and directing all incident resources to implement the plan and meet its goals and objectives.

Resources

Resources are all personnel and major pieces of apparatus on scene or en route on which status is maintained. Resources may be individual companies, task forces, strike teams, or other specialized units. Resources are considered to be *available* when they have checked in at the incident and are not currently committed to an assignment. It is imperative that the status of these resources be tracked so that they may be assigned when and where needed without delay.

NIMS-ICS Training

It is advantageous for all fire fighting personnel to receive NIMS-ICS training as part of their entry level training, recurring proficiency training, and professional development. NIMS-ICS courses are offered through the online resources of the National Fire Academy, the Federal Emergency Management Agency, and many state/tribal and local agencies. **Table 10.1, p. 388** identifies the appropriate courses for each level of responsibility.

Emergency Operations

To minimize the risk of injury and death to firefighters during emergency operations, fire departments should ensure that incident commanders perform the following:

- Conduct an initial size-up and risk assessment of incidents prior to committing to an interior attack.

- Maintain accountability of personnel on the scene by location and function.

- Establish rapid intervention Crews (RIC) and position them for immediate response to an emergency.

- Have at least four firefighters on the scene prior to making an interior attack (two firefighters inside the structure and two standing by outside). OSHA regulations require that if two firefighters enter a structure that has a hazardous atmosphere, two firefighters must be outside to provide emergency assistance if needed. This regulation is known as the Two In/Two Out Rule.

Table 10.1
NIMS-ICS Courses

Responder	Level Courses
Entry Level Responders And Disaster Workers	FEMA IS-700: NIMS, An Introduction ICS-100: Introduction to ICS 　*(or equivalent)*
First Line Supervisors	FEMA IS-700: NIMS, An Introduction ICS-100: Introduction to ICS 　*(or equivalent)* ICS-200: Basic ICS *(or equivalent)*
Middle Management	FEMA IS-700: NIMS, An Introduction FEMA IS-800: National Response Plan 　(NRP), An Introduction ICS-100: Introduction to ICS 　*(or equivalent)* ICS-200: Basic ICS *(or equivalent)* ICS-300: Intermediate ICS *(or equivalent)*
Command and General Staff	FEMA IS-700: NIMS, An Introduction FEMA IS-800: National Response Plan 　(NRP), An Introduction ICS-100: Introduction to ICS 　*(or equivalent)* ICS-200: Basic ICS *(or equivalent)* ICS-300: Intermediate ICS *(or equivalent)* ICS-400: Advanced ICS *(or equivalent)*

Personnel Accountability Systems

Personnel Accountability System — Method for identifying which emergency responders are working on an incident scene.

Each department must develop its own **personnel accountability system** that identifies and tracks all personnel working at an incident. The system should be standardized so that it is used at every incident. All personnel must be familiar with the system and participate when operating at an emergency incident. The system must also account for those individuals who respond to the scene in vehicles other than fire department apparatus.

Accountability is vital in the event of a serious accident or structural collapse. If the IC does not know who is on the fireground and where they are located, it is impossible to determine who and how many may be trapped inside or injured. Flashover (simultaneous ignition of room contents) and backdraft (fire explosion) may trap or injure firefighters. SCBAs can malfunction or run out of air. Firefighters can get lost in mazes of rooms and corridors. Too many firefighters have died because they were not discovered missing until it was too late.

Figure 10.16 A firefighter handing his personal identification tag to an accountability officer at an incident.

Tag System

A simple tag system can aid in accounting for personnel within the fireground perimeter. Personnel can be equipped with a personal identification tag **(Figure 10.16)**. Upon entering the fireground perimeter, firefighters leave their tags at a given location or with a designated person (command post, apparatus compartment, company officer, control officer, or sector officer). Tags can be attached to a control board or personnel identification (ID) chart for quick reference. Upon leaving the fireground perimeter, the firefighters collect their tags. This system enables officers to know exactly who is operating on the fireground.

SCBA Tag System

An SCBA tag system provides closer accountability for personnel inside a structure. All personnel entering a hazardous atmosphere must be required to wear full protective clothing with SCBA. These firefighters must be trained and certified for SCBA use. Each SCBA is provided with a tag containing the name of the user and the air pressure. The SCBA tag system does not replace the need for a traditional tag system or PASS telemetry.

Upon entering a building, personnel give their tags to a designated supervisor. The supervisor records time of entry and expected time of exit. This supervisor also does a brief check to ensure that all protective equipment is properly used and in place. This check provides complete accountability for those inside the structure and ensures that they are in proper gear. Firefighters leaving the danger area take back their tags so that the control officer knows who is safely outside and who is still inside the structure or danger area. Relief crews are sent in before the estimated time of the sounding of the low-pressure alarms.

Computer-Based Electronic Accountability Systems

While the tag and SCBA tag systems are still widely used, state-of-the-art wireless computer based electronic accountability/tracking systems are becoming more popular. These use bar code technology with scanners/readers and GPS or radar based transmitters that are placed on the responder's PPE or radio based tracking. The one feature that most of the electronic systems offer is rapid deployment and sensors that can detect and notify when crew members become immobile or call for assistance. The capability of remotely sounding a "Mayday" alarm, an evacuation alarm and verifying receipt by the IC or other firefighters on the scene greatly enhances fireground safety.

Although the electronic systems offer many advantages and improve safety of responders, manual accountability procedures such as lists of personnel inside IDLH areas face-to-face or radio roll calls (PAR), and other methods are the foundation of a solid accountability system. Manual accountability methods may be supplemented, but should not be replaced by an electronic accountability system.

Rapid Intervention Crews (RIC)

The primary purpose of a **rapid intervention crew (RIC)** is to provide a dedicated and specialized team of firefighters ready to rescue firefighters who become trapped in a structure. Rapid intervention crews are of vital importance at structural fires as they provide a designated emergency rescue team, eliminating the need to reassign other firefighters to this task.

The RIC responds to situations in which firefighters are disoriented, lost, or trapped in a structure. Ideally, a rapid intervention crew should respond with the first alarm units. Crew members should be fully equipped with protective clothing, SCBAs, lights and radios, axes, forcible entry tools, and other equipment they might require to perform a rescue operation **(Figure 10.17).** The RIC should report directly to the IC and be pre-positioned nearby. The minimum number of personnel in a rapid intervention crew is two firefighters, but the actual size of the team depends on the size and complexity of the incident.

NOTE: See FPP's *Rapid Intervention Teams* for more information.

Figure 10.17 Rapid Intervention Crew (RIC) personnel preparing to enter a structure to rescue firefighters trapped within.

Critical Incident Stress Management

One of the greatest, silent killers in any emergency responder's life is stress. Responders who have participated in an incident may, in turn, become victims of critical incident stress. Individuals may be able to cope with some amount of stress on their own, but many may need professional help.

Not everyone needs to seek professional help for everyday events, but everyone does need to know when to ask for help. If the stresses of fire and rescue become overwhelming, firefighters should seek out professionals – like the counselors who provide critical **incident stress management** – to help them handle stress. Like the counselors who provide **CIS Management**.

Critical incident stress debriefing (CISD) is peer-group or professional interaction immediately after a major incident. The recommended incidents to debrief include mass-casualty situations, loss of a child, and serious injury or loss of a coworker. When personnel should seek CISD ultimately depends upon the situation.

Because the injuries suffered by the victims in fire and rescue incidents sometimes can be severe or even fatal, emergency responders physically or emotionally affected by the incident should participate in a critical incident stress debriefing (CISD) process. Because individuals react to and deal with extreme stress in different ways — some more successfully than others — and because the effects of unresolved stresses tend to accumulate, participation in this type of process should not be optional.

The process should actually start *before* firefighters enter the scene if it is known that conditions exist there that are likely to produce psychological or emotional stress for the firefighters involved. Discovering these conditions is accomplished through a prebriefing process wherein the firefighters who are about to enter the scene are told what to expect so that they can prepare themselves.

If firefighters are required to work more than one shift in these conditions, they should go through a minor debriefing, sometimes called *defusing*, at the end of each shift. They should also participate in the full debriefing process within 72 hours of completing their work on the incident.

Critical Incident Stress Management (CISM) — Counseling designed to minimize the effects of psychological/emotional post-incident trauma on those at fire and rescue incidents who were directly involved with victims suffering from particularly gruesome or horrific injuries.

Chapter Summary

This chapter has covered how fire departments are organized and managed. Topics included the purposes of fire protection agencies, principles of organization (such as unity of command, span of control, division of labor, and discipline), and the various structures of local government. Types of fire departments are introduced, and the response considerations of automatic and mutual aid are discussed. The roles and types of fire department policies and procedures are described. The chapter closed with a brief overview of Incident Management Systems, which firefighters are likely to encounter from their first day of "active duty" on large and small incidents.

Review Questions

1. What are the common purposes that all fire protection agencies share?

2. What are the four basic organizational principles and how do these work to create effective teams?

3. How does the structure of local government affect the structure of fire and emergency services organizations?

4. What are the two most common ways of classifying public fire departments?

5. How are private fire departments different than public departments?

6. In what ways can automatic aid and mutual aid help departments with financial limitations?

7. What types of policies and procedures will fire and emergency services develop to govern the conduct of personnel?

8. What are the five organizational positions in the National Incident Management System-Incident Command System (NIMS-ICS)?

9. What is the purpose of using a Personnel Accountability System?

10. What are the benefits of a SCBA tag system that are not offered by a simple tag system?

Appendices

Contents

Appendix A

Fire and Emergency Services Higher Education (FESHE) Course Outcomes and NFPA® 1001 JPRs With Chapter References

FESHE Principles of Emergency Services Course Outcomes	
Course Outcome	**Chapter**
1. Illustrate and explain the history and culture of the fire service.	3
2. Analyze the basic components of fire as a chemical chain reaction, the major phases of fire, and examine the main factors that influence fire spread and fire behavior.	5
3. Differentiate between fire service training and education and explain the value of higher education to the professionalization of the fire service.	1
4. List and describe the major organizations that provide emergency response service and illustrate how they interrelate.	10
5. Identify fire protection and emergency-service careers in both the public and private sector.	1, 2
6. Define the role of national, state and local support organizations in fire and emergency services.	8
7. Discuss and describe the scope, purpose, and organizational structure of fire and emergency services.	10
8. Describe the common types of fire and emergency service facilities, equipment, and apparatus.	9
9. Compare and contrast effective management concepts for various emergency situations.	10
10. Identify and explain the components of fire prevention including code enforcement, public information, and public and private fire protection systems.	4, 6, 7
11. Recognize the components of career preparation and goal setting.	1
12. Describe the importance of wellness and fitness as it relates to emergency services.	1

NFPA® 1001 Job Performance Requirements (JPRs) With Page References

NFPA® 1001 (2008)

JPR Numbers	Chapter Reference	Page Reference
5.1.1	1, 2, 8, 10	9-14, 17-24, 43-82, 253-288, 361-391
5.3.1(A)	9	318, 335-338
5.3.2(A)	9	316-317, 332-334
5.3.5(A)	10	388-390
5.3.6(A)	9	319, 320-322
5.3.8(A)	5	192-196
5.3.10(A)	5, 6	170, 214-224
5.3.11(A)	5	169-193
5.3.12(A)	5, 6	177-181, 189-190, 201-207, 217-222
5.3.14(A)	7	241-248
5.3.16(A)	5	194-196
6.1.1	2, 10	47-49, 380-391
6.1.2	10	383-391
6.3.2(A)	6	207, 217-222
6.3.4(A)	4	136-147
6.5.1(A)	4	147-159
6.5.2(A)	4	159-164
6.5.3(A)	4, 7	156-157, 229-248

Tasks to be included in the test were chosen by a process of elimination. Tasks requiring special skills, 2 people to perform, were difficult to simulate, redundant, non-urgent, unsafe, or constituted a physical agility test were eliminated. The remaining tasks were then grouped into eight elements.

These elements are performed in the following sequence:

Stair Climb
Hose Drag
Equipment Carry
Ladder Raise
Forcible Entry
Search
Rescue
Ceiling Breach and Pull

The time, 10 minutes 20 seconds, was ultimately determined to be the maximum time allowed for an acceptable performance.

The Test

The exam is comprised of eight stations that will be completed in one continuous sequence. It is a Pass/Fail examination. The maximum time allowed for passing is 10 minutes and 20 seconds.

The candidate must wear long pants, appropriate footwear, a safety helmet with chinstrap, gloves and a 50 pound weighted vest during the entire exam. Watches and loose or restrictive jewelry are not allowed.

During the entire test candidates will wear a 50 pound (22.68 kg) vest to simulate the weight of PPE with SCBA. An additional 25 pounds (11.34 kg) (12.5 lbs [5.67 kg] per shoulder) will be added during the first event, but will be removed at the completion of that event.

The events are placed in a sequence that best simulates fire scene events, while allowing an 85ft (25.91 m) walk between events. This walk allows for approximately 20 seconds to recover and regroup before the next event. Running is not allowed between events.

- **Event #1 - Stair Climb**

  This event uses a StepMill stair climbing machine while wearing an additional shoulder weight (12.5 lbs [5.67 kg] per shoulder).

  Prior to beginning the timed CPAT there is a 20 second warm-up period on the StepMill at a rate of 50 steps per minute to establish balance and cadence. During the warm-up the candidate may grab a rail for balance, step off, and remount. If candidate steps off the entire 20 second period will begin again.

  At completion of the 20 second warm-up period the timed CPAT begins. The candidate will step on the StepMill for 3 minutes at a rate of 60 steps per minute. Handrails may only be used to momentarily re-establish balance.

The additional shoulder weight will be removed and the candidate will walk 85 feet (25.91 m) to Event #2.

Purpose -

This event combines three (3) critical tasks. It is intended to simulate climbing roughly 10-12 flights of stairs while carrying a hose pack, climbing stairs in full PPE and climbing ladders carrying tools.

Failures-

If candidate falls or dismounts the StepMill three (3) times during the warm-up period, the candidate fails the test. If the candidate falls, grasps any of the equipment, or dismounts the StepMill after the timed CPAT begins, the test is concluded and the candidate fails the test. During the test, the candidate is allowed to touch the wall or handrail for balance only momentarily. However, if the wall or handrail is grasped for more than a brief moment, or if the candidate uses them to bear weight on, the candidate will be warned. Only two warnings will be given. The third offense results in a failure.

Event #2 - Hose Drag

A fire nozzle is attached to a 200 foot (60 m) length of 1 ¾ inch (44 mm) fire hose. A mark 8 feet (2.24 m) back from the nozzle indicates the maximum amount of hose which may be draped across the candidates should or chest. A second mark 50 feet (15.24 m) back from the nozzle indicates the amount of hose which must be pulled to the candidate from a kneeling position.

Candidate will grasp a fire nozzle attached to the fire hose. Drape the hose over shoulder and across chest (not to pass the 8 foot [2.24 m] mark) and drag hose line as quickly as possible 75 feet (22.86m) to a drum. Make a 90 degree turn around drum and continue an additional 25 feet (7.62 m) to a box marked on the ground. Drop to at least one knee and pull 50 feet (15.24 m) of hose (up to the second mark) into the box. At least one knee must remain on the ground and candidate must stay in the box.

The candidate will then walk 85 feet (25.91 m) to the next event.

Purpose -

To simulate extending a dry hose line from an apparatus to the fire and advancing and uncharged attack line around obstacles while remaining stationary.

Failures -

If candidate fails to go around the drum or goes outside of the marked path the candidate fails. During the hose pull if the candidate does not keep at least one knee in contact with the ground the candidate will be warned only once. The second time neither knee is touching the ground the candidate fails. During the hose pull if the candidate's knees go outside the box they will be warned only once. The second time constitutes a failure.

- ### Event #3 - Equipment Carry

  This event uses two (2) power saws and a tool cabinet to simulate a tool compartment on a fire apparatus.

  The candidate removes two (2) saws from a cabinet one at a time and places them on the ground. Then pick them both up and carry them 75 feet (22.86 m) to a cone, around the cone and back replacing them in the cabinet.

  The candidate then walks 85 feet (25.91 m) to Event #4.

  Purpose -

  To simulate removing power tools from an apparatus, carrying them to the scene, and returning the equipment to the apparatus compartment.

  Failures -

  If a saw is dropped the candidate fails the test. Running is not allowed and candidate will only be warned once. If the candidate runs a second time they will fail.

- ### Event #4 -Ladder Raise

  Event uses two (2) 24 foot (7.32 m) extension aluminum fire department ladders. For safety a retractable lanyard is attached to the ladder the candidate raises.

The candidate must walk to the top rung of a 24 foot (7.32 m) extension ladder laying on the ground. Its butt is against a wall. Lift the top end from the ground and walk it to an upright position against the wall. This must be done in hand over hand fashion using each rung until the ladder is flush and stationary against the wall. Immediately proceed to a second prepositioned 24 foot (7.32 m) extension ladder. While standing in a box marked at the base of the ladder extend the fly section hand over hand until it hits the stop. Then, completely lower the fly hand over hand in a controlled manner.

The candidate will then walk 85 feet (25.91 m) to Event #4.

Purpose -
To simulate carrying a ladder to a structure and extending the ladder to a roof or window.

Failures -
If the candidate misses any rung during the raise only one warning is given. The second time a rung is missed the candidate fails. If the candidate allows the ladder to fall the candidate fails. If during the ladder extension the candidate's feet do not remain in the box only one warning is given. A second offense and the candidate fails. If the candidate does not maintain control of the ladder in a hand over hand manner, or lets the rope halyard slip in an uncontrolled manner the candidate fails.

- ### Event #5 - Forcible Entry
  This event uses a mechanized device located 39 inches (1 m) off the ground that measures cumulative force and a 10 pound (4.54 kg) sledge hammer.

  In this event, the candidate will use the 10 pound (4.54 kg) sledge hammer to strike the measuring device in the target area until the buzzer is activated. Candidate must keep both feet outside the toe box at all times.

  After the buzzer is activated, the candidate places the hammer on the ground.

  The candidate then walks 85 feet (25.91 m) to Event #6.

  ### Purpose -
  To simulate the use of force to open a locked door or breach a wall.

  ### Failures -
  If candidate does not maintain control of the hammer at all times or if the candidate releases the handle with both hands the candidate fails. If the candidate steps inside the toe box once the candidate will be warned. If the candidate steps inside the box a second time the candidate will fail.

- ### Event #6 - Search
  This event uses an enclosed search maze that has obstacles and narrow spaces.

  The candidate must crawl through a darkened tunnel maze that is approximately 3 feet (91.44 cm) high, 4 feet (121.92 cm) wide, and 64 feet (19.51 m) long with two (2) 90 degree turns. At a number of locations in the tunnel, the candidate must navigate over and under obstacles. In addition at two locations, the candidate must crawl through a narrowed space where the dimensions of the tunnel are reduced. The event is complete when candidate exits the tunnel.

  Movement through the maze is monitored. If the candidate chooses for any reason to end the event the candidate may simply rap sharply on the walls or call out. The candidate will be assisted out.

  The candidate then walks 85 feet (25.91 m) to Event #7.

  ### Purpose -
  To simulate searching an unpredictable area with limited visibility to find a victim.

  ### Failures -
  A request for assistance that requires opening an escape hatch or opening of the entrance or exit covers will constitute a failure.

- **Event #7 - Rescue**

This event uses a 165 pound (74.84 kg) weighted mannequin with a harness with shoulder handles.

The candidate must grasp the mannequin by one or both of the handles of the harness drag it 35 feet (10.67 m) to a pre-positioned drum, make a 180 degree turn around the drum, and return 35 feet (10.67 m) to the finish line. Candidate is not permitted to grasp or rest on the drum. It is permissible for the dummy to touch the drum. Candidate is permitted to drop or release the dummy to get a better grip. The entire mannequin must be dragged across the finish line.

The candidate releases the dummy and walks 85 feet(25.91 m) to the next event.

Purpose -

To simulate removing a victim or an injured partner from a fire scene.

Failures -

If the candidate grasps or rests on the drum one warning is given. If it happens again the candidate fails.

- **Event #8 - Ceiling Breach and Pull**

This event uses a mechanical device that measures overhead push and pull forces and a 6 foot (1.83 m) pike pole.

The candidate must remove the pike pole from a bracket and stand within a framework. The candidate places the point of the pike pole within a painted target on an overhead door area. By pushing upward, the candidate must fully push open the 60 pound (27.22 kg) hinged door three (3) times. Then using the hook side of the pike pole, an 80 pound (36.29 kg) ceiling device must be pulled fully downward five (5) times. Each series of pushes and pulls makes a set. The candidate must complete four (4) sets. If the candidate does not successfully complete a push or pull the examiner will call out *MISS* and that action must be done again successfully.

Adjusting the grip on the pole or allowing the pole to slip without the pole touching the ground does not result in a warning or failure. The candidate is allowed to re-establish a grip.

When the last repetition is completed, the examiner will call *TIME*. This will conclude the event and the test.

Purpose -

To simulate breaching and pulling down a ceiling to search for fire extension.

Failures -

One warning is given if the candidate drops the pole to the ground. If the pole is dropped, the candidate must pick it up and resume without assistance. A second drop will constitute a failure. The candidate must remain within the marked area. If the candidate steps out of the marked area, they will receive only one warning. A second instance will result in a failure.

PREHOSPITAL 9-1-1 EMERGENCY MEDICAL RESPONSE:

The Role of the United States Fire Service
in Delivery and Coordination

Authors and Contributors

Franklin D. Pratt, M.D., FACEP

Medical Director
Los Angeles County Fire Department

Medical Director
Emergency Department
Torrance Memorial Medical Center
Torrance, CA 90505

Assistant Clinical Professor
Geffen School of Medicine
UCLA

Paul E. Pepe, MD, MPH

Professor of Medicine, Surgery, Public
Health and Chair, Emergency Medicine
University of Texas Southwestern
Medical Center and the Parkland Health
and Hospital System

Director, City of Dallas Medical
Emergency Services
for Public Health, Public Safety and
Homeland Security

Steven Katz, M.D., FACEP, EMT-P

Associate Medical Director
Palm Beach County Fire Rescue
West Palm Beach, FL

President
National Paramedic Institute
Boynton Beach, FL

Chairman
Department of Emergency Medicine
Memorial Hospital West
Pembroke Pines, FL

David Persse, MD, EMT-P, FACEP

Physician Director
Houston Fire Department
Emergency Medical Services

Public Health Authority
Houston Department of Health and
Human Services

Associate Professor of Surgery
Baylor College of Medicine

Associate Professor of Emergency
Medicine
University of Texas Medical School
Houston

2

PREHOSPITAL 9-1-1 EMERGENCY MEDICAL RESPONSE: THE ROLE OF THE UNITED STATES FIRE SERVICE IN DELIVERY AND COORDINATION

ABSTRACT

Prehospital 9-1-1 emergency response is one of the essential public safety functions provided by the United States fire service in support of community health, security and prosperity. Fire service-based emergency medical services (EMS) systems are strategically positioned to deliver time critical response and effective patient care. Fire service-based EMS provides this pivotal public safety service while also emphasizing responder safety, competent and compassionate workers, and cost-effective operations. As the federal, state, and local governments consider their strategic plans for an 'all hazards' emergency response system, EMS should be included in those considerations and decision makers should recognize that the U.S. fire service is the most ideal prehospital 9-1-1 emergency response agency.

INTRODUCTION TO FIRE SERVICE-BASED EMS

EMS is an essential component of the public services provided in the United States. The Federal EMS Act of 1973 defined an EMS system as "an entity that provides for the arrangement of personnel, facilities, and equipment for the effective and coordinated delivery of health care services under emergency conditions in an appropriate geographic area" (EMS Act 1973, (P.L. 93-154)). Much of the dialogue in the public arena today concerning prehospital 9-1-1 emergency medical care often focuses on ambulance services and, accordingly, may ignore the important distinction between prehospital 9-1-1 emergency medical response and the other key uses of the ambulance-based, out-of-hospital providers for non-emergency medical and transportation services.

3

The primary purpose of this discussion is to underscore the reality today that the fire service has become the first-line medical responder for critical illness and injury in virtually every community in America. Regardless of whatever agency provides medical transportation services, the fire service is the agency that first delivers on-scene health care services under most true emergency conditions. Therefore, prehospital 9-1-1 emergency response, in support of community health, security and prosperity, is not only a key function of each community; it has become, almost universally, a principal duty of the fire service as well. In addition, fire service-based EMS systems are strategically positioned to deliver time critical response and effective patient care rapidly. Furthermore, the fire service-based EMS accomplishes this rapid first response while emphasizing responder safety, sending competent and compassionate workers, and delivering cost-effective operations.

Although the role of the fire service is central in 9-1-1 emergency medical response, financial, political, cultural and organizational factors often can make the conversation about prehospital care providers confusing and complex for many decision makers in local communities. The goal of this discussion is to resolve and demonstrate that the use of fire service equipment and personnel to provide 9-1-1 emergency response is the best approach for a community regardless of size. This basic premise is consistent with recent Institute of Medicine publications that have placed EMS at the intersection of public safety, public health, and medical care. The U.S. Fire Service is uniquely qualified to be at that intersection and in the following pages, the history, evolution, and current medical capabilities of the fire service will be reviewed.

The Maltese Cross and Its Legacy for Fire-Service Based EMS

During the Middle Ages, the Knights of Malta, the forerunners of the fire service, took care of travelers and specifically burn victims from the Crusades and associated battles. Eventually, the Knights of Malta adopted the Maltese Cross as their emblem and it has created a revered legacy for fire departments.

4

The Knights originally began their work as the creators, administrators and care givers in a hospital in Jerusalem. As such, they were known as the Hospitallers of Jerusalem, starting their work before the year 1000 AD. For the next two hundred years, they helped the sick and poor and they set up hospitals and hospices across Europe.

Eventually, the Hospitallers became firefighters out of necessity. The conflict of the Crusades often threatened the hospitals that they had founded. So, they adapted and even engaged in battle to protect their hospitals. As a result, they also became firefighters because one of the weapons of war at that time was the glass fire bomb. The fire bomb, thrown by the enemy, created a horrendous inferno. After rescuing a fellow knight from the inferno and extinguishing the fire, a Hospitaller was awarded a medal, shaped like a Maltese Cross to honor those actions.

As conflict continued, the Hospitallers needed an identifying mark for their armor. This was necessary because without identifying markings, it was difficult to tell who was who because everyone was wearing similar armor in battle. They adopted the Maltese Cross as their identifying mark. (Maltese Cross, 2007, Foster, 2007)

In essence, more than 1200 years ago, some of the earliest ancestors of the fire service were "all-hazards responders." They initially started as caregivers for the sick and then became firefighters to protect their own. These are two of the concepts firefighters still believe in today and hold as their most sacred responsibilities—caring for the sick and caring for their own.

Longstanding History of Fire Service-Based Medical Care in the U.S.

The fire service has formally been part of the 9-1-1 emergency care delivery system since EMS began in the late 1960's. Many of the original prehospital EMS providers were firefighters, who had "special" additional training in providing medical services during emergencies that occurred outside the hospital. Today, essentially every firefighter receives emergency medical training and the fire service provides the majority of medical services during emergencies that occur out of the hospital, just as it has done for the past

5

four decades. Of the 200 largest cities in the United States, 97% have fire service-based prehospital 9-1-1 emergency medical response (*JEMS* 200-City Survey, 2006) and the fire service provides advanced life support (ALS) response and care in 90% of the 30 most populated U.S. jurisdictions (cities and counties) (IAFF/IAFC Fire Operations Survey, 2005).

Although the origin of the modern relationship between emergency medicine and fire departments is cited as the 1960's, the involvement of the fire service in patient care began much earlier. For example, in 1937 a fire department ambulance in New York transported famous song writer Cole Porter to the hospital after a horseback riding accident.

While the fire service was involved in many famous anecdotal events, other accounts demonstrate its profound effect on public safety and patient care procedures. In 1921 Claude Beck, M.D., a surgeon at Western Reserve University in Cleveland, called the fire department so he could apply a "pulmotor," an artificial breathing apparatus, to attempt resuscitation in a patient who died unexpectedly during surgery (Beck, 1941). Dr. Beck continued to be involved in resuscitation and today is recognized as one of the founders of the science of resuscitation.

The following quote from the *Journal of the American Medical Association* in 1928 summarized the evolving relationship between fire department-based out-of-hospital emergency care and subsequent resuscitation in the hospital.

> "...inhalators are introduced: Cases of gas asphyxiation occur; the rescue crew of the fire department is called and resuscitates the patient. A physician sees the resuscitation and is impressed by the effectiveness of the treatment. Some time thereafter he finds himself confronted with a child which he has delivered, and which has come through a prolonged labor. It refuses to breath effectively, in spite of the application of all the ancient practices. The respiratory center has been depressed by the diminished blood supply to the brain resulting from compression of the head, and needs more than the

6

normal amount of carbon dioxide to stimulate breathing. So the physician calls in the fire department. If, as is often the case, the fire department succeeds where his medical skill and knowledge have failed, he calls for it again the next time. Now the hospitals in some cities are adopting the practice of calling for the inhalator whenever they have a baby who breathes poorly. In effect, *they add the rescue crew of the fire department to their board of consultants, and these new consultants thus contribute another service to the community over and above that for which the fire department is primarily organized.* Obviously, it is the hospitals that should be equipped to treat asphyxia -- asphyxia of every form -- and thus to help firemen overcome by smoke and gas, instead of relying on the fire department to help the hospital in such a matter as asphyxia of the newborn." (Henderson, *JAMA* 1928. note: italics added).

According to a historical account on the City's website, in 1947 in the city of Virginia, Minnesota, "the Fire Department took full possession of the ambulance along with a Pulmotor Resuscitator ... This would be the first time that ambulance personnel would be properly trained in first aid, and resuscitation procedures of that time" (City of Virginia, MN, 2007).

Such widespread anecdotes not only indicate longstanding involvement of the fire service in medical care, but it demonstrates the often-quoted mission of the fire service established in the 19th Century, "To Protect and Save Lives and Property." Clearly, protecting and saving lives is the first and foremost mission for these dedicated first responders.

Growth and Specialization of Fire Service-Based EMS

As illustrated by its history, the fire service has continuously adapted and changed to meet the current needs of a community. As EMS developed, the fire service was integrally involved. In the early stages, firefighters were chosen by expert physicians to take on the role of paramedic. This era of EMS in the fire service is represented well by

7

looking at the City of Miami Fire Rescue Department nearly half a century ago. The age-old firefighter mantra to "protect and save lives and property" is well-illustrated within the history books of the City of Miami Fire Rescue and serves as an important example of Fire Rescue today in the United States. Miami was the first city to call itself a "Fire Rescue" department. Miami Fire Rescue was also revolutionary in using the advancements of technology in 2-way radios to bridge physicians in the hospital with firefighter-paramedics in the prehospital setting.

In fact, the Rescue Division of Miami Fire Rescue was established in 1939 in order to give first aid to firefighters. Rescue One, the department's first rescue truck used to treat citizens, came on-line in 1941. In these early days, "Rescue" services were limited to basic first aid with transportation usually performed by funeral homes.

In 1964, Dr. Eugene Nagel, started to teach first aid and basic cardiopulmonary resuscitation (CPR) to the firefighters of Miami Fire Rescue. Dr. Nagel's goal was to improve out-of-hospital cardiac arrest survival in the community by using lessons learned from the "quick response" system in the hospitals and apply it to the prehospital setting. Dr. Nagel still reflects, "We chose firefighters because they were there, they were available, they were willing, and they were motivated. It was really quite simple" (Nagel interview, February 2007). According to Dr. Nagel, "The fire service is dispersed throughout America and is everywhere in our country. It is an efficient method for offering emergency care rather than creating a completely separate service with separate communications, vehicles, housing, and personnel. It worked well in Miami in the 1960's and continues to work well when integrated into the fire service. It is a natural fit" (Nagel interview, February 2007). Firefighters in Miami clearly demonstrated in the pioneer days of EMS that firefighters are ideal candidates and willing dispensers of high-quality EMS. In Miami, this started with basic first aid, and progressed to CPR, intravenous therapy, electrocardiographs, telemetry, and advanced airway intervention. During this same time period, similar efforts were underway using firefighters in the cities such as Baltimore, Columbus, Seattle, and Los Angeles. Providing firefighters training in lifesaving techniques and procedures has allowed them to deliver advances in medicine to

8

the prehospital 9-1-1 emergency care patient in a cost-effective and time-sensitive manner. Just as fire departments have evolved since the 1960's to provide prehospital emergency medical care, government oversight must evolve to cohesively organize, coordinate, and supervise the integrated delivery of emergency medical care from the scene to the hospital and even the rehabilitation and recovery phase. A critical link in that chain of survival and recovery is the rapid on-scene response of the Fire service, a service that cannot be underestimated and truly emphasized in planning, funding, support, research, and quality assurance.

The protection of life and property has been the mission of the fire service for over 200 years, but the fire department of the 21st century is evolving into a multidisciplinary public safety department. It not only handles most aspects of public safety (beyond law enforcement security issues), but it also will continue to provide advances in emergency medical care and many developing public health needs such as preparations for pandemics, disasters, and weapons of mass effect.

Today, the community-based fire station, with its ready availability of personnel 24 hours a day, coupled with the unique nature of medicine outside of the hospital, creates a symbiotic blend of the traditional public concepts and duties of the fire service with the potential for the most rapid delivery of advanced prehospital 9-1-1 emergency response and care. Traditionally, fire stations are strategically placed across geographic regions, typically commensurate with population densities and workload needs. This creates an all-hazard response infrastructure meeting the routine and catastrophic emergency needs of all communities regardless of the nature of the emergency. Accordingly, the fire service helps ensure the prosperity and security of all communities and providing prehospital 9-1-1 emergency medical care is consistent with its legacy going back 1200 years.

Types of Fire Service-Based EMS Systems

The fire service can be configured many ways to deliver prehospital 9-1-1 emergency medical care such as the following general configurations:

9

- Fire service-based system using cross-trained/multi-role firefighters. Firefighters are all-hazards responders, prepared to handle any situation that may arise at a scene including patient care and transport.

- Fire service-based system using employees who are not cross-trained as fire suppression personnel. Single role EMS-trained responders accompanying firefighter first-responders on 9-1-1 emergency medical calls.

- Combined system using the fire department for emergency response and a private or "third service" (police, fire, EMS) provider for transportation support. Single role emergency medical technicians and paramedics accompany firefighter first responders to emergency scenes to provide patient transport in a private or third service ambulance.

While there are pros and cons to the various system approaches, the emergency medicine (EM) literature indicates that the most likely time to create error in medical care is when care is transferred from one provider to another in a relatively short encounter time. Such circumstances require that the fire service regularly exercise the leadership needed to ensure that integration of the parts of the prehospital emergency care system are coordinated well, with maximum benefit to the patient and minimum risk to the community. For example, in the fire service-based EMS model in which the fire department provides extrication, triage and treatment services, and a separate private provider transports the patients, appropriate quality assurance measures must be in place. This quality assurance is most effective when the fire department, as the public agency, administers and monitors the performance requirements on-scene and within the transportation agreement.

10

National Incident Management System

The U.S. Fire Service-based emergency response and medical care system is the most effective, coordinated system worldwide. The National Incident Management System (NIMS) and other nationally-defined coordination plans ensure that fire service-based 9-1-1 emergency response and medical care always provides skilled medical services to the patient regardless of the circumstances surrounding the location and condition of the patient. In addition, the fire service has the day-to-day experience and ability to work smoothly with other participants in the prehospital 9-1-1 emergency medical care arena: private ambulance companies, law enforcement agencies, health departments, public works departments, the American Red Cross and other government and non-government agencies involved in medical care, disaster response and patient services. This type of universal coordination takes leadership, work, and the willingness to subordinate fire service prerogatives to those of the greater public need. The fire service is the creator of the unified command concept that brings everyone to the table, at the same time. Using the National Incident Management System, the fire service has superior ability to coordinate incidents of any size. As a result, it provides the best return on investment of public dollars to provide the delivery of prehospital 9-1-1 emergency medical service.

Emergency 9-1-1 Response is Different from Non-emergency and In-hospital Care

For government decision makers who do not work in the public safety environment on a day-to-day basis, it may be difficult to appreciate the differences between emergency response and ambulance transport. Unless one actually has used the EMS system in a medical emergency, he or she might be likely to define a call to 9-1-1 in a medical emergency as 'needing an ambulance.' However, with the recent advances in resuscitative medical care, particularly in cardiac emergencies, we now know that what occurs in the first few minutes after onset of the medical emergency will change the long term outcome. In many of these critical circumstances, what happens on-scene determines whether the patient lives or dies. Therefore, rapid, efficient and effective delivery of emergency response and care is dependent on immediately sending nearby

11

trained personnel to the scene of an emergency regardless of the vehicle or mode of transportation.

Ambulances, of course, are necessary to transport patients to a hospital where more definitive care may be needed. However, because ambulances are often busy evacuating, transporting and turning over patients at the hospital, the most reliable vehicle to ensure a rapid response generally is the neighborhood fire truck. It should be realized that the first emergency care provider who is responsible for competent care may arrive on a fire truck separate from an ambulance. This is the case in most communities in America.

There are sub-specialties of ambulance service in the out-of-hospital arena that must not be confused with 9-1-1 emergency response. For example, ambulance services are often employed for interfacility transfers for specialty care or the need to transfer patients from one hospital to another can provide a higher level of required care. These transfers may include critical care transfers between hospitals, but more often they may also be non-emergent interfacility transports or day transport for persons with home-delivered chronic care services. Such services typically are not performed by fire departments as a fundamental public policy device to better ensure dedicated 9-1-1 emergency services and thus provide security and prosperity for the community served.

Multi-Role Firefighters: Patient Safety from Multiple Perspectives

To further emphasize that the prehospital 9-1-1 emergency care patient should be considered a separate and distinct type of patient in the continuum of health care, consider the setting and the circumstances of emergency medical care delivery. These patients not only have medical needs, but they also need simultaneous physical rescue, protection from the elements and the creation of a safe physical environment as well as management of non-medical surrounding sociologic concerns. The fire service is uniquely equipped to simultaneously address all of these needs.

The mission of the fire service is to protect and save lives and property. There are no other conflicting agendas. The fire service-based prehospital, 9-1-1 emergency response

12

medical care system is designed to be part of society's safety net. Fire and prehospital 9-1-1 emergency response medical care are intimately intertwined. Separating them from the EMS focus only serves to polarize our country's already fragmented emergency response system.

All out-of-hospital emergency care and ambulance transport professionals are taught that scene safety is the primary objective at every emergency scene. However, many of today's non-fire service-based EMS professionals do not have the additional resources and often do not have the training to effectively secure a scene. When there is a strict medical orientation in their professional training and practice, adequate preparation to appropriately and safely provide emergency medical care to an emergency patient may be compromised. Scene safety issues are often not apparent until a crew is on-scene to assess the incident.

Decision makers should consider, 'What does a non-fire based EMS crew do on the scene of a motor vehicle accident when the car is engulfed in flames and occupants are trapped inside, and fire crews were not dispatched?' In many cases, a non-fire service-based EMS provider would need to request dispatch of a fire company after the initial scene size-up, further delaying care, and further increasing risk to rescuers and victims. Streamlining this approach into the fire service-based prehospital 9-1-1 emergency medical care system is quite arguably more effective from the perspective of scene safety, short response time, integrated rescue and treatment, and then transport to a medical facility. Regardless, the firefighter response is a key element of patient safety, both medically and environmentally.

In the era of homeland security threats and the spiraling growth of the commercial transport industry, the threat of hazardous materials (Haz-Mat) is center-stage. Again, fire service Haz-Mat teams are the front-line of protection and rapid delivery of medical care can be pre-empted by such chem-bio threats, but where rapid care can be given, it can be expedited directly by cross-trained fire-service Haz-Mat care providers.

13

Fire Service-Based EMS as the Health Care System Safety Net

Prehospital 9-1-1 emergency patient medical care is a major part of the safety net for the American healthcare system. They may be the provider of last resort for the needy, yet they can be one more mechanism for overloading the health care system. Nevertheless, to its credit, the fire service-based, prehospital 9-1-1 emergency patient medical care provides unconditional service to all members of our population. Therefore, the fire service must now become an integral part of the public health system and work closely with medical and public health experts to help alleviate unnecessary burdens on already overburdened hospital, medical and public health systems. Already part of local government, the fire service may be best positioned to sit at the table and help provide important data to facilitate creating solutions to pressing health care public policy issues.

Above all, rapid response times are a pivotal advantage of fire service-based, prehospital 9-1-1 emergency EMS systems. Now equipped with automated defibrillators to reverse sudden cardiac arrest, the fire truck, coupled with bystander CPR, has become one of the greatest life-saving tools in medical history. With stroke centers to treat stroke within the golden 3 hour window, cardiac catheterization centers to treat heart attack in the 90 minute door-to-balloon time, and trauma centers to treat hemorrhaging patients, time efficiency is a key component of the best designed EMS systems. The service most capable of rapid multi-faceted response, rapid identification and triage to the appropriate facility is a fire service-based EMS system.

EMS is Not an Ambulance Ride

One of the central themes of this discussion is concern over the common misconception that EMS begins with the transport of a patient in an ambulance to a hospital. This misunderstanding resulted essentially in funding of transport service providers but not providers of emergency medical care rendered at the scene. This funding aberrancy occurred in the 1960s as Medicare provided reimbursement for transportation of trauma patients to the hospital, long before the contemporary EMS system developed. About the same time, fire service delivery of 9-1-1 emergency medical care was becoming part of the fabric of the fire service. It was managed and funded as an integral component of

14

public safety service provided by a fire department. Thus, it was funded solely as part of the fire department budget.

Payment for transportation does not fairly portray the full picture of 9-1-1 emergency response and medical care. As the need to pay for EMS was realized, federal dollars for "emergency medical services" went to the perceived greatest area of need at that time, the need for transportation. These federal dollars even provided payment of non-emergency ambulance transport for the care of chronic medical problems. Even though much of the life-saving effect of EMS in today's circumstances will play out routinely on the scene long before ambulance arrival, the focus on transport and not medical care delivery remains. This distinction has been lost and, to this date, never totally reconciled. Especially considering the resource impact, educating the public and government officials about this distinction within the EMS system in the U.S. is a critical and timely issue in the era of homeland security and Haz-Mat threats.

Funding for Prehospital EMS

The fire service supports the recent Institute of Medicine recommendations for ensuring federal payment for emergency medical care not associated with transport. Although not labeled specifically for EMS activities, grant funds are received by fire departments and emergency management agencies to enhance EMS response capabilities throughout the United States. It is deceptive to imply that only funds awarded to single function EMS delivery agencies are the only dollars benefiting those receiving prehospital 9-1-1 emergency medical care services.

For example, Assistance to Firefighter Grants (AFG) are essential to ensuring that fire departments have the baseline response capability that prepares them to respond not only to local incidents but also to effectively participate in broader, national responses. Fire department 'response' is considered 'all-hazards', inclusive of emergency, prehospital 9-1-1 medical care services. The program is extraordinarily cost-effective, with low administrative overhead and direct payments to local fire departments. As almost all fire departments provide EMS at some level, AFG dollars support equipment purchases,

15

training efforts as well as public safety education and injury prevention efforts. In fiscal year 2006 (FY 2006), 4,726 grants were awarded to fire departments throughout the United States totaling $461,092,358.

Another example of federal funding of local emergency response systems is the Staffing for Adequate Fire and Emergency Response (SAFER) Grants. The single most important obligation the federal government should fulfill to enhance local preparedness and protect Americans against all-hazards—natural and man-made—is to assure that every fire department in the nation has sufficient numbers of adequately trained and equipped fire fighter/ EMS responders. In FY 2006, there were 242 SAFER awards totaling $96,151,433 provided to fire departments throughout the United States.

Both AFG and SAFER grants present the federal government with its best opportunity to assure a strong, emergency response component in every community in America.

Federal Oversight and Administration of EMS

EMS has many voices at the federal level including the Department of Health and Human Services, Department of Transportation, Department of Justice, and Department of Homeland Security. Each voice advocates for specific entities that provide EMS as part of its services. Congress appropriately has empowered all EMS-related agencies under the Federal Interagency Committee on Emergency Medical Services (FICEMS). Recently, the FICEMS has been strengthened and provides the mechanism to accomplish this "coordination of the voices." The leadership challenge is to bring all of the voices together. The FICEMS can do this, if given a chance and a mandate.

Conclusion

In terms of the rapid delivery of emergency medical care in the out-of-hospital environment, fire departments have the advantage of having a free-standing army ready to respond anytime and anywhere. Prehospital, 9-1-1 emergency response in support of community prosperity and security is one of the essential public safety functions provided by the United States fire service. Fire service-based EMS systems are strategically

16

positioned to deliver time critical response and effective patient care and scene safety. Fire service-based EMS accomplishes this while emphasizing responder and patient safety, providing competent and compassionate workers, and delivering cost-effective operations.

References

Beck CS. Resuscitation for cardiac standstill and ventricular fibrillation occurring during operation. Am J Surg 53 (4):273-279, 1941.

City of Virginia, Minnesota, VFD History, Emergency Medical Services History, http://www.virginiamn.us/VFD%20History.htm , April 2007

Emergency Medical Services Systems Act of 1973. (P.L. 93-154). 93rd Congress S 2410.

Eugene Nagel, Personal Interview, February 2007

Foster, M. *History of the Maltese Cross, as used by the Order of St John of Jerusalem* http://www2.prestel.co.uk/church/oosj/cross.htm   April 2007.

Henderson Y. *The Prevention and Treatment of Asphyxia in the Newborn.* JAMA 90(8):383-386, 1928.

Maltese Cross, http://en.wikipedia.org/wiki/Maltese_Cross_(symbol) April 2007.

Moore-Merrell, L., IAFF/IAFC Fire Department Operations Survey, March 2007

Pepe PE, Roppolo LP, Cobb LA. Successful systems for out-of-hospital resuscitation. In: Cardiopulmonary Arrest. Ornato JP and Peberdy MA, (eds); Humana Press, Totowa, NJ 2004; pp 649-681.

Williams, D.M., *2006 JEMS 200-City Survey: EMS From All Angles.* 2007, 38-53

17

Appendix D
Firefighter Life Safety Initiatives

The Firefighter Life Safety Summit held in Tampa, Florida, in March 2004, produced 16 major initiatives that will give the fire service a blueprint for making changes.

1. Define and advocate the need for a cultural change within the fire service relating to safety, incorporating leadership, management, supervision, accountability, and personal responsibility.

2. Enhance the personal and organizational accountability for health and safety throughout the fire service.

3. Focus greater attention on the integration of risk management with incident management at all levels, including strategic, tactical, and planning responsibilities.

4. Empower all firefighters to stop unsafe practices.

5. Develop and implement national standards for training, qualifications, and certification (including regular recertification) that are equally applicable to all firefighters, based on the duties they are expected to perform.

6. Develop and implement national medical and physical fitness standards that are equally applicable to all firefighters, based on the duties they are expected to perform.

7. Create a national research agenda and data collection system that relate to the initiatives.

8. Utilize available technology wherever it can produce higher levels of health and safety.

9. Thoroughly investigate all firefighter fatalities, injuries, and near misses.

10. Ensure grant programs support the implementation of safe practices and/or mandate safe practices as an eligibility requirement.

11. Develop and champion national standards for emergency response policies and procedures.

12. Develop and champion national protocols for response to violent incidents.

13. Provide firefighters and their families access to counseling and psychological support.

14. Provide public education more resources and champion it as a critical fire and life safety program.

15. Strengthen advocacy for the enforcement of codes and the installation of home fire sprinklers.

16. Make safety a primary consideration in the design of apparatus and equipment.

National Fallen Firefighters Foundation

www.firehero.org

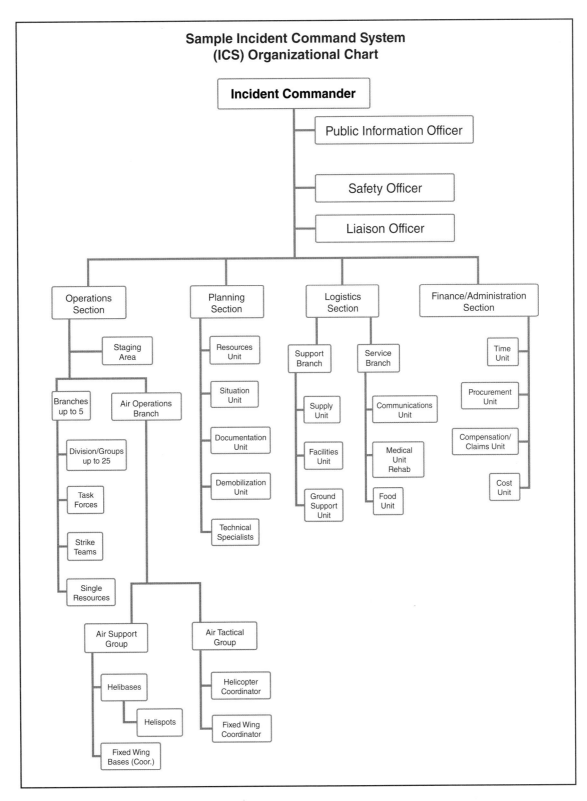

Sample Incident Command System
(ICS) Organizational Chart

Glossary

This glossary contains an extensive list of fire service terms and their definitions. Only the fire service definitions are given for the provided terms. In many cases, certain terms may have nonfire service applications that are not covered here. Also, the spellings and definitions are consistent with IFSTA and fire protection publications policy and may differ slightly from those used by other fire service organizations. Example: IFSTA uses one word for "firefighter," while the NFPA® uses two words for "fire fighter."

Entries have been alphabetized as though spaces and hyphens within the terms were not present. For example the entry **Fireproof** comes before **Fire-Protection System**, which comes before **Fire Wall**. Numerical entries (**9-1-1, 25 Percent Drain**) have been alphabetized by the first letter of their first numeral.

A

AAAE — *See* American Association of Airport Executives.

AAIB — *See* Air Accident Investigations Branch.

Abandonment — Termination of a first responder/patient relationship by the first responder, without consent of the patient and without care to the patient by qualified medical volunteers.

ABC — *See* American Board of Criminalistics.

A:B:C Extinguisher — *See* Multipurpose Fire Extinguisher.

ABC's — Airway, breathing, and circulation, the first three steps in the basic life support examination of any patient. Accompanied by control of severe bleeding, if necessary.

Abdominal Cavity — Large body cavity below the diaphragm and above the pelvis; contains the stomach with lower portion of the esophagus, small and large intestines (except sigmoid colon and rectum), liver, gallbladder, spleen, pancreas, kidney, and ureter.

Abeam — Directly off the side of a vessel; in a direction at right angles to the middle of the vessel's length. An object is said to be abeam when it is to the side of a vessel.

ABET — *See* Accreditation Board of Engineering and Technology.

Aboard — In or on a vessel; opposite of ashore.

Abort — (1) The act of terminating a planned aircraft maneuver, such as the takeoff or landing. (2) To terminate prematurely, or in the early stages.

Abrasion — Injury consisting of the loss of a partial thickness of skin from rubbing or scraping on a hard, rough surface. *Also known as* Brush Burn or Friction Burn.

Absolute Pressure — Gauge pressure plus atmospheric pressure.

Absorbent — Inert material or substance with no active properties that allow another substance to penetrate into the interior of its structure, and that can be used to pick up a liquid contaminant. An absorbent material is commonly used in the abatement of hazardous materials spills. Some examples of such absorbents are soil, diatomaceous earth, vermiculite, sand, and other commercially available products. *See* Contaminant.

Absorption — (1) Penetration of one substance into the structure of another, such as the process of picking up a liquid contaminant with an absorbent. *See* Absorbent and Contaminant. (2) Passage of materials (such as toxins) through some bodily surface into body fluids and tissue. *See* Routes of Entry and Toxin.

Academy — Training school; a place to train, learn, study, and achieve.

Accelerant — Material, usually a flammable or combustible liquid, that is used to initiate or increase the speed of a fire.

Accelerator — (1) Device attached to a dry-pipe sprinkler system for rapid removal of air in the system when a sprinkler operates. (2) Device, usually in the form of a foot pedal, used to control the speed of a vehicle by regulating the fuel supply.

Acceptance Testing — Preservice tests on fire apparatus or equipment, performed at the factory or after delivery, to assure the purchaser that the apparatus or equipment meets bid specifications. *Also known as* Proof Test.

Access — (1) Place or means of entering a structure. (2) Roadways allowing fire apparatus to travel to an emergency. *See* Egress.

Access Hole — (1) Starter hole into which a cutting tool may be inserted to continue cutting a piece of sheet metal. (2) Space made in a door crack with a manual prying tool to facilitate the placement of a spreading tool.

Accessibility — Ability of fire apparatus to get close enough to a building, structure, site, or emergency scene to conduct emergency operations. *See* Access.

Accident — (1) Unplanned, uncontrolled event (or sequence of events) resulting from unsafe acts and/or occupational conditions; can result in injury, death, or property damage. Typically caused by persons who are either unaware or uninformed of potential hazards, ignorant of safety policies, or who fail to follow safety procedures.

Accident Investigation — Fact-finding rather than fault-finding procedures that look for causes of accidents; leads to analyzing causes in order to prevent similar accidents.

Accidental Fire Cause — Cause classification for a fire that does not involve a deliberate human act to ignite or spread the fire into an area where the fire should not be.

Accommodation Ladder — Vessel's own gangway (usually one on each side) fitted with means of raising and lowering; also a set of steps or ladder used for getting from one deck to another.

Accommodation Spaces — Areas of a vessel designed for living; subdivided into officer, crew, and passenger accommodations. *Also known as* Cabins.

Accordion Fold — Method of folding a salvage cover; when completed, resembles the bellows of an accordion.

Accordion Load — Arrangement of fire hose in a hose bed or compartment in which the hose lies on edge with the folds adjacent to each other.

Accreditation Board of Engineering and Technology (ABET) — Organization that provides accreditation, promotion, and advancement of education in applied science, computing, engineering, and technology.

Acetylene (C_2H_2) — Colorless gas that has an explosive range from 2.5 percent to 100 percent; used as a fuel gas for cutting and welding operations.

ACGIH® — *See* American Conference of Governmental Industrial Hygienists®.

Acid — Compound containing hydrogen that reacts with water to produce hydrogen ions; a proton donor; a liquid compound with a pH less than 7. Acidic chemicals are corrosive. *See* Base, Corrosive, and pH.

Acoustic Search Device — Sensitive equipment used to listen for victims' responses in a collapsed structure.

Acquired Building — Structure acquired by the authority having jurisdiction from a property owner for the purpose of conducting live fire training or rescue training evolutions. *Also known as* Acquired Structure.

Acquired Immune Deficiency Syndrome (AIDS) — Fatal viral disease that is spread through direct contact with bodily fluids from a previously infected individual.

Acrolein ($CH_2 = CHCHO$) — Toxic gas produced by the burning of wood, paper, cotton, plastic materials, oils, or fats. When inhaled, acrolein can cause nose and throat irritation, nausea, shortness of breath, pulmonary edema, lung damage, or death.

Action Plan — Written plan of how objectives are to be achieved. *See* Incident Action Plan.

Activation Energy — Amount of energy that must be added to an atomic or molecular system to begin a reaction.

Active Listening — Method of listening characterized by maintaining eye contact with the message sender, imagining the sender's upcoming points, taking notes or mentally summarizing key points, paraphrasing especially important points, nodding the head, and thinking or saying something such as, "I understand."

Actual Mechanical Advantage — Something less than the theoretical mechanical advantage, due to the friction in a system.

Actuate — To set into operation; this term is often used to refer to an installed fire protection system or its components.

Actuator Valve — Valve that controls the flow of hydraulic oil from an aerial apparatus hydraulic system to the hydraulic cylinders.

Acute — Characterized by sharpness or severity; having rapid onset and a relatively short duration. *See* Chronic.

Acute Exposure — Single exposure (dose) or several repeated exposures to a substance within a short time period.

Acute Exposure Guideline Levels — Airborne concentration of a substance at or above which it is predicted that the general population, including "susceptible" but excluding "hypersusceptible" individuals, could experience notable discomfort. Established by the Environmental Protection Agency (EPA).

Acute Health Effects — Health effects that occur or develop rapidly after exposure to a substance. *See* Chronic Health Effects.

Acute Myocardial Infarction (AMI) — Critical phase of a heart attack where blockage of a coronary artery produces a number of signs and symptoms, particularly chest pain, nausea, heavy sweating, anxiety, and pallor. *Also known as* Heart Attack.

Acute Radiation Syndrome (ARS) — Serious illness that occurs when the entire body (or most of it) receives a high dose of radiation, usually over a short period of time.

ADA — *See Americans with Disabilities Act of 1990 - Public Law 101-336.*

Adapter — Fitting for connecting hose couplings that have dissimilar threads but the same inside diameter. *See* Fitting, Increaser, and Reducer.

Addiction — State of being strongly dependent upon some agent, such as drugs, tobacco, or alcohol.

Adhesion — Act of binding together substances of unlike compositions.

Adiabatic — Process of thermodynamic change of state in which no heat is added or subtracted from a system; adiabatic compression always results in warming, while adiabatic expansion always results in cooling.

Adjunct — An accessory or auxiliary agent, such as an oral airway.

Adjustable Flow Nozzle — Nozzle designed so that the amount of water flowing through the nozzle can be increased or decreased at the nozzle; usually accomplished by adjusting the pattern of the stream.

Adjustable Fog Nozzle — Nozzle designed to allow the discharge pattern to be adjusted from straight stream to full fan fog; suitable for applying water, wet water, or foam solution. Some adjustable fog nozzles allow the rate of flow to be adjusted as well.

Adjutant — Firefighter assigned to drive and assist a chief officer. *Also known as* Chief's Aide.

Administration — Government agency having authority over port operations.

Administrative Law — Body of law created by an administrative agency in the form of rules, regulations, orders, and decisions to carry out the regulatory powers and duties of the agency. *See* Law.

Administrative Search Warrant — Court order that allows investigators the right to enter a scene after the fire department has left the scene, or to reenter the scene if the investigator arrived while the fire department had control of the scene.

Admission — Statement that implicates the speaker in the commission of a crime.

Admission Valve — Pressure regulator valve that lets the air flow to the user.

Admixture — Ingredients or chemicals added to concrete mix to produce concrete with specific characteristics.

Adrenaline — Chemical released by the body that causes the breathing rate to increase and the body to prepare for "fight or flight."

Adsorbent — Material, such as activated carbon, that has the ability to condense or hold molecules of other substances on its surface.

Advanced Exterior Fire Fighting — Offensive fire fighting requiring the use of personal protective equipment, including self-contained breathing apparatus (SCBA), and performed outside a structure when the fire has progressed beyond the incipient phase.

Advanced Life Support (ALS) — Advanced medical skills performed by trained medical personnel, such as the administration of medications, or airway management procedures to save a patient's life.

Advancing Line — Line of fire hose that is moved forward.

Adverse Weather Condition — Any atmospheric condition, such as rain, snow, or cold, that creates additional problems or considerations for emergency personnel.

Adze — Chopping tool with a thin, arched blade set at a right angle to the handle. *Also spelled* Adz.

Aerate — To mix with air.

Aeration — Introduction of air into a foam solution; creates bubbles that result in finished foam.

Aerator — Device for introducing air into dry bulk solids to improve flow ability.

Aerial Apparatus — Fire fighting vehicle equipped with a hydraulically operated ladder, elevating platform, or other similar device for the purpose of placing personnel and/or water streams in elevated positions.

Aerial Attack — Use of aircraft to apply extinguishing agents to wildland fires. *See* Attack Methods (2).

Aerial Device — General term used to describe the hydraulically operated ladder or elevating platform attached to a specially designed fire apparatus.

Aerial Device Certification Testing — Pre-service testing, usually performed by a third-party testing agency, designed to give an unbiased opinion as to whether or not a piece of apparatus meets its design specifications and is worthy of being placed in service.

Aerial Fuels — Standing and supported live and dead combustibles that are not in direct contact with the ground; consists mainly of foliage, twigs, branches, stems, cones, bark, and vines.

Aerial Ignition — Use of an airborne incendiary device to assist in backfiring, burning out, or prescribed fires. Devices are normally carried in or suspended from helicopters.

Aerial Ladder — Power-operated ladder, usually employing hydraulics, that is mounted on a special truck chassis.

Aerial Ladder Platform — Power-operated ladder, usually employing hydraulics, with a passenger-carrying device attached to the end of the ladder.

Aerial Ladder Truss — Assembly of bracing bars or rods in triangular shapes that form a rigid framework for the aerial device.

Aerobic Capacity — Measure of cardiovascular fitness that takes into account oxygen capacity and efficiency of the lungs and blood in the cardiovascular and respiratory systems.

Aerodrome — *See* Airport.

Aerosol — Form of mist characterized by highly respirable, minute liquid particles. *See* Mist.

Aerosolize — To produce a fine mist or spray characterized by highly respirable, minute liquid particles.

Aesthetics — Branch of philosophy dealing with the nature of beauty, art, and taste.

AFA-CWA — *See* Association of Flight Attendants-CWA.

AFCI — *See* Arc-Fault Circuit Interrupter.

Affective — Descriptive of a person's attitudes, values, and habits.

Affective Learning Domain — Learning domain that involves emotions, feelings, attitudes, values, and habits. *See* Learning Domain.

AFFF — *See* Aqueous Film Forming Foam.

Affidavit — Sworn written statement.

Affiliation — Socio-psychological concept that shows that people tend to act as a group - even with people they do not know very well - and that generally no one leaves in an emergency until everyone leaves together.

Affirmative — Clear text radio term for "yes."

Affirmative Action — Administrative law adopted by the equal employment opportunity commission to implement the requirements of Title VII of the *Civil Rights Act of 1964*.

Affirmative Action Programs — Employment programs designed to make a special effort to identify, hire, and promote special populations where the current labor force in a jurisdiction or labor market is not representative of the overall population.

A-Frame — (1) Vertical lifting device that can be attached to the front or rear of the apparatus; consists of two poles attached several feet (meters) apart on the apparatus and whose working ends are connected to form the letter A. A pulley or block and tackle through which a rope or cable is passed is attached to the end of the frame. (2) A type of building construction in which a steep, gabled roof forms the major structural supports for the entire building.

A-Frame Ladder — Type of ladder that is hinged in the middle and can be used as a stepladder or a short extension ladder.

A-Frame Stabilizer — Stabilizing device that extends at an angle down and away from the chassis of an aerial fire apparatus.

AFSA — *See* American Fire Sprinkler Association.

Aft — Direction toward the back end or stern of a vessel, such as a ship or aircraft; term used relative to some other part of a vessel indicating the direction toward the stern. *Also known as* After.

After Action Reviews — Learning tools used to evaluate a project or incident to identify and encourage organizational and operational strengths and to identify and correct weaknesses.

Aftercooler — Air compressor component that cools the air that has been heated during compression.

Afterpeak — Area in the hull at the extreme rear end of a vessel; usually used for storage. *See* Forepeak.

Agency for Toxic Substances and Disease Registry (ATSDR) — Lead U.S. public health agency responsible for implementing the health-related provisions of the Comprehensive Environmental Response, Compensation and Liability Act (CERCLA); charged with assessing health hazards at specific hazardous waste sites, helping to prevent or reduce exposure and the illnesses that result, and increasing knowledge and understanding of the health effects that may result from exposure to hazardous substances.

Agency Representative — Individual from an assisting or cooperating agency who has been assigned to an incident and has full authority to make decisions on all matters affecting that agency's participation at the incident. Agency representatives report to the incident liaison officer.

Agent — Generic term used for materials that are used to extinguish fires.

Aggravate — To worsen; to make worse.

Aggregate — (1) Gravel, stone, sand, or other inert materials used in concrete. These materials may be fine or coarse. (2) Term used in fire prevention and building codes to describe the sum total of individual parts or components of an assembly or feature, such as in units of exit.

Agroterrorism — Terrorist attack directed against agriculture, such as food supplies or livestock. *Also known as* Agricultural Terrorism.

Aground — Vessel resting wholly or partly on the ground instead of being entirely supported by the water. If done intentionally, a vessel is said to "take the ground"; if by accident, it is said to have "run aground."

Ahead — In front of a vessel; may indicate direction (an object may lie ahead) or movement (proceed at "full speed ahead").

AHJ — *See* Authority Having Jurisdiction.

AIDS — *See* Acquired Immune Deficiency Syndrome.

Aileron — Movable hinged rear portion of an airplane wing. The primary function of the ailerons is to roll or bank the aircraft in flight.

Air — Gaseous mixture that composes the earth's atmosphere; composed of approximately 21 percent oxygen, 79 percent nitrogen, plus trace gases.

Air Accident Investigations Branch (AAIB) — Part of the United Kingdom's Department of Transport that investigates civil aircraft accidents and other serious incidents.

Air-Aspirating Foam Nozzle — Foam nozzle designed to provide the aeration required to make the highest quality foam possible; most effective appliance for the generation of low-expansion foam.

Air Attack — (1) Using fixed-wing aircraft or helicopters to apply fire retardants or extinguishing agents on a wildland fire. Aircraft can also be used to transport crews, supplies, and equipment, or provide medical evacuation and reconnaissance. (2) Incident Management System term for the air attack coordinator.

Air Bag — (1) Inflatable bag built into the steering wheel, dashboard, or doors of an automobile that inflates immediately when the vehicle is impacted. (2) Large inflatable bag onto which persons can leap to escape danger. (3) *See* Air Lifting Bag.

Air Bank — *See* Air Cascade System.

Air Bill — Shipping document prepared from a bill of lading that accompanies each piece or each lot of air cargo. *See* Bill of Lading and Shipping Papers.

Air Bottle — *See* Air Cylinder.

Air Cascade System — Group of large breathing air cylinders connected and equipped with the proper fittings to replenish self-contained breathing apparatus (SCBA) cylinders. Generally, three or more large air cylinders, each usually with a capacity of 300 cubic feet (8 490 L), from which SCBA cylinders are recharged.

Air Chamber — Chamber filled with air that eliminates pulsations caused by the operation of piston or rotary-gear pumps.

Air Chisel — *See* Pneumatic Chisel.

Airco — One of several names for the plane carrying the air attack coordinator.

Aircraft Accident — Occurrence during the operation of an aircraft in which any person suffers death or serious injury, or in which the aircraft receives damage.

Aircraft Attitude — Angle of the aircraft front to rear while in flight. *Also known as* Attitude.

Aircraft Classes — Classification of aircraft by weight for various purposes. (Canadian terms are in parentheses.)

Heavy (heavy) aircraft are capable of takeoff weight of 300,000 pounds (136 078 kg) or more, whether or not the aircraft is operating at this weight during a particular phase of flight.

Large (medium) aircraft are capable of takeoff weight of more than 12,500 pounds (5 670 kg), maximum certified takeoff weight up to 300,000 pounds (136 078 kg).

Small (light) aircraft are capable of takeoff weight of 12,500 pounds (5 670 kg) or less.

Aircraft Familiarization — Process of teaching personnel to become familiar with the various aircraft operated in an airport; includes familiarization with fuel capacity, fuel tank locations, emergency exit locations, operation of emergency exits, and passenger seating capacity.

Aircraft Fire Apparatus — Fire apparatus specifically designed for aircraft crash fire fighting/rescue operations.

Aircraft Hangar, Group I — Classification of aircraft hangar that has a single fire area in excess of 40,000 feet (12 192 m), has an access door height in excess of 28 feet (8.5 m), houses aircraft with a tail height in excess of 28 feet (8.5 m), and/or houses strategically important military aircraft.

Aircraft Hangar, Group II — Classification of aircraft hangar that has a single fire area that is less than 40,000 feet (12 192 m) and an access door height that is less than 28 feet (8.5 m). Construction type and fixed fire suppression systems also are used to determine Group II qualifications.

Aircraft Hangar, Group III — Classification of aircraft hangar that has aircraft access doors that are less than 28 feet (8.5 m) in height and a single fire area that is less than those given for the various types of building construction found in NFPA® 409, Standard on Aircraft Hangars.

Aircraft Incident — Non-accidental occurrence associated with the operation of an aircraft that affects or could affect continued safe operation if not corrected.

Aircraft Rescue and Fire Fighting (ARFF) — Term used to describe actions required by rescue and fire fighting personnel to handle aircraft incidents and accidents.

Aircraft Rescue and Fire Fighting (ARFF) Apparatus — Motor-driven vehicle designed and constructed for the purpose of aircraft rescue and fighting fires; capable of delivering Class B foam and providing specified levels of pumping, water, hose, rescue capacity, and personnel.

Aircraft Rescue and Fire Fighting Working Group (ARFFWG) — Non-profit international organization dedicated to the sharing of aircraft rescue and fire fighting information between airport firefighters, municipal fire departments, and all others concerned with aircraft fire fighting.

Aircraft Tug — Special, low-profile vehicle designed to tow aircraft on the airport ramp or push aircraft backwards away from an airport gate. *Also known as* Pushback Tractor or Tug.

Aircraft Velocity — Speed of an aircraft relative to its surrounding air mass. *Also known as* Airspeed.

Air Cylinder — Metal or composite cylinder or tank that contains the supply of compressed air for the breathing apparatus. *Also known as* Air Bottle or Air Tank.

Air Drop — Process of dropping water, short-term fire retardant, or long-term fire retardant from an air tanker or helicopter onto a wildland fire.

Air-Entrained Concrete — Concrete with air entrapped in its structure to improve its resistance to freezing.

Airfield — *See* Airport.

Airfoil — Any surface, such as an airplane wing, aileron, elevator, rudder, or helicopter rotor, designed to obtain reaction from the air through which it travels. This reaction keeps the aircraft aloft and controls its flight attitude and direction.

Airframe — (1) Major components of an aircraft, such as the fuselage, wings, stabilizers, and flight control surfaces, that are necessary for flight. (2) Basic model of an aircraft; for example, the Boeing 707 airframe has both civilian and military applications in a variety of configurations.

Air-Handling System — *See* Heating, Ventilating, and Air-Conditioning System (HVAC).

Air Lift Axle — Single air-operated axle that, when lowered, will convert a vehicle into a multiaxle unit, providing the vehicle with a greater load carrying capacity.

Air Lifting Bag — Inflatable, envelope-type device that can be placed between the ground and an object and then inflated to lift the object. It can also be used to separate objects. Depending on the size of the bag, it may have lifting capabilities in excess of 75 tons (68 040 kg).

Air Line Connection — *See* Chuck.

Air Line Pilots Association, International (ALPA) — Largest airline pilot union in the world, representing 61,000 pilots who fly for 40 U.S. and Canadian airlines.

Airline Respirator — *See* Airline Respirator System and Supplied Air Respirator (SAR).

Airline Respirator System — System in which breathing air is continuously supplied to the respirator user from a remote source of air. *Also known as* Supplied Air Respirator System. *See* Supplied Air Respirator.

Air Lock — (1) Intermediate chamber between places of unequal atmospheric pressure or temperature. (2) Situation that can develop in a centrifugal pump that has not been properly primed; rapid revolution of the impeller may create an air lock, which prevents priming the pump.

Air Mask — *See* Self-Contained Breathing Apparatus.

Air Mass — Extensive body of air, usually 1,000 miles (1 609 km) or more across, having the same properties of temperature and moisture in a horizontal plane.

Air Operations Area (AOA) — Area of an airport where aircraft are expected to operate, such as taxiways, runways, and ramps.

Air Pack — *See* Self-Contained Breathing Apparatus.

Air Pocket — (1) Condition that occurs during drafting when a portion of hard suction hose is elevated higher than the intake of the pump. (2) Void created by a cave-in. (3) Confined space where air is trapped in the top of a vehicle that has sunk beneath the water. (4) Condition of the atmosphere (as a local down current) that causes an airplane to drop suddenly.

Airport — Land used for aircraft takeoffs and landings. *Also known as* Aerodrome or Airfield.

Airport Control Tower — Building or unit built to house traffic control service for the movement of aircraft and vehicles in an airport operations area.

Airport Emergency Plan — Plan formulated by airport authorities to ensure prompt response to all emergencies and other unusual conditions, in order to minimize the extent of personal and property damage.

Airport Familiarization — Process of teaching personnel to become familiar with airport buildings, runways and taxiways, access roads, and surface features that may enhance or obstruct the prompt and safe response to accidents/incidents on the airport.

Airport Firefighter — Firefighter trained to prevent, control, or extinguish fires that are in or adjacent to aircraft. *Also known as* ARFF Firefighter.

Airport Fire Protection — Specialized branch of the fire service dealing with airports and aircraft.

Airport Flight Information Service — Air traffic services units that provide airport flight information service, search and rescue service, alerting service to aircraft at non-controlled airports, and assistance to aircraft in emergency situations.

Airport Ground Control — Control of aircraft and vehicular traffic on the ground operating in the airport movement area by the airport control tower.

Airport Operation Area (AOA) — Area of an airport where aircraft are expected to operate, such as taxiways, runways, and ramps.

Air-Pressure Sprinkler System — Sprinkler system in which air pressure is used to force water from a storage tank into the system.

Air Purification System — System designed to produce compressed breathing air for use in respiratory protection equipment.

Air-Purifying Respirator (APR) — Respirator with an air-purifying filter, cartridge, or canister that removes specific air contaminants by passing ambient air through the air-purifying element; may have a full or partial facepiece.

Air-Reactive Material — Substance that reacts or ignites when exposed to air at normal temperatures. *Also known as* Pyrophoric. *See* Reactive Material, Reactivity, and Water-Reactive Material.

Air Scoop — Hood or open end of an air duct that introduces air into an automobile, aircraft, or engine for combustion, cooling, or ventilation.

Airspeed — *See* Aircraft Velocity.

Air Spring — Flexible, air-inflated chamber on a truck or trailer in which the air pressure is controlled and varied to support the load and absorb road shocks.

Air-Supply Unit — Apparatus designed to refill exhausted SCBA air cylinders at the scene of an ongoing emergency.

Air-Supported Structure — Membrane structure that is fully or partially held up by interior air pressure.

Air Support Group Supervisor — Individual responsible to the air operations branch director for logistical support and management of helibase and helispot operations, and maintenance of a liaison with fixed-wing aircraft bases.

Air Surface Detection Equipment (ASDE) — Short-range radar displaying the airport surface, used to track and guide surface traffic in low-visibility weather conditions. ASDE may be used to direct radio-equipped emergency vehicles to known accident sites.

Air Tactical Group Supervisor — Individual responsible to the air operations branch director for the coordination of fixed-wing and/or rotary-wing aircraft operations over an incident.

Air Tank — *See* Air Cylinder.

Air Tanker — Any fixed wing aircraft certified by FAA as being capable of transport and delivery of fire retardant solutions.

Air Traffic Control (ATC) — Federal Aviation Administration (FAA) division that operates control towers at major airports.

Airway — (1) Metal or plastic framework designed to fit the curvature of the mouth and throat to prevent air passageways from closing. (2) A passage for carrying air from the nose or mouth to the lungs. (3) Channel of a designated radio frequency for broadcasting or other radio communications. (4) Designated route along which airplanes fly from airport to airport.

Aisle — Passageway between sections of seats in rows.

Alarm — Any signal or message from a person or device indicating the existence of a fire, medical emergency, or other situation requiring the need for emergency fire services response.

Alarm Assignment — Predetermined number of fire units assigned to respond to an emergency.

Alarm Center — *See* Telecommunications Center.

Alarm Check Valve — Type of check valve installed in the riser of an automatic sprinkler system that transmits a water flow alarm when the water flow in the system lifts the valve clapper.

Alarm Circuit — (1) Electrical circuit connecting two points in a fire alarm system; for example, from the signal device to the fire station, from the central alarm center to all fire stations, or from the sending device to the audible alarm services. (2) The circuit on a fire alarm system that connects the alarm initiating devices, such as the smoke detectors to the fire alarm control panel.

Alarm-Indicating Device — Bell, horn, chime, loudspeaker, or similar device that is actuated by a signal from an alarm-initiating device.

Alarm-Initiating Device — Mechanical or electrical device that activates an alarm system. There are three basic types of alarm-initiating devices: manual, products-of-combustion detectors, and extinguishing system activation devices. *See* Initiating Device.

Alarm System — System by which occupants and/or emergency personnel can be alerted to the existence of a hostile fire.

Alcohol-Resistant AFFF Concentrate (AR-AFFF) — Aqueous film forming foam that is designed for use with polar solvent fuels. *See* Aqueous Film Forming Foam and Foam Concentrate.

Alkali — Strong base. *See* Acid, Base, Caustic, and pH.

All Clear — (1) Signal that a danger has passed. (2) Signal given to the incident commander that a specific area has been checked for victims and none have been found, or that all found victims have been extricated from an entrapment.

Allergen — Material that can cause an allergic reaction of the skin or respiratory system. *Also known as* Sensitizer.

Allergic Reaction — Local or general (systemic) reaction to an allergen; usually characterized by hives, tissue swelling, or difficulty breathing.

All Hands — Fire service jargon for an emergency incident engaging all companies on the first-alarm assignment; may be followed by multiple alarms.

All-Hazard Concept — Provides a coordinated approach to a wide variety of incidents; all responders use a similar, coordinated approach with a common set of authorities, protections, and resources.

Allocated Resources — Resources dispatched to an incident that have not been checked in with the incident commander.

Alloy — Substance or mixture composed of two or more metals (or a metal and nonmetallic elements) fused together and dissolved into each other to enhance the properties or usefulness of the base metal.

ALPA — *See* Air Line Pilots Association, International.

Alpha Particle — Energetic, positively charged particles (helium nuclei) emitted from the nucleus during radioactive decay that rapidly lose energy when passing through matter. *See* Alpha Radiation, Beta Particle, and Gamma Rays.

Alpha Radiation — Consists of particles having a large mass and a positive electrical charge; least penetrating of the three common forms of radiation. It is normally not considered dangerous to plants, or to animals or people unless it gets into the body. *See* Beta Radiation, Gamma Radiation, and Radiation (2).

ALS — *See* Advanced Life Support.

Alternate Airport — Airport to which an aircraft may proceed if a landing at the intended airport becomes inadvisable.

Alternating Current (AC) Circuit — Electrical circuit in which the current can move through the circuit in both directions and the flow can be constantly reversing.

Altitude — Geographic position of a location or object in relation to sea level. The location may be either above, below, or at sea level.

Aluminize — To coat with aluminum.

Aluminum Alloy Ladder — Ladder made of aluminum and other materials, such as magnesium, to make the ladder lightweight but strong.

Alveoli — Air sacs of the lungs; place where oxygen is passed to the blood and carbon dioxide is passed from the blood.

Ambient Temperature — Temperature of the surrounding environment.

Ambu-Bag — Trade name for a device that is used to provide the manual ventilation of a patient during cardiopulmonary resuscitation.

Ambulance — Ground vehicle that provides patient transport capability and is equipped with basic or advanced life support equipment and personnel.

American Association of Airport Executives (AAAE) — Professional organization for airport management that offers or co-sponsors emergency response and ARFF related training conferences.

American Board of Criminalistics (ABC) — National peer-review group that certifies forensic scientists in specific disciplines, including fire debris analysis.

American Conference of Governmental Industrial Hygienists (ACGIH) — Organization that promotes the free exchange of ideas and experiences and the development of standards and techniques in industrial health. *See* Biological Exposure Indices (BEI®).

American Fire Sprinkler Association (AFSA) — Nonprofit, international association representing open shop fire sprinkler contractors, dedicated to the educational advancement of its members and the promotion of the use of automatic fire sprinkler systems.

American National Standards Institute (ANSI) — Voluntary standards-setting organization that examines and certifies existing standards and creates new standards.

American Society for Testing and Materials (ASTM) — Voluntary standards-setting organization that sets guidelines on characteristics and performance of materials, products, systems and services; for example the quality of concrete or the flammability of interior finishes.

American Society of Mechanical Engineers (ASME) — Voluntary standards-setting organization concerned with the development of technical standards, such as those for respiratory protection cylinders.

Americans with Disabilities Act (ADA) of 1990 - Public Law 101-336 — Federal statute intended to remove barriers, physical and otherwise, that limit access by individuals with disabilities.

American Wire Gauge (AWG) — Measurement unit for the diameter of wire. Larger AWG numbers indicate smaller diameters than smaller AWG numbers; for example, No. 14 AWG wire is smaller than No. 8 AWG wire.

Amidships — Center of a vessel's length, halfway between the bow and the stern.

Ammeter — (1) Instrument for measuring electric current in amperes. (2) Gauge that indicates both the amount of electrical current being drawn from and provided to the vehicle's battery.

Ammonium Nitrate and Fuel Oil (ANFO) — High explosive blasting agent made of common fertilizer mixed with diesel fuel or oil; requires a booster to initiate detonation. *See* Detonation, Explosive (1), and High Explosive.

Ampacity — Current-carrying capacity of conductors or equipment; expressed in amperes.

Amperage — Strength of an electrical current, expressed in amperes.

Ampere — Basic unit of electrical current; amount of current sent by one volt through one ohm of resistance. May be abbreviated either by A or I.

Amphitheater Room Setup — Room arrangement in which the chairs are positioned in a slight semicircle to provide for better eye contact between the educator and the audience and to improve the audience's line of sight to a screen or video monitor. *Also known as* Auditorium-Style Setup.

Amputation — Complete removal of an appendage.

Analysis — Ability to divide information into its most basic components. *See* Cost-Benefit Analysis and Impact Analysis.

Anaphylaxis — Severe systemic allergic reaction characterized by hives, itching, difficulty breathing, and possible circulatory collapse. *Also known as* Anaphylactic Shock.

Anarchism — Political belief that society should be organized without a coercive, compulsory government.

Anatomy — Structure of the body or the study of body structure.

Anchor — (1) Metal device used to hold down the ends of trusses or heavy timber members at the walls. (2) Reliable or principal support. (3) Something that serves to hold an object firmly. (4) A single object used to secure a rope rescue system. *Also known as* Anchor Points. (5) Heavy device used to hold a ship or boat in position.

Anchorage — Designated areas, identified on navigational charts, where ships may safely anchor.

Anchor Light — Light a vessel carries when at anchor; must be visible for 2 miles (3.22 km) at night in every direction. Vessels over 150 feet (45.7 m) must carry two lights visible for 3 miles (4.83 km).

Anchor Point — (1) Solid base or point from which pulling or pushing operations can be initiated. (2) Point from which a fire line is begun; usually a natural or man-made barrier that prevents fire spread and the possibility of the crew being "flanked" while constructing the fire line. Examples include lakes, ponds, streams, roads, earlier burns, rockslides, and cliffs.

Anchor System — Total combination or anchor points, slings, and carabiners used to create attachment points for a rope rescue system.

Ancillary Ladder — Small ladder attached to an elevating platform to be used as an escape route for platform passengers in the event of a mechanical failure of the aerial device.

Andragogy — Study of adult education and its methods of teaching and learning.

ANFO — *See* Ammonium Nitrate and Fuel Oil.

Angina Pectoris — Spasmodic pain in the chest caused by insufficient blood supply to the heart; aggravated by exercise or tension and relieved by rest or medication.

Angle of Approach — (1) On a vehicle, the smallest angle made between the road surface and a line drawn from the front point of ground contact of the front tire to any projection of the apparatus ahead of the front axle — the front overhang. (2) Angle formed by level ground and a line from the point where the front tires of a vehicle touch the ground to the lowest projection at the front of the apparatus. The angle of approach should be at least 16 degrees.

Angle of Approach/Departure — Relationship described in degrees that is created by an incline from or to a road surface.

Angle of Departure — (1) On a vehicle, the smallest angle made between the road surface and a line drawn from the rear point of ground contact of the rear tire to any projection of the apparatus behind the rear axle — the rear overhang. (2) Angle formed by level ground and a line from the point where the rear tires of a vehicle touch the ground to the lowest projection at the rear of the apparatus. The angle of departure should be at least 8 degrees.

Angle of Inclination — Pitch for portable non-self-supporting ground ladders. The preferred angle of inclination is 75 degrees.

Angle of Loll — Angle at which an imbalanced vessel is leaning and to which the vessel will stabilize. *See* List and Loll.

Angle of Repose — Greatest angle above the horizontal plane at which loose material, such as soil, will lie without sliding.

Annealed — Soft state in metal caused by controlled application of heat and cold.

Annealed Glass — Glass that has slowly cooled during the forming process to relieve internal stresses of the quenching process; commonly found glass that breaks into large pieces and shards when broken.

Annual Leave — Vacation time allowed emergency services personnel per year.

ANSI — *See* American National Standards Institute.

Antenna — Device connected to a receiver, transmitter, or transceiver that is intended to radiate the transmitted signal and/or to receive a signal.

Anterior — Situated in front of, or in the forward part of. In anatomy, used in reference to the belly surface of the body.

Anthrax — Non-contagious, potentially fatal disease caused by breathing, eating, or absorbing through cuts in the skin the bacteria known as Bacillus anthracis.

Anti-Electrocution Platform — Slide-out platform mounted beneath the side running board or rear step of an apparatus equipped with an aerial device. This platform is designed to minimize the chance of the driver/operator being electrocuted should the aerial device come in contact with energized electrical wires or equipment.

Antibiotic — Antimicrobial agent made from a mold or a bacterium that kills or slows the growth of other microbes, specifically bacteria; examples include penicillin and streptomycin. Antibiotics are ineffective against viruses.

Antidote — Substance that will counteract the effects of a poison or toxin.

Antifogging Chemical — Chemical used to prohibit fogging inside the facepiece.

Anti-Shim Device — *See* Dead Latch.

Antisubmarine Device — Any device designed to prevent a driver from sliding forward and becoming wedged or trapped beneath the dashboard of a vehicle.

Anxiety — Feeling of apprehension, uncertainty, or fear.

Aorta — Largest artery in the body; originates at the left ventricle of the heart.

Apartment — Subdivision of residential property classification consisting of structures that contain three or more living units equipped with independent bathroom and cooking facilities. *Also known as* Apartment House, Garden Apartment, or Tenement.

Apnea — Cessation of breathing; the absence of respiration.

A-Post — Front post area of a vehicle where the door is connected to the body.

Apparatus — Motor-driven vehicle or group of vehicles designed and constructed for the purpose of fighting fires; may be of different types such as engines, water tenders, and ladder trucks.

Apparatus Bay — Area of the fire station where apparatus are parked. *Also known as* Apparatus Room.

Apparatus Engine — Diesel or gasoline engine that powers the apparatus drive train and associated fire equipment. *Also known as* Power Plant.

Appliance — Generic term applied to any nozzle, wye, siamese, deluge monitor, or other piece of hardware used in conjunction with fire hose for the purpose of delivering water.

Application — (1) Lesson plan component in which the instructor provides opportunities for participants to practice, or to apply cognitive information to skills learned in a lesson. *See* Lesson Plan. (2) The third of the four teaching steps in which students use or apply what the educator has taught; the step in which students practice using new ideas, information, techniques, and skills. *See* Application Step.

Application Rate — Minimum amount of foam solution that must be applied to an unignited fire, spill, or spill fire to either control vapor emission or extinguish the fire; measured per minute per square foot (or square meter) of area to be covered.

Application Step — Third step, in the four-step teaching method of conducting a lesson, in which the learner is given the opportunity to apply what has been learned and to perform under supervision and assistance.

Applicator Pipe — Curved pipe attached to a nozzle for precisely applying water over a burning object.

Apprenticeship — Labor organization professional development program requiring at least three years of fire service experience supplemented with related technical instruction. Apprentices are subject to probationary periods, the length of which is stipulated by local programs. The fire service apprenticeship training program was developed by the International Association of Fire Chiefs and the International Association of Firefighters, and was accepted by the Department of Labor's Bureau of Apprenticeship and Training on July 11, 1975.

Approach Clothing — Special personal protective clothing designed to protect the firefighter from radiant heat while approaching the fire. It typically consists of standard turnout gear with an aluminized outer coating.

Approach Lights — System of lights arranged to assist an airplane pilot in aligning his or her aircraft with the runway for landing.

Approach Sequence — Order in which aircraft are positioned while on approach or while awaiting approach clearance.

Approach-Avoidance — Decision-making problem; refers to an inner conflict within the person in charge that results in an inability to make a decision.

Approved — Acceptable to the authority having jurisdiction.

Apron — Airport area intended to accommodate aircraft for purposes of loading or unloading passengers or cargo, refueling, parking, or maintenance. *Also known as* Ramp.

Aqueous Film Forming Foam (AFFF) — Synthetic foam concentrate that, when combined with water, can form a complete vapor barrier over fuel spills and fires and is a highly effective extinguishing and blanketing agent on hydrocarbon fuels. *See* Alcohol-Resistant AR-AFFF Concentrate, Foam Concentrate, and Foam System.

AR-AFFF — *See* Alcohol-Resistant Aqueous Film Forming Foam.

Arc — High-temperature luminous electric discharge across a gap or though a medium such as charred insulation. Arcs produce very high temperature.

Arc-Fault Circuit Interrupter (AFCI) — Electronic device, generally part of a circuit breaker, that detects arcing conditions caused by an energized conductor contacting either a neutral conductor or a grounded object.

Arch — Curved structural member in which the interior stresses are primarily compressive. Arches develop inclined reactions at their supports.

Arched Roof — Any of several different types of roofs, all of which are curved or arch shaped, resembling the top half of a horizontal cylinder. Typical applications are found on supermarkets, auditoriums, bowling centers, sports arenas, and aircraft hangars.

Arc Mapping — Visual documentation of the path of electrical arcs at a scene.

Area Ignition — Simultaneous or nearly simultaneous ignition of several individual wildland fires that are spaced in such a way as to add to and influence the main body of the fire and each other in a way that produces a hot, fast-moving fire or blowup throughout the area. Area ignition is a cause of blowup and great fire spread.

Area of Origin — Location in which the ignition source and material first ignited actually came together for the first time.

Area of Refuge — (1) Space protected from fire in the normal means of egress either by an approved sprinkler system, separation from other spaces within the same building by smokeproof walls, or location in an adjacent building. (2) Two-hour-rated building compartment containing one elevator to the ground floor and at least one enclosed exit stairway. (3) Area where persons who are unable to use stairs can temporarily wait for instructions or assistance during an emergency building evacuation. (4) In wildland fire fighting, a safe area.

Area Separation Wall — Wall that provides a complete separation of building compartments, dividing the building into distinct areas.

ARFF — *See* Aircraft Rescue and Fire Fighting.

ARFF Firefighter — *See* Airport Firefighter.

ARFFWG — *See* Aircraft Rescue and Fire Fighting Working Group.

Armormax® — A combination of numerous synthetic fibers used to form an opaque composite ballistic armor.

Around-the-Pump Proportioner — Apparatus-mounted foam proportioner in which a small quantity of water is diverted from the apparatus pump through an inline proportioner; there it picks up the foam concentrate and carries it to the intake side of the pump. It is the most common apparatus-mounted foam proportioner in service. *See* Foam Proportioner and Proportioning.

Arrest — (1) Sudden cessation or stoppage. (2) Restricting a person's movement or freedom, usually in a legal or law enforcement action.

Arresting System — Device used to engage an aircraft and absorb forward momentum in case of an aborted takeoff or landing.

Arrhythmia — Any disturbance in the rhythm of the heart.

Arrow Pattern — *See* Pointer Pattern.

Arson — Crime of willfully, maliciously, and intentionally starting an incendiary fire or causing an explosion to destroy one's property or the property of another. Precise legal definitions vary among jurisdictions, wherein it is defined by statutes and judicial decisions. *See* Firesetting.

Arson Hotline — Telephone line and operation set up for the purpose of receiving information, often given anonymously, on arson crimes.

Arson Immunity Law — Law stating that insurance companies must release all information and documentation when requested to a public entity when there is reason to suspect a fire under investigation was intentionally set. The released information is considered confidential until it is used in court proceedings, and the insurance company that released the information is granted immunity under the law for breaking any confidentiality requirements it may have to its clients.

Arson Investigator — Public sector fire investigator who primarily investigates intentionally set fires; may be tasked with locating and arresting arsonists and interviewing suspects. May also have limited law enforcement powers, such as the power of arrest and authorization to carry a weapon.

Arsonist — Person who commits an act of arson.

Arson Kit — Kit containing equipment used to detect, collect, protect, and preserve evidence of arson and to aid in determining the cause of a fire.

Arson Strike Force — Special purpose, short-term mobilization of a team or teams of investigators, together with allied resources, that applies high intensity investigative efforts to a major arson incident or series of incidents.

Arson Task Force — Legal or quasi-legal bodies or private advisory committees established to set policy and implement new programs based upon information gathered about local arson activity. Arson task forces are not investigative units.

Arteriosclerosis — Generic name for several conditions that cause the walls of the arteries to become thickened, hard, and inelastic.

Artery — Blood vessel that carries blood away from the heart.

Articulated Transit Bus — Passenger-carrying bus constructed with two sections, a tractor and a trailer, which are connected by a pivoting joint.

Articulating Aerial Platform — Aerial device that consists of two or more booms that are attached with hinges and operate in a folding manner. A passenger-carrying platform is attached to the working end of the device.

Articulating Boom — Arm portion or structural support member of an aerial device consisting of two or more sections that are hinged and rotate in a vertical plane in a folding manner.

Articulation — (1) The action or manner of jointing or interrelating. (2) A joint or juncture between bones or cartilages.

Artifacts — Remains of materials involved in the fire that are in some way related to ignition, development, or spread of the fire or explosion.

Artificial Respiration — Movement of air into and out of the lungs by artificial means. *Also known as* Artificial Resuscitation, Pulmonary Resuscitation, and Rescue Breathing.

Artificial Resuscitation — *See* Artificial Respiration.

Asbestos — Fibrous carcinogenic substance (noncombustible magnesium silicate minerals) used for fireproofing, brake linings, roofing compositions, and other purposes such as insulation and ceiling materials in older buildings. Inhaled asbestos fibers travel to the lungs, causing scarring, reduced lung capacity, and cancer.

Ascender — Mechanical contrivance, used when climbing rope, that allows upward but not downward movement.

ASCLD — *See* Association of Crime Laboratory Directors.

Ash — Powdery residue left when organic material is burned completely or is oxidized by chemical means.

Ashore — Leaving a vessel and stepping on land; opposite of aboard.

ASME — *See* American Society of Mechanical Engineers.

Aspect — (1) Position facing a particular direction; exposure. (2) Compass direction toward which a slope faces.

Asphyxia — Suffocation.

Asphyxiant — Any substance that prevents oxygen from combining in sufficient quantities with the blood or from being used by body tissues. *See* Chemical Asphyxiant and Simple Asphyxiant.

Asphyxiation — Condition that causes death because of a deficient amount of oxygen and an excessive amount of carbon monoxide and/or other gases in the blood.

Aspirate — To inhale foreign material into the lungs.

Aspiration — Adding air to a foam solution as the solution is discharged from a nozzle. *Also known as* Aeration.

Aspirator — Suction device for removing undesirable material from the throat of a patient.

Assay — To analyze or estimate.

Assembly — (1) All component or manufactured parts necessary for and fitted together to form a complete machine, structure, unit or system. (2) Occupancy classification of buildings, structures, or compartments (rooms) that are used for the gathering of 50 or more persons. *See* Occupancy Classification.

Assembly Area — Area designated in the employee emergency action plan in which employees displaced by an evacuation are to assemble.

Assessment — Process used to find out the knowledge, skills, and abilities possessed by a learner; can be accomplished by observation or by special assessment activities such as quizzes and tests.

Assessment Stop — Distant location at which first responders can safely stop and evaluate the situation, complete donning their protective clothing and SCBA, and report conditions to the telecommunications center.

Assigned Resources — Resources on an incident that have been checked in and assigned an objective.

Assignment — Work that must be performed by learners outside class in order to reach a skill level, meet an objective, and/or prepare for the next lesson.

Assisting Agency — Agency directly contributing suppression, rescue, support, or service resources to another agency.

Association of Crime Laboratory Directors (ASCLD) — Association that provides criteria used to judge whether a facility and its practices provide an atmosphere conducive to the quality of work necessary in the forensic field.

Association of Flight Attendants-CWA (AFA-CWA) — The world's largest labor union for flight attendants, representing over 50,000 flight attendants at 22 airlines.

Asthma — Respiratory condition marked by attacks of labored breathing, wheezing, a sense of constriction in the chest, and coughing or gasping.

ASTM — *See* American Society for Testing and Materials.

Astragal — Molding that covers the narrow opening between adjacent double doors in the closed position.

ATF — *See* Bureau of Alcohol, Tobacco, Firearms and Explosives.

Atherosclerosis — Common form of arteriosclerosis characterized by fat deposits in the walls of the arteries.

Athwartship — Direction from side to side; to move across a vessel is to move athwartships.

Atmosphere — Area within the confined space where dust, vapors, mists, or other hazardous materials may exist.

Atmospheric Ceiling — Level in the atmosphere at which a heated column ceases to rise.

Atmospheric Displacement — System or method of applying water fog in a superheated area, causing the water to be converted into steam that expands and displaces the atmosphere in a burning room or building.

Atmospheric Pressure — Force exerted by the atmosphere at the surface of the earth due to the weight of air. Atmospheric pressure at sea level is about 14.7 psi (101 kPa) and is measured as 760 mm of mercury on a barometer. Atmospheric pressure increases as elevation decreases, and decreases as elevation increases.

Atmospheric Stability — Degree to which vertical motion in the atmosphere is enhanced or suppressed. Vertical motion and smoke dispersion are enhanced in an unstable atmosphere. Stability suppresses vertical motion and limits smoke dispersion. *See* Inversion (1).

Atmospheric Storage Tank — Class of fixed facility storage tanks. Pressures range from 0 to 0.5 psi (0 to 3.4 kPa) {0 to 0.03 bar}. *Also known as* Nonpressure Storage Tank. *See* Cone Roof Storage Tank, External Floating Roof Tank, Floating Roof Storage Tank, Horizontal Storage Tank, Internal Floating Roof Tank, Lifter Roof Storage Tank, Low-Pressure Storage Tank, and Pressure Storage Tank.

Atmospheric Temperature — Measure of the warmth or coldness of the air.

Atomic Number — Number of protons in an atom.

Atomic Weight — Physical characteristic relating to the mass of molecules and atoms. A relative scale for atomic weights has been adopted, in which the atomic weight of carbon has been set at 12, although its true atomic weight is 12.01115.

Atrium — (1) Upper chamber of the left or right side of the heart. (2) Open area in the center of a building, extending through two or more stories, similar to a courtyard but usually covered by a skylight, to allow natural light and ventilation to interior rooms.

ATSDR — *See* Agency for Toxic Substances and Disease Registry.

Attack — (1) To set upon forcefully. (2) Any action to control fire. (3) In ICS/IMS, used to describe the units attacking the fire.

Attack Hose — Hose between the attack pumper and the nozzle(s); also, any hose used in a handline to control and extinguish fire. Minimum size is 1½ inch (38 mm).

Attack Line — (1) Hoseline connected to a pump discharge of a fire apparatus ready for use in attacking a fire; may or may not be preconnected. In contrast, supply lines are connected to a water supply with a pump. (2) Fire streams used to attack, contain, or prevent the spread of a fire.

Attack Methods — (1) Tactics for interior fire-suppression operations, including direct, indirect, and combination attacks. (2) Tactics for wildland fire-suppression operations, including aerial, direct, flank, frontal, indirect, mobile, pincer, and tandem attacks.

Attack Pumper — (1) Pumper that is positioned at the fire scene and is directly supplying attack lines. (2) Light truck equipped with a small pump and water tank. *Also known as* Midi-pumper or Mini-pumper.

Attic — Concealed and often unfinished space between the ceiling of the top floor and the roof of a building. *Also known as* Cockloft or Interstitial Space.

Attic Fold — Method of folding a salvage cover that aids in spreading within the tight confines of an attic, where lateral movement is difficult.

Attic Ladder — Term commonly used for a folding ladder or combination ladder that is especially useful for inside work, and is used to access an attic through a scuttle or similar restricted opening. Attic ladders generally come in 6- to 14-foot (1.8-4.2 m) lengths.

Audible Alarm — Bell, whistle, or other sound-producing alerting device attached to a self-contained breathing apparatus, personal alert safety system, or fixed fire protection system.

Audience — Person or persons receiving a message. *Also known as* Receiver.

Audiometric Test — Examinations used to determine the extent of temporary or permanent shifts in thresholds of hearing acuity. These tests make it possible to grade occupational noise exposures and, when necessary, recommend appropriate hearing conservation procedures.

Audiovisual Materials — Instructional materials that can be heard as well as seen. Note: This category includes flipcharts, mark-and-wipe boards, and chalkboards, even though there is no audio element involved.

Auditorium Raise — Method of extending a ladder perpendicularly and holding it in place from four opposite points of the compass by four guy ropes attached to the top of the ladder. *Also known as* Church Raise or Steeple Raise.

Auditorium-Style Room Setup — *See* Amphitheater Room Setup.

Auger — (1) Screwlike shaft that is turned to move grain or other commodities through a farm implement. (2) Tool for boring holes in floors.

Auger Wagon — Large wagon containing a power take-off-driven auger for unloading purposes. Widely used in agriculture to transport and unload grain, silage, loose forage, stover, and other loose materials.

Authority — Relates to the empowered duties of an official to perform certain tasks. In the case of a fire inspector, the level of an inspector's authority is commensurate with the enforcement obligations of the governing body.

Authority Having Jurisdiction (AHJ) — Term used in codes and standards to identify the legal entity, such as a building or fire official, that has the statutory authority to enforce a code and to approve or require equipment; may be a unit of a local, state, or federal government, depend-

ing on where the work occurs. In the insurance industry it may refer to an insurance rating bureau or an insurance company inspection department.

Autocratic Leadership — Leadership style in which the leader makes decisions independently of others, informing them only after the decision has been made.

Autoexposure — *See* Lapping.

Autoignition — Ignition that occurs when a substance in air, whether solid, liquid, or gaseous, is heated sufficiently to initiate or cause self-sustained combustion without an external ignition source. *See* Autoignition Temperature, Ignition, and Ignition Temperature.

Autoignition Temperature — Minimum temperature to which a fuel (other than a liquid) in the air must be heated in order to start self-sustained combustion; no external ignition source is required. *See* Autoignition, Ignition, and Ignition Temperature.

Autoinjector — Spring-loaded syringe filled with a single dose of a life-saving drug.

Automatic Aid — Written agreement between two or more agencies to automatically dispatch predetermined resources to any fire or other emergency reported in the geographic area covered by the agreement. These areas are generally located near jurisdictional boundaries or in jurisdictional "islands."

Automatic Alarm — (1) Alarm actuated by heat, gas, smoke, flame-sensing devices, or waterflow in a sprinkler system; the alarm is then conveyed to local alarm bells or the fire station. (2) Alarm box that automatically transmits a coded signal to the fire station, telecommunications center, or alarm company to give the location of the alarm box.

Automatic Closing Door — Self-closing door normally held in the open position by an automatic releasing device such as a magnetic hold-open device. When the door is released by the hold-open device, it closes.

Automatic Fire Detection Systems — Heat, gas, and flame detectors used in nonresidential buildings.

Automatic Hydrant Valve — Valve that opens automatically when connected to a hydrant, to allow water to flow into the supply line.

Automatic Location Identification (ALI) — Enhanced 9-1-1 feature that displays the address of the party calling 9-1-1 onscreen for use by the public safety telecommunicator; usually used in tandem with automatic number identification (ANI) services. This feature is also used to route calls to the appropriate public safety answering point (PSAP) and can store information in its database regarding all emergency services (police, fire, and medical) that respond to that address.

Automatic Nozzle — Fog stream nozzle that automatically corrects itself to provide a good stream at the proper nozzle pressure.

Automatic Number Identification (ANI) — Enhanced 9-1-1 feature that displays the phone number of the party calling 9-1-1 onscreen for use by the public safety telecommunicator; usually used in tandem with automatic location identification (ALI) services.

Automatic Oscillating Foam Monitor — Large-capacity foam system that is designed to operate automatically when a fire-detection system activates; may be found in aircraft hangars, tank farms, and loading racks. *See* Foam Monitor, Manual Foam Monitor, and Remote-Controlled Foam Monitor.

Automatic Sprinkler Kit — Kit containing the tools and equipment required to close an open sprinkler.

Automatic Sprinkler System — System of water pipes, discharge nozzles, and control valves designed to activate during fires by automatically discharging enough water to control or extinguish a fire. *Also known as* Sprinkler System. *See* Riser and Sprinkler.

Automatic Suppression Systems — Fire suppression systems that sense heat, smoke, or gas, and activate automatically. These include sprinkler, standpipe, carbon dioxide, and halogenated systems, as well as fire pumps, dry chemical agents and their systems, foam extinguishers, and combustible metal agents.

Automatic Vehicle Locator (AVL) — System that uses global positioning satellites to determine the exact location of units in the field. This information is relayed to public safety telecommunications centers to help determine the closest unit to send during an emergency.

Autonomic Nervous System — Part of the nervous system concerned with the regulation of body functions not controlled by conscious thought.

Autorotation — Flight condition in which the lifting rotor of a rotary wing aircraft is driven entirely by action of the air when in flight, or, as in the case of a helicopter, after an engine failure.

Auxiliary — (1) Additional fire fighting equipment or staffing that are not part of the regular complement assigned to the fire service. (2) A group organized to assist the fire department.

Auxiliary Alarm System — System that connects the protected property with the fire department alarm telecommunications center by either a municipal master fire alarm box or a dedicated telephone line.

Auxiliary Deadbolt — Deadbolt bored lock. *Also known as* Tubular Deadbolt.

Auxiliary Hydraulic Pump — Electrically operated, positive displacement pump used to supply hydraulic oil through the hydraulic system of an aerial device in the event that the main hydraulic pump fails.

Auxiliary Lock — Lock added to a door to increase security.

Auxiliary Power Unit (APU) — (1) Power unit installed in most large aircraft to provide electrical power and pneumatics for ground power, air conditioning, engine start, and backup power in flight. (2) Mobile units that are moved from one aircraft to another to provide a power boost during engine startup.

Available Fire Flow — Actual amount of water available from a given hydrant; determined by testing.

Available Resources — Resources not assigned to an incident and available for an assignment.

Average Daily Consumption — Average of the total amount of water used each day during a one-year period.

Avoidance — (1) Socio-psychological concept that shows that people feel they can protect themselves psychologically by denying unpleasant situations; thus, during the first moments of a fire, people tend to search for other, safer explanations for the cues they see, smell, and hear. (2) Effect of a decision-making problem. The person in charge might try to avoid being in charge, especially when faced with an approach-avoidance dilemma.

Avulsion — Forcible separation or detachment; the tearing away of a body part.

Awareness Level — Lowest level of training established by the National Fire Protection Association® for first responders at hazardous materials incidents. *See* Operational Level.

Awareness Materials — Fire and life safety teaching materials that attempt to make the audience more aware of a problem or situation. *Also known as* Promotional Materials.

AWG — *See* American Wire Gauge.

Awning Window — Type of swinging window that is hinged at the top and swings outward, often having two or more sections.

Axe — Forcible entry tool that has a pick or flat head and a blade attached to a wood or fiberglass handle. *Also known as* Firefighter's Axe.

Axial Load — Load applied to the center of the cross section of a member and perpendicular to that cross section. It can be either tensile or compressive and creates uniform stresses across the cross section of the material.

B

BA — Short for breathing apparatus. *See* Self-Contained Breathing Apparatus (SCBA).

Baby Bangor — Short-length tapered-truss wood ladder. *Also known as* Attic Ladder.

Back Burn — Process of burning vegetation in advance of an oncoming wildland fire in order to establish a firebreak that will stop the spread of the fire.

Back Flushing — Cleaning a fire pump or piping by flowing water through it in the opposite direction of normal flow.

Back Pressure — Pressure loss or gain created by changes in elevation between the nozzle and pump.

Backdraft — Instantaneous explosion or rapid burning of superheated gases that occurs when oxygen is introduced into an oxygen-depleted confined space. The stalled combustion resumes with explosive force; may occur because of inadequate or improper ventilation procedures. *See* Flashover and Rollover.

Backfill — Coarse dirt or other material used to build up the ground level around foundation walls, in order to provide a slope for drainage away from the foundation.

Backfire — Fire set along the inner edge of a control line to consume the fuel in the path of a wildland fire and/or change the direction of force of the fire's convection column.

Backfiring — (1) Technique used in the indirect attack method for wildland fires; involves intentionally setting a fire between the control line and the advancing fire to deprive the fire of fuel. The intent is for the backfire to meet the advancing fire some distance from the control line. Backfiring can be dangerous and is illegal in some places. (2) Leakage of the fuel-air explosion past the valves in a gasoline engine due to worn valves or bad valve timing.

Backing Fire — Fire spreading (or ignited to spread) into (against) the wind or downslope. A fire spreading on level ground in the absence of wind is a backing fire.

Backing Material — Material used to take up space or fill gaps behind shoring system parts.

Backlash — (1) Sudden violent backward movement or reaction. (2) Reverse bouncing motion that occurs when the motion of an aerial device is abruptly halted.

Backpack — (1) Tank-type extinguisher carried on the firefighter's back by straps. The unit has a pump built into the nozzle, and is used extensively to fight wildland fires. (2) Pack used to carry hose on firefighters' backs. (3) Assembly that holds the air cylinder and regulator of the self-contained breathing apparatus to the wearer. *Also known as* Backplate.

Backplate — *See* Backpack (3).

Backsplash — Vertical surface at the back of a countertop.

Backstay — Line made of rope or wire supporting a mast (vertical pole); extends from the top of the mast to the stern.

Backup Knot — A second knot tied in the short tail of a knot or bend to ensure that the primary knot or bend cannot come undone by itself during use.

Backwards — Slang for making a reverse lay; as in "Lay a backwards."

Bacteria — Microscopic, single-celled organisms. *See* Rickettsia and Virus.

Badge — Indicator of rank worn on a firefighter's or an officer's uniform.

Baffle — (1) Intermediate partial bulkhead that reduces the surge effect in a partially loaded liquid tank. (2) Divider used to separate beds of hose into two or more compartments. (3) Device to deflect, check, or regulate flow. (4) Partition placed in vehicular or aircraft water tanks to reduce shifting of the water load when starting, stopping, or turning.

Bag-Valve Mask — Portable artificial ventilation unit consisting of a face mask, a one-way valve, and an inflatable bag; can be used on a nonbreathing or breathing patient.

Bagging — Spreading of a salvage cover to catch water from above, particularly in an attic; used in salvage and overhaul operations.

Balanced Pressure Proportioner — Foam concentrate proportioner that operates in tandem with a fire water pump to ensure a proper foam concentrate-to-water mixture.

Bale Hook — Tool used for moving bales or boxed goods, and for moving and overhauling stuffed furniture or mattresses. *Also known as* Baling Hook or Hay Hook.

Ballast — Additional weight placed low in the vessel's hull to improve its stability; may be steel, concrete, or water. *See* Ballasting, Ballast Tank, and Trim.

Ballasting — Process of filling empty tanks with seawater to increase a vessel's stability. *See* Ballast, Ballast Tank, and Trim.

Ballast Tank — Watertight compartment that holds liquid ballast. *See* Trimming Tank.

Ballistics — Science of projectiles, their motion, and their effects.

Balloon Throw — Method of spreading a salvage cover; uses air trapped under the cover to float it into place over the materials to be protected.

Balloon-Frame Construction — Type of structural framing used in some single-story and multistory wood frame buildings; studs are continuous from the foundation to the roof, and there may be no fire stops between the studs.

Ball Valve — Valve having a ball-shaped internal component with a hole through its center that permits water to flow through when aligned with the waterway.

Baluster — Vertical member supporting a handrail.

Balustrade — Entire assembly of a handrail including its supporting members (newel posts and balusters).

Band — Range of frequencies defined between two definite limits.

Bandage — Material used to hold a dressing in place.

Banding Method — Means of attaching a coupling to a fire hose using tightly wound strands of narrow-gauge wire or steel bands.

Bang Out — Slang for "to dispatch" or "to be dispatched."

Bangor Ladder — *See* Pole Ladder.

Bank-Down Application Method — Method of foam application that may be employed on an ignited or unignited Class B fuel spill. The foam stream is directed at a vertical surface or object that is next to or within the spill area; foam deflects off the surface or object and flows down onto the surface of the spill to form a foam blanket. *Also known as* Deflection. *See* Rain-Down Application Method and Roll-On Application Method.

Bar Joist — Open web truss constructed entirely of steel, with steel bars used as the web members.

Barge — Long, large vessel used for transporting goods on inland waterways; usually flat-bottomed, self-propelled, or towed or pushed by another vessel. *See* Cargo Vessel and Lighter.

Barometer — Instrument used to measure atmospheric pressure.

Barrel — Measure of liquid volume used in the marine industry; for petroleum, 1 barrel = 42 U.S. gallons (159 liters).

Barrel Strainer — Cylindrical strainer that is attached to a hard suction hose to prevent the induction of foreign debris into the pump during drafting operations.

Barrier — Any obstruction of the spread of fire; typically an area devoid of combustible fuel.

Bar-Screw Jack — Jack used to hold loads under compression; commonly used in shoring work or other similar evolutions.

Basal Skull Fracture — Fracture involving the base of the cranium.

Base — (1) Bottom of something; a foundation or support. (2) Location at which the primary Incident Management Logistics functions are coordinated and administered; the incident command post may be co-located with the base. There is only one base per incident. (3) At a high-rise fire, the location where reserve companies are staged until needed. *Also known as* Level II Staging. (4) Lowest or widest section of a non-self-supporting extension ladder. Also, the bottom end of any non-self-supporting ground ladder. (5) Any alkaline or caustic substance; corrosive water-soluble compound or substance containing group forming hydroxide ions in water solution that reacts with an acid to form a salt. *See* Acid, Alkali, Caustic, Corrosive, and pH.

Base Leg — Flight path at right angles to the landing runway off the approach end.

Base Radio — Fixed, nonmobile radio at a central location.

Base Rails — Lower chords of the aerial ladder to which the rungs, trusses, and other portions of the ladder are attached. *Also known as* Beams.

Base Section — *See* Bed Section.

Baseline Data — Data and statistics gathered before an education program starts; educators compare baseline data with data collected after the program has concluded in order to determine educational gain.

Basement Plans — Drawings showing the below-ground view of a building. The thickness and external dimensions of the basement walls are given, as are floor joist locations, strip footings, and other attached foundations.

Basic Life Support (BLS) — Emergency medical treatment administered without the use of adjunctive equipment; includes maintenance of airway, breathing, and circulation, as well as basic bandaging and splinting.

Basket Stabilizer — Device used to support the basket portion of an elevating platform device in the stowed position during road travel.

Batch Mixing — Production of foam solution by adding an appropriate amount of foam concentrate to a water tank before application; the resulting solution must be used or discarded following the incident. *See* Premixing.

Batt Insulation — Blanket insulation cut in widths to fit between studs, and in short lengths to facilitate handling.

Battalion — Fire department organizational subdivision consisting of several fire service companies in a designated geographic area. A battalion is usually the first organizational level above individual companies or stations. *Also known as* District.

Battalion Chief — Chief officer assigned to command a fire department battalion. *Also known as* District Chief.

Batten — (1) Thin iron bar used to hold down the coverings of hatches on merchant vessels. (2) Strip of wood used to keep cargo away from the hull of a vessel or to prevent it from shifting.

Batten Door — *See* Ledge Door.

Battering — Act of creating an opening in a building component by striking and breaking it with a tool, such as a sledge or ram.

Battering Ram — Large metal pipe with handles and a blunt end used to break down doors or create holes in walls.

Battery — (1) Unlawful, intentional and unauthorized touching of or application of force to a person without his or her consent. (2) Number of similar articles, items, or devices arranged, connected, or used together; for example, a grouping of artillery pieces for tactical purposes. (3) The electrical power supply for a vehicle, handlights, or other electrically powered device.

Battery Bank — Group of vehicle batteries clustered in one location.

Battle's Sign — Purplish discoloration above the bone behind the ear indicating a skull fracture.

Bay — Compartment or section in a fire station where the fire apparatus is parked.

Beam — (1) Structural member subjected to loads, usually vertical loads, perpendicular to its length. (2) Main structural member of a ladder supporting the rungs or rung blocks. *Also known as* Rail or Side Rail. (3) Width of a vessel measured at the widest point.

Beam Block — *See* Truss Block.

Beam Bolts — Bolts that pass through both rails at the truss block of a wooden ladder to tie the two truss rails together.

Beam Raise — Raising a ladder to the vertical position with only one beam in contact with the ground, instead of with both beams on the ground as with a flat raise.

Bearing Wall — *See* Load-Bearing Wall.

Bearing Wall Structures — Common type of structure that uses the walls of a building to support spanning elements such as beams, trusses, and pre-cast concrete slabs.

Becket Bend — Knot used for joining two ropes; particularly well suited for joining ropes of unequal diameters or joining a rope and a chain. *Also known as* Sheet Bend.

Becquerel (Bq) — International System unit of measurement for radioactivity, indicating the number of nuclear decays/disintegrations a radioactive material undergoes in a certain period of time. *See* Curie (Ci), Radiation (2), and Radioactive Material (RAM).

Bed Ladder — Lowest section of a multi-section ladder.

Bed Ladder Pipe — Non-telescoping section of pipe, usually 3 or 3½ inches (76 mm or 89 mm) in diameter, attached to the underside of the bed section of the aerial ladder for the purpose of deploying an elevated master stream.

Bed Section — Bottom section of an extension ladder. *Also known as* Base Section.

Bedded Position — Extension ladder with the fly section(s) fully retracted.

Behavior — In psychology, any response or reaction to a stimulus, such as instruction.

Behavior Change — Change in a person's actions because of an increase in knowledge.

Behavioral Objective — Measurable and precise statement of intent that specifically describes behavior that the learner is expected to exhibit as a result of instruction. Behavioral objectives also indicate the conditions under which the behavior is to be performed (given certain equipment, a specific time period for completion, etc.) and the required standard of performance — a percentage (75 percent), a number (9 out of 10), a time constraint (within 1 minute), or an NFPA® (or OSHA, SOP, etc.) requirement. The term is often interchangeably used with the terms educational objective, outcome objective, and enabling objective. *See* Enabling Objective, Objective (1), and Performance Objective.

BEI® — *See* Biological Exposure Indices.

Belay — Climber's term for a safety line.

Below Minimum — Weather conditions below the minimum prescribed by regulation for a particular operation, such as the takeoff or landing of aircraft.

Below-Grade Hazards — Includes open pits creating flooding, or contaminated atmospheres.

Below-Grade Operation — (1) Rescue activity that occurs at the bottom or slope of an open pit or trench, for example, freeing an equipment operator from an overturned backhoe that lies on the slope of an excavation. (2) Per OSHA 1926.650, any open operation such as that in an open trench for footings and foundations.

Belowground Operation — (1) Activity that occurs below the surface of the earth, for example, rescue and search operations in a mine or mine shaft. (2) Per OSHA 1926.800, operation with earth cover such as mining and tunneling. *Also known as* Underground Operation.

Belt System — *See* Loop System.

Belt Weather Kit — Belt-mounted case with pockets fitted for anemometer, compass, sling psychrometer, slide rule, water bottle, pencils, and book of weather report forms.

Bench Trial — Court proceeding in which the judge alone acts as the trier of fact.

Benchmark — (1) Permanently affixed mark such as a stake driven into the ground that establishes the exact elevation of a place; used by surveyors in measuring site elevations or as a starting point for surveys. (2) Anything that serves as a standard against which others may be measured.

Bend — Two rope ends tied together.

Bent — Supporting legs of a bridge in a plane perpendicular to its length.

Benzene (C_6H_6) — Highly toxic carcinogen produced by the burning of PVC plastics or gasoline. Inhalation of high levels can cause unconsciousness and death from respiratory paralysis.

Berm — Outside or downhill side of a ditch or trench; a mound or wall of earth.

Bernoulli's Equation — Mathematical expression of the principle of conservation of energy applied to hydraulics.

Berth — Mooring or docking a vessel alongside a pier, wharf, or bulkhead. *See* Berthing Area and Mooring.

Berthing Area — Space at a wharf or pier for docking a vessel; place where a vessel comes to rest.

Berthing Space — Bed or bunk space on a vessel.

Beta Particle — Particle that is about 1/7,000th the size of an alpha particle but has more penetrating power. The beta particle has a negative electrical charge. *See* Alpha Particle, Beta Radiation, and Gamma Rays.

Beta Radiation — Type of radiation that can cause skin burns. *See* Alpha Radiation, Gamma Radiation, and Radiation (2).

Bias — Highly personal or unreasoned distortion of judgment; prejudice.

Bid Bond — Deposit provided to the apparatus purchaser from the manufacturer in order to ensure that the manufacturer will take the bid made if offered. This prevents damages to the purchaser should the bidder default on any part of the deal. The bond is returned to the manufacturer when the contract is executed.

Bifold Doors — Doors designed to fold in half vertically.

Big Line — Slang for a hoseline of at least 2-inch (51 mm) diameter, especially when used as a handline.

Big Stick — Slang for a mechanically raised main ladder or an aerial ladder truck. Originally, aerial ladders were made of wood, hence the term "big stick."

Bight — Element of a knot formed by simply bending the rope back on itself (creating a loop) while keeping the sides parallel.

Bile — Fluid secreted by the liver that is concentrated and stored in the gall bladder.

Bilge — Lowest inner part of a vessel's hull; flat part of the bottom of a vessel.

Bilge Pump — Small pump, located in the bilge, used to remove internal water.

Bill of Lading — Shipping paper used by the trucking industry (and others) indicating origin, destination, route, and product; placed in the cab of every truck tractor. This document establishes the terms of a contract between a shipper and a carrier. It serves as a document of title, a contract of carriage, and a receipt for goods. *See* Lading and Shipping Papers.

Billy Pugh Net — Rope net or basket designed to be suspended beneath a helicopter for transporting personnel and/or equipment.

Bimetallic — Strip or disk composed of two different metals that are bonded together; used in heat detection equipment.

Biochemical — Involving chemical reactions in living organisms.

Biodegradable — Capable of being broken down into innocuous products by the actions of living things, such as microorganisms.

Biological Agent — Viruses, bacteria, or their toxins which are harmful to people, animals, or crops. When used deliberately to cause harm, may be referred to as a Biological Weapon.

Biological Attack — Intentional release of viruses, bacteria, or their toxins for the purpose of harming or killing citizens. *See* Terrorism and Weapons of Mass Destruction.

Biological Death — Condition present when irreversible brain damage has occurred, usually 4 to 10 minutes after cardiac arrest.

Biological Exposure Indices (BEI®) — Guidance value recommended for assessing biological monitoring results that is established by the American Conference of Governmental Industrial Hygienists (ACGIH).

Biological Toxin — Poison produced by living organisms. *See* Poison and Toxin.

Biological Weapon — *See* Biological Agent.

Bird Box — *See* Connection Box.

Bird Cage Construction — *See* Unibody Construction.

Bitter End — *See* Working End.

Bitts — Single or twin set of upright wood or steel posts located on deck along the sides of a vessel; used for securing mooring lines. *See* Bollard.

Bituminous Material — Refers to materials that contain tar or asphalt-like materials. Bituminous materials used in roofing include tar and tar-impregnated papers.

Black — Area already burned by a wildland fire. *Also known as* Burn.

Blacken — To "knock down" a fire; to reduce a fire by extinguishing all visible flame. As the flame is extinguished, the fire is said to be blackened.

Blacklining — Ensuring that there are no unburned fuels adjacent to the control line by burning out such areas; burning out adjacent to a control line in order to widen and strengthen it.

Bladder-Tank Balanced-Pressure Proportioner — Type of mobile or fixed foam system that uses water to displace foam concentrate in a storage tank and force it into a proportioning system. *See* Foam Proportioner and Proportioning.

Blanch — To become white or pale.

Blank — Thin piece of metal inserted between flanges in a pipe system to isolate part of the system.

Blank Flange — Device that attaches to the end of a pipe in order to cap the end.

Blanket — (1) Thick layer of insulating material between two layers of heavy waterproof paper. (2) Layer of foam over a fuel.

Blast Area — Area affected by the blast wave from an explosion.

Blast Pressure Wave — Shock wave created by rapidly expanding gases in an explosion.

Blast-Pressure Front — Expanding edge of the pressure in a detonation or deflagration that causes the majority of damage in an explosion.

Blasting Cap — *See* Detonator.

Bleed — (1) Process of releasing a liquid or gas under pressure, such as releasing air from the regulator or cylinder of a self-contained breathing apparatus. (2) Internal or external loss of blood.

Bleeder Valve — Valve on a gate intake that allows air from an incoming supply line to be bled off before allowing the water into the pump.

Blended Gasoline — Gasoline that has oxygen added to it to increase the efficiency of the combustion of the fuel. *Also known as* Reformulated Gasoline.

BLEVE — *See* Boiling Liquid Expanding Vapor Explosion.

Blind Hoistway — Used for express elevators that serve only upper floors of tall buildings. There are no entrances to the shaft on floors between the main entrance and the lowest floor served.

Blister Agent — Chemical warfare agent that burns and blisters the skin or any other part of the body it contacts. *Also known as* Vesicant. *See* Chemical Warfare Agent.

Blitz Attack — To aggressively attack a fire from the exterior with a large diameter (2½-inch [65 mm] or larger) fire stream.

Block — In personnel management, a division of an occupational analysis consisting of a group of related tasks with one factor in common. *See* Unit.

Block and Tackle — Series of pulleys (sheaves) contained within a wood or metal frame; used with rope to provide a mechanical advantage for pulling operations.

Blood Agent — *See* Chemical Asphyxiant.

Blood Poisons — *See* Chemical Asphyxiant.

Blood Pressure (BP) — Pressure exerted by the flow of blood against the arterial walls.

Blood Volume — Total amount of blood in the heart and the blood vessels.

Bloodborne Pathogens — Pathogenic microorganisms that are present in the human blood and can cause disease in humans. These pathogens include (but are not limited to) hepatitis B virus (HBV) and human immunodeficiency virus (HIV).

Blow-Down Valve — Manually operated valve that has the function of quickly reducing tank pressure to atmospheric pressure.

Blower — Large-volume fan used to blow fresh air into a building or other confined space; often used in positive-pressure ventilation (PPV). Blowers are most often powered by gasoline engines, but some have electric motors.

Blowup — Sudden, dangerously rapid increase in fireline intensity at a wildland fire; caused by any one or more of several factors, such as strong or erratic wind, steep uphill slopes, large open areas, and easily ignited fuels. Blowup is sufficient to preclude direct attack or to change the incident action plan; often accompanied by violent convection and may have other characteristics of a firestorm. *See* Flare-Up.

BLS — *See* Basic Life Support.

Blunt Start — *See* Higbee Cut.

Board of Appeals — Group of people, usually five to seven, with experience in fire prevention, building construction, and/or code enforcement, who are legally constituted to arbitrate differences of opinion between fire inspectors and building officials, property owners, occupants or builders.

Boat — (1) Small craft capable of being carried on board a vessel. (2) Naval slang for a submarine.

Boat Deck — Uppermost deck on which lifeboats and other lifesaving appliances are stowed; used as a promenade space on passenger vessels. *See* Deck.

Boat Hook — Long pole with distinctive hook at the end used for fending off other boats and retrieving or picking up mooring lines.

Boatswain — Petty officer on a merchant vessel who has charge of the deck crew, hull maintenance, and related work. *Also known as* Bosun.

BOCA — *See* Building Officials and Code Administrators International, Inc.

Body Bag — Device used to remove the bodies of deceased victims. The bags are made of rubber or plastic and are widely used in disasters.

Body Language — Nonverbal communication including but not limited to body posture and gestures; represents a large portion of communication in human interactions.

Body-on-Chassis Construction — Method of school bus or recreational vehicle construction where the manufacturer installs the body unit onto a commercially available chassis constructed by another manufacturer.

Bogie — Tandem arrangement of aircraft landing gear wheels with a central strut. The bogie swivels up and down so that all wheels stay on the ground as the attitude of the aircraft changes, or the slope of the ground surface changes.

Boiler Room — Compartment containing boilers but not containing a station for operating or firing the boilers.

Boilerplate — Standardized or formulaic language.

Boiling Liquid Expanding Vapor Explosion (BLEVE) — Rapid vaporization of a liquid stored under pressure upon release to the atmosphere following major failure of its containing vessel. Failure is the result of overpressurization caused by an external heat source, which causes the vessel to explode into two or more pieces when the temperature of the liquid is well above its boiling point at normal atmospheric pressure. *See* Boiling Point.

Boiling Point — Temperature of a substance when the vapor pressure exceeds atmospheric pressure. At this temperature, the rate of evaporation exceeds the rate of condensation. At this point, more liquid is turning into gas than gas is turning back into a liquid. *See* Condensation, Physical Properties, and Vapor Pressure.

Boilover — Overflow of burning crude oil from an open top container when the hot oil reaches the water level in the tank. The water flashes to steam causing a violent expulsion of the material as a froth.

Bollard — Stout vertical post (single or double) on a pier or wharf used for securing a vessel's mooring lines; common along piers where large vessels are moored. *See* Bitts.

Bolster — *See* Chair.

Bolt Cutters — Cutting tool designed to make a precise, controlled cut; used for cutting wire, fencing, bolts, and small steel bars.

Bolted Fault — Condition occurring when two conductors in a circuit come into firm, direct contact with each other. *Also known as* Dead Short.

Bomb Line — Slang for a portable master stream device that is preconnected to a short length (less than 200 feet [61 m]) of hose for rapid deployment.

Bomb Squad — Crew of emergency responders specially trained and equipped to deal with explosive devices.

Bombproof Anchor Point — (1) Slang reference to an anchor that is absolutely immovable, such as a huge boulder, a large tree, or a fire engine. (2) Any anchor point capable of withstanding forces in excess of those that might be generated by the rescue operation or even catastrophic failure (and resultant shock load) of a raising or lowering system.

Bonding — (1) Connection of two objects with a metal chain or strap in order to neutralize the static electrical charge between the two; similar to Grounding. (2) Gluing two objects together.

Boneyarding — During mop-up, spreading materials that are no longer burning in an area within the black that has been cleared of all burning or hot fuels.

Boom — (1) Pole rigged for use as a crane on board a vessel. (2) Floating object used to confine materials on the surface of the water.

Booms — Telescoping or articulating arm portions of an elevating platform aerial device.

Booster Apparatus — *See* Brush Apparatus.

Booster Hose — Non-collapsible rubber-covered, rubber-lined hose usually wound on a reel and mounted somewhere on an engine or water tender; used for the initial attack and extinguishment of incipient and smoldering fires. This hose is most commonly found in ½-, ¾-, and 1-inch (13 mm, 19 mm, and 25 mm) diameters and is used for extinguishing low-intensity fires and mop-up. *Also known as* Booster Line, Hard Line, and Red Line.

Booster Pump — Fire pump used to boost the pressure of the existing water supply within a fixed fire protection system.

Booster Reel — Mounted reel on which booster hose is carried.

Booster Tank — *See* Water Tank.

Bored Lock — *See* Cylindrical Lock.

Botts' Dots — Round, nonreflective raised pavement markers.

Bounce Flash — Lighting technique used to reduce glare or reflection by pointing the flash at a nearby surface rather than at the subject.

Bourdon Gauge — Most common type of gauge used to measure water pressures.

Bourdon Tube — Part of a bourdon gauge that has a curved, flat tube that changes its curvature as pressure changes. This movement is then transferred mechanically to a pointer on the dial.

Bow — Front end or forward part of a vessel; opposite of the stern.

Bow Thruster — Large propeller mounted in a tunnel located in the forward part of the vessel used to assist the vessel in docking and undocking; reduces the need for assistance from tugs.

Bowline Knot — Knot used to form a loop in natural fiber rope.

Bowstring Truss — Lightweight truss design noted by the bow shape, or curve, of the top chord.

Box — Shortened term for a public or private fire alarm box.

Box Alarm — (1) Signal transmitted from a fire alarm box. (2) Predetermined response assignment to an emergency call.

Box Crib — Stabilization platform constructed by creating opposing layers of pieces of cribbing.

Box Lock — Lock mortised into a door. *Also known as* Mortise Lock.

Box Stabilizer — Two-piece aerial apparatus stabilization device consisting of an extension arm that extends directly out from the vehicle, and a lifting jack that extends from the end of the extension arm to the ground. *Also known as* H-Jack.

Box-Beam Construction — Method of construction for aerial device booms consisting of four sides welded together to form a box shape with a hollow center. Hydraulic lines, air lines, electrical cords, and waterways may be encased within the center or on the outside of the box beam.

Boyle's Law — Law stating that the volume of a gas varies inversely with the applied pressure. The formula is $P_1 V_1 = P_2 V_2$, where:

P_1 = original pressure

V_1 = original volume

P_2 = final pressure

V_2 = final volume

B-Post — Post between the front and rear doors on a four-door vehicle, or the door-handle-end post on a two-door car.

BP — *See* Blood Pressure.

Bq — *See* Becquerel.

Brace Lock — Rim lock equipped with a metal rod that serves as a brace against the door.

Brace — Pieces of wood attached between components of shoring systems for stability. *Also known as* Lacing.

Bracketing — Taking a photograph at the setting recommended by the camera meter and then manually adjusting the exposure setting one or two f-stops above and below the recommended exposure.

Braid-on-Braid Rope — Rope constructed with both a braided core and a braided sheath. The appearance of the sheath is that of a herringbone pattern.

Braided Hose — Non-woven rubber hose manufactured by braiding one or more layers of yarn, each separated by a rubber layer, over a rubber tube and encased in a rubber cover.

Braided Rope — Rope constructed by uniformly intertwining strands of rope together (similar to braiding a person's hair).

Brainstorm — Process of identifying as many ideas as possible without any initial evaluation, debate, agreement, or consensus.

Brake Limiting Valve — Valve that allows the vehicle's brakes to be adjusted for the current road conditions.

Brakes — Long wooden handles on early hand pump fire engines that firefighters moved up and down to pump water from the reservoir to the pump's discharge.

Braking Distance — Distance the vehicle travels from the time the brakes are applied until it comes to a complete stop.

Braking Prusik — A Prusik attached onto a main line using a three-wrap Prusik hitch to grab the line and prevent it from moving.

Branch — Organizational level of an incident management system having functional/geographic responsibility for major segments of incident operations. The branch level is organizationally between section and division/sector/group.

Branch Circuit — Wiring between the point of application (outlets) and the final overcurrent device protecting the circuit.

Branch Line — Pipes in an automatic sprinkler system to which the sprinklers are directly attached.

Brands — Large, burning embers that are lifted by a fire's thermal column and carried away with the wind.

Brass — Brasswork or brass appliances carried on fire apparatus; may now be chrome-plated or made of light-weight alloys.

Breach — To make an opening in a structural obstacle (such as a masonry wall) without compromising the overall integrity of the wall to allow access into or out of a structure for rescue, hoseline operations, ventilation, or to perform other functions.

Breach of Duty — Any violation or omission of a legal or moral duty; neglect or failure to fulfill the duties of an office or employment in a just and proper manner.

Break a Line — To disconnect hoselines for any purpose, especially to break and roll up hose after a fire operation; to disconnect a hose coupling.

Breakaway/Frangible Fences and Gates — Fences and gates designed and constructed to collapse when impacted by large vehicles, in order to allow rapid access to accident sites.

Break Bulk Cargo — Loose, non-containerized cargo commonly packaged in bags, drums, cartons, crates, etc.

Break Bulk Carrier — Ship designed with large holds to accommodate a wide range of products such as vehicles, pallets of metal bars, liquids in drums, or items in bags, boxes, and crates. *See* Cargo Vessel.

Break Bulk Terminal — Shore facility handling cargo shipped in bags, steel drums, cartons, crates, or pallets. Typical cargoes are rolls of paper, bags of fertilizer, coils of wire, or packages of steel.

Breaking — To destroy a structural obstacle in order to gain access to victims or perform other functions.

Breakover — *See* Slopover.

Breakover Angle — Angle formed by level ground and a line from the point where the rear tires of a vehicle touch the ground to the bottom of the frame at the wheelbase midpoint. This angle should be at least 10 degrees.

Breast Timber — Strut that holds a horizontal compression load, keeping sheeting in place for shoring.

Breathing Air — Compressed air that is filtered and contains no more contaminants than are allowed by standards.

Breathing Apparatus Support Unit — Mobile unit designed and constructed for the purpose of providing specified level of breathing air support capacity and personnel capable of refilling self-contained breathing apparatus (SCBA) at remote incident locations. These units may be equipped with either compressor- or cascade-type reservicing systems.

Breathing Tube — Low-pressure hose that extends from the regulator to the SCBA facepiece.

Breathing-Air Compressor — Compressor specifically designed to compress air for breathing-air cylinders.

Bresnan Distributor Nozzle — Cellar nozzle in which the head rotates when water flows through it.

Brick Veneer — Single layer of bricks applied to the inside or outside surface of a wall for esthetic and/or insulation purposes.

Brick-Joisted — Brick or masonry wall structure with wooden floors and roof. Commonly known as ordinary construction.

Bridge — (1) To span a gap by placing a ladder, usually between two structures. (2) Control center on modern mechanized vessels; forward part of a vessel's super-structure. (3) Persons in charge of a vessel.

Bridge Truss — Heavy-duty truss, usually made of heavy wooden members with steel tie rods, that has horizontal top and bottom chords and steeply sloped ends.

Bridging — Construction technique of adding diagonal cross braces between joists.

British Thermal Unit (Btu) — Amount of heat energy required to raise the temperature of one pound of water one degree Fahrenheit. One Btu = 1.055 kilo joules (kJ).

Brix Scale — Measurement of the mass ratio of a foam concentrate to water in a finished foam solution.

Broadside Collision — *See* Side-Impact Collision.

Broken Stream — Stream of water that has been broken into coarsely divided drops.

Bronchial Asthma — Constriction of the bronchial tubes in response to irritation, allergies, or other stimulus.

Brush — Collective term that refers to stands of vegetation dominated by bushes, shrubby, woody plants, or small low-growing trees; usually of a type undesirable for livestock or timber management and of little or no commercial value.

Brush Apparatus — *See* Wildland Fire Apparatus.

Brush Burn — Scrape or adhesion created when the skin is rubbed across a rough surface; not actually a thermal or chemical burn. *Also known as* Abrasion.

Brush Hook — Heavy cutting tool designed primarily to cut brush at the base of the stem; used in much the same way as an axe. Has a wide blade generally curved to protect the blade from being dulled by rocks.

Brush Patrol — *See* Wildland Fire Apparatus.

Brush Pumper — *See* Wildland Fire Apparatus.

BTU — *See* British Thermal Unit.

Bucket Brigade — Early fire fighting technique in which people formed two lines between a fire and a water source. One line (usually composed of men) would pass buckets of water toward the fire to be applied onto the fire, and the other line (composed of women and children) would return the empty buckets to be refilled.

Buddy Breathing System — *See* Team Emergency Conditions Breathing.

Buddy System — Safety procedure used in rescue work; when rescuers work in a hazardous area, at least two rescuers must remain in contact with each other at all times.

Budget — Plan for action, with associated costs, for the coming year.

Buff — Person other than a firefighter who is interested in fires, fire departments, and firefighters as a hobby. *Also known as* Fire Fan or Spark.

Buggie — Slang for a chief's vehicle.

Bugles — Insignia depicting early speaking trumpets used to designate the rank of fire department personnel.

Building Code — Body of local law, adopted by states/provinces, counties, cities, or other governmental bodies to regulate the construction, renovation, and maintenance of buildings. *See* Code and Occupancy Classification.

Building Department — Local governmental agency responsible for enforcing various codes and regulations.

Building Engineer — Person who is familiar with and responsible for the operation of a building's heating, ventilating, and air-conditioning (HVAC) system and other essential equipment.

Building Marking System — Standardized system used to identify and document (on the actual structure) the location of victims and hazards within that structure.

Building Officials and Code Administrators International, Inc. (BOCA) — Organization that provides model codes for city and state adoption; the model codes are for building, mechanical, plumbing, and fire prevention. BOCA joined with the Southern Building Code Congress International (SBCCI) and the International Conference of Building Officials (ICBO) to form the International Code Council (ICC).

Building Packaging — Process of protecting the building from outside threats, such as inclement weather.

Building Permit — Authorization issued from the appropriate authority having jurisdiction (AHJ) before any new construction, addition, renovation, alteration, or demolition of buildings or structures occurs. *See* Authority Having Jurisdiction (AHJ).

Building Survey — Portion of the pre-incident planning process during which the company travels to a building and gathers the necessary information to develop a pre-incident plan for the building.

Built-Up Membrane Roof — Use of several overlapping layers of roofing felt applied to a roof deck with intervening layers of roofing cement. The layers are then saturated with a bituminous material that may be either tar or asphalt. *See* Built-Up Roof.

Built-Up Roof — Roof covering made of several alternate layers of roofing paper and tar, with the final layer of tar being covered with pea gravel or crushed slag.

Bulk Cargo — Homogeneous cargo (oil, grain, coal, bricks, lumber, or ore) stowed loose in a hold and not enclosed in any container such as boxes, bales, or bags.

Bulk Cargo Carrier — Ship carrying either liquid or dry goods stowed loose in a hold and not enclosed in any container. *See* Cargo Vessel.

Bulk Container — Cargo tank container attached to a flatbed truck or rail flat car used to transport materials in bulk. This container may carry liquids or gases. *See* Container (1).

Bulk Packaging — Packaging, other than a vessel or barge, including transport vehicle or freight container, in which hazardous materials are loaded with no intermediate form of containment; has (a) a maximum capacity greater than 119 gallons (450 L) as a receptacle for a liquid, (b) maximum net mass greater than 882 pounds (400 kg) and a maximum capacity greater than 119 gallons (450 L) as a receptacle for a solid, or (c) water capacity greater than 1,000 pounds (454 kg) as a receptacle for a gas. Reference: *Title 49 CFR 171.8. See* Nonbulk Packaging and Packaging (1).

Bulk Terminal — Handling area for cargoes (unpackaged commodities carried in holds and tanks of cargo vessels and tankers) that are loaded and unloaded by conveyors, pipelines, or cranes. A liquid bulk terminal handles cargoes such as fuel and lubricating oils and chemicals. A dry bulk terminal handles cargoes such as coal or grain. *See* Dry Bulk Terminal and Liquid Bulk Terminal.

Bulkhead — (1) Upright partition that separates one aircraft compartment from another. Bulkheads may strengthen or help give shape to the structure and may be used for the mounting of equipment and accessories. *See* Main Transverse Bulkheads and Main Watertight Subdivision. (2) Structure on the roof of a building through which the interior stairway opens onto the roof. *Also known as* Penthouse. (3) A vertical row of wood or metal pilings, or stone blocks along the shore line, that has been back-filled to protect the shore from erosion, or form a berth for shipping.

Bulldozer — Any tracked vehicle with a blade for exposing mineral soil. *Also known as* Dozer. *See* Dozer Tender and Dozer Transport.

Bulwark — Wall built around the edge of a vessel's upper deck.

Bumper — Structure designed to provide front- and rear-end protection of a vehicle.

Bumper Line — Preconnected hoseline located on the apparatus bumper.

Bumper Struts — Bumpers that incorporate energy absorbing struts to make them less vulnerable to damage in low-speed collisions.

Bung — Cork or other type of stopper used in a barrel, cask, or keg.

Bunk — Firefighter's bed.

Bunk Room — Dormitory area where firefighters sleep.

Bunker Clothes — *See* Personal Protective Equipment. *Also known as* Bunker Gear.

Buoyancy (B) — Tendency or capacity to remain afloat in a liquid as a result of the upward force of a fluid upon a floating object. *See* Center of Buoyancy.

Bureau of Alcohol, Tobacco, Firearms and Explosives (ATF) — Division of U.S. Department of Justice that enforces federal laws and regulations relating to alcohol, tobacco, firearms, explosives, and arson.

Bureau of Mines — Former name for the Mine Safety and Health Administration. *See* Mine Safety and Health Administration.

Bureaucratic Leadership — Style of leadership in which the leader has a low degree of concern for workers and production.

Burn — (1) To be on fire; to consume fuel during rapid combustion. (2) Geographical area over which a fire has passed. *Also known as* Black. (3) Tissue injury caused by heat, electrical, current, or chemicals.

Burnback Resistance — Ability of a foam blanket to resist direct flame impingement such as would be evident in a partially extinguished petroleum fire.

Burn Building — Training structure specially designed to contain live fires for the purpose of fire suppression training.

Burn Center — Medical facility especially designed, equipped, and staffed to treat severely burned patients.

Burning Out — Intentionally setting a fire to natural cover fuels inside the control line to widen the line; used as a direct attack technique, usually within 10 feet (3 m) of the line. Burning out is done on a small scale in order to consume unburned fuel and aid control-line construction. Burning out should not be confused with "backfiring,"
which is a larger-scale tactic to eliminate large areas of unburned fuels in the path of a fire, or to change the direction of force of a convection column.

Burning Point — *See* Fire Point.

Burning Velocity — Velocity of the flame front in an explosion relative to the unburned gases ahead of it.

Burnout — (1) Building that has been denuded of almost all combustible material. Also refers to a burned wildland area. (2) A work-related psychological disorder resulting from stress.

Burn Pattern — *See* Fire Patterns.

Burns, Degree of — First degree: reddened skin; second degree: blisters; third degree: deep skin destruction. Major types of burns: heat, chemical, electrical, and radiation.

Burst Test — Destructive test on a 3-foot (.9 m) length of hose to determine its maximum strength.

Butt — (1) One coupling of a fire hose. (2) Hydrant outlet. (3) Heel (lower end) of a ladder. (4) Act of steadying a ladder that is being climbed.

Butt Spurs — Metal safety plates or spikes attached to the butt end of ground ladder beams.

Butterfly Roof — V-shaped roof style resembling two opposing shed roofs joined along their lower edges.

Butterfly Valve — Type of control valve that uses a flat circular plate in the pipe which rotates ninety degrees across the cross section of the pipe to control the flow. *See* Gate Valve.

Buttress — Structure projecting from a wall designed to receive lateral pressure action at a particular point.

Byline — Line at the beginning of a news story, magazine article, or book giving the author's name.

Bypass Breathing — Emergency procedure in which the self-contained breathing apparatus (SCBA) wearer closes the mainline valve and opens the bypass valve for air when a regulator malfunctions.

Bypass Valve — Valve on a self-contained breathing apparatus (SCBA) that when opened allows air to bypass its normal route through the regulator; used when a regulator malfunctions.

Bypass-Type Balanced-Pressure Proportioner — Foam proportioning system that discharges foam through a pump separate from the water supply pump; most commonly found in airport crash vehicles and in fixed-site facilities. It is one of the most accurate types of foam proportioning systems in use. *See* Foam Proportioner and Proportioning.

C

CAA — *See* Civil Aviation Authority.

Cabin — (1) Aircraft passenger compartment that may be separated and may contain a cargo area. (2) *See* Accommodation Spaces.

Cable Hanger — Device used to test the structural strength of aerial ladders.

Cables — Flexible structural members used to support roofs, brace tents, and restrain pneumatic structures.

CABO — *See* Council of American Building Officials.

CAD — *See* Computer-Aided Design.

C.A.F.I. — *See* Canadian Association of Fire Investigators.

CAFS — *See* Compressed Air Foam System.

Caisson — (1) Watertight structure within which construction work is carried out underwater. (2) Protective sleeve used to keep water out of an excavation for a pier. (3) Protective hardened steel sleeves located inside automobile B- and C- posts that are designed to protect seatbelt pretensioners from being cut.

Calcination — Process of driving free and chemically bound water out of gypsum; also describes chemical and physical changes to the gypsum component itself.

Calcined — Process that heats a substance to a high temperature but below the melting or fusing point, causing loss of moisture, reduction or oxidation, and decomposition of carbonates and other compounds.

Calendering — Fire hose inner tube manufacturing process in which rubber is pressed between opposing rollers to produce a flat sheet. A tube is then formed by lapping and bonding together the edges of the sized sheet.

Calibrate — To standardize or adjust the increments on a measuring instrument.

Calibration Curve — Generic method for identifying the concentration of a substance, such as foam, in an unknown sample by comparing the unknown to a set of standard samples of known concentration.

California FIRESCOPE Incident Command System — *See* Incident Command System (ICS).

Call Back — Process of notifying off-duty firefighters to return to their stations for service.

Call Box — *See* Telephone Alarm Box.

Call Firefighter — *See* Paid-On-Call Firefighter.

Calorie — Amount of heat needed to raise the temperature of one gram of water one degree Celsius. *See* Joule.

Cam — Part of a mortise lock cylinder that moves the bolt or latch as the key is turned.

Camber — Low vertical arch placed in a beam or girder to counteract deflection caused by loading.

Camlock Fastener — Trade name given to a quick-disconnect screw-type fastener, designed to open with a quarter or half turn (similar to Dzus fasteners).

Can Man — Slang for a firefighter, usually from a truck or ladder company, whose role is to carry a pump can and some other tool, often a pike pole.

Canadian Association of Fire Investigators (C.A.F.I.) — Professional organization for fire investigators in Canada offering training and professional development opportunities.

Canadian Centre for Occupational Health and Safety (CCOHS) — Canadian federal government agency that provides information and policy development regarding work-related injury, illness prevention initiatives, and occupational health and safety information.

Canadian Charter of Rights and Freedoms — Portion of the Canadian Constitution containing due process clauses. Section 7 states that "Everyone has the right to life, liberty and security of the person and the right not to be deprived thereof except in accordance with the principles of fundamental justice."

Canadian Coast Guard (CCG) — Marine law enforcement and rescue agency in Canada; responsible for the safety, order, and operation of maritime traffic.

Canadian Electrical Code® (CEC®) — Manual providing safety standards for installation of electrical wiring and electrical systems in Canada.

Canadian Nuclear Safety Commission — Agency responsible for regulating almost all uses of nuclear energy and nuclear materials in Canada.

Canadian Standards Association (CSA) — Canadian standards-writing organization.

Canadian Transportation Emergency Centre (CANUTEC) — Canadian center that provides fire and emergency responders with 24-hour information for incidents involving hazardous materials; operated by Transport Canada, a department of the Canadian government. *See* Chemical Transportation Emergency Center (CHEMTREC®) and Emergency Transportation System for the Chemical Industry (SETIQ).

Canine Search — Use of disaster-trained search dogs and handlers for the location of victims.

Canister Apparatus — Type of breathing apparatus that uses filtration, adsorption, or absorption to remove toxic substances from the air; generally referred to as a gas mask. Canister apparatus are not acceptable for use in fire fighting operations or IDLH atmospheres.

Cannula — Tube used to enter a duct or cavity. A nasal cannula is often used to administer supplemental oxygen.

Canopy — (1) Transparent enclosure over the cockpit of some aircraft. (2) Level or area containing the crowns of the tallest vegetation containing the leaves of trees and brush present (living or dead), usually above 20 feet (6.1 m).

Canteen Unit — Emergency vehicle that provides food, drinks, and other rehabilitative services to emergency workers at extended incidents.

Cantilever — (1) Projecting beam or slab supported at one end. (2) Type of collapse void in which one end of a floor or roof section that has collapsed remains suspended and unsupported.

Cantilever Fire Wall — Free standing fire wall that is commonly found in large churches and shopping malls.

Cantilever Operation — *See* Unsupported Tip.

Cantilever Roof — Roof structure extending from the edge of the building that is anchored at only one end.

Cant Strip — Angular board installed at the intersection of a roof deck and a wall to avoid a sharp right angle when the roofing is installed.

CANUTEC — *See* Canadian Transport Emergency Centre.

Capability Assessment for Readiness (CAR) — Self-assessment survey-type instrument conducted by states to assess their operational readiness and emergency management capabilities; created by the U.S. Federal Emergency Management Agency (FEMA), in partnership with National Emergency Management Association (NEMA) and state emergency managers in 1997.

Capacity — Maximum ability of a pump or water distribution system to deliver water. Also the maximum quantity of water that can be contained in a tank.

Capacity Indicator — Device installed on a tank to indicate capacity at a specific level.

Capacity Stencil — Number stenciled on the exterior of tank cars to indicated the volume of the tank.

Capillaries — Tiny blood vessels in the body's tissues in which the exchange of oxygen and carbon dioxide take place.

Capital Budget — Budget intended to fund large, one-time expenditures, such as those for fire stations, fire apparatus, or major pieces of equipment.

Capital Grant — Money gained through a large-scale fund-raising activity in which the funds raised will support a building or other so-called "capital expense", such as a large computer system.

Captain — (1) Rank used in some departments for a company officer. (2) Commander of a vessel. See Master.

Captain of the Port (COTP) — U.S. Coast Guard officer who has broad powers over all vessels in a port area in the U.S.; equivalent to Harbormaster in the United Kingdom.

CAR — *See* Capability Assessment for Readiness.

Car Terminal — Facility for loading and unloading vessels specially designed to transport automobiles.

Carabiner — Steel or aluminum D-shaped snap link device for attaching components of rope rescue systems together. In rescue work, carabiners should be of a positive locking type, with a 5,000-pound (2 268 kg) minimum breaking strength. *Also known as* Biner, Crab, or Snap Links.

Carbonaceous — Made of or containing carbon.

Carbonaceous Material — Material that contains carbon.

Carbon Dioxide (CO$_2$) — Colorless, odorless, heavier than air gas that neither supports combustion nor burns; used in portable fire extinguishers as an extinguishing agent to extinguish Class B or C fires by smothering or displacing the oxygen. CO$_2$ is a waste product of aerobic metabolism. *See* Combustion and Fire Exinguisher.

Carbon Dioxide System — Extinguishing system that uses carbon dioxide as the primary extinguishing agent; designed primarily to protect confined spaces because the gaseous agent is easily dispersed by wind.

Carbon Monoxide (CO) — Colorless, odorless, dangerous gas (both toxic and flammable) formed by the incomplete combustion of carbon. It combines with hemoglobin more than 200 times faster than oxygen does, thus decreasing the blood's ability to carry oxygen.

Carbon Monoxide Detector — Device designed to detect the presence of carbon monoxide (CO) and sound an alarm to prevent personnel within the structure from being poisoned by the colorless and odorless gas.

Carbon Monoxide Poisoning — Sometimes lethal condition in which carbon monoxide molecules attach to hemoglobin, decreasing the blood's ability to carry oxygen.

Carboxyhemoglobin (COHB) — Hemoglobin saturated with carbon monoxide and therefore unable to absorb needed oxygen.

Carboy — Cylindrical container of about 5 to 15 gallons (19 L to 57 L) capacity for corrosive or pure liquids. Made of glass, plastic, or metal, with a neck and sometimes a pouring tip; cushioned in a wooden box, wicker basket, or special drum. *See* Container (1).

Carcinogen — Cancer-producing substance.

Cardiac Arrest — Sudden cessation of heartbeat.

Cardiac Monitoring — Monitoring the status of the electrical activity of the heart.

Cardiopulmonary Resuscitation (CPR) — Application of rescue breathing and external cardiac compression used on patients in cardiac arrest to provide an adequate circulation and oxygen to support life.

Cardiopulmonary System — Heart and lungs.

Cardiovascular System — Body's system of blood vessels and associated organs that support the flow of blood through the body.

Career Fire — Jargon used to describe a large fire.

Career Fire Department — Fire department composed of full-time, paid personnel.

Career Firefighter — Person whose primary employment is as a firefighter within a fire department. Also spelled Career Fire Fighter.

Cargo Container — *See* Container (1).

Cargo Manifest — Document or shipping paper listing all contents carried by a vehicle or vessel on a specific trip.

Cargo Plan — View of a vessel showing all the storage space available for cargo; shows the amount and type of cargo carried, its destination, and how it will be stowed.

Cargo Tank — *See* Cargo Tank Truck.

Cargo Tank Truck — Motor vehicle commonly used to transport hazardous materials via roadway. *Also known as* Cargo Tank, Tank Motor Vehicle, and Tank Truck. *See* Compressed-Gas Tube Trailer, Corrosive Liquid Tank, Cryogenic Liquid Tank, Dry Bulk Cargo Tank, Elevated Temperature Materials Carrier, High-Pressure Tank, Low-Pressure Chemical Tank, and Nonpressure Liquid Tank.

Cargo Vessel — Ship used to transport cargo (dry bulk, break bulk, roll-on/roll off, and container) via waterways. *See* Barge, Break Bulk Carrier, Bulk Cargo Carrier, Container Vessel, and Roll-on/Roll-off Vessel.

Carline Supports — Structural members used in the construction of buses. They are designed to strengthen the sidewall of the bus where it might come into contact with a car during a collision.

Carotid Artery — Principal artery of the neck, easily felt on either side of the trachea.

Carriage — Main support for the stair treads and risers. *Also known as* Stringer.

Carryall — Waterproof carrier or bag used to carry and catch debris or used as a water sump basin for immersing small burning objects.

Cartridge Filter Respirators — Type of respiratory protection that utilizes special filter cartridges to filter out specific airborne contaminants.

Cascade Air Cylinders — Large air cylinders that are used to refill smaller SCBA cylinders.

CAS Number — Number assigned by the American Chemical Society's Chemical Abstract Service that uniquely identifies a specific compound.

Cascade Systems — Three or more large air cylinders, each usually with a capacity of 300 cubic feet (8,490 L), that are interconnected, and from which smaller SCBA cylinders are recharged.

Case — Housing for any locking mechanism.

Case Law — Laws based on judicial interpretations and decisions rather than created by legislation.

Case Study — Discussion in which a group reviews real or hypothetical events. *See* Discussion.

Casement Window — Window hinged along one side, usually designed to swing outward, with the screen on the inside.

Cast Coupling — Coupling manufactured by a process in which molten metal is poured into a mold and allowed to cool, after which the mold is removed from the hardened coupling.

Cast-in-Place Concrete — Common type of concrete construction. Refers to concrete that is poured into forms as a liquid and assumes the shape of the form in the position and location it will be used.

Caster — Roller on the bottom of a chair or piece of furniture; also spelled castor.

Catalyst — Substance that modifies (usually increases) the rate of a chemical reaction without being consumed in the process.

Catch a Hydrant — Process in which a firefighter dismounts the fire apparatus at the hydrant, connects the fire hose to the hydrant, and turns on the water.

Catch Basin — *See* Portable Tank.

Catchall — Retaining basin, usually made from salvage covers, to impound water dripping from above.

Caternary Wire System — Series of overhead wires used to transmit electrical power to buses, locomotives, and trams at a distance from the energy supply point. *See* Caternary System.

Caulk — Non-hardening paste used to fill cracks and crevices. Also spelled Calk.

Caustic — (1) Corrosive material that burns or destroys tissue by chemical action, as opposed to heat. (2) Substance having the destructive properties of a base. *See* Acid, Alkali, and Base.

Cave-In — Collapse of unsupported trench walls.

Cavitation — Condition in which vacuum pockets form due to localized regions of low pressure at the vanes in the impeller of a centrifugal pump, causing vibrations, loss of efficiency, and possibly damage to the impeller. *See* Centrifugal Pump and Impeller.

Cavity — Hollow or space, especially within the body or one of its organs. For example, the abdominal cavity is bounded by the abdominal walls, the diaphragm, and the pelvis.

CBRNE — *See* Chemical, Biological, Radiological, Nuclear, and Explosive.

CCG — *See* Canadian Coast Guard.

CCOHS — *See* Canadian Centre for Occupational Health and Safety.

CD-R — Abbreviation for Compact Disc-Recordable.

CD-ROM — Abbreviation for Compact Disc-Read-Only Memory.

CD-RW — Abbreviation for Compact Disc-Rewritable.

CDC — *See* Centers for Disease Control and Prevention.

Cease-and-Desist Order — Court order prohibiting a person or business from continuing a particular course of conduct.

CEC® — *See Canadian Electrical Code®.*

Ceiling — (1) Height of the base of the lowest layer of clouds when over half of the sky is obscured; reported as "broken," "overcast," "obscuration," or "partial obscuration." (2) Non-load-bearing structural component separating a living/working space from the underside of the floor or roof immediately above.

Ceiling Concentration — Maximum allowable concentration of dust, vapors, mists, or other hazardous materials that may exist in a confined space.

Ceiling Jet — Horizontal movement of a layer of hot gases and combustion by-products from the center point of the plume, when the vertical development of the rising plume is redirected by a horizontal surface such as a ceiling.

Cell — (1) Small cavity or compartment. (2) Smallest structural unit of living matter capable of functioning independently.

Cell Electrolyte Level — In apparatus terms, the level of water that is within the vehicle's batteries.

Cellar Pipe — Special nozzle for attacking fires in basements, cellars, and other spaces below the attack level.

Cellulosic Materials — Organic materials, such as cotton or wood, composed of cells.

Celsius — International temperature scale on which the freezing point is 0°C (32°F) and the boiling point is 100°C (212°F) at normal atmospheric pressure at sea level. *Also known as* Centigrade. *See* Fahrenheit Scale and Temperature.

Celsius Scale — International temperature scale on which the freezing point is 0°C (32°F) and the boiling point is 100°C (212°F) at normal atmospheric pressure at sea level. *Also known as* Centigrade Scale. *See* Fahrenheit Scale and Temperature.

Cement — Any adhesive material or variety of materials which can be made into a paste with adhesive and cohesive properties to bond inert aggregate materials into a solid mass by chemical hardening. For example, portland cement is combined with sand and/or other aggregates and water to produce mortar or concrete.

Cementitious — Containing or composed of cement; having cementlike characteristics.

Center of Buoyancy — Geometrical center of the underwater volume of a body; considered to be the point through which all forces of buoyancy are acting vertically upwards with a force equal to the weight of a body. *See* Buoyancy.

Center of Gravity — Point through which all the weight of a vessel and its contents may be considered as concentrated, so that if supported at this point, the vessel would remain in equilibrium in any position. *See* Gravity.

Center Rafter Cut — *See* Louver Cut.

Centerline — Imaginary line running the length of a vessel, from the point of the bow to the center of the stern; equidistant from the port and starboard sides of a vessel.

Centers for Disease Control and Prevention (CDC) — U. S. government agency for the collection and analysis of data regarding disease and health trends.

Certified Fire and Explosion Investigator Program — Fire investigator certification program offered by the National Association of Fire Investigators (NAFI) through its National Certification Board in the U.S.

Certified Fire Investigator Program (CFI) — Fire investigator certification program offered by the International Association of Arson Investigators (IAAI).

Centigrade — *See* Celsius.

Centigrade Scale — *See* Celsius Scale.

Central Fire Station — Headquarters station that contains administrative offices, special equipment, fire apparatus, and personnel.

Central Neurogenic Hyperventilation — Abnormal pattern of breathing seen in severe illness or injury involving the brain and characterized by very heavy, rapid breathing.

Central Processing Unit (CPU) — Part of a computer that actually possesses information.

Central Station Alarm System — System that functions through a constantly attended location (central station) operated by an alarm company. Alarm signals from the protected property are received in the central station and are then retransmitted by trained personnel to the fire department alarm telecommunications center.

Central Station Monitoring — Alarm systems that are monitored by a third party (usually a private alarm company) at a constantly attended location (central station) instead of a direct connection. Alarm signals from the protected property are received in the central station and are then retransmitted by trained personnel to the fire department alarm telecommunications center.

Centrifugal Pump — Pump with one or more impellers that rotate and utilize centrifugal force to move the water. Most modern fire pumps are of this type. *See* Impeller, Multistage Centrifugal Pump, Self-Priming Centrifugal Pump, and Single-Stage Centrifugal Pump.

CERCLA — *See* Comprehensive Environmental Response, Compensation and Liability Act.

Certificate of Occupancy — Issued by a building official after all required electrical, gas, mechanical, plumbing, and fire protection systems have been inspected for compliance with the technical codes and other applicable laws and ordinances.

Certification — (1) A certified statement. (2) Refers to a manufacturer's certification; for example, that a ladder has been constructed to meet requirements of NFPA® 1931. (3) Issuance of a document that states one has demonstrated the knowledge and skills necessary to function in a field.

Certification Tests — Pre-service tests for aerial device, ladder, pump, and other equipment conducted by an independent testing laboratory prior to delivery of an apparatus. These tests ensure that the apparatus or equipment will perform as expected after being placed into service.

Certified Shop Test Curves — Results, which are plotted on a graph, of the test performed by the manufacturer on its pump before shipping.

Cervical Collar — Device used to immobilize and support the neck.

Cervical Spine — First seven bones of the vertebral column, located in the neck.

C-Factor — Factor used in hydraulic formulas (usually the Hazen-Williams formula) to account for the roughness of the inner surface of piping or fire hose. The C-factor decreases as the sediment, incrustation, and tuberculation within the pipe increases.

CFEI — See Certified Fire and Explosion Investigator Program.

CFI — See Certified Fire Investigator Program.

CFM — See Cubic Feet Per Minute.

CFR — (1) *See* Code of Federal Regulations. (2) *See* Crash Fire Rescue.

CGA — See Compressed Gas Association.

Chafing Block — Blocks placed under hoselines to protect the hose covering from damage due to rubbing against the ground or concrete.

Chain Hose Tool — Tool used to carry, secure, and otherwise aid in handling hose.

Chain of Command — (1) Order of rank and authority in the fire and emergency services. (2) The proper sequence of information and command flow as described in the National Incident Management System - Incident Command System (NIMS-ICS).

Chain of Custody — Continuous changes of possession of physical "evidence" that must be established in court to admit such material into evidence.

Chain Reaction — Series of self-sustaining changes, each of which causes or influences a similar reaction.

Chain Saw — Gas- or electric-powered saw that operates by rotating a chain of small cutting blades around an oblong bar.

Chair — In construction, device of bent wire used to hold reinforcing bars in position in reinforced concrete. *Also known as* Bolster.

Chamois — Soft pliant leather used for drying furniture and contents or for removing small amounts of water.

Change Order — Client's written order to a contractor, issued after execution of a construction contract, which authorizes a change in the construction work, project completion time, and/or cost of the project. *See* Contractor.

Channeling Devices — Items such as signs, road flares, and cones intended to guide traffic away from the active zones at an incident or accident.

Char — Carbonaceous material formed by incomplete combustion of an organic material, commonly wood; the remains of burned materials.

Char Gauge — Blunt-ended, thin probe similar to dial calipers or tire-tread gauges that is inserted into blistered char to measure the depth of char.

Charge — To pressurize a fire hose or fire extinguisher.

Charged Building — Building heavily laden with heat, smoke, and gases, and possibly in danger of having a backdraft.

Charged Line — Hose loaded with water under pressure and prepared for use.

Charging Station — Group of equipment assembled in a location to refill self-contained breathing apparatus cylinders.

Charles' Law — Scientific law that says the increase or decrease of pressure in a constant volume of gas is directly proportional to corresponding increase or decrease of temperature. If a gas is confined so it cannot expand, its pressure will increase or decrease in direct proportion to temperature. The formula is stated as $P_1T_1 = P_2T_2$, where:

P_1 = original pressure

T_1 = original temperature

P_2 = final pressure

T_2 = final temperature

Charter Warning — Name for the advisement of rights read to a suspect in Canada. *See* Canadian Charter of Rights and Freedoms and Miranda Warning.

Chase — Vertical or horizontal space in a building used to route pipes, wires, ducts, or other utility or mechanical systems. Usually surrounded with a fire-rated enclosure. *See* Pipe Chase.

Chassis — Basic operating system of a motor vehicle consisting of the frame, suspension system, wheels, and steering mechanism, but not the body.

Chauffeur — *See* Fire Apparatus Driver/Operator.

Cheater Bar — Piece of pipe added to a prying tool to lengthen the handle and provide additional leverage.

Check-In — Process or location used by assigned resources to report in at an incident.

Checklists — Detailed lists generally prepared for the maintenance of equipment or apparatus or for installed fire protection equipment to ensure that the inspector does not overlook an item that needs to be checked regularly. They may also be used during pre-incident planning and fire prevention inspections.

Checkrail Window — Type of window usually consisting of two sashes, known as the upper and lower sashes, that meet in the center of the window. Checkrail or double-hung windows may be made of either wood or metal, but the construction design is quite similar.

Checks — Cracks or breaks in wood.

Check Valve — Automatic valve that permits liquid flow in only one direction. For example, the inline valve that prevents water from flowing into a foam concentrate container when the nozzle is turned off or there is a kink in the hoseline.

Chemical Agent — Chemical substance that is intended for use in warfare or terrorist activities to kill, seriously injure, or incapacitate people through its physiological effects.

Chemical Asphyxiant — Substance that reacts to prevent the body from being able to use oxygen. *Also known as* Blood Poison, Blood Agent, or Cyanogens Agent. *See* Asphyxiant.

Chemical Attack — Deliberate release of a toxic gas, liquid, or solid that can poison people and the environment. *See* Chemical Warfare Agent, Terrorism, and Weapon of Mass Destruction.

Chemical, Biological, Radiological, Nuclear, or Explosive (CBRNE) Type Weapon — *See* Weapon of Mass Destruction.

Chemical Burns — Burns caused by contact with acids, lye, and vesicants such as tear gas, mustard gas, and phosphorus.

Chemical Carrier — Tank vessel that transports multiple specialty and chemical commodities. *See* Tanker.

Chemical Chain Reaction — One of the four sides of the fire tetrahedron representing a process occurring during a fire. Vapor or gases are distilled from flammable materials during initial burning; atoms and molecules are then released from these vapors and combine with other radicals to form new compounds; these compounds are again disturbed by the heat, releasing more atoms and radicals that again form new compounds and so on. Interrupting the chain reaction will stop the overall reaction; this is the extinguishing mechanism utilized by several extinguishing agents. *See* Self-Sustained Chemical Reaction.

Chemical Change — When a substance changes from one type of matter to another.

Chemical Compound — Homogeneous substance consisting of two or more elements and having properties different from the constituent elements.

Chemical Degradation — Process that occurs when the characteristics of a material are altered through contact with chemical substances.

Chemical Entry Suit — Protective apparel designed to protect the firefighter's body from certain liquid or gaseous chemicals. May be used to describe both Level A and Level B protection.

Chemical Explosion — Rapid, exothermic reactions in which an ignition source initiates the explosion (or an increase in temperature self-initiates it), and combustion propagates along the blast-pressure front of the reaction in all directions.

Chemical Flame Inhibition — Extinguishment of a fire by interruption of the chemical chain reaction.

Chemical Foam — Foam produced as a result of a reaction between two chemicals, an alkaline solution and an acid solution, which unite to form a gas (carbon dioxide) in the presence of a foaming agent that traps the gas in fire-resistive bubbles. Chemical foam is not commonly used today. *See* Mechanical Foam.

Chemical Heat Energy — Heat produced from a chemical reaction including combustion, spontaneous heating, heat of decomposition, and heat of solution; sometimes occurs as a result of a material being improperly used or stored. Some materials may simply come in contact with each other and react, or they may decompose and generate heat.

Chemical Properties — Relating to the way a substance is able to change into other substances. Chemical properties reflect the ability to burn, react, explode, or produce toxic substances hazardous to people or the environment. *See* Physical Properties.

Chemical Protective Clothing (CPC) — Clothing designed to shield or isolate individuals from the chemical, physical, and biological hazards that may be encountered during operations involving hazardous materials. *See* Level A Protection, Personal Protective Equipment (PPE), and Special Protective Clothing (1).

Chemical Reaction — Change in the composition of matter that involves a conversion of one substance into another.

Chemical Transportation Emergency Center (CHEMTREC®) — Center established by the American Chemistry Council that supplies 24-hour information for incidents involving hazardous materials. *See* Canadian Transport Emergency Centre (CANUTEC) and Emergency Transportation System for the Chemical Industry (SETIQ).

Chemical Warfare Agent — Chemical substance intended for use in warfare or terrorist activities, to kill, seriously injury, or seriously incapacitate people through their physiological effects. *See* Blister Agent, Chemical Agent, Chemical Attack, Choking Agent, Nerve Agent, and Vomiting Agent.

CHEMTREC® — *See* the Chemical Transportation Emergency Center®.

Chevron Room Setup — Room arrangement in which the chairs are positioned in a fan or V-formation, thus placing more members of the audience closer to the educator and allowing participants to see each other. *Also known as* Fan-Style Room Setup or Herringbone Room Setup.

Cheyne-Stokes Respiration — Abnormal breathing pattern characterized by rhythmic increase and decrease in depth of ventilations, with regularly recurring periods during which breathing stops.

Chief — (1) Incident Management System title for individuals responsible for command of the functional sections: operations, planning, logistics, and finance/administrative. (2) Short for chief of department or fire chief. (3) Term used to verbally address any chief officer.

Chief Complaint — Problem for which a patient seeks help; usually stated in a word or short phrase.

Chief of Department — Highest ranking member of the fire department; in some instances, designated as the director or administrator.

Chief Engineer — Senior engineering officer responsible for the satisfactory working and upkeep of the main and auxiliary machinery on board a vessel.

Chief Officer — (1) Any of the higher officer grades, from district or battalion chief to the chief of the fire department. (2) Deck officer immediately responsible to a vessel's master on board a merchant vessel; officer next in rank to the master. *Also known as* Chief Mate, First Mate, or Mate.

Chief's Aide — *See* Adjutant.

Chief Steward — Person in charge of the steward's department, responsible for the comfort and service of passengers on passenger vessels; obtains and regulates the issue of provisions and stores, and is in charge of the inspection and proper storage of provisions.

Chimney — Steep, narrow draws or canyons in which heated air rises rapidly as it would in a flue pipe.

Chimney Effect — Created when a ventilation opening is made in the upper portion of a building, and air currents throughout the building are drawn in the direction of the opening. Also occurs in wildland fires when the fire advances up a V-shaped drainage swale. *See* Stack Effect.

Chimney Rods — Poles connected to a chimney brush.

Chlorinated Polyethylene (CPE) — Widely used synthetic roofing material used in single-ply membrane roofs.

Chock — (1) Cast metal ring mounted to the deck edge to control a mooring line or prevent chafing of the line; closed chock requires one end of the mooring line to pass through the center of the chock, open chock allows the line to be dropped in from the top. (2) Piece of wood or other material placed at the side of cargo to prevent rolling or moving sideways. *See* Fairlead. (3) Wooden, plastic, or metal block constructed to fit the curvature of a tire; placed against the tire to prevent apparatus rolling. *Also known as* Wheel Block.

Choking Agent — Chemical warfare agent that attacks the lungs, causing tissue damage. *See* Chemical Warfare Agent.

Chord — Top or bottom longitudinal member of a truss; main members of trusses, as distinguished from diagonals.

Chronic — Marked by long duration; recurring over a period of time. *See* Acute.

Chronic Health Effects — Long-term effects from either a one-time or repeated exposure to a hazardous substance. *See* Acute Health Effects.

Chronic Health Hazards — Hazards that may cause long-term health effects from either a one-time or repeated exposure to a substance.

Chronic Obstructive Pulmonary Disease (COPD) — Term for several diseases that result in obstructive problems in the airways.

Chuck — Portable fire hydrant carried on the apparatus, with one or more gated connections for the hose. The device screws into a special flush hydrant connection on the water main or a special main. *Also known as* Air Line Connection.

Chuck Key — Key used to tighten or loosen the bit in a power drill.

Church Raise — *See* Auditorium Raise.

Churning — (1) Movement of smoke being blown out of a ventilation opening, only to be drawn back inside by the negative pressure created by the ejector because the open area around the ejector has not been sealed. *Also known as* Recirculation. (2) Rotation of a centrifugal pump impeller when no discharge ports are open, so that no water flows through the pump.

Chute — Salvage cover arrangement that channels excess water from a building. A modified version can be made with larger sizes of fire hose.

Ci — *See* Curie.

Cilia — Tiny hairlike projections that help move mucus from the lungs.

Circle System — *See* Loop System.

Circuit — Complete path of an electrical current.

Circuit Breaker — Device (basically an on/off switch) designed to allow a circuit to be opened or closed manually, and to automatically interrupt the flow of electricity in a circuit when it becomes overloaded.

Circular Saw — Gas- or electric-powered saw whose circular blade rotates at a high speed to produce a cutting action; a variety of blades may be used, depending on the material being cut. *Also known as* Rotary Rescue Saw.

Circular-Shaped Pattern — Fire pattern that appears on the undersides of horizontal surfaces such as ceilings or tables; formed when the plume generated by a fire spreads out across the horizontal surface.

Circulating Feed — Fire hydrant that receives water from two or more directions.

Circulating System — *See* Loop System.

Circulation Relief Valve — Small relief valve that opens and provides enough water flow into and out of the pump to prevent the pump from overheating when it is operating at churn against a closed system.

Circulator Valve — Device in a pump that routes water from the pump to the supply in order to keep the pump cool when hoselines are shut down.

Circulatory System — Bodily system consisting of the heart and blood vessels.

Circumstantial Evidence — Facts from which presumptions or inferences are made; indirect evidence. For example, seeing a person flee from the scene of an arson is circumstantial or indirect evidence that the person committed the crime; seeing the person set the fire is direct evidence.

CIS — *See* Critical Incident Stress.

CISD — *See* Critical Incident Stress Debriefing.

Cistern — Water storage receptacle that is usually underground and may be supplied by a well or rainwater runoff.

Citation — Legal reprimand for failure to comply with existing laws or regulations; notice of a violation of law. *See* Violation.

Citizens Band (CB) Radio — Low-power radio transceiver that operates on frequencies authorized by the Federal Communications Commission (FCC) for public use with no license requirement.

Civil Aviation Authority (CAA) — United Kingdom's regulatory aviation authority; responsible for regulating all UK civil aviation functions, including airspace policy, safety regulations, economic regulation, and consumer protection.

Civil Liability — Legal responsibility for fulfilling a specified duty or behaving with due regard for the rights and safety of others.

Civil Support Team (CST) — Provides military (usually National Guard) support to civil authorities such as emergency managers.

Civil Wrong — Wrongdoing for which an action for damages may be brought. *Also known as* Tort.

Cladding — Exterior finish or skin.

Clappered Siamese — Hose appliance that has one discharge and two or more intakes equipped with hinged gates that prevent water from being discharged through an open intake.

Clapper Valve — Hinged valve that permits the flow of water in one direction only.

Class A Fire — Fires involving ordinary combustibles such as wood, paper, cloth, and similar materials.

Class A Foam — *See* Class A Foam Concentrate.

Class A Foam Concentrate — Foam specially designed for use on Class A combustibles; these hydrocarbon-based surfactants are essentially wetting agents that reduce the surface tension of water and allow it to soak into combustible materials more easily than plain water. Class A foams are becoming increasingly popular for use in wildland and structural fire fighting. *Also known as* Class A Foam. *See* Finished Foam and Foam Concentrate.

Class A Fuels — Ordinary combustible solids such as wood, grass, rubber, cloth, paper, and plastics.

Class A Poison — Poisonous gases or liquids, of which a very small amount of the gas or vapor of the liquid is dangerous to life.

Class B Fire — Fires of flammable and combustible liquids and gases such as gasoline, kerosene, and propane.

Class B Foam — *See* Class B Foam Concentrate.

Class B Foam Concentrate — Foam specially designed for use on ignited or un-ignited Class B flammable or combustible liquids. *Also known as* Class B Foam. *See* Finished Foam and Foam Concentrate.

Class B Poison — Toxic substance that presents a severe health hazard if released during transportation.

Class C Fire — Fires involving energized electrical equipment.

Class D Fire — Fires of combustible metals such as magnesium, sodium, and titanium.

Class K Fire — Fires in cooking appliances that involve combustible cooking media, such as vegetable or animal oils and fats; commonly occurring in commercial cooking facilities such as restaurants and institutional kitchens.

Class I Harness — Ladder-belt-type harness that is worn around the wearer's waist and used only to secure firefighters to a ladder or other object. *Also known as* Pompier Belt. *See* Life Safety Harness.

Class II Harness — Sit-type harness designed to support the weight of two people (victim and rescuer). *See* Life Safety Harness.

Class III Harness — Sit-type harness designed to support two people. However, this type has additional support over the shoulders that is designed to prevent the wearer from becoming inverted on the rope. *See* Life Safety Harness.

Claustrophobia — Pathological fear of confined spaces.

Claw Tool — Forcible entry tool having a hook and a fulcrum at one end and a prying blade at the other.

Clean Agent — Fire suppression media that leaves little or no residue when used.

Clean-Burn Pattern — Fire pattern found on noncombustible surfaces where there has been direct contact with or intense radiant heat on the surface; the direct flame contact burns away any accumulated soot or smoke deposits on the surface, leaving demarcation lines.

Cleanout Fitting — Fitting installed in the top of a tank to facilitate washing the tank's interior.

Clear Dimensions — Interior compartment measurements made from the inside surface of one wall to the inside surface of the opposite wall.

Clear Text — Use of plain English in radio communications transmissions. No ten codes or agency specific codes are used when using clear text.

Clear Vision — Central focus of human vision; provides sharp, in-focus pictures.

Clear Width — Actual unobstructed opening size of an exit. *See* Exit.

Cleat — (1) Fitting consisting of two arms fastened on deck, around which mooring lines may be secured. (2) Strip of wood or metal to give additional strength, prevent warping, or hold in place. (3) Small pieces of wood used to secure other parts of a shoring system.

Clerestory — Windowed space that rises above lower stories to admit air, light, or both.

Clevice — U-shaped shackle attached with a pin or bolt to the end of a chain.

Clevis Hook — Type of hook attached at the end of a rope, web sling, or chain engineered for rapid connection; commonly used during vehicle extrication and rescue incidents.

Clinical Death — Term that refers to the lack of signs of life, where there is no pulse and no blood pressure; occurs immediately after the onset of cardiac arrest.

Clinker — Stony matter fused together by heat.

Closed-Circuit Breathing Apparatus — Respiratory protection system in which the exhalations of the wearer are rebreathed, after carbon dioxide has been effectively removed and a suitable oxygen concentration restored from resources composed of compressed oxygen, chemical oxygen, or liquid oxygen; usually long-duration device systems. Not approved for fire fighting operations. *Also known as* Oxygen-Breathing Apparatus (OBA) or Oxygen-Generating Apparatus.

Closed Fracture — Fracture in which there is no break in the overlying skin.

Closed Sprinkler — Sprinkler that is equipped with a heat-sensitive element, such as a fusible link or frangible bulb, that is rated at a fixed temperature; when heat rises past the preset temperature, the link melts or the bulb bursts, causing the head to open. May be used in wet-pipe, dry-pipe, or pre-action sprinkler systems. *See* Foam-Water Sprinkler and Open Sprinkler.

Cloud — Ball-shaped pattern of an airborne hazardous material where the material has collectively risen above the ground or water at a hazardous materials incident. *See* Cone, Hemispheric Release, and Plume.

Clove Hitch — Knot that consists of two half hitches; its principal use is to attach a rope to an object such as a pole, post, or hose.

CNC — *See* Condensation Nuclei Counter.

CNG — *See* Compressed Natural Gas.

CO — *See* Carbon Monoxide.

CO₂ — *See* Carbon Dioxide.

Coaching — Process in which instructors direct the skills performance of individuals by observing, evaluating, and making suggestions for improvement.

Coach Space — Standard seating areas within a train car or airliner.

Coalition — Formal, mutual relationship between or among organizations who agree to help each other in specific ways to reach a specific goal; relationship is often formalized with a written agreement that spells out what kind of help each organization will provide the other.

Coaming — Raised framework around deck or bulkhead openings; used to prevent entry of water.

Coarse Aggregates — Crushed stone, gravel, cinders, shale, lava, pumice, vermiculite, etc.

Cockloft — Concealed space between the top floor and the roof of a structure. *See* Attic.

Cockpit — Fuselage compartment occupied by pilots while flying the aircraft.

Cockpit Voice Recorder — Recording device installed in most large civilian aircraft to record crew conversation and communications; intended to assist in an accident investigation by helping to determine the probable cause of the accident.

Code 1 — Operation of an emergency vehicle under non-emergency response conditions. Driver proceeds at his or her convenience, no warning devices are being used, and all traffic laws are followed.

Code 2 — Operation of an emergency vehicle in which the driver proceeds immediately, obeys all traffic laws, and uses visual warning devices but no audible warning devices. This is prohibited in most jurisdictions.

Code 3 — Operation of an emergency vehicle under emergency response conditions using visual and audible warning devices.

Code — Body or collection of systematically arranged laws, rules, and regulations, usually pertaining to one subject area; examples include a mechanical code, a building code, an electrical code, or a fire code. They are enacted by a legislative body to become law in a particular jurisdiction. *See* Building Code, Regulation, and Standard.

Codes — (1) Body of systematically arranged laws, usually pertaining to one subject area, such as a mechanical code, a building code, an electrical code, or a fire code. (2) A collection of rules and regulations enacted by a legislative body to become law in a particular jurisdiction

Code Enforcement — Process of enforcing a body of law aimed at reducing fire and life-safety hazards as well as mandating the proper installation and maintenance of building/structure fire and life-safety features to provide adequate community fire prevention.

Code Enforcement Officer — *See* Inspector.

Code for Safety to Life from Fire in Buildings and Structures — Old title of NFPA® 101, *Life Safety Code®*.

Code of Federal Regulations (CFR) —Books or documents containing the specific U.S. regulations provided for by law; complete body of U.S. federal law.

Coefficient of Discharge — Correction factor used in hydraulic calculations to account for irregularities in the shape of the hydrant discharge orifice. Frequently applied in computing the flow from a hydrant.

Coercion — Act of forcing or compelling someone (by use of threats, authority, or any other means) to comply, perform an act, or make a choice.

Coercive Power — Power to punish or impose sanctions on those who fail to behave in a prescribed manner.

COFC — *See* Container-on-Flatcar.

Coffer Dam — (1) Watertight enclosure, usually made of sheet piling, that can be pumped dry to permit construction inside. (2) Narrow, empty space (void) between compartments or tanks of a vessel that prevents leakage between them; used to isolate compartments or tanks.

COG — *See* Continuity of Government.

Cognitive Evaluation — Assessment of knowledge that shows cognitive or knowing level by requiring that learners respond appropriately to questions on various types of tests.

Cognitive Learning Domain — Learning that relates to knowledge and intellectual skills (facts and information), emphasizing thought rather than feeling or movement and involving the learning of concepts and principles. *See* Learning Domain.

COHb — *See* Carboxyhemoglobin.

Cohesion — Act of binding together substances of like composition.

Coil Spring Suspension — Suspension system consisting of numerous spirally-bound, elastic steel bodies that recover their shape after being compressed, bent, or stretched.

Cold Smoke — Smoke from a fire that lacks any substantial heat.

Cold Trailing — Constructing a minimum fire line along the perimeter of a wildland fire after the perimeter is relatively cold, in order to ensure no further advance of the fire. Accomplished by carefully inspecting and feeling with the hand to detect any fire, digging out every live spot, and trenching any live edge.

Collapse Zone — Area beneath a wall in which the wall is likely to land if it loses structural integrity.

Collapsible Ladder — *See* Folding Ladder.

Collar Method — Means of attaching a coupling to a hose with a two- or three-piece collar, which is bolted into place.

Collision Beam — (1) Structural member within a vehicle door designed to prevent the door from collapsing inward if struck. (2) Heavy-gauge steel member strategically located in the sidewall of a bus. Collision beams limit penetration of an object into the passenger compartment of a vehicle.

Collision Bulkhead — Stronger-than-normal bulkhead located forward to control flooding in the event of a head-on collision.

Colorimetric Tube — Small tube that changes color when contaminated air is drawn through it. *Also known as* Detector Tube.

Column — Vertical supporting member.

Column Footing — Square pad of concrete that supports a column.

Combination Aircraft — Large aircraft with a passenger cabin in the front of the aircraft and a separate cargo compartment in the rear of the aircraft. *Also known as* Combies.

Combination Apparatus — Piece of fire apparatus designed to perform more than one function; usually called Triple Combinations, Quads, or Quints.

Combination Attack — Battling a fire by using both a direct and an indirect attack; this method combines the steam-generating technique of a ceiling level attack with an attack on the burning materials near floor level. A water or foam stream is moved around a compartment in an O, T, or Z pattern; this movement allows the extinguishing agent to be applied to the fire and to the surrounding uninvolved fuel. *See* Attack Methods (1).

Combination Detection and Alarm Systems — Systems that have both fire and burglar alarms, with the fire alarm signal overriding the burglar alarm.

Combination Detector — Alarm-initiating device that is capable of detecting an abnormal condition by more than one means. The most common combination detector is the fixed-temperature/rate-of-rise heat detector.

Combination Fire Department — Organization in which some of the firefighters receive pay while other personnel serve on a voluntary basis. In Canada, a combination fire department is called a Composite Department.

Combination Ladder — Ladder that can be used as either a single, extension, or A-frame ladder.

Combination Lay — Hose lay in which two or more hoselines are laid in either direction - water source to fire or fire to water source.

Combination Nozzle — Nozzle designed to provide either a solid stream or a fixed spray pattern suitable only for mop-up. Not to be confused with an adjustable fog nozzle.

Combination Packaging — Shipping container consisting of one or more inner packagings secured in a nonbulk outer packaging. *See* Packaging (1).

Combination Smoke Detector — Smoke-sensing device consisting of both photoelectric and ionization smoke detectors.

Combination Spreader/Shears — Powered hydraulic tool consisting of two arms equipped with spreader tips that can be used for pulling or pushing. The insides of the arms contain cutting shears.

Combination System — Water supply system that is a combination of both gravity and direct pumping systems. It is the most common type of municipal water supply system.

Combine — Large, self-propelled machine that cuts, threshes, and cleans crops as it drives across a field.

Combined-Agent Vehicle — Type of rapid intervention vehicle that is designed to apply multiple types of fire-extinguishing agents on aircraft crash incidents.

Combplate — Grooved plate at the top of an escalator. The grooves in the plate mesh with matching ridges in the stair treads to prevent shoes from being caught in the crevice as the stair treads move under the plate.

Combustible Gas Detector — Indicates the explosive levels of combustible gases.

Combustible Liquid — Liquid having a flash point at

or above 100°F (37.8°C) and below 200°F (93.3°C). *See* Flammable Liquid and Flash Point.

Combustion — Exothermic chemical reaction that is a self-sustaining process of rapid oxidation of a fuel, producing heat and light. *See* Flammable Liquid, Flash Point, Noncombustible, and Oxidation.

Come-Along — Manually operated pulling tool that uses a ratchet/pulley arrangement to provide a mechanical advantage.

Command — (1) Act of directing, ordering, and/or controlling resources by virtue of explicit legal, agency, or delegated authority. (2) Term used on the radio to designate the incident commander. (3) Function of NIMS-ICS that determines the overall strategy for the incident, with input from throughout the ICS structure.

Command Post (CP) — Designated physical location of the command and control point where the incident commander and command staff function during an incident, and where those in charge of emergency units report to be briefed on their respective assignments. The command post may be co-located with the base. *See* Incident Command Post.

Command Staff — In a fully developed fireground organization, the Information Officer (PIO), Safety (ISO), and Liaison Officer, who report directly to the IC.

Comm Center — *See* Telecommunications Center.

Commercial Aviation Aircraft — Airline, commuter, cargo, and fire fighting aircraft.

Commercial Chassis — Truck chassis produced by a commercial truck manufacturer. These chassis are in turn outfitted with a rescue or fire fighting body.

Commercial Motor Coach — Custom-built bus designed to carry groups of people to a specific destination, usually a long distance away. These buses may run regularly scheduled routes, or they may be specially chartered. *Also known as* Charter Bus and Touring Bus.

Commissioner — Member of city or county government; the fire commissioner represents the fire department on the government ruling body. In some cases, there is no commissioner, and the fire chief is the ranking official directly responsible to the government.

Commodity Flowcharting — Portrays the movement of a tangible item, such as money or stolen property, through a system.

Common Brick — Fired clay brick with a plain, unfinished surface.

Common Conductor — *See* Grounded Conductor.

Common Freight — Goods, other than passengers' baggage, transported to a specific destination by a regularly scheduled hauler, such as a bus or train.

Common Hazard — Condition likely to be found in almost all occupancies and generally not associated with a specific occupancy or activity.

Common Law — Law not created by legislative action but based on certain commonly held customs, traditions, and beliefs within a particular culture.

Common Path of Travel — Route of travel used to determine measured egress distances in code enforcement. The common path of travel is considered to be down the center of a straight corridor and a 1-foot (0.3 m) radius around each corner. *Also known as* Normal Path of Travel.

Communicable Disease — Disease that is transmissible from one person to another.

Communication — (1) Two-way process of transmitting and receiving some type of message. (2) Exchange of ideas and information that conveys an intended meaning in a form that is understood. (3) Ongoing process that educators and their audiences use to complete the exchange of information and attitudes about fire and life safety.

Communications Center — *See* Telecommunications Center.

Communication Barriers — Poor listening habits or environments that get in the way of communication.

Communications Unit — (1) Functional unit within the service branch of the logistics section of the incident management system; responsible for the incident communications plan, installation and repair of communications equipment, and operation of the incident communications center. (2) Vehicle used to provide the major part of an incident communications center.

Community Master Plan — Medium- to long-range plan for the growth and development of a community; generally written through the interaction of all city agencies that may be affected by future developments.

Companionway — Interior stair-ladder, usually enclosed, that is used to travel from deck to deck.

Company — (1) Basic fire fighting organizational unit consisting of firefighters and apparatus; headed by a company officer. (2) Term that encompasses the whole crew of a vessel.

Company Log — Record of the activities of a fire company; usually kept by a company officer.

Company Officer — Individual responsible for command of a company. This designation is not specific to any particular fire department rank (may be a firefighter, lieutenant, captain, or chief officer if responsible for command of a single company).

Comparison Sample — Evidence collected from undamaged areas or materials to offer a comparison to similar materials damaged by a fire.

Compartment — Interior space (room) of a vessel; numbered from forward to aft with odd numbers on starboard side and even numbers on port side.

Compartmentation — (1) Series of barriers designed to keep flames, smoke, and heat from spreading from one room or floor to another. (2) Subdividing of a vessel's hull by transverse watertight bulkheads; may allow a vessel to stay afloat under certain flooding conditions. *See* One-Compartment Subdivision.

Compartmentalization — Systematic venting of a structure by controlling which windows and doors are opened at any given time.

Compartmentation Systems — Series of barriers designed to keep flames, smoke, and heat from spreading from one room or floor to another; barriers may be doors, extra walls or partitions, fire-stopping materials inside walls or other concealed spaces, or floors.

Compartment Syndrome — Occurs when a patient's limb has been entrapped for four to six hours; at this point, the crushed tissue in the involved limb begins to give off toxins, which decreases the potential for saving the limb.

Compensation/Claims Unit — Functional unit within the finance/administrative section of an incident management system; responsible for financial concerns resulting from injuries or fatalities at an incident.

Compensatory Measure — Measure intended to compensate for a code deficiency; may be either administrative or physical. Provides approximately the same level of safety performance as the intent of the deficient element that it replaces.

Competency-Based Learning (CBL) — Training based upon the competencies of a profession or job; competencies are the absolute standards or criteria of performance. Emphasis is on what the learner will learn. *Also known as* Criterion-Referenced Learning or Performance-Based Learning.

Complaint — (1) Objection to an existing condition that is brought to the attention of a fire prevention bureau or a building department, usually by a citizen. (2) In court, a formal charge or accusation.

Complement — (1) All firefighters assigned to a working unit, or the number of units assigned to a given alarm. (2) Equipment assigned to a piece of apparatus.

Complex Buildings — Structures such as manufacturing, health care, or multi-use buildings that are more structurally complex than single-family dwellings.

Complex Loop — Piping system that is characterized by one or more of the following: more than one inflow point, more than one outflow point, and/or more than two paths between inflow and outflow points. *Also known as* Grid System or Gridded Piping System.

Compliance — Meeting the minimum standards set forth by applicable codes or regulations. *See* Code and Regulation.

Composite Cylinder — Lightweight air cylinder made of more than one material; often aluminum wrapped with fiberglass.

Composite Department — *See* Combination Fire Department.

Composite Materials — Plastics, metals, ceramics, or carbon-fiber materials with built-in strengthening agents. These materials are much lighter and stronger than the metals formerly used for such aircraft components as panels, skin, and flight controls.

Composite Packaging — Single container made of two different types of material. *See* Packaging (1).

Composite Panels — Produced with parallel external face veneers bonded to a core of reconstituted fibers.

Compound — Substance consisting of two or more elements that have been united chemically.

Compound Fracture — Open fracture; a fracture in which there is an open wound of the skin and soft tissues.

Compound Gauge — Pressure gauge capable of measuring above and below atmospheric pressure; commonly used to measure the intake pressure on a fire pump.

Compound Tackle — Two or more blocks reeved with more than one rope.

Comprehensive Environmental Response, Compensation and Liability Act (CERCLA) — U.S. law that created a tax on the chemical and petroleum industries, and provided broad federal authority to respond directly to releases or threatened releases of hazardous substances that may endanger public health or the environment.

Comprehensive Test — Type of test typically given in the middle (midterm) or at the end (final) of instruction that measures terminal performance of program participants and whether they have achieved program objectives. *See* Test.

Compress — Folded cloth or pad used for applying pressure to stop hemorrhage, or as a wet dressing.

Compressed Air — Air under greater than atmospheric pressure; used as a portable supply of breathing air for SCBA or to operate pneumatic tools.

Compressed Air Foam System (CAFS) — Generic term used to describe a high-energy foam-generation system consisting of a water pump, a foam proportioning system, and an air compressor (or other air source) that injects air into the foam solution before it enters a hoseline.

Compressed Gas — Gas that, at normal temperature, exists solely as a gas when pressurized in a container, as opposed to a gas that becomes a liquid when stored under pressure. *See* Gas, Liquefied Compressed Gas, and Nonflammable Gas.

Compressed Gas Association (CGA) — Trade association that writes standards pertaining to the use, storage, and transportation of compressed gases.

Compressed Gas (Tube) Trailer — Cargo tank truck that carries gases under pressure; may be a large single container, an intermodal shipping unit, or several horizontal tubes. *Also known as* Tube Trailer. *See* Cargo Tank Truck.

Compressed Natural Gas — Natural gas that is stored in a vessel at pressures of 2,400 to 3,600 psi (16 800 kPa to 25 200 kPa).

Compression — Vertical and/or horizontal forces that tend to push the mass of a material together; for example, the force exerted on the top chord of a truss.

Compressor — Machine designed to compress air or gas.

Computer-Aided Design (CAD) — Computer technology used to design, draw, or draft technical products, rooms, or entire buildings in two or three dimensions; it is also used to create animations from static drawings and to convert existing drawings and diagrams into computer models.

Computer-Aided Instruction (CAI) — Instructional approach that uses the computer to present instruction to the student on an individualized, self-paced basis.

Concealed Space — Structural void that is not readily visible from a living/working space within a building, such as areas between walls or partitions, ceilings and roofs, and floors and basement ceilings through which fire may spread undetected; also includes soffits and other enclosed vertical or horizontal shafts through which fire may spread.

Concentrated Load — Load that is applied at one point or over a small area.

Concentration — (1) Quantity of a chemical material inhaled for purposes of measuring toxicity. (2) Percentage (mass or volume) of a material dissolved in water (or other solvent). *See* Dose and Lethal Concentration, 50 Percent Kill (LC$_{50}$).

Concrete — Strong, hard building material produced from a mixture of portland cement and an aggregate filler/binder to which water is added to form a wet, moldable slurry that sets into a rigid building material. Concrete is fireproof, watertight, and comparatively inexpensive to make. The aggregates used in concrete are inert mineral ingredients that reduce the amount of cement that otherwise would be needed. In structural concrete, the filler/binder is usually sand and/or gravel. Lightweight concrete, used as sound-proofing material, may use sand and/or vermiculite.

Concrete Admixture — Substance added to concrete to aid in imparting color, waterproofing, controlling workability, controlling the hardening process, and entraining air.

Concrete Block — Large rectangular brick used in construction; the most common type is the hollow concrete block. *Also known as* Concrete Masonry Units (CMU).

Concrete Block Brick Faced — Wall construction system that includes one wythe of concrete blocks with a brick wythe attached to the outside. *See* Course, Header Course, and Wythe.

Condensation — Process of going from the gaseous to the liquid state.

Condensation Nuclei Counter (CNC) — Quantitative fit-test protocol using a counting instrument that quantitatively fit-tests respirators with the use of a probe. The probed respirator has a special sampling device installed on the respirator that allows the probe to sample the air from inside the mask.

Condition — Part of an educational objective that describes under what provisions and with what resources the learner should be able to act or fulfill the objective.

Conduction — Physical flow or transfer of heat energy from one body to another, through direct contact or an intervening medium, from the point where the heat is produced to another location, or from a region of high temperature to a region of low temperature. *See* Convection, Heat, Heat Transfer, Law of Heat Flow, and Radiation.

Conductivity — Ability of a substance to conduct an electrical current.

Conductivity Readings — Form of nondestructive testing used on aluminum aerial devices. Changes in the integrity of material in a certain area will be reflected by a divergence of conductivity readings.

Conductor — Substance or material that transmits electrical or thermal energy. *See* Dielectric, Semiconductor, and Thermocouple.

Cone — Triangular-shaped pattern of an airborne hazardous material release with a point source at the breach and a wide base downrange. *See* Cloud, Hemispheric Release, and Plume.

Cone Roof Storage Tank — Fixed-site vertical atmospheric storage tank that has a cone-shaped pointed roof with weak roof-to-shell seams that are intended to break when excessive overpressure results inside. Used to store flammable, combustible, and corrosive liquids. *Also known as* Dome Roof Tank. *See* Atmospheric Storage Tank, External Floating Roof Tank, and Internal Floating Roof Tank.

Conference Discussion — Discussion in which a group directs its thinking toward solving a common problem.

Confine a Fire — To restrict the fire within determined boundaries established either prior to the fire or during the fire. *Also known as* Confinement.

Confined Space — Space or enclosed area not intended for continuous occupation, having limited (restricted access) openings for entry or exit, providing unfavorable natural ventilation and the potential to have a toxic, explosive, or oxygen-deficient atmosphere.

Confinement — (1) The process of controlling the flow of a spill and capturing it at some specified location. (2) Fire fighting operations required to prevent fire from extending from the area of origin to uninvolved areas or structures. *See* Confine a Fire and Containment.

Conflagration — Large, uncontrollable fire covering a considerable area and crossing natural fire barriers such as streets; usually involves buildings in more than one block and causes a large fire loss. Forest fires can also be considered conflagrations.

Connection Box — Contains fittings for trailer emergency and service brake connections and an electrical connector to which the lines from the towing vehicle may be connected. *Formerly known as* Bird Box, Junction Box, or Light Box.

Consensus — General agreement; the judgment or agreement arrived at by most of those in a group.

Consensus Standard — Rules, principles, or measures that are established though agreement of the members of the standards-setting organization.

Consent — In terms of legal right of entry, refers to the granting of access to a scene by the lawful owner of the property where the incident occurred; consent is a courtesy on the part of the private property owner and as such may be withheld at any time.

Conservation of Energy — Law of physics that states that the total amount of energy in an isolated system remains constant. As a result, energy cannot be created or destroyed.

Consignee — Person who is to receive a shipment.

Consist — Rail shipping paper that contains a list of cars in the train by order; indicates the cars that contain hazardous materials. Some railroads include information on emergency operations for the hazardous materials on board with the consist. *Also known as* Train Consist. *See* Shipping Papers and Waybill.

Consistency — Quality of finished foam that has small bubbles of equal size - an important quality for all types of foam. *See* Finished Foam.

Constant Pressure Relay — Method of establishing a relay water supply utilizing two or more pumpers to supply the attack pumper. This method reduces the need for time-consuming and often confusing fireground calculations of friction loss.

Constitutional Law — Law based on the Constitution; all state/provincial laws must be consistent with the respective federal constitution.

Constrict — To be made smaller by drawing together or squeezing.

Construction Classification — Classification given to a particular building by a building code, based on its construction materials, methods, and ability to resist the effects of a fire situation. *See* Building Code.

Construction Plan — Visual depiction of how a building and all of its many components are to come together; serves as a medium for conveying information to those who need it for the construction of a building. *See* Floor Plan, Plot Plan, and Site Plan.

Consumable Materials — Instructional materials limited to one-time use because they are designed to be "consumed" or used up.

Consumer Product Safety Commission (CPSC) — U.S. government agency charged with protecting the public from unreasonable risks of serious injury or death from more than 15,000 types of consumer products under the agency's jurisdiction, including hazardous materials intended for consumer purchase and use. CPSC also operates the National Electronic Injury Surveillance System (NEISS) database, collecting data based on a sample of hospital emergency rooms and focusing on the role of consumer products in fire and burn injuries.

Contact Paper — Vinyl- or paper-like material that has a strong adhesive pre-applied to one side.

Contagious — Capable of being transmitted from one person to another, by contact or close proximity.

Contained Fire — Fire whose progress has been stopped but for which the control line is not yet finished.

Container — (1) Article of transport equipment that is: (a) of a permanent character and strong enough for repeated use; (b) specifically designed to facilitate the carriage of goods by one or more modes of transport without intermediate reloading; and (c) fitted with devices permitting its ready handling, particularly its transfer from one mode to another. The term "container" does not include vehicles. *Also known as* Cargo Container or Freight Container. (2) Box of standardized size used to transport cargo by truck or railcar when transported overland or by cargo vessels at sea; sizes are usually 8 by 8 by 20 feet or 8 by 8 by 40 feet (2.4 m by 2.4 m by 6 m or 2.4 m by 2.4 m by 12.2 m). See Bulk Container, Carboy, Container Specification Number, Container Terminal, Container Vessel, Dewar, Intermodal Container, Reefer Container, Refrigerated Intermodal Container.

Container Chassis — Trailer chassis consisting of a frame with locking devices for securing and transporting a container as a wheeled vehicle.

Container-on-Flatcar (COFC) — Rail flatcar used to transport highway transport containers.

Container Ship — Ship specially equipped to transport large freight containers in horizontal, or more commonly, vertical container cells. The containers are usually loaded and unloaded by special cranes.

Container Specification Number — Shipping container number preceded by letters "DOT" that indicates the container has been built to U.S. federal specifications.

Container Terminal — Facility for loading and unloading cargoes shipped in standard 20 foot or 40 foot long containers and their stowage; usually accessible by truck, railroad, and marine transportation. See Container and Reefer Container.

Container Vessel — Ship specially equipped to transport large freight containers in horizontal or, more commonly, vertical container cells; containers are usually loaded and unloaded by special cranes. See Cargo Vessel.

Containment — Act of stopping the further release of a material from its container. See Confinement.

Contaminant — Foreign substance that compromises the purity of a given substance. See Contamination.

Contamination — (1) Condition of impurity resulting from mixture or contact with foreign substance. (2) In terms of fire investigation, refers to anything that can taint physical evidence. See Contaminant, Decontamination, and Surface Contamination.

Contents — Furnishings, merchandise, and any machinery or equipment not part of the building structure.

Continuity of Government (COG) — Process to ensure continuation of the government. See Continuity of Operations (COOP).

Continuity of Operations (COOP) — Defining plans for the continuity of operations in all state agencies and an overall plan for the continuity of government; includes emergency evacuation procedures, firm definitions of the leader's emergency powers, line of succession for all agency officials, and plans and programs for business continuity in the private sector. See Continuity of Government (COG).

Continuous Halyard — Halyard on which both ends are attached to the bottom rung of the fly section of an extension ladder. The rope is run from the bottom rung of the fly section, down around the bottom rung of the bed section, and back up to the bottom rung of the fly section.

Contractor — Individual who performs construction on a property for a predetermined cost or fee.

Contractual Entry — Legal entry to a scene by those with a privately defined jurisdiction, such as private investigators representing an insurance company that insures the property where the incident occurred.

Contractual Sleeve Binding — Method of attaching couplings to fire hose with a tension ring that compresses a nylon sleeve to lock the hose onto the coupling shank.

Continuous Fuels — Fuels distributed uniformly over an area, thereby providing a continuous path for fire to spread. See Fuel Continuity.

Control — Point in time when progress of a fire has been halted, such as when the perimeter spread of a wildland fire has been halted and can reasonably be expected to hold under foreseeable conditions. When the fire is under control, the release of fire fighting resources can begin.

Control a Fire — To complete control line around a fire, any spot fire there from, and any interior island to be saved; to burn out any unburned area adjacent to the fire side of the control lines; and to cool down all hot spots that are immediate threats to the control line until the lines can reasonably be expected to hold under foreseeable conditions.

Control Agent — Material used to contain, confine, neutralize, or extinguish a hazardous material or its vapor.

Control Center — Telecommunications center used by the fire service for emergency communications. There are also mobile command posts that can be taken directly to the fire scene and function as the incident operational control center.

Control Zones — See Hazard-Control Zones.

Controlled Airport — Airport having a control tower in operation; the tower is usually staffed by FAA personnel.

Controlled Breathing — Technique for consciously reducing air consumption by forcing exhalation from the mouth and allowing natural inhalation through the nose.

Controlled Burning — Fires intentionally set in vegetative fuels for the purpose of burning debris or accumulations of wildland fuels, such as grass and brush, to reduce available fuel and prevent the occurrence of uncontrolled wildland fires. May be done as part of a fuel-management program to prevent or reduce the rate of spread of wildland fires. *See* Prescribed Burning.

Controller — Electric control panel used to switch a fire pump on and off and to control its operation.

Control Line — Inclusive term for all constructed or natural barriers (or combinations thereof) and treated fire edges that ultimately contain and control the fire; not to be confused with fire line.

Control Pedestal — Central location for most or all of the aerial device controls. Depending on the type and manufacturer of the apparatus, the control pedestal may be located on the turntable, on the rear or side of the apparatus, or in the elevating platform. *Also known as* Pedestal.

Control Zones — System of barriers surrounding designated areas at emergency scenes intended to limit the number of persons exposed to the hazard, and to facilitate its mitigation. At a major incident there will be three zones — restricted (hot), limited access (warm), and support (cold). *See* Hazard-Control Zones.

Convection — Transfer of heat by the movement of heated fluids or gases, usually in an upward direction. *See* Conduction, Heat, Heat Transfer, Law of Heat Flow, and Radiation.

Convection Column — Rising column of heated air or gases above a continuing heat or fire source. *Also known as* Thermal Column.

Convenience Outlet — Electrical outlet that can be used for lamps and other appliances.

Convenience Stair — Stair that usually connects two floors in a multistory building.

Convergent Volunteers — Individuals who arrive at the scene of a disaster or emergency in order to help, but were not dispatched to the scene through official channels.

Convulsant — Poison that causes an exposed individual to have convulsions. *See* Poison.

Convulsion — Seizure or violent involuntary contraction (or series of contractions) of the voluntary muscles.

Cooling — (1) Act of lowering the temperature of the fuel and adjacent surfaces. (2) Reduction of heat by the quenching action or heat absorption of the extinguishing agent.

COOP — *See* Continuity of Operations.

Cooperating Agency — Agency supplying assistance to the incident control effort, other than direct suppression, rescue, support, or service functions; for example, the Red Cross, a law enforcement agency, or a telephone company.

Cooperative Agreement — Written agreement between fire protection agencies agreeing to cooperate in actions or share resources for a common good.

Cope Steel — To cut a flange section in order to avoid interference with other structural members.

COTP — *See* Captain of the Port.

Copyright Law — Law designed to protect the competitive advantage developed by an individual or organization as a result of their creativity. *See* Law and Statute.

Corbel — Bracket or ledge made of stone, wood, brick, or other building material projecting from the face of a wall or column used to support a beam, cornice, or arch. *See* Corbelling.

Corbelling — Use of a corbel to provide additional support for an arch. *See* Corbel.

Core Temperature — Body temperature measured in deep structures such as the lungs or liver.

Corner Fittings — Strong metal devices located at the corners of a container having several apertures that normally provide the means for handling, stacking, and securing the freight container.

Corner Structures — Vertical frame components located at the corners of a container; integral with the corner fittings.

Cornice — Concealed space near the eave of a building; usually overhanging the area adjacent to exterior walls.

Coronary Arteries — Blood vessels that supply blood to the walls of the heart.

Coroner — Official chiefly responsible for investigating deaths, particularly some of those happening under unusual circumstances, and determining the cause of death. *See* Medical Examiner.

Corpus Delicti — Evidence of substantial and fundamental facts necessary to prove the commission of a crime.

Corrective Maintenance — Reactive maintenance or repairs that are performed as a result of a breakdown or mechanical failure.

Corrosive — Having the property of burning, irritating, or destroying human skin tissue and severely corroding steel. *See* Acid, Base, and Corrosive Material.

Corrosive Liquid Tank — Cargo tank truck that carries corrosive liquids, usually acids. *See* Cargo Tank Truck.

Corrosive Material — Gaseous, liquid, or solid material that can burn, irritate, or destroy human skin tissue and severely corrode steel. *Also known as* Corrosive. *See* Hazardous Material.

Corrugated — Formed into ridges or grooves; serrated.

Corrugated Hose — Hose shaped into folds or parallel and alternating ridges and grooves to improve flexibility.

Cost-Benefit Analysis — Systematic methodology to compare costs and benefits to make cost-effective funding decisions on projects. *See* Analysis and Impact Analysis.

Cost Unit — Functional unit within the finance/administrative section of an incident management system; responsible for tracking costs, analyzing cost data, making cost estimates, and recommending cost-saving measures.

Council of American Building Officials (CABO) — Former umbrella organization for BOCA (Building Officials and Code Administrators), ICBO (International Conference of Building Officials), and SBCCI (Southern Building Code Congress International). These agencies have merged to form the International Code Council (ICC).

Counseling — Advising learners or program participants on their educational progress, career opportunities, personal anxieties, or sudden crises in their lives.

Counterbalance Valve — Valves designed to prevent unintentional or undesirable motion of an aerial device from position.

Countermeasures — Devices or systems designed to prevent sensor-guided weapons from locking onto and destroying a target.

County — Political subdivision of a state, province, or territory for administrative purposes and public safety. *Also known as* Parish.

Coupling — Fitting permanently attached to the end of a hose; used to connect two hoselines together, or to connect a hoseline to a device such as a nozzle, appliance, discharge valve, or hydrant.

Course — Horizontal layer of individual masonry units. *See* Header Course and Wythe.

Course Description — Relates the basic goals and objectives of the course in a broad, general manner. It is designed to provide a framework and guide for further development of the course and also communicate the course content.

Course Objectives — Specific identification of the planned results of a course of instruction.

Course Outline — List of jobs and information to be taught to fulfill previously identified needs and objectives.

Courts of Queen's Bench — Canadian equivalent of the U.S. Federal Court System.

Cover — (1) Practice of moving unassigned fire companies into stations that have been emptied by another emergency. (2) To cover exposures by placing primary fire streams in advantageous positions to protect buildings or rooms exposed to heat and fire. (3) To protect with a salvage cover. (4) General term used to described brush, grasses, and other natural ground covers.

Covert — Not in the open; secret.

Covered Floating Roof Tank — *See* Internal Floating Roof Tank.

Cover Letter — Letter explaining or containing additional information about an accompanying communication.

Cowl Flaps — Adjustable sections or hinged panels on the engine cowling of reciprocating engines; used to control the engine temperature.

Cowling — Removable covering around aircraft engines.

CP — *See* Command Post.

CPC — *See* Chemical Protective Clothing.

CPE — *See* Chlorinated Polyethylene.

C-Post — Post nearest the rear door handle on a four-door vehicle. On a two-door vehicle, the rear roof post is considered to be the C-post.

CPR — *See* Cardiopulmonary Resuscitation.

CPSC — *See* Consumer Product Safety Commission.

CPU — *See* Central Processing Unit.

Cradle — Rest designed to support the free end of the aerial device during road travel.

Crash Fire Rescue (CFR) — Old term used to describe the fire and rescue services provided at airport facilities. *Currently known as* Aircraft Rescue and Fire Fighting.

Crawl Space — Area between ground and floor, ceiling and floor above, or ceiling and roof, or any other structural void with a vertical dimension that does not allow a person to stand erect within the space. These spaces often contain ductwork, plumbing, and wiring.

Crazing — Formation of patterns of short cracks throughout a pane of glass, such as windows and mirrors, from the heat of fire. It is thought to be the result of heating of one side of a pane while the other side remains cool.

Creeping Fire — Fire burning with a low flame height and spreading slowly.

Creosote — Highly flammable byproduct of combustion composed of tars and other hydrocarbons that are distilled from carboniferous fuels as they burn; generally collects on cooler surfaces of flues and chimneys.

Crew — Organized group or specific number of emergency services personnel, under the leadership of a crew leader or other designated supervisor, that has been assembled for an assignment such as search, ventilation, or hoseline deployment and operations. The number of personnel in a crew should not exceed recommended span-of-control limits of three to seven people. Sometimes referred to as a "company" in municipal fire departments.

Crew List — Part of a vessel's papers listing the names and nationalities of every member of the crew, the capacity in which each member serves, and the amount of wages each member receives.

Crew Transport — Any vehicle capable of transporting a specified number of fire crew personnel in a specified manner.

Cribbing — (1) Varying lengths of hardwood, usually 4 x 4 inches (100 mm by 100 mm) or larger, used to stabilize vehicles and collapsed buildings during extrication incidents. (2) Process of arranging planks into a crate-like construction. *Also known as* Shoring.

Crime Concealment Fire — Intentionally set fire intended to destroy evidence of another crime such as a homicide or burglary.

Criminal Law — Law intended to protect society by identifying certain conduct as criminal, and specifying the sanctions to be imposed on those who engage in criminal activity.

Criminal Search Warrant — Warrant issued with the intent of collecting evidence specifically to prove that a fire or explosion was intentionally set; issued when an administrative search leads to an investigator having probable cause that an arson or other crime was committed.

Crisis Communication — Preincident, incident, and postincident information or threat advisories provided to the public and news media.

Crisis Counseling — Programs to help relieve grieving, stress, or mental health problems caused or aggravated by a disaster or its aftermath.

Criterion — (1) Standard on which a decision or judgment is based. (2) One of the three requirements of evaluation. (3) The standard against which learning is compared after instruction. (4) The expected learning outcome; examples are Behavioral Objectives or NFPA® standards. Plural for the term is criteria.

Criterion-Referenced Learning — *See* Competency-Based Learning.

Criterion-Referenced Testing — Measurement of individual performance against a set standard or criteria, not against other students. Mastery learning is the key element to criterion-referenced testing. *See* Mastery and Test.

Critical Angle — Angle between legs of an anchor; it must be less than 90 degrees to avoid excessive loading of individual anchor points and components in an anchor system.

Critical Angle of List — Point at which critical events will occur. Not a point that remains constant in all cases; it is determined by stability calculations made by qualified personnel along with their professional judgment. *See* List and Heel.

Critical Incident Stress (CIS) — Physical, mental, or emotional tension caused when persons have been exposed to a traumatic event where they have experienced, witnessed, or been confronted with an event or events that involve actual death, threatened death, serious injury, or threat of physical integrity of self or others. *See* Post-Traumatic Stress Disorder (PTSD) and Stress (3).

Critical Incident Stress Debriefing (CISD) — Counseling designed to minimize the effects of psychological/emotional post-incident trauma on those at fire and rescue incidents who were directly involved with victims suffering from particularly gruesome or horrific injuries. *See* Post-Traumatic Incident Debriefing.

Critical Incident Stress Management (CISM) — Comprehensive crisis intervention system composed of 7 elements: pre-crisis preparation, a disaster or large scale incident, defusing, critical incident stress debriefing, one-on-one crisis intervention/counseling, family/organizational crisis intervention, and follow-up/referral mechanisms.

Critical Infrastructure — Systems, assets, and networks, whether physical or virtual, so vital that the incapacity or destruction of such systems and assets would have a debilitating impact on security, national economic security, national public health or safety, or any combination of those matters. *See* Infrastructure.

Critical Radiant Flux — Description of the amount of heat required to ignite a floor covering specimen in the critical radiant flux test; expressed as Btu per ft^2 (Watts per cm^2).

Critical Rescue and Fire Fighting Access Area (CRFFAA) — Rectangular area surrounding a runway. Its width extends 500 feet (150 m) outward from each side of the runway centerline, and its length extends 3,300 feet (1 100 m) beyond each runway end.

Cross Contamination — (1) Contamination of people, equipment, or the environment outside the hot zone without contacting the primary source of contamination. *Also known as* Secondary Contamination. *See* Contamination, Decontamination, and Hazard-Control Zones. (2) Evidence in one location at the scene that is moved to another location at the scene.

Crossover Line — Pipe that is installed in a bulk storage tank piping system that allows product unloading from either side of the tank.

Crosswind — Wind that is blowing in a direction from the side of an aircraft or foam stream; can affect a foam distribution pattern. *See* Downwind, Headwind, and Wind.

Croup — Common viral infection *Seen* in small children; characterized by spasm of the larynx and resulting upper airway obstruction.

Crow Bar — Prying tool with a blade at either end; one end is significantly curved to provide additional mechanical advantage.

Crowd Control — Limiting access to an emergency scene by curious spectators and other non-emergency personnel.

Crown Fire — Fire that advances from top to top (canopy) of closely spaced trees or shrubs, more or less independent of a surface fire. Crown fires are sometimes classed as running or dependent to distinguish the degree of independence from the surface fire.

Crown Out — Fire that rises from ground level into the tree crowns and advances from treetop to treetop.

Cruising — Driving a vehicle in such a manner that an even speed and engine rpm is maintained. It is best to operate at 200 to 300 rpm below the maximum rpm recommended by the manufacturer.

Crushable Bumpers — Polystyrene foam or fluoroelastomer devices designed to absorb energy by flexing when struck.

Crush Points — Places within the frame of a vehicle that are designed to collapse, crush, deform, and otherwise absorb (not transmit) forces so as to minimize the impact on the passengers.

Crush Syndrome — Potentially fatal condition that occurs as a result of crushing pressure on a part of the body, typically the lower extremities. When blood flow to and from the injured area is absent for four to six hours, the injured tissue begins to die, giving off toxins; a sudden release of pressure allows the toxins to flow into the bloodstream and to have an effect on other bodily organs.

Cryogenics — The study of materials at very low temperatures.

Cryogens — Gases that are converted into liquids by being cooled below -150°F (-101°C). *Also known as* Refrigerated Liquids and Cryogenic Liquid. *See* Cryogenic Liquid Storage Tank and Cryogenic Liquid Tank.

Cryogenic Liquid — *See* Cryogens.

Cryogenic Liquid Storage Tank — Heavily insulated, vacuum-jacketed tanks used to store cryogenic liquids; equipped with safety-relief valves and rupture disks. *See* Cryogen.

Cryogenic Liquid Tank — Cargo tank truck that carries gases that have been liquefied by temperature reduction. *See* Cryogens and Cargo Tank Truck.

CSA — *See* Canadian Standards Association.

CST — *See* Civil Support Team.

CT — Abbreviation used for a measure of toxicity determined by multiplying exposure concentration (C) in ppm by the time of exposure (T) in minutes and expressed as the CT product or ppm per minute.

Cubic Feet per Minute — Measure of a volume of material flowing past or through a specified measuring point.

Cumulonimbus Clouds — Ultimate growth of a cumulus cloud into an anvil-shaped cloud with considerable vertical development, usually with fibrous ice crystal tops, and usually accompanied by lightning, thunder, hail, and strong winds.

Cumulus Clouds — Principal low-cloud type shaped into individual cauliflower-like cells of sharp nonfibrous outline, and having less vertical development than cumulonimbus clouds.

Curb Weight — Weight of an empty fire apparatus off the assembly line with no tools, water, equipment, or passengers.

Curbside — Side of a trailer nearest the curb when it is traveling in a normal forward direction (right-hand side); opposite to roadside.

Curie (Ci) — English System unit of measurement for radioactivity, indicating the number of nuclear decays/disintegrations a radioactive material undergoes in a certain period of time. *See* Becquerel, Radiation (2), and Radioactive Material (RAM).

Curing — (1) Maintaining conditions to achieve proper strength during the hardening of concrete. (2) Manufacturing step in making fire hose; the process of applying heat and pressure to "set" the shape of the tube and to increase its smoothness.

Curling — Method for raising a one-firefighter ladder from a flat rest position in preparation for carrying.

Current — (1) Rate of electrical flow in a conductor; measured in amperes. (2) The horizontal movement of water.

Curriculum — Broad term that refers to the sequence of presentation, the content of what is taught, and the structure of ideas and activities developed to meet the learning needs of learners and achieve desired educational objectives; also the teaching and learning methods involved, how learner attainment of objectives is assessed, and the underlying theory and philosophy of education.

Curriculum Development — Using analysis, design, and evaluation to create a series of presentations that adhere to the four teaching steps (preparation, presentation, application, and evaluation) and address the learning needs of a particular audience or program. *Also known as* Instructional Design.

Curtain Boards — *See* Draft Curtains.

Curtain Door — Door used as a barrier to fire, consisting of interlocking steel plates or of a continuous formed spring steel "curtain." Curtain doors are often mounted in pairs, one door on the inside and the other on the outside of an opening.

Curtain Wall — Non-load-bearing exterior wall attached to the outside of a building with a rigid steel frame. Usually the front exterior wall of a building intended to provide a certain appearance.

Custom Chassis — Truck chassis designed solely for use as a fire or rescue apparatus.

Customer Service — Quality of an organization's relationship with individuals who have contact with the organization. There are internal customers such as the various levels of personnel and trainees, and external customers such as other organizations and the public. Customer service is the way these individuals, personnel, and organizations are treated, and their levels of satisfaction.

Cutters — *See* Powered Hydraulic Shears.

Cutting Tool — Hand or power tool used to cut a specific kind of material.

Cyanogen Agent — *See* Chemical Asphyxiant.

Cyanosis — Blueness of the skin due to insufficient oxygen in the blood.

Cyber Terrorism — Premeditated, politically motivated attack against information, computer systems, computer programs, and data which result in violence against noncombatant targets by sub-national groups or clandestine agents.

Cylinder — (1) Component of a locking mechanism that contains coded information for operating that lock, usually with a key. (2) Air tank portion of a self-contained breathing apparatus.

Cylinder Guard — Metal plate that covers a lock cylinder to prevent forceful removal.

Cylinder Plug — Part of a lock cylinder that receives the key. *Also known as* Key Plug.

Cylinder Pressure Gauge — Gauge attached to the cylinder outlet that indicates the pressure in the cylinder.

Cylinder Shell — External case of a lock cylinder.

Cylindrical Lock — Lock having the lock cylinder contained in the knob. *Also known as* Bored Lock.

D

Damage — Loss, injury, or deterioration caused by the negligence, design, or accident of one person to another in respect to another person's property.

Damage Control Locker — Compartment containing fire fighting/emergency equipment.

Damages — Compensation to a person for any loss, detriment, or injury whether to his person, property, or rights through the unlawful act, omission, or negligence of another.

Damping Mechanism — Structural element designed to control vibration.

Dangerous Cargo Manifest — Invoice of cargo used on ships, containing a list of all hazardous materials on board and their location on the ship.

Dangerous Goods — (1) Any product, substance, or organism included by its nature or by regulation in any of the nine United Nations classifications of hazardous materials. (2) Term used to describe hazardous materials in Canada. (3) Term used in the U.S. and Canada for hazardous materials aboard aircraft. *See* Hazardous Material (1).

Dangerous Goods Guide to Initial Emergency Response (IERG) — Canada's equivalent of the DOT *Emergency Response Guidebook.*

Darcy-Weisbach Method — Technique used to determine pressure loss due to fluid friction in a piping system.

Data — Facts, numbers, and information used as a basis for reasoning, discussion, or calculation. The singular form of the term is *datum.*

Database — Computer software program that serves as an electronic filing cabinet; used to create forms, record and sort information, develop mailing lists, organize libraries, customize telephone and fax lists, and track presentation and program outcomes.

dB — *See* Decibel.

DBH — *See* Diameter at Breast Height.

Deadbolt — Movable part of a deadbolt lock that extends from the lock mechanism into the door frame to secure the door in a locked position.

Dead-End Corridor — Corridor in which egress is possible in only one direction. *See* Egress.

Dead-End Hydrant — Fire hydrant located on a dead-end main that receives water from only one direction.

Dead-End Main — Water main that is not looped and in which water can flow in only one direction.

Dead Fuels — Fuels with no living tissue in which moisture content is governed almost entirely by atmospheric moisture (relative humidity and precipitation), dry-bulb temperature, and solar radiation.

Dead Latch — Sliding pin or plunger that operates as part of a dead-locking latch bolt. *Also known as* Anti-Shim Device.

Dead Load — Weight of the structure, structural members, building components, and any other features permanently attached to the building that are constant and immobile.

Dead Locking — *See* Latch Bolt.

Deadman Switch — Foot pedal located below the aerial device control pedestal. This pedal must be depressed in order for the aerial device controls to be operable.

Dead-Man Valve — Spring-loaded valve that controls the flow of fuel from the loading rack to the tank vehicle or rail tank car. It is designed to shut off immediately when the operator releases the handle.

Dead Shore — Shore that is applied vertically to support a horizontal load; for example, an unstable floor. *Also known as* Vertical Shore.

Decibel (dB) — (1) Unit used to express relative difference in power between acoustic and electrical signals; equal to 10 times the logarithm of the ratio of the two levels. (2) Unit for expressing the relative intensity of sounds on a scale from 0 for the least perceptible sound to about 130 for the average pain level; degree of loudness.

Deck — Continuous, horizontal surface (floor) running the length of a vessel; some may not extend the whole length of a vessel, but they always reach from one side to the other. *See* Boat Deck, Main Deck, Poop Deck, Tank Top, Tween Deck, Upper Deck, and Weather Deck.

Deck Gun — *See* Turret Pipe.

Deckhead — *See* Overhead (1).

Decking — *See* Sheathing (2).

Deck Pipe — *See* Turret Pipe.

Declared Emergency — Aircraft emergency in which the aircraft crew is aware that there is a problem and notifies the airport authorities of the emergency before they prepare to land.

Decoding — Translating a message to find its meaning.

Decomposition — Chemical change in which a substance breaks down into two or more simpler substances. Result of oxygen acting on a material that results in a change in the material's composition. Oxidation occurs slowly, sometimes resulting in the rusting of metals. *See* Oxidation and Pyrolysis.

Decon — *See* Decontamination.

Decontaminate — To remove a foreign substance that could cause harm; frequently used to describe removal of a hazardous material from a person, clothing, or area.

Decontamination — Process of removing a hazardous foreign substance from a person, clothing, or area. *Also known as* Decon. *See* Contamination, Decontamination Corridor, Definitive Decontamination, Emergency Decontamination, Gross Decontamination, Mass Decontamination, Patient Decontamination, and Technical Decontamination.

Decontamination Corridor — Area where decontamination is conducted. *See* Decontamination.

Dedicated Railcar — Car set aside by the product manufacturer to transport a specific product. The name of the product is painted on the car.

Deep-Seated Fire — Fire that has moved deep into piled or bulk materials such as hay, baled cotton, or paper.

Defamation — Publication of anything that injures the good name or reputation of a person or brings disrepute to a person. *See* Libel and Slander.

Defendant — Party accused of alleged wrongdoing in a civil proceeding, or the party accused of a felony (indictable offense) in a criminal proceeding.

Defense Mechanisms — Systems, such as nasal hair, mucus, or cilia, that protect the body from invasion by foreign particles and injury.

Defensive Fire Attack — Exterior fire attack that is limited to controlling the spread of a fire, with an emphasis on exposure protection. *Also known as* Defensive Attack.

Defensive Mode — Commitment of a fire department's resources to protect exposures when the fire has progressed to a point where an offensive attack is not effective; deploying resources to limit the growth of an emergency incident rather than mitigating it. *See* Defensive Strategy.

Defensive Operations — Operations in which responders seek to confine the emergency to a given area without directly contacting the hazardous materials involved. *See* Nonintervention Operations and Offensive Operations.

Defensive Strategy — Overall plan for incident control established by the incident commander that involves protection of exposures as opposed to aggressive, offensive intervention. *See* Nonintervention Strategy, Offensive Strategy, and Strategy.

Defibrillation — Process of stopping very rapid contractions of the heart (fibrillation) by delivering a direct electric shock to the patient's heart with a device called a defibrillator. This is a common emergency procedure that is administered by paramedics and other specially trained emergency medical technicians.

Definitive Decontamination — Decontaminating further after technical decontamination; may involve sampling and/or lab testing and is usually conducted by hospital staff or other experts. *See* Decontamination and Technical Decontamination.

Deflagration — (1) Chemical reaction producing vigorous heat and sparks or flame and moving through the material (as black or smokeless powder) at less than the speed of sound. A major difference among explosives is the speed of this reaction. (2) Intense burning, a characteristic of Class B explosives.

Deformation — (1) Alteration of form or shape. (2) Projection on the surface of reinforcing bars to prevent the bars from slipping through the concrete. *Also known as* Set.

Defusing — Informal discussion with incident responders conducted after the incident has been terminated, either at the scene or after the units have returned to quarters. During the discussion commanders address possible chemical and medical exposure information, identify damaged equipment and apparatus that require immediate attention, identify unsafe operating procedures, assign information gathering responsibilities to prepare for the post-incident analysis, and reinforce the positive aspects of the incident.

Degradation — *See* Chemical Degradation.

Dehydration — Process of removing water or other fluids.

Delayed Treatment — Classification for patients with serious but not life threatening injuries; these patients may need additional care but may not need that care immediately.

Delegation — Providing subordinates with the authority, direction, and resources needed to complete an assignment.

Deluge Sprinkler System — Fire-suppression system that consists of piping and open sprinklers. A fire detection system is used to activate the water or foam control valve. When the system activates, the extinguishing agent is expelled from all sprinkler heads in the designated area. *See* Dry-Pipe Sprinkler System, Preaction Sprinkler System, and Wet-Pipe Sprinkler System.

Deluge Valve — Automatic valve used to control water to a deluge sprinkler system.

Demand-Type Breathing Apparatus — Breathing apparatus with a regulator that supplies air to the facepiece only when the wearer inhales or when the bypass valve has been opened; no longer approved for fire fighting or IDLH situations. *Also known as* Negative-Pressure Breathing Apparatus.

Demand Valve — Valve within the self-contained breathing apparatus regulator that lets breathing air pass to the wearer when the wearer inhales.

Demobilization Unit — Functional unit within the planning section of an incident management system; responsible for assuring orderly, safe, and efficient demobilization of resources committed to the incident.

Democratic Leadership — Leadership style in which the leader is team-oriented and gives authority to the group; the group makes suggestions and decisions. *Also known as* Participative Leadership.

Demography — The statistical study of human population, especially the size, density, distribution, and other vital statistics of a group of people.

Demonstration — Instructional /teaching method in which the instructor/educator actually performs a task or skill, usually explaining the procedure step-by-step.

Density — Mass per unit of volume of a substance. The density of any substance is obtained by dividing the mass by the volume.

Deodorization — Action taken following a fire to remove smoke odors from an atmosphere.

Department of Defense (DoD) — Administrative body of the executive branch of the U.S. Federal Government that encompasses all branches of the U.S. military.

Department of Energy (DOE) — Administrative body of the executive branch of the U.S. Federal Government that manages national nuclear research and defense programs, including the storage of high-level nuclear waste.

Department of Homeland Security (DHS) — U.S. agency that has the missions of preventing terrorist attacks, reducing vulnerability to terrorism, and minimizing damage from potential attacks and natural disasters; includes the Federal Emergency Management Agency (FEMA), U.S. Coast Guard (USCG), and Office for Domestic Preparedness (ODP).

Department of Housing and Urban Development (HUD) — U.S. government agency that oversees home ownership, low-income housing assistance, fair housing laws, homelessness, aid for distressed neighborhoods, and housing development programs.

Department of Justice (DOJ) — Administrative body of the executive branch of the U.S. Federal Government that assigns primary responsibility for operational response to threats or acts of terrorism within U.S. territory to the Federal Bureau of Investigation (FBI). *See* Terrorism.

Department of Labor (DOL) — Administrative body of the executive branch of the U.S. Federal Government that is responsible for overseeing labor policy, regulation, and enforcement.

Department of Transportation (DOT) — U.S. federal agency that is responsible for transportation policy, regulation, and enforcement; regulates the transportation of hazardous materials. *Formerly known as* Interstate Commerce Commission.

Dependable Lift — Height a column of water may be lifted in sufficient quantity to provide a reliable fire flow. Lift may be raised through a hard suction hose to a pump, taking into consideration the atmospheric pressure and friction loss within the hard suction hose; dependable lift is usually considered to be 14.7 feet (4.48 m). *See* Lift.

Deposition — Process during which the witness answers questions under oath posed by the attorneys for each party; sworn testimony taken out of court. Not specifically delineated as a separate portion of discovery in Canada.

Depression — Emotional state in which there are extreme feelings of sadness, dejection, lack of worth, and emptiness. Mild symptoms include lack of motivation and inability to concentrate; more serious symptoms include sleeping and eating disorders and other severe changes of bodily functions, such as inactivity.

Depth of Calcination — Measurement of the depth of fire damage in gypsum board.

Depth of Char — Measurement of the depth of fire damage in wood.

Depth of Field — Range that is in focus both in front of and behind the subject of a photograph.

Dermis — True skin; a dense, elastic layer of fibrous tissue that lies beneath the epidermis (the outer skin). It is laced with blood vessels, nerve fibers, and receptor organs for sensations of touch, pain, heat, and cold. It also contains muscular elements, hair follicles, and oil and sweat glands.

Descent Device — Friction or mechanical device used to control a descent down a fixed line or to lower a load.

Desiccant — Substance that has a high affinity for water and is used as a drying agent.

Designated Employee — Employee trained to use portable fire extinguishers or small hoselines to fight incipient fires in the employee's immediate work area.

Designated Length — Length marked on the ladder.

Design Build — Concept involving the use of a single organization to both design and build a facility, rather than engaging separate firms to perform these activities; may be used to refer a design-build project or a design-build firm.

Detailed View — Additional, close-up information shown on a particular section of a larger drawing. *See* Elevation View, Plan View, and Sectional View.

Det Cord —*See* Detonator Cord.

Detector Tube — *See* Colorimetric Tube.

Detention Window — Window designed to prevent exit through the opening.

Deterrence — Discouraging or preventing someone from acting in a hazardous manner, or preventing a hazardous incident from happening; maintenance of legal powers for the purpose of inhibiting hazardous actions.

Detonation — (1) Supersonic thermal decomposition, which is accompanied by a shock wave in the decomposing material. (2) Explosion with an energy front that travels faster than the speed of sound. (3) High explosive that decomposes extremely rapidly, almost instantaneously. *See* Explosive (1) and (2) and High Explosive.

Detonator — Device used to trigger less sensitive explosives, usually composed of a primary explosive; for example, a blasting cap. Detonators may be initiated mechanically, electrically, or chemically. *Also known as* Initiator. *See* Detonation.

Detonator Cord — (1) Flexible explosive tape put around the outer edge of the inside of the canopy of some military aircraft to separate the Plexiglas® from the metal frame, in order to facilitate rescue or egress. (2) A flexible cord containing a center core of high explosive used to detonate other explosives. *Also known as* Det Cord.

Deutsches Institut fur Normung (DIN) — Nongovernmental organization established in Germany to develop consensus standards to ensure quality and conformity in materials, testing, and processes; similar to ANSI in the U.S..

Dewar — All-metal container designed for the movement of small quantities of cryogenic liquids within a facility; not designed or intended to meet Department of Transportation (DOT) requirements for the transportation of cryogenic materials. *See* Container and Cryogen.

Dewatering — Process of removing water from a vessel.

Dew Point — Temperature at which the water vapor in air precipitates as droplets of liquid.

DFDR — *See* Digital Flight Data Recorder.

DHS — *See* Department of Homeland Security.

Diabetes Mellitus — Complex disorder that is mainly caused by the failure of the pancreas to release enough insulin into the body; high levels of sugar in the blood and urine. Symptoms include the need to urinate often, increased thirst, weight loss, and increased appetite.

Diameter at Breast Height (DBH) — Means by which the relative size of trees is expressed. If a tree trunk measured at breast height is 20 inches (508 mm) or more in diameter, it is considered a large tree. A tree with a DBH of less than that is considered a small tree.

Diaphoresis — Profuse sweating that occurs with a fever, physical exertion, exposure to heat, or stress.

Diaphragm — Dome-shaped muscle that separates the chest cavity from the abdominal cavity. This muscle has holes through which pass the large artery (aorta), esophagus, and large vein (vena cava).

Diatomaceous Earth — Light siliceous material consisting chiefly of the skeletons of diatoms (minute unicellular algae); used especially as an absorbent or filter. *Also known as* Diatomite.

Diatomite — *See* Diatomaceous Earth.

Dicing — Ventilation exit opening created by making multiple cuts in the sheathing perpendicular to the ridge beam.

Dielectric — Material that is a poor conductor of electricity; usually applied to tools that are used to handle energized electrical wires or equipment. *See* Conductor.

Dielectric Heating — Heating that occurs as a result of the action of pulsating either direct current (DC) or alternating current (AC) at high frequency on a nonconductive material.

Differential Dry-Pipe Valve — Valve in a dry-pipe sprinkler system in which relatively low air pressure is used to hold the valve closed and thus hold the water back.

Differential Manometer — Device whose primary application is to reflect the difference in pressures between two points in a system.

Diffuser — Equipment used for breaking up the stream of water from a fire hydrant. Also effective for diverting the flow of debris from the hydrant water stream.

Diffusion — (1) Process by which oxygen moves from alveoli to the blood cells in the thin-walled capillaries. (2) Process by which hazardous materials pass through protective clothing.

Digester — Large, circular container used at sewage treatment plants to cleanse raw sewage.

Digital Flight Data Recorder (DFDR) — Digital recording device on large civilian aircraft to record data such as aircraft airspeed, altitude, heading, and acceleration, in order to be used as an aid to accident investigation. *Also known as* Black Box.

Digital Memory Card — Storage device used on DSLR cameras and other digital devices to store captured images and data files; can be removed from the camera and easily uploaded to a computer. Also allows for immediate review, editing, and/or deletion of captured images.

Digital Single-Lens Reflex (DSLR) Camera — Digital camera that uses a mechanical mirror system and prism to direct light from the lens to an optical viewfinder on the back of the camera.

Dike — (1) Temporary dam constructed of readily available objects to obstruct the flow of a shallow stream of water to a depth that will facilitate drafting operations. (2) Temporary or permanent barrier that contains or directs the flow of liquids.

Diked Area — Area surrounding storage tanks or loading racks that is designed to retain spilled fuel and fire-extinguishing agents such as water and foam. *See* Nondiked Area.

Dilution — Application of water to a water-soluble material to reduce the hazard. *See* Dissolution and Water Solubility.

Dimensioning — Indicating or determining size and position in space relative to existing conditions.

Dimpled — Depressed or indented, as on a metal surface to aid in gripping.

DIN — *See* Deutsches Institut fur Normung.

Dip Tube — Tube installed in a pressurized container from the top to the bottom to permit expelling of the contents, liquid or solid, out of the top of the container.

Direct Attack — (1) In structural fire fighting, an attack method that involves the discharge of water or a foam stream directly onto the burning fuel. *See* Attack Methods (1). (2) In wildland fire fighting, an operation where action is taken directly on burning fuels by applying an extinguishing agent to the edge of the fire or close to it. *See* Attack Methods (2).

Direct-Connect Alarms — Alarm systems that are connected directly to a local police or fire department from the protected property.

Direct Current (DC) Circuit — Electrical circuit in which the current moves through the circuit in only one direction.

Direct Injection — Application method where foam concentrate is injected directly into the water stream at the pump before it enters the hoseline. *See* Semisubsurface Injection and Subsurface Injection.

Directional Anchor — Anchor that is capable of supporting a load in only a limited direction.

Directional Foam Spray Nozzle — Foam delivery device that consists of a small foam nozzle used to protect areas such as loading racks by applying the extinguishing agent onto the surface beneath tanker trucks.

Directive — Authoritative instrument or order issued by a superior officer.

Direct Lines — Phone lines leased or dedicated to a specific purpose used as point-to- point communication. These lines are not connected to the public telephone network and therefore do not have a dial tone. *Also known as* Private Lines.

Direct Loss — Loss caused directly by a fire; can be either primary damage or secondary damage.

Director — Title for individuals responsible for command of a branch in an incident management system.

Direct Order — Command or assignment to a subordinate that specifies the desired behavior or outcome.

Directory — Computer table of identifiers and references to the corresponding items or data; for example a computer listing of files stored on a hard drive.

Direct Pumping System — Water supply system supplied directly by a system of pumps rather than elevated storage tanks.

Direct Reading Conductivity Meter — Device designed to directly measure the specific conductivity of a solution and provide a reading on a display.

Dirty Bomb — *See* Radiological Dispersal Device (RDD).

Disability — According to the *Americans with Disabilities Act (ADA)*, a person has a disability if he or she has a physical or mental impairment that substantially limits a major life activity.

Disaster Recovery Center (DRC) — Facility established in a centralized location within or near the disaster area at which disaster victims (individuals, families, or businesses) apply for disaster aid.

Discharge Outlet, Type I — Foam delivery device that conducts and delivers finished foam onto the burning surface of a liquid without submerging it or agitating the surface; no longer manufactured and considered obsolete, but may still be found in some fixed-site applications.

Discharge Outlet, Type II — Foam delivery device that delivers finished foam onto the surface of a burning liquid, partially submerges the foam into the surface, and produces limited agitation on the surface of the burning liquid.

Discharge Outlet, Type III — Foam delivery device that delivers finished foam in a manner that causes it to fall directly onto the surface of the burning liquid and does so in a way that causes general agitation; includes master streams and handlines.

Discharge Velocity — Linear velocity or rate at which water flows through and travels from an orifice.

Discipline — To maintain order through training and/or the threat or imposition of sanctions; setting and enforcing the limits or boundaries for expected performance.

Discontinuity — Interruption of the typical structure of a weldment, such as inhomogeneity in the mechanical, metallurgical, or physical characteristics of the material or weldment.

Discovery — Means by which the plaintiff (one party) obtains information from the opposing party (defendant) to prove its allegation.

Discrimination — Measure of the extent to which any item in a test is answered more or less successfully by learners who do well or poorly on a test overall, thereby discriminating between them. Ideally, items that do not discriminate would be omitted from revised versions of the test. *Also known as* Discrimination Index.

Discussion — (1) Instructional method in which an instructor generates interaction with and among a group. There are several formats of discussion: guided, conference, case study, role-play, and brainstorming. In each type, it remains the responsibility of the instructor to steer the group discussion or activity to meet lesson objectives. (2) Teaching method by which students contribute to the class session by using their knowledge and experience to provide input. (3) The exchange of ideas between an educator and the audience. (4) Two-way communication between sender and receiver. *See* Case Study and Role-Playing.

Disentanglement — Aspect of vehicle extrication relating to the removal and/or manipulation of vehicle components to allow a properly packaged patient to be removed from the vehicle. Sometimes referred to as *removing the vehicle from the patient*.

Disinfect — Destroy, neutralize, or inhibit the growth of harmful microorganisms.

Dislocation — State of being misaligned; the condition that results when the surfaces of two bones are no longer in proper contact.

Dispatch — (1) To direct fire companies to respond to an alarm. (2) Radio designation for the dispatch center; for example, "Engine 65 to Dispatch, send me a second alarm."

Dispatcher — Person who works in the telecommunications center and processes information from the public and emergency responders.

Dispatching — Process by which an alarm is received at the telecommunications center, retransmitted to the emergency responders, and acknowledged when received.

Dispersion — Act or process of being spread widely. *See* Engulf (1) and Vapor Dispersion.

Displaced Runway Threshold — Temporary relocation of a runway threshold (beginning or end) because of maintenance or other activity on the runway.

Displacement — (1) Volume or weight of a fluid displaced by a floating body of equal weight. (2) Amount of water forced into the pump, thus displacing air.

Disseminate — To spread about or scatter widely.

Dissipate — To cause to spread out or spread thin to the point of vanishing.

Dissolution — Act or process of dissolving one thing into another, such as dissolving a gas in water. *See* Concentration (2) and Dilution.

Distance Learning — Method of instruction through which the instructors and participants rarely meet face-to-face, but communicate by correspondence, electronic mail (e-mail), radio, and television. *See* Open Learning.

Distention — State of being expanded or swollen, particularly of the abdomen.

Distortion — State of being twisted out of normal or natural shape or position.

Distress — More stress than a person can reasonably be expected to handle; in other words, when stress controls the person.

Distribution System — That part of an overall water supply system that receives the water from the pumping station and delivers it throughout the area to be served.

Distributor Nozzle — Nozzle used to create a broken stream that is usually used on basement fires.

District — *See* Response District.

Diuretic — Product that tends to increase the flow of urine.

Diurnal — (1) Daily; especially pertaining to cyclic actions of the atmosphere that are completed within 24 hours and that recur every 24 hours. (2) A tide pattern that has one high and one low in a 24-hour period.

Diverter Valve — *See* Selector Valve.

Diving Accident Network — Hotline that can advise physicians and rescue personnel about diving mishaps.

Division — NIMS-ICS organizational level having responsibility for operations within a defined geographic area. It is composed of a number of individual units that are assigned to operate within a defined geographical area.

Division of Labor — Subdividing an assignment into its constituent parts in order to equalize the workload and increase efficiency.

Documentation Unit — Functional unit within the planning section of an incident management system; responsible for recording/protecting all documents relevant to the incident.

DoD — *See* Department of Defense.

DOE — *See* Department of Energy.

Dog — To lock levers or bolts and thumbscrews on watertight doors.

Dogs — *See* Pawls.

Dog the Hatches — Close the doors.

DOJ — *See* Department of Justice.

DOL — *See* Department of Labor.

Dollies — *See* Supports.

Domains of Learning — Areas of learning and classification of learning objectives; these are known as the cognitive (knowledge), affective (attitude), and psychomotor (skill performance) learning domains.

Dome Roof — Hemispherical roof assembly, usually supported only at the outer walls of a circular or many-sided structure.

Dome Roof Tank — *See* Cone Roof Storage Tank.

Domestic Consumption — Water consumed from the water supply system by residential and commercial occupancies.

Domineering Attitude — Effect of a decision-making problem in which the leader tries to control every facet of the operation.

Donning Mode — State of positive-pressure SCBA when the donning switch is activated.

Donning Switch — Device on a positive-pressure regulator that, when activated, stops airflow while the unit is being donned. Airflow is resumed with the user's first inhalation.

Donut Roll — Length of hose rolled up for storage and transport.

Door Closer — Mechanical device that closes a door. *Also known as* Self-Closing Door.

Door Hold-Open Device — Mechanical device that holds a door open and releases it upon a signal. Usually a magnetic device used to hold fire or smoke door assemblies in the open position.

Doorjamb — Sides of the doorway opening.

Door/Roof Posts — Structural members that surround the doors and support the roofs of vehicles. *Also known as* Pillars.

Door/Window Schedule — Table that lists the door/window location on a plan, the dimensions of the opening, and any other construction information. *See* Schedule.

Dormitory — Subdivision of residential property classification with structures, or spaces in structures, that provide group sleeping accommodations for more than 16 unrelated people; these occupants are housed in one room or a group of rooms under joint occupancy and single management. These rooms lack individual cooking facilities, and meals may or may not be provided.

Dose — Quantity of a chemical material ingested or absorbed through skin contact; employed in measuring toxicity. *See* Concentration (1) and Lethal Dose, 50 Percent Kill (LD_{50}).

Dosimeter — Detection device used to measure an individual's exposure to an environmental hazard such as radiation or sound.

DOT — *See* Department of Transportation.

DOT 3AA — DOT specification for type and material of steel self-contained breathing apparatus or cascade cylinder construction.

Double-Acting Hydraulic Cylinder — Hydraulic cylinder capable of transmitting force in two directions.

Double Bottom — Extra watertight floor within a vessel above the outer watertight hull; void or tank space between the outer hull of a vessel and the floor of a vessel. *Also known as* Inner Bottom or Tank Top.

Double-Edge Snap Throw — Method of spreading a salvage cover similar to the single-edge snap throw; intended to cover two groupings located on either side of a narrow aisle.

Double Figure-Eight Knot — Knot used to tie ropes of equal diameters together.

Double-Hung Window — Window having two vertically moving sashes.

Doubles — Truck combination consisting of a truck tractor and two semi-trailers coupled together. *Formerly known as* Double-Bottom or Double-Trailer.

Double-Trailer — *See* Doubles.

Doughnut-Shaped Pattern — Ring-shaped fire pattern formed on a floor when a pool of flammable liquid is ignited; the center of the ring is protected from fire damage while the edge of the ring will show a circular demarcation line.

Downstream — (1) Direction of airflow from a high-pressure source to a low-pressure source; for example, when the facepiece is downstream from the air cylinder. (2) Direction in which the current of a moving body of water is flowing.

Downwind — Wind that is blowing in a direction from behind a person or aircraft. *See* Crosswind, Headwind, and Wind.

Downwind Leg — Flight path parallel to the landing runway in the direction opposite to landing.

Dozer — *See* Bulldozer.

Dozer Tender — Ground vehicle (service unit) with personnel capable of maintenance, minor repairs, and limited fueling of bulldozers.

Dozer Transport — Heavy vehicle carrying a bulldozer to an incident.

Draft — (1) Process of acquiring water from a static source and transferring it into a pump that is above the source's level; atmospheric pressure on the water surface forces the water into the pump where a partial vacuum was created. (2) Vertical distance between the water surface and the lowest point of a vessel; depth of water a vessel needs in order to float. Draft varies with the amount of cargo, fuel, and other loads on board. *See* Draft Marks.

Draft Curtains — Noncombustible barriers or dividers hung from the ceiling in large open areas that are designed to minimize the mushrooming effect of heat and smoke and impede the flow of heat. *Also known as* Curtain Boards and Draft Stops.

Draft Marks — Numerals on the ends of a vessel indicating the depth of the vessel in the water. *See* Draft.

Draft Stops — *See* Draft Curtains.

Drafting Operation — *See* Draft.

Drafting Pit — Underground reservoir of water from which to draft for pumper testing; usually located at a training center.

Drag — (1) Procedure of dragging hooks through water to find drowning victims. (2) Rescue procedure for removing victims from a fire area.

Drag Chute — Parachute device installed on some aircraft that is deployed on landing roll to aid in slowing the aircraft to taxi speed.

Drainage Dropout Rate — *See* Drainage Time.

Drainage Time — Amount of time it takes foam to break down or dissolve. *Also known as* Drainage, Drainage Dropout Rate, or Drainage Rate. *See* Quarter-Life.

Drain Valve — (1) Valve on a pump discharge that facilitates the removal of pressure from a hoseline after the discharge has been closed. (2) Valve on an elevated waterway system to facilitate the drainage of water from the system before stowing.

Drawn to Scale — Dimensions that are reduced proportionally on construction plans to the actual size of the building or component. *See* Construction Plan.

DRC — *See* Disaster Recovery Center.

Dressing — Clean or sterile covering applied directly to a wound; used to stop bleeding and to prevent contamination of the wound.

Drift Smoke — Smoke that has been transported from its point of origin and in which convective, columnar motion no longer dominates.

Drill — Exercise conducted to practice and/or evaluate training already received; the process of skill maintenance.

Drill Schedule — Calendar for training sessions in manipulative skills for firefighters or fire companies.

Drill Tower — Tall fire training structure, normally more than three stories high, used by training personnel to develop realistic fire service situations, especially for ladder and rope evolutions. *Also known as* Tower.

Driver — (1) Engine or motor used to turn a pump. (2) *See* Fire Apparatus Driver/Operator.

Driver/Operator — *See* Fire Apparatus Driver/Operator.

Driver Reaction Distance — Distance a vehicle travels while a driver is transferring the foot from the accelerator to the brake pedal after perceiving the need for stopping.

Driver's Side — Side of a vehicle that is on the same side as the steering wheel.

Drive Train — *See* Power Train.

Drivewheel Horsepower — Power available at the wheels to move the vehicle.

Drop — To drop water or retardant from an aircraft.

Drop Bar — Metal or wooden bar that serves as a locking device when placed or dropped into brackets across a swinging door.

Drop-Forged Coupling — Coupling made by raising and dropping a drop hammer onto a block of metal as it rests on a forging die, thus forming the metal into the desired shape.

Drop Frame — Two-level frame section of a trailer that provides proper coupler height at the forward end and a lower height for the remainder of the length.

Drop Height — Most effective and safest altitude of an aircraft when fire-extinguishing agents are dropped on wildland fires.

Droplet Contact — Means of transmitting a communicable disease indirectly by spray droplets from an infected person's coughing or sneezing.

Drop Panel — Type of concrete floor construction in which the portion of the floor above each column is dropped below the bottom level of the rest of the slab, increasing the floor thickness at the column.

Drop Zone — Target area for air tankers, helicopters, and cargo dropping.

Drowning Machine — Colloquial term for the convection currents resulting when water floods over a low-head dam.

Dry Adiabatic Lapse Rate — Rate of decrease in temperature of a mass of dry air as it is lifted adiabatically through an atmosphere in hydrostatic equilibrium.

Dry Air Mass — Portion of the atmosphere that has a relatively low dew point temperature and where the formation of clouds, fog, or precipitation is unlikely.

Dry-Barrel Hydrant — Fire hydrant that has its operating valve at the water main rather than in the barrel of the hydrant. When operating properly, there is no water in the barrel of the hydrant when it is not in use. These hydrants are used in areas where freezing may occur.

Dry Bulk Cargo Tank — Cargo tank truck that carries small, granulated, solid materials; generally does not carry hazardous materials, but in some cases may carry fertilizers or plastic products that can burn and release toxic products of combustion. *See* Cargo Tank Truck.

Dry Bulk Carrier — Cargo tank that carries small, granulated, solid materials; generally does not carry hazardous materials, but in some cases may carry fertilizers or plastic products that can burn and release toxic products of combustion.

Dry Bulk Terminal — Facility equipped to handle dry goods, such as coal or grain, that are stored in tanks and holds on a vessel. *See* Bulk Terminal.

Dry Chemical — (1) Any one of a number of powdery extinguishing agents used to extinguish fires; the most common include sodium or potassium bicarbonate, monoammonium phosphate, and potassium chloride. (2) Extinguishing system that uses dry chemical powder as the primary extinguishing agent; often used to protect areas containing volatile flammable liquids.

Dry Dock — Enclosed area into which a vessel floats but where water is then removed, leaving the vessel dry for repairs, cleaning, or construction.

Dry Foam — Foam that has a very high air-to-foam solution ratio. This foam will cling to horizontal surfaces.

Dry Hoseline — Hoseline without water in it; an uncharged hoseline.

Dry Hydrant — (1) Permanently installed pipe that has pumper suction connections installed at static water sources to speed drafting operations. (2) Hydrant that is permanently out of service; these may be found in old abandoned complexes or similar structures. It is important to make a distinction between these two uses of the term.

Dry Lightning Storm — Lightning storm during which little or no rain reaches the ground.

Dry-Pipe Sprinkler System — Fire-suppression system that consists of closed sprinklers attached to a piping system that contains air under pressure. When a sprinkler activates, air is released, activating the water or foam control valve and filling the piping with extinguishing agent. Dry systems are often installed in areas subject to freezing. *See* Deluge Sprinkler System, Preaction Sprinkler System, and Wet-Pipe Sprinkler System.

Dry Powder — Extinguishing agent suitable for use on combustible metal fires.

Dry Standpipe System — (1) Standpipe system that has closed water supply valves or that lacks a fixed water supply. (2) Any of several standpipe systems in which the piping contains water only when actually being used.

Dry Thunderstorm — Storm, including lightning, during which little or no rain reaches the ground.

Drywall — System of interior wall finish using sheets of gypsum board and taped joints. *See* Wallboard.

DSLR — *See* Digital Single-Lens Reflex Camera.

Dual-Issue Leadership — Leadership style in which the leader has a high degree of concern for both workers and production.

Dual Pumping — Operation where a strong hydrant is used to supply two pumpers by connecting the pumpers intake-to-intake. The second pumper receives the excess water not being pumped by the first pumper, which is directly connected to the water supply source. Sometimes incorrectly referred to as *tandem pumping*.

Duct — (1) Tube or passage that confines and conducts airflow throughout the aircraft for pressurization, air conditioning, etc. (2) Channel or enclosure, usually of sheet metal, used to move heating and cooling air through a building. (3) Hollow pathways used to move air from one area to another in ventilation systems.

Ductile — Capable of being shaped, bent, or drawn out.

Due Course of Law — *See* Due Process.

Due Process — Conduct of legal proceedings according to established rules and principles for the protection and enforcement of private rights, including notice and the right to a fair hearing before a tribunal with the power to decide the case. *Also known as* Due Course of Law or Due Process of Law. *See* Due Process Clause.

Due Process Clause — Constitutional provision that prohibits the government from unfairly or arbitrarily depriving a person of life, liberty, or property. *See* Due Process.

Due Process of Law — *See* Due Process.

Duff — Matted, partly decomposed leaves, twigs, and bark beneath the litter of freshly fallen twigs, needles, and leaves lying under trees and brush.

Dummy Coupler — Fitting used to seal the opening in an air brake hose connection (gladhands) when the connection is not in use; a dust cap.

Dump Line — *See* Waste Line.

Dunnage — Loose packing material (usually wood boards and wedges) that is placed around cargo in a vessel's hold to support, protect, or prevent it from moving while the vessel is at sea.

Duplex Occupancy — Two-family dwelling in which the families live side by side; one family occupies the left half of the structure and the other occupies the right half.

Durable Agents — *See* Gelling Agents.

Dust — Solid particle that is formed or generated from solid organic or inorganic materials by reducing its size through mechanical processes such as crushing, grinding, drilling, abrading, or blasting.

Dust Devil — *See* Whirlwind.

Dust Explosion — Rapid burning (deflagration), with explosive force, of any combustible dust. Dust explosions generally consist of two explosions: a small explosion or shock wave creates additional dust in an atmosphere, causing the second and larger explosion.

Dutchman — Extra fold placed along the length of a section of hose as it is loaded, so that its coupling rests in proper position.

Duty — (1) Obligation that one has by law or contract. (2) Fire-related responsibility assigned to a member by the fire brigade organizational statement.

Dye-Penetrant Testing — Form of nondestructive testing in which the surface of the test material is saturated with a dye or fluorescent penetrant, and a developer is applied. Dyes bleed visibly to the surface indicating defects; fluorescents show the defective areas under ultraviolet light.

Dynamic — Amount of stretch built into a rope. Dynamic ropes have a large amount of stretch, in order to reduce the shock on the climber and anchor systems; they are used for recreational climbing, where long falls may occur.

Dynamic Load — Loads that involve motion. They include the forces arising from wind, moving vehicles, earthquakes, vibration, or falling objects, as well as the addition of a moving load force to an aerial device or structure. *Also known as* Shock Loading.

Dynamic Rope — Rope that stretches farther than a static rope stretches.

Dynamic Stress — Stress imposed on an aerial device while it is in motion, resulting from a dynamic load.

Dyspnea — Painful or difficult breathing; rapid, shallow respirations.

Dzus Fastener — Trade name given to a half-turn fastener with a slotted head. This type of fastener is used on engine cowlings, cover plates, and access panels throughout the aircraft.

E

EAP — *See* Employee Assistance Program.

Eave — Lower border of a roof that overhangs the wall.

Ebb Tide — Falling tide.

EBS — Emergency building shores.

EBSS — *See* Emergency Breathing Support System.

Eccentric Load — Load perpendicular to the cross section of the structural member, but which does not pass through the center of the cross section. An eccentric load creates stresses that vary across the cross section, and may be both tensile and compressive.

ECO — *See* Entry Control Officer.

Economic Factor — Includes expenses caused by the loss of tools, apparatus, equipment, manpower, property, and systems, in addition to legal expenses.

Economizer — Assembly of coils in a vessel's stack (chimney), designed to transfer heat rising up the stack to water within the tubes. *See* Fiddley and Stack.

Edema — Condition in which fluid escapes into the body tissues and causes local or generalized swelling.

Education — Process of teaching, instructing, or training individuals in new skills or additional knowledge, or preparing individuals for some kind of action or activity; what teachers do to bring about learning in their students. May or may not involve formal classroom instruction.

Educational Objective — *See* Behavioral Objective and Learning Objective.

Educator — Person charged with the responsibilities of conducting program presentations, directing the instructional process, teaching and demonstrating skills, imparting new information, leading discussions, and evaluating mastery to ensure that learning has taken place.

Eduction — Process used to mix foam concentrate with water in a nozzle or proportioner; concentrate is drawn into the water stream by the Venturi method. *Also known as* Induction. *See* Venturi Principle.

Eductor — (1) Portable proportioning device that injects a liquid, such as foam concentrate, into the water flowing through a hoseline or pipe. *See* Foam Proportioner and Proportioning. (2) Syphon used to remove water from flooded basements. (3) Venturi device that uses water pressure to draw foam concentrate into a water stream for mixing; also enables a pump to draw water from an auxiliary source. *Also known as* Inductor.

EEO — *See* Equal Employment Opportunity.

Efflorescence — White soluble salt crystals consisting of calcium and magnesium sulfates that form as white powder on the surface of masonry walls; caused by water that penetrates the masonry.

Effluent — Fluid that flows from a pipe or similar outlet; most commonly used to describe waste products from industrial processes.

Egress — (1) Place or means of exiting a structure or vehicle. (2) Escape or evacuation. *See* Access, Exit, and Means of Egress.

EIFS — *See* Exterior Insulation and Finish Systems.

Ejection Seat — Aircraft seat capable of being ejected in an emergency to catapult the occupant clear of the aircraft.

EKG — *See* Electrocardiogram.

Elastomer — Generic term for the a group of synthetic rubber-like materials such as butyl rubber, neoprene, and silicone rubber used in facepiece seals, low-pressure hoses, and similar SCBA components.

Electric Arc — Visible discharge of electricity across a gap or between electrodes.

Electric Fence — Livestock-retaining fence that uses an electric current to deliver a shock, in order to discourage animals from trying to escape.

Electrical Burns — Burns caused by contact with electrical current or power, such as high-power wires or lightning.

Electrical Heat Energy — Heat energy that is electrical in origin; includes resistance heating, dielectric heating, heat from arcing, and heat from static electricity. Poorly maintained electrical appliances, exposed wiring, and lightning are sources of electrical heat energies.

Electrical Service — Conductor and equipment for delivering energy from the electrical supply system to the wiring system of the premises.

Electrical Shock — Injury caused by electricity passing through the body; severity of injury depends upon the path the current takes, the amount of current, and the resistance of the skin.

Electrical Systems — Wiring systems designed to distribute electricity throughout a building or vehicle.

Electrocardiogram (EKG) — Test used to observe the function of the heart. *Also known as* EKG.

Electrode — Conductor used to establish electrical contact in a circuit.

Electrolysis — Chemical change, especially decomposition of water and other inorganic compounds in a water solution (electrolyte), when an electric current is passed through the substance.

Electrolyte — (1) Substance that dissociates into ions in solution or when fused, thereby becoming electrically conducting. (2) Energy component within the human body that can be lost through sweating.

Electromotive Force (EMF) — *See* Voltage.

Electron — Minute component of an atom that possesses a negative charge.

Electronic Bulletin Board — Computer application that allows network users to communicate in specific subject areas, such as fire safety, education, public safety, health, or travel. Users can post messages, and then other users of the bulletin board can respond.

Element — Most simple substance that cannot be separated into more simple parts by ordinary means.

Elevated Master Stream — Fire stream in excess of 350 gpm (1 400 L/min) that is deployed from the tip of an aerial device.

Elevated Storage — Water storage reservoir located above the level of the system it is being used to supply, in order to take advantage of head pressure.

Elevated Temperature Material — Material that when offered for transportation or transported in bulk packaging is (a) in a liquid phase and at temperatures at or above 212°F (100°C), (b) intentionally heated at or above their liquid phase flash points of 100°F (38°C), and (c) in a solid phase and at a temperature at or above 464°F (240°C). *See* Bulk Packaging, Elevated Temperature Materials Carrier, and Flash Point.

Elevated Temperature Materials Carrier — Cargo tank truck or cargo truck carrying large metal pots that transport elevated-temperature materials.

Elevating Master Stream Device — *See* Water Tower.

Elevating Platform — Work platform attached to the end of an articulating or telescoping aerial device.

Elevating Water Device — Articulating or telescoping aerial device added to a fire department pumper to enable the unit to deploy elevated master stream devices; these aerial devices range from 30 to 75 feet (9 m to 23 m) in height.

Elevation — (1) Height of a point above sea level or some other datum point. (2) Drawing or orthographic view of any of the vertical sides of a structure, or vertical views of interior walls.

Elevation Cylinder — Hydraulic cylinders used to lift the aerial device from its bed to a working position. *Also known as* Hoisting Cylinder.

Elevation Loss — *See* Elevation Pressure.

Elevation Pressure — Gain or loss of pressure in a hoseline due to a change in elevation. *Also known as* Elevation Loss.

Elevation View — Architectural drawing that shows the vertical view of a building, including floors, building height, and grade of surrounding ground. *See* Detailed View, Plan View, and Sectional View.

Elevator — (1) Hinged, movable control surface at the rear of the horizontal stabilizer of an aircraft. It is attached to the control wheel or stick and is used to control the pitch up or down or to hold the aircraft in level flight. (2) Passenger-carrying car in a multistory building. (3) Tall structure used to store grain or feed at an agricultural site.

Elliptical — (1) Large, cylindrical, oblong water tank that is used on tankers or tenders. (2) Having the shape of an ellipse; an elliptical cross section is frequently used for the tank-on-tank vehicles.

ELT — *See* Emergency Locator Transmitter.

Embezzlement Fire — Type of concealment fire designed to cover a "paper trail" of financial documents that incriminate the arsonist.

Embolism — Sudden blocking of an artery or vein by a clot or foreign material that has been carried by the blood.

Emergency — Sudden or unexpected event or group of events that require immediate action to mitigate.

Emergency Breathing Support System (EBSS) — Escape-only respirator that provides sufficient self-contained breathing air to permit the wearer to safely exit the hazardous area; usually integrated into an airline supplied-air respirator system.

Emergency Decontamination — Removing contamination on individuals in potentially life-threatening situations with or without the formal establishment of a decontamination corridor. *See* Decontamination and Decontamination Corridor.

Emergency Lighting System — (1) System of interior and exterior low-power incandescent and/or fluorescent lights that are designed to assist passengers in locating and using aircraft emergency exits, but that are not bright enough to assist aircraft rescue and fire fighting personnel in carrying out search and rescue operations. (2) Battery-operated floodlights in a building that are designed to activate when normal power supply is interrupted.

Emergency Locator Transmitter (ELT) — Radio transmitter carried by most aircraft. The radio is activated by impact forces; once activated, the ELT transmits a variable tone on emergency frequencies to aid in location of the accident site.

Emergency Management — Process of managing all types of emergencies and disasters by coordinating the actions of numerous agencies through all phases of disaster or emergency activity.

Emergency Medical Services (EMS) — Initial medical evaluation/treatment provided to employees and others who become ill or are injured. These services may be provided by an in-house emergency response team or by an outside provider.

Emergency Medical Technician (EMT) — Professional-level provider of basic life support emergency medical care. Requires certification by some authority.

Emergency Operations — Activities involved in responding to the scene of an incident and performing assigned duties in order to mitigate the emergency.

Emergency Operations Center (EOC) — Facility that houses communications equipment and staff that are used to coordinate the response to an emergency.

Emergency-Relief Device — Device that is designed to relieve pressure on a vessel or container to prevent over-pressurization; may be a rupture disk, relief valve, or similar device. *See* Rupture Disk.

Emergency Responder — Qualified member of a fire and emergency services organization that provides search and rescue, fire suppression, medial, hazardous materials, or specialized protection services. The organization may be publicly or privately managed and funded.

Emergency Response Guidebook (ERG) — Manual that aids emergency response and inspection personnel in identifying hazardous materials placards and labels. It also gives guidelines for initial actions to be taken at hazardous materials incidents. Developed jointly by Transport Canada (TC), U.S. Department of Transportation (DOT), and the Secretariat of Transport and Communications of Mexico (SCT). *Formerly known as* North American Emergency Response Guidebook (NAERG).

Emergency Response Organization — Fire brigade or emergency medical response team.

Emergency Response Plan — Document that contains information on the actions that may be taken by a governmental jurisdiction to protect people and property before, during, and after an emergency.

Emergency Resource List — Directory held by a local jurisdiction that includes contact information for specific equipment not normally carried in the jurisdiction's inventory; should include agreements, contact numbers and equipment information. Jurisdictions should contract with more than one company for equipment, to provide redundancy in case the primary contractor is unable to supply the needed resource.

Emergency Traffic — Urgent radio traffic; a request for other units to clear the radio waves for an urgent message. *Also known as* Priority Traffic.

Emergency Transportation System for the Chemical Industry (SETIQ) — Emergency response center for Mexico. *See* Canadian Transport Emergency Centre (CANUTEC) and Chemical Transportation Emergency Center (CHEMTREC®).

Emergency Truck — Van or similar-type vehicle used to carry portable equipment and personnel.

Emergency Valve — Self-closing tank outlet valve. *See* Emergency Valve Operator and Emergency Valve Remote Control.

Emergency Valve Operator — Device used to open and close emergency valves. *See* Emergency Valve and Emergency Valve Remote Control.

Emergency Valve Remote Control — Secondary means, remote from tank discharge openings, for operation in event of fire or other accident. *See* Emergency Valve Operator and Emergency Valve.

Emergency Vehicle Technician (EVT) — Individual trained to perform emergency response vehicle inspections, diagnostic testing, maintenance, repair procedures, and operational testing. The NFPA® recognizes three levels of EVTs.

Emetic — Agent that causes vomiting.

EMF — *See* Electromotive Force.

Empennage — Aircraft tail assembly, including the vertical and horizontal stabilizers, elevators, and rudders.

Emphysema — Lung disease in which there is destruction of the alveoli, resulting in labored breathing and increased susceptibility to infection; a chronic obstructive pulmonary disease.

Employee Assistance Program (EAP) — Program that may be provided by an employer to employees and their families to aid in solving work or personal problems.

Employee Emergency Action Plan — OSHA-required plan that all employers must devise to inform all their employees of how they are to react to a fire or other emergency in the workplace. Employers with more than ten employees must put their plan in writing and keep it available to their employees.

EMS — *See* Emergency Medical Services.

EMT — *See* Emergency Medical Technician.

Emulsifier — Compound that supports one insoluble liquid in suspension in another liquid; for example, foam concentrate that is designed to mix with the fuel that it is covering, break the fuel into small droplets, and encapsulate it. The resulting emulsion is rendered nonflammable. *See* Foam Concentrate.

Emulsion — An insoluble liquid suspended in another liquid. *See* Insoluble.

Enabling Legislation — Legislation that gives appropriate officials the authority to implement or enforce the law.

Enabling Objective — *See* Behavioral Objective and Learning Objective.

Encapsulating — Completely enclosed or surrounded, as in a capsule.

Enclosed Structure — Any structure that may expose occupants to hazards such as trapped heat or accumulations of smoke or toxic gases.

Encoding — Putting a message into words.

Encrypting — Type of data security in which a signal is converted to bits of data, to which an algorithm is then applied.

End Impact — Ultimate goal; a long-term way of evaluating program effectiveness. For the fire and life safety educator, the end impact is the decrease of fires and injuries.

End-of Service-Life Indicator (ESLI) — Visual indicator that alerts the user when the APR canister or cartridge has reached its limit and is no longer providing breathable air.

End-of-Service-Time Indicator (ESTI) — Warning device that alerts the user that the respiratory protection equipment is about to reach its limit and that it is time to exit the contaminated atmosphere; its alarm may be audible, tactile, visual, or any combination thereof.

Endothermic Heat Reaction — Chemical reaction in which a substance absorbs heat energy.

Energizers — Quick, attention-getting exercises that raise the energy level of participants (and perhaps the educator as well), promote readiness for learning, create excitement, overcome the effects of fatigue, and develop a sense of shared fun. *Also known as* Spice.

Energy — Capacity to perform work; occurs when a force is applied to an object over a distance, or when a chemical, biological, or physical transformation is made in a substance.

Energy-Absorbing Liner — Portion of helmet designed to cushion blows to the head.

Engine — Ground vehicle providing specified levels of pumping, water, and hose capacity, and staffed with a minimum number of personnel. *Also known as* Fire Department Pumper.

Engine Company — Group of firefighters assigned to a fire department pumper who are primarily responsible for providing water supply and attack lines for fire extinguishment.

Engineer — (1) Fire protection or fire prevention personnel qualified by professional engineering credentials. (2) A member of the engineering profession. (3) *See* Fire Apparatus Driver/Operator.

Engine House — Firehouse, fire station, or fire hall.

Engine Numbers — For identification, engines of multiengine aircraft are numbered consecutively 1, 2, 3, 4, etc., as seen from the pilot's seat. They are numbered left to right across the aircraft even though some may be mounted on the wings or on the tail of the aircraft.

Engine Pressure — *See* Net Pump Discharge Pressure.

Engulf — (1) Dispersion of material as defined in the General Emergency Behavior Model (GEBMO); an engulfing event occurs when matter and/or energy disperses and forms a danger zone. (2) To flow over and enclose; in the fire service, this refers to being enclosed in flames. *See* Dispersion and Vapor Dispersion.

Enhanced 9-1-1 — Emergency telephone service that provides selective routing, automatic number identification (ANI), and automatic location identification (ALI).

Enhanced Performance Glass (EPG) — Laminated glass that provides higher levels of security as well as additional impact protection and sound proofing.

Enhanced Strike Team — Engine strike team to which a water tender is assigned to operate as part of the team.

Entombed — Condition of being trapped and/or pinned inside a collapsed structure by components of the structure itself.

Entrain — To draw in and transport solid particles or gasses by the flow of a fluid.

Entrainment — The drawing in and transporting of solid particles or gases by the flow of a fluid.

Entry Clothing — Personal protective clothing that is designed for entering into total flame and for specialized work inside industrial furnaces and ovens. *Also known as* Fire Entry Suit.

Entry Control Board — Record-keeping clipboard equipped with a clock, tables, and slots for tallies; used by entry control officers in the United Kingdom, Australia, and New Zealand to keep track of all firefighters wearing SCBA.

Entry Control Officer (ECO) — Command position at a confined space rescue operation responsible for keeping account of rescuers who enter the hazard zone.

Entry Point — Ventilation opening through which replacement air enters the structure; usually the same opening that rescue or attack crews use to enter the structure. *Also known as* Entry Opening.

Envelopment — Attacking key or critical segments around the entire fire perimeter at the same time.

Envenomization — Poisonous effects caused by the bites, stings, or deposits of insects, spiders, snakes, or other poison-carrying animals.

Environment — (1) Circumstances, objects, and conditions by which one is surrounded. (2) The physical area in which an evaluation is done.

Environmental Change — Change in a learner's surroundings, particularly the home or workplace, after a fire and life safety outreach activity. *See* Outreach Activity.

Environmental Lapse Rate — Rate of temperature change with elevation, determined by the vertical distribution of temperature at a given time and place.

Environmental Protection Agency (EPA) — U.S. government agency that creates and enforces laws designed to protect the air, water, and soil from contamination; responsible for researching and setting national standards for a variety of environmental programs.

Environment Canada — Agency responsible for preserving and enhancing the quality of the natural environment (including water, air, and soil quality), conserving Canada's renewable resources, and coordinating environmental policies and programs for the federal government of Canada.

EOC — Emergency operations center; a centrally located facility where information is gathered/disseminated, and response actions are determined during disaster and emergency situations. *Also known as* Command Post or Disaster Operations Center.

EPA — *See* Environmental Protection Agency.

EPDM — *See* Ethylene Propylene Diene Monomer.

Epicenter — Center of a seated explosion, located at the center point of the seismic shock wave created by the explosion.

Epidemic — Occurrence of more cases of disease than expected in a given area, or among a specific group of people, over a particular period of time.

Epilepsy — Chronic brain disorder marked by seizures; usually associated with alteration of consciousness, abnormal motor behavior, and psychic or sensory disturbances.

Equal — In terms of specifying apparatus, it means the same level of quality, standard, performance, or design - but not necessarily identical.

Equal Employment Opportunity (EEO) — Personnel management responsibility to be sensitive to the social, economic, and political needs of a jurisdiction or labor market.

Equal Employment Opportunity Law — Law that applies to protected groups of individuals who have experienced past workplace discrimination.

Equilibrium — When the support provided by a structural system is equal to the applied loads.

Equipment — General term for portable tools or appliances carried on the fire apparatus that are not permanently attached to or part of the apparatus.

Equipment Strip — Removal of essential fire fighting tools and equipment at the fire scene before a pumper proceeds to the water source.

Equivalency — Alternative practices that are acceptable for meeting a minimum level of code mandated fire protection. In prescriptive code practice, equivalencies are difficult to produce; compensatory measures are more common.

ERG — *See Emergency Response Guidebook.*

Escape Route — Pathway to safety; can lead to an already burned area, a previously constructed safety area, a meadow that will not burn, or a natural rocky area that is large enough to allow evacuating personnel to take refuge without being burned. When escape routes deviate from a defined physical path, they must be clearly marked (flagged).

Escape Time — Time required for an individual to exit a hazardous atmosphere without incurring injury or death.

Escape Trunk — Vertical, enclosed shaft with a ladder, providing an escape path for crew stationed in low areas of a vessel.

ESLI — *See* End-of-Service-Life Indicator.

Esophagus — Portion of the digestive tract that lies between the throat and the stomach.

Established Burning — Fire stage in which fuel continues to burn without an external heat source.

ESTI — *See* End-of-Service-Time Indicator.

Ethylene Propylene Diene Monomer (EPDM) — Synthetic, M-class rubber used in single-ply membrane roofs.

Etiologic Agent — Living microorganism, such as a germ, that can cause human disease; a biologically hazardous material.

Eustress — Just enough stress to allow one to perform well; in other words, the person controls the stress.

Eutectic Alloying — When two metals form an alloy that has a lower melting temperature than either of the two original metals.

Evacuation — (1) Process of leaving or being removed from a potentially hazardous location. (2) Organized, phased, and supervised withdrawal, dispersal, or removal of civilians from a dangerous area, and their reception and care in safe areas. *See* Shelter in Place.

Evacuation Chute — Aircraft-door-connected escape slides that when deployed will inflate and extend to the ground; pneumatic in operation, most are deployed automatically by opening the door, though some require manual activation, normally a short pull on a lanyard. Many may be disconnected from the aircraft and used for a flotation device in water crashes. *Also known as* Evacuation Slide.

Evacuation System — System intended to allow people to escape to safety during a fire; includes egress systems (exit access, exit, and exit discharge) as well as doors, panic hardware, horizontal exits, stairs, smokeproof towers, fire-escape stairs, escalators, moving sidewalks, elevators, windows, and exit lighting and signs.

Evaluation — (1) Systematic and thoughtful collection of information for decision-making; consists of criteria, evidence, and judgment. (2) Last of the four teaching steps in which the fire and life safety educator finds out whether the educational objectives have been met. (3) Process that examines the results of a presentation or program to determine whether the participants have learned the information or behaviors taught; consists of criteria, evidence, and judgment. *See* Formative Evaluation, Lesson Plan, and Summative Evaluation.

Evaluation Instrument — Physical means used to evaluate or test a learner's mastery of the educational objectives taught; may be written, oral, or performance-based.

Evaluation Step — Fourth step in conducting a lesson in which the student demonstrates that the required degree of proficiency has been achieved.

Evaluation Strategy — Plan for conducting an evaluation; includes the type of evaluation instrument to be used, the information or behaviors to be evaluated, and the methods used to interpret the evaluation instrument.

Evaporation — Process of a solid or liquid turning into gas.

Event Flowcharting — Method for chronologically displaying the movements of events or occurrences, either over time or through a system.

Evidence — (1) One of three requirements of evaluation; the information, data, or observation that allows the instructor to compare what was expected to what actually occurred. (2) In law, something legally presented in court that bears on the point in question. (3) Information collected and analyzed by an investigator.

Evolution — (1) Sequential operation, or set or prescribed action that results in an effective fireground activity. (2) Operation of fire and emergency services training covering one or several aspects of fire fighting. *Also known as* Practical Training Evolution.

EX — Rating symbol used on lift trucks that are safe for use in atmospheres containing flammable vapors or dusts.

Excavation — Opening in the ground that results from a digging effort.

Excelsior — Slender, curled wood shavings used for starting fires or packing fragile items.

Excepted Packaging — Container used for transportation of materials that have very limited radioactivity. *See* Industrial Packaging, Packaging (1), Strong, Tight Container, Type A Packaging, and Type B Packaging.

Exclusionary Evidence — Evidence collected to show that a particular device or scenario can be ruled out, in relation to the ignition or fire spread scenario.

Exclusionary Rule — Judicially established evidentiary rule that excludes from admission at trial any evidence seized in a manner considered unreasonable by an interpretation of the Fourth Amendment of the U.S. Constitution.

Exhalation Valve — One-way valve that lets exhaled air out of the self-contained breathing apparatus facepiece.

Exhaust Area — Area behind a jet engine where hot exhaust gases present a danger to personnel.

Exhauster — Device that speeds the discharge of air from a dry-pipe sprinkler system.

Exhaust System — Ventilation system designed to remove stale air, smoke, vapors, or other airborne contaminants from an area. *See* Heating, Ventilating, and Air-Conditioning (HVAC) System.

Exigent Circumstances — Right of entry stating that the fire department does not require a warrant to enter a property to suppress a fire, or to remain on the property for a reasonable amount of time afterward in order to determine the origin and cause of the fire.

Exit — Portion of a means of egress that is separated from all other spaces of the building structure by construction or equipment, and provides a protected way of travel to the exit discharge. *See* Clear Width, Egress, Exit Discharge, Means of Egress, and Travel Distance.

Exit Access — Portion of a means of egress that leads to the exit; for example, hallways, corridors, and aisles. *See* Exit and Means of Egress.

Exit Capacity — According to building code requirements, the maximum number of people who can discharge through a particular exit; determined by the useable width of the exit. *See* Exit.

Exit Device — *See* Panic Hardware.

Exit Discharge — That portion of a means of egress that is between the exit and a public way. *See* Exit and Means of Egress.

Exit Lighting — Lighting intended to help people see on their way out of a structure.

Exit Opening — In ventilation, the opening that is made or used to release heat, smoke, and other contaminants into the atmosphere.

Exit Sign — Lighted sign indicating the direction/location of an exit from a structure.

Exit Stairs — Stairs that are used as part of a means of egress. The stairs may be part of either the exit access or the exit discharge, when conforming to requirements in the NFPA®101, *Life Safety Code®. See* Exit, Exit Access, Exit Discharge, Means of Egress, and NFPA® 101, *Life Safety Code®.*

Exothermal — Characterized by or formed with the evolution of heat.

Exothermic Heat Reaction — Chemical reaction between two or more materials that changes the materials and produces heat.

Expander — (1) Device that enlarges the expansion rings used for securing threaded couplings to fire hose. (2) Inner component of a screw-in expander coupling.

Expansion Joint — Flexible joint in concrete used to prevent cracking or breaking because of expansion and contraction due to temperature changes.

Expansion Ratio — Ratio of the finished foam volume to the volume of the original foam solution. *Also known as* Expansion. *See* Aeration and Foam Expansion.

Expansion Ring — Malleable metal band that binds fire hose to a threaded coupling by compressing the hose tightly against the inner surface of the coupling.

Expansion Ring Method — Means of attaching a threaded coupling to a fire hose; a metal expansion ring is placed inside the end of the hose and then expanded, in order to compress the hose tightly against the inner surface of the coupling.

Expellant Gas — Any of a number of inert gases that are compressed and used to force extinguishing agents from a portable fire extinguisher. Nitrogen is the most commonly used expellant gas. *See* Inert Gas.

Expert Power — Sufficiently strong perception that a leader's expertise, knowledge, and abilities will produce a desirable outcome, so that others will willingly follow that leader.

Expert Witness — Person with sufficient skill, knowledge, or experience in a given field so as to be capable of drawing inferences or reaching conclusions or opinions that an average person would not be competent to reach.

Explosion — physical or chemical process that results in the rapid release of high pressure gas into the environment. *See* Backdraft and Boiling Liquid Expanding Vapor Explosion.

Explosion-Dynamics Analysis — Process of following force vectors backwards toward the initial compartment where an explosion occurred.

Explosion-Proof Equipment — Equipment encased in a rigidly built container so that it can withstand an internal explosion and prevent ignition of a surrounding flammable or explosive atmosphere.

Explosive — (1) Any material or mixture that will undergo an extremely fast self-propagation reaction when subjected to some form of energy. *See* Detonation, High Explosive, and Magazine. (2) Materials capable of burning or bursting suddenly and violently. *See* Detonation, Low Explosive, and Magazine.

Explosive Atmosphere — Any atmosphere that contains a mixture of fuel to air that falls within the explosive limits for that particular material.

Explosive Breathing Technique — Individual emergency conditions breathing technique used by a firefighter wearing SCBA during accidental submersion; the firefighter holds his or her breath, rapidly inhales and exhales, and then holds breath again.

Explosive Device — Contrivance built to cause an explosion; commonly known as a bomb, though this is not always an accurate description. *See* Incendiary Device.

Explosive Limit — *See* Flammable Limit.

Explosive Range — Range between the upper and lower flammable limits of a substance. *See* Flammable Range.

Explosive Spalling — Spalling that occurs violently, throwing out bits of concrete-like projectiles.

Exposure — Contact with a substance by swallowing, breathing, or touching the skin or eyes. Exposure may be short-term (acute exposure), of intermediate duration, or long-term (chronic exposure).

Exposure Bag — Special neoprene bag into which a person is placed for field treatment of hypothermia.

Exposure Concentration — Measure of toxicity; expressed in parts per million (ppm) and abbreviated C.

Exposure Limit — Maximum length of time an individual can be exposed to an airborne substance before injury, illness, or death occurs.

Exposure Protection — Covering any object in the immediate vicinity of the fire with water or foam.

Exposures — (1) Structure or separate part of the fireground to which a fire could spread. (2) People, property, systems, or natural features that are or may be exposed to the harmful effects of a hazardous materials emergency. (3) NFPA® defines exposure as the heat effect from an external fire that might cause ignition of or damage to an exposed building. (4) Direction in which a slope faces. (5) General surroundings of a site with special reference to its openness to winds and sunshine.

Exposure Time — Length of exposure; expressed in minutes, and abbreviated T.

EX Symbol — Rating symbol used on lift trucks that are safe for use in atmospheres containing flammable vapors or dusts. *See* Lift Truck.

Extend — (1) To extend a hoseline by adding hose, straightening, or rerouting the hose already laid. (2) To increase the reach of an extension ladder or aerial device by raising the fly section.

Extended-Attack Fire — (1) Wildland fire that has not been contained or controlled by initial-attack forces and for which more fire fighting resources are arriving, en route, or being ordered by the incident commander. (2) Situation in which a fire cannot be controlled by initial-attack resources within a reasonable period of time.

Extension Cylinders — Hydraulic cylinders that control the extension and retraction of the fly sections of an aerial device.

Extension Fly Locks — Devices that prevent the fly sections of a ground or aerial ladder from retracting unexpectedly.

Extension Ladder — Sectional ladder of two or more parts that can be extended to various heights.

Extension Ram — Powered hydraulic tool designed for straight pushing operations; may extend as far as 63 inches (1 600 mm). *Also known as* Ram.

Exterior — (1) The outside of a building. (2) The outside of a vehicle; body panels, glass, bumpers, and other components.

Exterior Exposure — Building or other combustible object located close to the fire building that is in danger of becoming involved due to heat transfer from the fire building.

Exterior Fire Protection — Protection of structures from the exterior with no interior fire fighting.

Exterior Insulation and Finish Systems (EIFS) — Exterior cladding or covering systems composed of an adhesively or mechanically fastened foam insulation board, reinforcing mesh, a base coat, and an outer finish coat. *Also known as* Synthetic Stucco.

Exterior Stairs — Stairs separated from the interior of a building by walls.

External Floating Roof Tank — Fixed-site vertical storage tank that has no fixed roof but relies on a floating roof to protect its contents and prevent evaporation. *Also known as* Open-Top Floating Roof Tank. *See* Cone Roof Tank, Floating Roof Storage Tank, and Internal Floating Roof Tank.

External Respiration — Inhalation and exhalation of air into and from the lungs.

External Water Supply — Any water supply to a fire pump from a source other than the vehicle's own water tank, or any water supply to an aerial device from a source other than the vehicle's own fire pump.

Extinguish — To put out a fire completely.

Extinguisher — Portable fire fighting appliance designed for use on specific types of fuel and classes of fire.

Extinguisher Hose — Braided, rubber-covered hose used on extinguishers that is made to withstand pressures up to 1,250 psi (8 618 kPa).

Extinguishing Agent — Substance used for the purpose of controlling or extinguishing a fire.

Extremely Hazardous Substance — Chemicals determined by the Environmental Protection Agency (EPA) to be extremely hazardous to a community during an emergency spill or release, because of their toxicity and physical/chemical properties. There are 402 chemicals listed under this category. *See* Hazardous Substance.

Extreme Rescue Load — Normally considered to be 600 pounds (272.15 kg).

Extrication — Incidents involving the removal and treatment of victims who are trapped by some type of man-made machinery or equipment.

Extrication Collar — Device used for spinal immobilization.

Extrication Group — Group within the incident management system that is responsible for extricating victims.

Extrude — To shape heated plastics or metal by forcing them through dies.

Extruded Coupling — Coupling manufactured by the process of extrusion.

F

FAA — *See* Federal Aviation Administration.

Facade — Fascia added to some buildings with flat roofs to create the appearance of a mansard roof. *Also known as* False Roof or Fascia.

Face — *See* Wall.

Facepiece — Part of a self-contained breathing apparatus that fits over the face; includes the head harness, facepiece lens, exhalation valve, and connection for either a regulator or a low-pressure hose. *Also known as* Mask.

Faceshield — Protective shield attached to the front of a fire helmet. *Also known as* Helmet Faceshield.

Facilitator — (1) Instructor role in which he or she encourages productive interaction of group members; instructor does not display personal expertise, but channels and enhances the expertise of others. (2) Person in a group whose basic job is to stimulate others to participate in the group discussion.

Facilities Unit — Functional unit within the support branch of the logistics section of an incident management system; provides fixed facilities for an incident, including the incident base, feeding areas, sleeping areas, sanitary facilities, and a formal command post.

FACP — *See* Fire Alarm Control Panel.

Factory Certified — Qualification of fire department personnel who attend special manufacturers' repair schools to become formally qualified in certain testing and maintenance procedures.

Factory Raise — *See* Hotel Raise.

Fact Sheet — List of facts and material that allow a reporter to write an in-depth article; may be several pages long, and includes historical perspective, anecdotal material, statistics, and local data.

Fact Testimony — When a witness is presenting factual information based on his or her personal observations. *Also known as* Lay Testimony.

FACU — *See* Fire Alarm Control Unit.

Fahrenheit Scale — Temperature scale on which the freezing point is 32°F (0°C) and the boiling point at sea level is 212°F (100°C) at normal atmospheric pressure. *See* Celsius Scale and Temperature.

Failure Point — Point at which material ceases to perform satisfactorily; depending on the application, this can involve breaking, permanent deformation, excessive deflection, or vibration.

Fainting — Momentary loss of consciousness caused by insufficient blood supply to the brain. *Also known as* Syncope.

Fairing — An auxiliary structure or the external surface either attached to, or a part of the roof of a large truck that serves to reduce drag.

Fairlead — Chock or opening, sometimes fitted with a roller device designed to lead a rope or line from one part of a vessel to another (change line direction); also controls lines and minimizes chafing. *See* Chock (1).

Fall Line — Portion of a rope, in a block and tackle system, that runs between the standing block and the leading block or the power source. *Also known as* Pull Line, Pulling Line, and Weft Yarn.

Fallout — Radioactive particles descending from a cloud after a nuclear detonation.

False Ceiling — Additional suspended ceiling below the true original ceiling, forming a concealed space.

False Front — Additional facade on the front of a building applied after the original construction for decoration; often creates a concealed space.

False Roof — *See* Facade.

Family Education Rights and Privacy Act of 1974 — Legislation that provides that an individual's school records are confidential, and that information contained in those records may not be released without the individual's prior written consent.

Family-of-Eight Knots — Series of rescue knots based on a figure-eight knot.

Fan — Generic term used interchangeably for both blowers and smoke ejectors.

Fan Light — Semicircular window, usually over a doorway, with muntins radiating like the ribs of a fan.

Fan-Style Room Setup — *See* Chevron Room Setup.

Fantail — Back part of a vessel that hangs out over the water; a stern overhang.

Farm Implement — Any piece of farm machinery.

Fascia — (1) Flat horizontal or vertical board located at the outer face of a cornice. (2) Broad flat surface over a storefront or below a cornice.

Fast — To securely attach a vessel to a wharf or dock.

Fast Attack Mode — When the first-arriving unit at a fire makes a quick offensive attack on the fire. *Also known as* Fast Attack.

Fast Track — Method to reduce the overall time for completion of a project through phasing the design and construction process.

Fatality — Someone who has died as the result of the incident.

Fax — To send a hard copy facsimile (copy) of print or illustrative material via telephone lines.

FBI — *See* Federal Bureau of Investigation.

FCC — *See* Federal Communications Commission.

FDC — *See* Fire Department Connection.

FDIC — *See* Fire Department Instructors Conference.

Febrile Convulsions — Convulsions brought on by fever, occuring most oftenly in children.

Federal Aviation Administration (FAA) — Subdivision of the U.S. Department of Transportation that is involved with the regulation of civil aviation.

Federal Bureau of Investigation (FBI) — Agency within the U.S. Department of Justice that investigates the theft of hazardous materials, collects evidence for crimes, and prosecutes criminal violation of federal hazardous materials laws and regulations. The FBI is also the lead agency on terrorist incident scenes. *See* Terrorism.

Federal Communications Commission (FCC) — U.S. government agency charged with the control of all radio and television communications; acts as the main regulator of radio frequencies in both the public and private sectors.

Federal Emergency Management Agency (FEMA) — Agency within the U.S. Department of Homeland Security (DHS) that is responsible for emergency preparedness, mitigation, and response activities for events including natural, technological, and attack-related emergencies.

Federal Freedom of Information Act — Legislation used as a model for many state laws designed to make government information available to the public.

Feedback — (1) Student responses generated by questions, discussions, or opportunities to perform that demonstrate learning or understanding. (2) In communications, responses that clarify and ensure that the message was received and understood.

Feeder Line — *See* Relay-Supply Hose.

Feed Main — Pipe connecting the sprinkler system riser to the cross mains; these cross mains directly service a number of branch lines on which the sprinklers are installed.

Felony — Serious crime punishable by a fine, incarceration, and/or death, depending on the severity of the crime and the jurisdiction. *See* Indictable Offense.

FEMA — *See* Federal Emergency Management Agency.

Female Coupling — Threaded swivel device on a hose or appliance with internal threads designed to receive a male coupling with external threads of the same thread and diameter.

Femoral Artery — Principal artery of the thigh; allows pulse to be felt in the groin area.

Femur — Bone that extends from the pelvis to the knee; longest and largest bone in the body.

Fender — (1) Exterior body portion of a vehicle adjacent to the front or rear wheels. (2) Buffer between the side of a vessel and a dock, or between two vessels to lessen shock and prevent chafing. (3) Body material that surrounds the front tires; starts at the front of the vehicle, proceeds around the front tire and ends at the fire wall.

FFAPR — *See* Full-Facepiece Air-Purifying Respirator.

FFFP — *See* Film Forming Fluoroprotein Foam.

FIBC — *See* Flexible Intermediate Bulk Container.

Fiber — Solid particle whose length is several times greater than its diameter.

Fiberboard — Lightweight insulation board made of compressed cellulose fibers; often used in suspended ceilings.

Fiberglass — Composite material consisting of glass fibers embedded in resin.

Fiber-Optic Search Device — Very small camera on a flexible arm that allows viewing in a confined space with limited access.

Fibrillation — Rapid, ineffective contraction of the heart.

Fibula — Smaller of the two bones of the lower leg.

Fiddley — Vertical space extending from the engine room to a vessel's stack (chimney). *See* Economizer and Stack.

FIDO — *See* Fire Incident Data Organization.

Field Mobile Mechanic — Motor-driven vehicle designed and constructed for the purpose of providing a specified level of equipment capacity and mechanically trained personnel.

Field Sketch — Rough drawing of an occupancy that is made during an inspection. The field sketch is used to make a final inspection drawing.

Field Unit — *See* Brush Apparatus or Wildland Fire Apparatus.

Fifth Wheel — Device used to connect a truck tractor or converter dolly to a semitrailer in order to permit articulation between the units. It is generally composed of a lower part consisting of a trunnion, plate, and latching mechanism mounted on the truck tractor (or dolly), and a kingpin assembly mounted on the semitrailer. *See* Semitrailer.

Fifth-Wheel Pickup Ramp — Steel plate designed to lift the front end of a semitrailer to facilitate the engagement of the kingpin into the fifth wheel.

Figure Eight — Forged metal device in the shape of an eight; used to help control the speed of a person descending a rope.

Figure-Eight Knot — Knot used to form a loop in the end of a rope; should be used in place of a bowline knot when working with synthetic fiber rope.

File Server — Computer that contains program files available to all workstations in a computer network.

Filler Yarn — Threads running crosswise in fabrics or woven hose.

Fillet Weld — Weld made in the interior angle of two pieces of metal placed at right angles to each other.

Fill Hose — Short section of hose carried on apparatus, equipped with booster tanks to fill the tank from a hydrant or another truck.

Fill Opening — Opening on top of a tank used for filling the tank; usually incorporated into a manhole cover.

Fill Site — Location at which tankers/tenders will be loaded during a water shuttle operation.

Fill-The-Box — Slang for a request by a unit responding on a reduced assignment to send the balance of the assignment.

Film Forming Fluoroprotein Foam (FFFP) — Foam concentrate that combines the qualities of fluoroprotein foam with those of aqueous film forming foam. *See* Foam Concentrate.

Filter Basket — Fine mesh screen that is attached to the end of the foam concentrate pickup hose to prevent sediment from entering the system and clogging the proportioner.

Filter Breathing — Individual emergency conditions breathing technique used by a firefighter with a depleted air supply. The firefighter inserts the regulator end of the low-pressure hose into a pocket or glove, or inside the turnout coat, to help filter smoke particles and to protect the firefighter from inhaling superheated air.

Filter Canister — Filtration device containing chemicals to filter out harmful substances through adsorption or absorption on negative-pressure respirators. This should not be used for fire fighting or Immediately Dangerous to Life or Health (IDLH) atmospheres.

Fin — Fixed or adjustable airfoil attached longitudinally to an aircraft to provide a stabilizing effect in flight.

Final Approach — Portion of the landing pattern in which the aircraft is lined up with the runway and is heading straight in to land.

Final Disposition — Point in the chain of custody where a piece of evidence is determined to no longer have value as evidence; options at this point may include permanent storage, return to the owner, or authorized destruction.

Finance/Administrative Unit — Component of an incident management system responsible for documenting the ongoing financial impact of the incident; oversees the documentation of time and costs associated with personnel, as well as the documentation of private resources used throughout the incident. Includes the time unit, procurement unit, compensation/claims unit, and the cost unit.

Financial Profiling — Investigative tool that allows the investigator to organize and display the financial data of an individual or organization onto a graph or chart.

Fine Aggregates — Usually sand.

Finger — Long, narrow extension of a fire projecting from the main body of a wildland fire.

Finish — (1) Arrangement of hose usually placed on top of a hose load and connected to the end of the load. *Also known as* Hose Load Finish. (2) Fine or decorative work required for a building or one of its parts. (3) Finishing material used in painting.

Finished Foam — Extinguishing agent formed by mixing a foam concentrate with water and aerating the solution for expansion. *Also known as* Foam. *See* Foam Blanket, Foam Concentrate, and Foam Solution.

Fink Truss — Monoplane truss common in residential construction, in which all chords and diagonal members are in the same plane.

Fire — Rapid oxidation of combustible materials accompanied by a release of energy in the form of heat and light.

Fire Alarm — (1) Call announcing a fire. (2) Bell or other device summoning a fire company to respond to a fire or other emergency.

Fire Alarm Control Panel (FACP) — System component that receives input from both automatic and manual fire alarm devices and may provide power to detection devices or communication devices; can be a local control unit or a master control unit. *Also known as* Fire Alarm Control Unit.

Fire Alarm Control Unit (FACU) — *See* Fire Alarm Control Panel (FACP).

Fire Alarm Signal — Continuous rapid ringing of a vessel's bell for a period of not less than 10 seconds, supplemented by the continuous ringing of the general alarm bells for not less than 10 seconds.

Fire Alarm System — (1) System of alerting devices that takes a signal from fire detection or extinguishing equipment and alerts building occupants or proper authorities of a fire condition. (2) System of interconnected alarm-initiating and alarm-indicating devices designed to alert personnel to the existence of a fire in the protected premises. The alarm system may or may not be connected to a fire suppression system. (3) System used to dispatch fire department personnel and apparatus to emergency incidents. *Also known as* Fire Alarm Signaling System. *See* Fire Alarm Control Unit (FACU), Fire Detection System, Initiating Device, and Signaling Device.

Fire and Life Safety Inspector — *See* Inspector.

Fire Apparatus — Any fire department emergency vehicle used in fire suppression or other emergency situations.

Fire Apparatus Driver/Operator — Firefighter who is charged with the responsibility of operating fire apparatus to, during, and from the scene of a fire operation, or at any other time the apparatus is in use. The driver/operator is also responsible for routine maintenance of the apparatus and any equipment carried on the apparatus. This is typically the first step in the fire department promotional chain. *Also known as* Chauffeur, Driver/Operator, or Engineer.

Fireball — Brief, roughly spherical fire suspended in the air, resulting from ignitable gases released during an explosion; may occur during or after an explosive reaction.

Fire Behavior — (1) Manner in which fuel ignites, flames develop, and heat and fire spread; sometimes used to refer to the characteristics of a particular fire. (2) Manner in which a fire reacts to the variables of fuel, weather, and topography. *See* Fire Dynamics.

Fire-Behavior Forecast — Prediction of probable fire behavior, usually prepared by a fire-behavior officer in support of fire-suppression or prescribed-burning operations.

Fire Blanket — Blanket stored in a case in a kitchen or similar location that is intended to be wrapped around a victim whose clothing catches fire.

Fireboat — Vessel or watercraft designed and constructed for the purpose of fighting fires; provides a specified level of pumping capacity and personnel for the extinguishment of fires in the marine environment. *Also known as* Marine Unit.

Fire Bomb — Incendiary device used to start an arson fire; usually hand-thrown so that it will break, spill its flammable contents, and ignite.

Firebreak — Natural or man-made (constructed) barrier that is devoid of vegetation and stops or slows the advance of a wildland fire.

Fire Brigade — (1) Organization of industrial plant personnel trained to use fire fighting equipment within the plant, and who are assigned to carry out fire prevention activities and basic fire fighting duties and responsibilities. The full-time occupation of brigade members may or may not involve fire suppression and related activities. (2) Term used in some countries, outside the U.S., in place of fire department.

Fire Brigade Apparatus — Emergency response vehicles used by fire brigade personnel for fire suppression, rescue, or other specialized functions.

Fire Brigade Management Official — Individual designated by the senior facility manager as the person responsible for the organization, management, and operation of the industrial fire brigade.

Fire Brigade Organizational Statement — OSHA-required statement that must be prepared by all employers who choose to have a fire brigade. The document must include a statement that establishes the existence of the brigade; the basic organizational structure; the type, amount, and frequency of training to be provided; the expected number of members; and the functions that the brigade is to perform at the workplace.

Fire Broom — Broom used in wildland fire fighting.

Fire Bucket — Bucket with a round bottom, usually painted red and marked with the word *fire* to discourage use for purposes other than fire fighting; frequently kept filled with water, sand, or other fire extinguishing material. *Also known as* Fire Pail.

Fire Buff — (1) A fire department enthusiast. (2) A person attracted to fires.

Fire Bug — Common slang term to describe an arsonist or pyromaniac; especially a repeating fire setter. Also describes a person who not only sets fires but also enjoys watching them.

Fire Building — (1) Building in which a fire originated and is in progress. (2) Training building in which fire fighting is practiced. *Also known as* Burn Building.

Fire Camp — Camp near a large wildland fire for coordinating agencies, communications, logistics, and support.

Fire Cause — (1) Agency or circumstance that started a fire or set the stage for one to start; source of a fire's ignition. (2) The sequence of events that allows the source of ignition and the fuel to come together. (3) The combination of fuel supply, heat source, and a hazardous act that results in a fire.

Fire Cause Classification — One of four established classifications for the cause of a fire; accidental, natural, incendiary, or undetermined.

Fire Cause Determination — Process of establishing the cause of a fire incident through careful investigation and analysis of the available evidence.

Fire Commissioner — In the U.S., a politically appointed or elected manager of the fire department; usually has authority over the fire chief, who is a civil servant. In Canada, the position is responsible for fire prevention activities. *See* Fire Marshal.

Fire Control Plan — Set of general arrangement plans for each deck that illustrate fire stations, fire-resisting bulkheads, and fire-retarding bulkheads, together with particulars of fire detecting systems, manual alarm systems, fire extinguishing systems, fire doors, means of access to different compartments, and ventilating systems (including locations of dampers and fan controls). Plans are stored in a prominently marked weather-tight enclosure outside the house, for the assistance of land-based fire fighting personnel.

Fire Control Zone — Uninvolved area immediately surrounding a fire, wide enough to protect fire brigade members and others from the adverse effects of the fire.

Fire Curtain — Aluminized device on a rod, designed to be unrolled to reflect radiant heat from operators or crew members on some apparatus, bulldozers, or tractor-plows.

Fire Cut — Angled cut made at the end of a wood joist or wood beam that rests in a masonry wall to allow the beam to fall away freely from the wall in case of failure of the beam. This helps prevent the beam from acting as a lever to push against the masonry.

Fire Damper — (1) Device that automatically interrupts airflow through all or part of an air-handling system, thereby restricting the passage of heat and the spread of fire. (2) Device installed in air ducts that penetrate fire-resistant-rated vertical or horizontal assemblies; prohibits the transfer of heat or flames through the ducts at the point where the duct passes through the assembly. *See* Duct and Smoke Damper.

Fire Department Connection (FDC) — Point at which the fire department can connect into a sprinkler or standpipe system to boost the water pressure and flow in the system. This connection consists of a clappered siamese with two or more 2½-inch (64 mm) intakes or one large-diameter (4-inch [102 mm] or larger) intake. *Also known as* Fire Department Sprinkler Connection. *See* Standpipe System.

Fire Department Emergency Communications Systems — Detection and alarm systems that transfer information from whomever reports a fire to fire service personnel.

Fire Department Instructors Conference (FDIC) — Annual meeting of fire department training officials.

Fire Department Physician — Physician designated by a fire department to treat members of the department.

Fire Department Pumper — Fire apparatus having a permanently mounted fire pump with a rated discharge capacity of 750 gpm (3 000 L/min) or greater. This apparatus may also carry water, hose, and other portable equipment.

Fire Department Sprinkler Connection — *See* Fire Department Connection.

Fire Department Water Supply Officer — Officer in charge of all water supplies at the scene of a fire; duties include placing pumpers at the most advantageous hydrants or other water sources, and directing supplementary water supplies, including water shuttles and relay pumping operations. This may also be a permanent, full-time staff position with responsibility for coordinating, with other local agencies, water supply projects of concern to the fire department.

Fire Detection System — System of detection devices, wiring, and supervisory equipment used for detecting fire or products of combustion, and then signaling that these elements are present. *See* Fire Alarm Control Unit (FACU), Fire Alarm System, Initiating Device, and Signaling Device.

Fire Devil — Small cyclone or twister that forms when heated fire gases rise and cooler air rushes into the resulting low-pressure areas; most common in forest fires but can also be encountered in large structural fires.

Fire District — Designated geographic area where fire protection is provided, usually through a supporting tax, or an area where fire prevention codes are enforced.

Fire Door — Specially constructed, tested, and approved fire-rated door assembly designed and installed to prevent fire spread by automatically closing and covering a doorway in a fire wall to block the spread of fire through the door opening. *See* Fire Wall.

Fire Door Assembly — Listed and labeled assembly consisting of door, frame, and hardware. Rated in terms of hours of fire protection; for example, a one-hour fire door assembly.

Fire Drill — Training exercise to ensure that the occupants of a building can exit the building in a quick and orderly manner in case of fire.

Fire Dynamics — Applying the tools of chemistry and physics to gain a technical understanding of how fires ignite, grow, and spread. *Also known as* Fire Behavior.

Fire Edge — Boundary of a fire at a given moment.

Fire Effect — In fire investigations, the changes to materials or loss of materials, such as melting, calcinations, or char; sometimes confused with Fire Pattern.

Fire Entry Suit — *See* Entry Clothing.

Fire Escape — (1) Means of escaping from a building in case of fire; usually an interior or exterior stairway or slide, independently supported and made of fire-resistive material. (2) Traditional term for an exterior stair, frequently incorporating a movable section of noncombustible construction, that is intended as an emergency exit; usually supported by hangers installed in the exterior wall of the building. The traditional fire escape is narrower than required stairways and is no longer allowed by codes, except as an existing feature. They have been associated with frequent failures.

Fire Extinguisher — Portable fire fighting device designed to combat incipient fires. *See* Carbon Dioxide (CO_2) and Incipient Phase.

Firefighter — Active member of the fire department. *Also spelled* Fire Fighter.

Firefighter's Axe — *See* Axe.

Firefighter's Carry — One of several methods of lifting and carrying a disabled victim to safety.

Firefighter's Smoke Control Station (FSCS) — Interface between the smoke management system and the fire response forces.

Fire Fighting Ensemble — Protective gear used for fire fighting that consists of protective pants, coat, boots, gloves, hood, and helmet.

Fire Flank — Side of a wildland fire.

Fire Flow — (1) Quantity of water available for fire fighting in a given area. It is calculated in addition to the normal water consumption in the area. (2) The amount of water required to extinguish a fire in a timely manner.

Fire Flow Testing — Procedure used to determine the rate of water flow available for fire fighting at various points within the distribution system.

Fire Front — Part of a fire within which continuous flaming combustion is taking place; assumed to be the leading edge of the fire perimeter. In surface fires, the fire front may be mainly smoldering combustion.

Fire-Gas Detector — Device used to detect gases produced by a fire within a confined space.

Fire Gases — Gases produced as combustion occurs.

Fireground — Area around a fire and occupied by fire fighting forces.

Fireground Commander — *See* Incident Commander.

Fireground Perimeter — Work area surrounding the fire building.

Fire Guard — Person trained and assigned to watch for fires and life safety hazards during specified periods or events.

Fire Hall — *See* Fire Station.

Fire Hazard — Any material, condition, or act that contributes to the start of a fire or that increases the extent or severity of fire. *See* Hazard.

Fire Hazard Severity Rating System — System of adjectives used to describe fire danger to the public; ranges from *low* to *extreme*.

Fire Hook — Hook, on the end of a rope or pole, used to pull combustible roofing materials such as thatch from burning buildings. These devices could also be used to hook into the gables of a building, or a ring installed on the gable, to pull that end of the building down. Because these hooks were carried on early ladder trucks, these trucks became known as "hook and ladder companies". The pike pole is a modern variation of the fire hook. *See* Pike Pole.

Fire Hose Float — Water-rescue flotation device made from inflated fire hose.

Fire House — *See* Fire Station.

Fire Hydrant — Upright metal casing that is connected to a water supply system and is equipped with one or more valved outlets to which a hoseline or pumper may be connected to supply water for fire fighting operations. *Also known as* Hydrant.

Fire Hydraulics — Science that deals with water in motion, as it applies to fire fighting operations.

Fire Incident Data Organization (FIDO) — NFPA® organization that maintains a database that is one of the main sources of information (data, statistics) about fires in the U.S. Provides an in-depth look at reported fires involving three or more civilian deaths, one or more firefighter deaths, or large dollar loss, as well as some other particularly interesting types of fires, such as high-rise fires.

Fire Inspector — Fire personnel assigned to inspect property with the purpose of enforcing fire regulations.

Fire In The United States — USFA publication based largely on fire data submitted to the National Fire Incident Reporting System (NFIRS) by roughly 13,000 fire departments; presented in an easy-to-understand format that relies heavily on the extensive use of charts and graphs.

Fire Investigator — Public or private sector individual tasked with discovering the origin and cause of a fire, as well as who may be responsible or liable for a fire.

Fireline Intensity — Rate of heat energy released per unit time per unit length of fire front. Numerically, it is the product of the heat of combustion, quantity of fuel consumed in the fire front, and the rate of spread of a fire in Btu per second per foot (kilojoules per second per meter) of fire front.

Fire Line Tape — Plastic marking tape strung around an emergency scene to keep bystanders away from the action.

Fire Lines — (1) Boundaries established around a fire area to prevent access except for emergency vehicles and persons having a right and need to be present. (2) In wildland fire fighting, part of a control line that is scraped or dug to mineral soil; also, a general term for the area where fire fighting activities are taking place. The wildland equivalent of the term *fireground* as used in structural fire fighting.

Fire Load — (1) The amount of fuel within a compartment; expressed in pounds per square foot, and obtained by dividing the amount of fuel present by the floor area. Fire load is used as a measure of the potential heat release of a fire within a compartment. (2) Maximum amount of heat that can be produced if all the combustible materials in a given area burn. *Also known as* Fuel Load.

Fire Loss In Canada — One of the main sources of information (data, statistics) about fires in Canada; compiled from data provided by the Association of Canadian Fire Marshals and Fire Commissioners and the government agency Statistics Canada.

Fire Main System — System that supplies water to all areas of a vessel; composed of fire pumps, piping (main and branch lines), control valves, hose, and nozzles.

Fire Mark — Distinctive metal or wooden marker once produced by insurance companies for identifying their policyholders' buildings.

Fire Marshal — Highest fire prevention officer of a state, province, county, or municipality. In Canada, this officer is *also known as* the Fire Commissioner.

Fire Medical Apparatus — Motor-driven vehicle, designed and constructed for the purpose of providing medical care with a specified level of equipment capacity and medically trained personnel; this unit is not used to transport patients to medical facilities. *Also known as* Non-Transport Fire Medical Apparatus.

Fire Pail — *See* Fire Bucket.

Fire Partition — Fire barrier that extends from one floor to the bottom of the floor above or to the underside of a fire-rated ceiling assembly; provides a lower level of protection than a fire wall. An example is a one-hour rated corridor wall. *See* Fire Wall.

Fire Patterns — Visible or measurable physical effects that remain after a fire. *Also known as* Burn Patterns.

Fire Perimeter — Edge of a wildland fire.

Fireplay — Child's involvement with fire materials without the approval or supervision of parents; usually involves lighting matches or lighters.

Fire Plow — Heavy-duty plowshare or disc plow pulled by a tractor to construct a fireline.

Fire Plug — Wooden plug inserted into holes drilled into early wooden water main systems; when the plug was removed, water could be obtained for fire fighting purposes. Fire hydrants evolved from fire plugs. *See* Fire Hydrant.

Fire Point — Temperature at which a liquid fuel produces sufficient vapors to support combustion once the fuel is ignited. The fire point is usually a few degrees above the flash point. *Also known as* Burning Point. *See* Flash Point.

Fire Police — Members, usually of a volunteer fire department, who respond with the fire department and assist the police with traffic control, crowd control, and scene preservation and security; common only in the mid-Atlantic states of the U.S. *Also known as* Special Police.

Fire Prevention — (1) Part of the science of fire protection that deals with preventing the outbreak of fire by eliminating fire hazards through such activities as inspection, code enforcement, education, and investigation programs. (2) Division of a fire department responsible for conducting fire prevention programs of inspection, code enforcement, education, and investigation. *Also known as* Fire Prevention Bureau.

Fire Prevention Bureau — Division of the fire department responsible for conducting fire prevention programs of inspection, code enforcement, education, and investigation. *Also known as* Fire Prevention.

Fire Prevention Code — Body of law enacted for the purpose of enforcing fire prevention and safety regulations, thus providing fire safety through the elimination of fire hazards and maintenance of fire protection equipment. *See* Code.

Fire Prevention Week — Week proclaimed each year by the President of the United States to commemorate the anniversary of the great Chicago conflagration on October 9, 1871; takes place the week in which October 9 falls.

Fireproof — Obsolete term for resistance to fire; a misnomer because all materials with the exception of water will burn at some point. Other terms such as fire resistive or fire resistant should be used to indicate a material's degree of resistance to fire.

Fire Protection — Actions taken to limit the adverse environmental, social, political, economic, and life-threatening effects of fire.

Fire Protection Engineer (FPE) — Graduate of an accredited institution of higher education who has specialized in engineering science related to fire protection.

Fire-Protection Rating — Designation indicating the duration of a fire-test exposure to which a fire door assembly or fire window assembly was exposed, and for which it successfully met all acceptance criteria.

Fire-Protection System — System designed to protect structure and minimize loss due to fire.

Fire Pump — (1) Water pump used in private fire protection to provide water supply to installed fire protection systems. (2) Water pump on a piece of fire apparatus. (3) Centrifugal or reciprocating pump that supplies seawater to all fire hose connections aboard a ship.

Fire-Rated Glass — Type of glass that does not use interior wires. These fire-rated glass panels are made from a combination of glass and plastic.

Fire Report — Official report on a fire kept as a permanent record; generally prepared by the officer in charge of the fire operation.

Fire Resistance — The ability of a structural assembly to maintain its load-bearing ability under fire conditions.

Fire-Resistance Directory — Directory that lists building assemblies that have been tested and given fire-resistance ratings. Published by Underwriters Laboratories.

Fire-Resistance Rating — Rating assigned to a material or assembly after standardized testing by an independent testing organization; identifies the amount of time a material or assembly will resist a typical fire, as measured on a standard time-temperature curve.

Fire Resistant — Capacity of structural components to resist higher heat temperatures for certain periods of time. Lesser degree of resistance to fire than *fireproof*.

Fire Resistive — Ability of a structure or a material to provide a predetermined degree of fire resistance; usually according to building and fire prevention codes and given in hour ratings.

Fire Retardant — Any substance, except plain water, that when applied to another material or substance will reduce the flammability of fuels or slow their rate of combustion by chemical or physical action.

Fire Risk — Probability that a fire will occur and the potential for harm it will create in terms of the number of incidents, injuries, or deaths per capita. (**NOTE:** Depending on the source of information, the per capita unit may be one thousand people or one million people.)

Fire Science — Study of the behavior, effects, and control of fire.

Fire Season — Period of the year during which wildland fires are likely to occur, spread, and damage wildland areas sufficiently to warrant organized fire suppression.

Fire Separation — Horizontal or vertical assembly of fire-resistant materials that is designed to impede or slow the spread of fire.

Fire Service — Organized fire prevention, fire protection, fire training, and fire fighting services, including the members of such organizations individually and collectively who assist in preventing and combating fires.

Fire Service Hose — Specially constructed hose designed to withstand the hazards of the fire scene.

Firesetter — Person who starts a fire, usually deliberately and maliciously.

Firesetting — Intentional act of lighting a fire, usually deliberately and maliciously, that creates a disturbance or harms people, animals, or objects. *See* Arson.

Fire Shelter — Aluminized tent carried by firefighters that offers personal protection by means of reflecting radiant heat and providing a volume of breathable air in a fire-entrapment situation.

Fire Standard Certified (FSC) — Indication on packs of cigarettes in the U.S. that indicates that the cigarettes are "fire-safe" and will self-extinguish if left lit and unattended.

Fire Station — (1) Building in which fire suppression forces are housed. *Also known as* Fire Hall or Fire House. (2) Location on a vessel with fire fighting water outlet (fire hydrant), valve, fire hose, nozzles, and associated equipment.

Fire Stop — Solid materials, such as wood blocks, used to prevent or limit the vertical and horizontal spread of fire and the products of combustion; installed in hollow walls or floors, above false ceilings, in penetrations for plumbing or electrical installations, in penetrations of a fire-rated assembly, or in cocklofts and crawl spaces.

Fire Storm — Violent convective atmospheric disturbance caused by a large continuous area of intense fire (conflagration), in which a rising column of heated air creates intense winds toward the fire center, encompassing the entire fire area. Often characterized by destructively violent surface indrafts, near and beyond the perimeter, and sometimes by tornado-like whirls.

Fire Stream — Stream of water or other water-based extinguishing agent after it leaves the fire hose and nozzle until it reaches the desired point.

Fire Suppressant — Agent used to extinguish the flaming and smoldering phases of combustion by direct application to the burning fuel.

Fire Suppression — All work and activities connected with fire-extinguishing operations, beginning with discovery and continuing until a fire is completely extinguished.

Fire Swatter — Fire-suppression tool consisting of a flap of belting fabric fastened to a long handle; used in direct attack for beating out flames along a fire edge.

Fire Tetrahedron — Model of the four elements/conditions required to have a fire. The four sides of the tetrahedron represent fuel, heat, oxygen, and chemical chain reaction.

Fire Trap — Slang for an old structure in such a deteriorated state that it is highly susceptible to fire, has inadequate protective equipment and exits, and is considered likely to contribute to major loss of life in case of fire.

Fire Triangle — Plane geometric figure of an equilateral triangle that is used to explain the conditions necessary for fire. The sides of the triangle represent heat, oxygen, and fuel. The fire triangle was used prior to the general adaptation of the fire tetrahedron, which includes a chemical chain reaction. *See* Fire Tetrahedron.

Fire Tube — *See* Heating Tube.

Fire Wall — (1) Fire rated wall with a specified degree of fire resistance, built of fire-resistive materials and usually extending from the foundation up to and through the roof of a building, that is designed to limit the spread of a fire within a structure or between adjacent structures. (2) Bulkhead separating an aircraft engine from the aircraft fuselage or wing. (3) The partition between the engine compartment and the passenger compartment of a vehicle. It is designed to protect vehicle occupants from the engine and its associated hazards.

Fire Wall Assembly — All of the components needed to provide a separating fire wall that meets the requirements of a specified fire-resistance rating.

Fire Wardens — Individuals appointed by the city of New Amsterdam and other early American cities in an attempt to prevent fires by inspecting chimneys and hearths. They were empowered to cite residents for failing to meet the city fire codes. Similar to the fire wards of early Boston.

Fire Wards — Individuals appointed by the city of Boston after 1631 in an attempt to prevent fires. They were provided badges and staffs of office and assigned to different parts of the city. Similar to the fire wardens of New Amsterdam and other early American cities.

Fire Watch — Usually refers to someone who has the responsibility to tour a building or facility on at least an hourly basis, look for actual or potential fire emergency conditions, and send an appropriate warning if such conditions are found.

Fire Weather — Weather conditions that influence fire ignition, behavior, and suppression.

Fire Weather Forecast — Weather prediction specially prepared for use in wildland fire control.

Firewhirl — Spinning vortex column of ascending hot air and gases rising from a fire and carrying smoke, debris, and flame aloft. *Also known as* Fire Devil or Fire Whirlwind.

Fire Wire — Length of wire rope or chain hung from the bow and stern of a vessel in port to allow the vessel to be towed away from the pier in case of fire. *Also known as* Emergency Towing Wire or Fire Warp.

Firing Out — Act of lighting backfires with a torch, fusee, or other device, to accomplish burning out or backfiring that will impede the growth of an uncontrolled wildland fire. *See* Backfire, Backfiring, and Burning Out.

First Aid — Immediate medical care given to a patient until he or she can be transported to a medical facility.

First Alarm — Initial fire department response to a report of an emergency.

First-Degree Burn — Burn affecting only the outer skin layers; will cause redness and pain but not blisters or scars.

First-Due — Apparatus that should reach the scene of an emergency first based on the pre-fire attack plan. *Also known as* First-In.

First Responder (EMS) — (1) First person arriving at the scene of an accident or medical emergency who is trained to administer first aid and basic life support. (2) Level of emergency medical training, between first aider and emergency medical technician levels, that is recognized by the authority having jurisdiction (AHJ).

Fiscal — Having to do with finances and money.

Fissionable — Capable of splitting the atomic nucleus and releasing large amounts of energy.

Fitting — Device that facilitates the connection of hoselines of different sizes to provide an uninterrupted flow of extinguishing agent. *See* Appliance.

Five-Minute Escape Cylinder — Small air cylinder used as a backup air source with airline respirators.

Five-Step Planning Process — Systematic planning and action process composed of five steps: 1) identification of major fire problems, 2) selection of the most cost-effective objectives for the education program, 3) design of the program itself, 4) implementation of the program plan, and 5) evaluation of the fire safety program to determine impact.

Fixed-Flow Direct-Injection Proportioner — Fixed-site foam system that provides foam at a preset rate. Foam concentrate and water are provided to the proportioner by two separate pumps that operate at preset rates. *See* Foam Proportioner and Proportioning.

Fixed Foam Extinguishing System — Complete installation of piping, foam concentrate storage, water supply, pumps, and delivery systems used to protect a specific hazard such as a petroleum storage facility. *See* Portable Foam Extinguishing System and Semifixed Foam Extinguishing System.

Fixed Monitor System — Fire suppression system employing stationary master stream devices (monitors) in areas where large quantities of water or foam will be needed in the event of a fire.

Fixed Stare — Condition while operating an apparatus in which the driver/operator becomes absorbed with particular details rather than maintaining the constant eye movement that ensures safe driving.

Fixed-Temperature Device — Fire alarm initiating device that activates at a predetermined temperature.

Fixed-Temperature Heat Detector — Temperature-sensitive device that senses temperature changes and sounds an alarm at a specific point, usually 135°F (57°C) or higher.

Fixed Window — Window that is set in a fixed or immovable position and cannot be opened for ventilation.

Flagger — Individual assigned to direct the flow of traffic using a flag, flashlight, paddle, wand, sign, or other device.

Flag State — Nation in which a vessel is registered.

Flail Chest — Condition in which several ribs are broken, each in at least two places.

Flame — Light of various colors given off by burning gases or vapors during the combustion process; visible, luminous body of a burning gas.

Flame Depth — Depth of the fire front; horizontal distance between the leading and trailing edges of the fire front.

Flame Detector — Detection and alarm device used in some fire detection systems, generally in high-hazard areas; detects light/flames in the ultraviolet wave spectrum (UV detectors), or detects light in the infrared wave spectrum (IR detectors). *Also known as* Light Detector.

Flame Front — (1) Outermost edge or surface of the flame. (2) Combustion area that lags behind the blast-pressure front in a deflagration; marks where expanding gases are igniting during an explosion. *See* Blast-Pressure Front.

Flame Height — Average maximum vertical extension of flames at the leading edge of the fire front; occasional flashes that rise above the general level of flames are not considered. This distance is less than the flame length if flames are tilted due to wind or slope.

Flame Impingement — Points at which flames contact the surface of a container or other structure.

Flame Interface — Area or surface between the gases or vapors and the visible flame.

Flame Length — Distance between the flame tip and the midpoint of the flame depth at the base of the flame (generally the ground surface); an indicator of fire intensity.

Flame Out — Unintended loss of combustion in turbojet engines resulting in the loss of engine power.

Flameover — Condition that occurs when a portion of the fire gases trapped at the upper level of a room ignite, spreading flame across the ceiling of the room. *See* Rollover.

Flame Propagation Rate — Velocity at which combustion travels through a gas or over the surface of a liquid or solid.

Flame Resistant — Materials that are not susceptible to combustion to the point of propagating a flame after the ignition source is removed.

Flame Speed — Velocity of the flame front relative to the center of the explosion.

Flame Spread — Movement of a flame away from the ignition source.

Flame Spread Rating — (1) Numerical rating assigned to a material based on the speed and extent to which flame travels over its surface. (2) Measurement of the propagation of flame on the surface of materials or their assemblies as determined by recognized standard tests. *See* Steiner Tunnel Test.

Flame Test — Test designed to determine the flame spread characteristics of structural components or interior finishes.

Flame Zone — Area of any individual fire where flames are visible.

Flammability — Fuel's susceptibility to ignition.

Flammable — Capable of burning and producing flames. *See* Flammable Gas, Flammable Liquid, Flammable Solid, and Nonflammable.

Flammable/Combustible Liquid Pit — Training prop designed to provide controlled burns of flammable or combustible liquids; used in training for the extinguishment of flammable/combustible liquid fires.

Flammable and Explosive Limits — Upper and lower concentrations of a vapor, expressed in percent mixture with an oxidizer, that will produce a flame at a given temperature and pressure.

Flammable/Explosive Range — Percentage of a gas vapor concentration in the air that will burn if ignited.

Flammable Gas — Any material (except an aerosol) that is a gas at 68°F (20°C) or less and that (a) is ignitable and will burn at 14.7 psi (101.3 kPa) when in a mixture of 13 percent or less by volume with air, or (b) has a flammable range at 14.7 psi (101.3 kPa) by volume with air at least 12 percent regardless of the lower limit. *See* Flammable, Gas, Lower Flammable Limit (LFL), Nonflammable Gas, and Upper Flammable Limit (UFL).

Flammable Limit — Percentage of a substance in air that will burn once it is ignited. Most substances have an upper flammable limit (too rich) and a lower flammable limit (too lean). *Also known as* Explosive Limit. *See* Flammable Range, Lower Flammable Limit (LFL), and Upper Flammable Limit (UFL).

Flammable Liquid — Any liquid having a flash point below 100°F (37.8°C) and a vapor pressure not exceeding 40 psi absolute (276 kPa) {2.76 bar}. *See* Combustible Liquid, Flammable, Flash Point, Polar Solvent Fuel, and Vapor Pressure.

Flammable Material — Substance that ignites easily and burns rapidly.

Flammable Range — Range between the upper flammable limit and lower flammable limit in which a substance can be ignited. *Also known as* Explosive Range. *See* Flammable Limit.

Flammable Solid — Solid material (other than an explosive) that (a) is liable to cause fires through friction or retained heat from manufacturing or processing, or (b) ignites readily and then burns vigorously and persistently, creating a serious transportation hazard. *See* Flammable.

Flank — One side of a wildland fire.

Flank Attack — Attacking a fire on the flanks or sides of a wildland fire and working along the fire edge toward the head of the fire. *Also known as* Flanking Attack. *See* Attack Methods (2).

Flanking — Attacking the sides of the fire from a less active area or from an anchor point; the intent being to have the two crews attacking the flanks meet at the head of the fire.

Flanks of Fire — Parts of a fire's perimeter that are roughly parallel to the main direction of spread.

Flaps — Adjustable airfoils attached to the leading or trailing edges of aircraft wings to improve aerodynamic performance during takeoff and landing. They are normally extended during takeoff, landing, and slow flight.

Flare-Up — Sudden acceleration in rate of spread or intensification of a fire. Unlike blowup, a flare-up is of relatively short duration and does not radically change existing control plans. *See* Blowup.

Flashback — Spontaneous reignition of fuel when the blanket of extinguishing agent breaks down, or is compromised through physical disturbance.

Flash Fire — Type of fire that spreads rapidly through a vapor environment.

Flash Fuels — Wildland ground cover fuels that are easily ignited and burn rapidly; examples include grass, leaves, pine needles, fern, tree moss, and some kinds of slash. *Also known as* Flashy Fuels.

Flashing — (1) Liquid-tight rail on top of a tank that contains water and spillage and directs it to suitable drains; may be combined with DOT overturn protection. (2) Sheet metal used in roof and wall construction to keep water out.

Flashing Drain — Metal or plastic tube that drains water and spillage from flashing to the ground.

Flashover — Stage of a fire at which all surfaces and objects within a space have been heated to their ignition temperature, and flame breaks out almost at once over the surface of all objects in the space. *See* Backdraft, Ignition Temperature, and Rollover.

Flash Point — Minimum temperature at which a liquid gives off enough vapors to form an ignitable mixture with air near the surface of the liquid. *See* Fire Point.

Flash Resistant — Aircraft materials that are not susceptible to burning violently when ignited.

Flat — Two-family dwelling in which the families live one above the other; one family occupies the entire ground floor (and basement if there is one) while the second family occupies the entire second floor (and attic if there is one) of a building.

Flat-Head Axe — Axe with a cutting edge on one side of the head and a blunt or flat head on the opposite side.

Flat Load — Arrangement of fire hose in a hose bed or compartment, in which the hose lies flat with successive layers one upon the other.

Flat Plate — Plain floor slab about 8 inches (203 mm) thick that rests on columns spaced up to 22 feet (6.7 m) apart and depends on diagonal and orthogonal patterns of reinforcing bars for structural support because the slab lacks beams; simplest and most economical floor system.

Flat Raise — Raising a ladder with the heel of both beams touching the ground.

Flat Roof — Roof that has a slope not exceeding 2 inches (51mm) vertical for each 12 inches (305 mm) horizontal; generally has a slight pitch to facilitate runoff.

Flat Slab — Type of concrete floor construction that provides a flat surface for the underside of the floor finish.

Flat-Slab Concrete Frame — Construction technique consisting of concrete slabs supported by concrete columns.

Flesch Grade Level Index — *See* Flesch Reading Ease.

Flesch Reading Ease — Readability index. *Also known as* Flesch Grade Level Index.

Flexible Intermediate Bulk Container (FIBC) — *See* Intermediate Bulk Container (IBC).

Flight — (1) Series of steps between takeoff and landing of an aircraft. (2) Series of stairs or steps between two landings.

Flight Controls — General term applied to devices that enable the pilot to control the direction of flight and attitude of the aircraft.

Flight Data Recorder — Recording device on large civilian aircraft to record aircraft airspeed, altitude, heading, acceleration, and other flight data to be used as an aid to accident investigation. *Also known as* Black Box.

Flight Deck — Cockpit on a large aircraft that is separated from the rest of the cabin.

Flight Service Station — Facility from which aeronautical information and related aviation support services are provided to aircraft. This also includes airport and vehicle advisory services for designated uncontrolled airports.

Flipchart — Teaching aid consisting of a large easel and tablet.

Floating Dock Strainer — Strainer designed to float on top of the water; used for drafting operations. This eliminates the problem of drawing debris into the pump and reduces the required depth of water needed for drafting.

Floating Foundation — Foundation for which the volume of earth excavated will approximately equal the weight of the building supported. Thus, the total weight supported by the soil beneath the foundation remains about the same, and settlement is minimized because of the weight of the building.

Floating Pump — Small, portable pump that floats on the water source.

Floating Ribs — Two lowest pairs of ribs; so called because they are connected only to vertebrae in the back.

Floating Roof Storage Tank — Atmospheric storage tank that stands vertically, and is wider than it is tall. The roof floats on the surface of the liquid to eliminate the vapor space. *See* Atmospheric Storage Tank and Lifter Roof Storage Tank.

Flood Tide — Rising tide.

Floor Plan — Architectural drawing showing the layout of a floor within a building as seen from above. It outlines the location and function of each room. *See* Construction Plan, Plot Plan, and Site Plan.

Floor Runner — Heavy plastic or canvas placed on a floor to protect the floor's surface or covering from firefighter traffic; used during salvage operations.

Flow — Motion characteristic of water.

Flow Hydrant — Hydrant from which the water is discharged during a hydrant flow test. *See* Test Hydrant.

Flowmeter — Mechanical device installed in a discharge line that senses the amount of water flowing and provides a readout in units of gallons per minute (liters per minute).

Flow Pressure — Pressure created by the rate of flow or velocity of water coming from a discharge opening. *Also known as* Plug Pressure.

Flow Test — Tests conducted to establish the capabilities of water supply systems. The objective of a flow test is to establish quantity (gallons or liters per minute) and pressures available at a specific location on a particular water supply system.

Fluid — Any substance that can flow, has a definite mass and volume at constant temperature and pressure but no definite shape, and that is unable to sustain shear stresses. Fluids include both gases and liquids.

Fluid-Applied Membrane — Roof coating material that is applied as a liquid and allowed to cure; includes neoprene, silicone, polyurethane, and butyl rubber. Typically applied to curved roof surfaces such as domes.

Fluid Mechanics — Branch of physics dealing with the behavior of fluids, particularly with respect to their reaction to forces applied to them.

Fluorinated Surfactants — (1) Chemicals that lower the surface tension of a liquid, in this case fire fighting foams. (2) Surface-active substance where the hydrophobic (incapable of dissolving in water) part of the substance molecule contains fluorine; has the ability to lower aqueous surface tension, improve wetting, and remain chemically stable when exposed to heat, acids, and bases as well as reducing and oxidizing agents.

Fluoroprotein Foams — Protein foam concentrate with synthetic fluorinated surfactants added. These surfactants enable the foam to shed, or separate from, hydrocarbon fuels. *See* Foam Concentrate.

Flush Bolt — Locking bolt that is installed flush within a door.

Flush Hydrant — Hydrant installed in a pit below ground level such as near the runway area of airports or other locations where aboveground hydrants would be unsuitable.

Flyer — Another term for a brochure.

Flying Shore — Shore for vertical surfaces, such as a wall, that is braced against another vertical surface.

Fly Rope — *See* Halyard.

Fly Section — Extendable section of ground extension or aerial ladder. *Also known as* Fly.

FM — *See* FM Global.

FMD — *See* Foot and Mouth Disease.

FM Global (FM) — Fire research and testing laboratory that provides loss control information for the Factory Mutual System and anyone else who may find it useful.

Foam — Extinguishing agent formed by mixing a foam concentrate with water and aerating the solution for expansion; for use on Class A and Class B fires. Foam may be protein, synthetic, aqueous film forming, high expansion, or alcohol type. *Also known as* Finished Foam. *See* Foam Concentrate and Foam System.

Foam Blanket — Covering of foam applied over a burning surface to produce a smothering effect; can be used on unignited surfaces to prevent ignition. *See* Foam Stability.

Foam Chamber — Foam delivery device that is mounted on storage tanks; applies foam onto the surface of the fuel in the tank. *See* Alcohol-Resistant AFFF Concentrate, Aqueous Film Forming Foam, Class A Foam Concentrate, Class B Foam Concentrate, Emulsifier, Film Forming Fluoroprotein Foam, Fluoroprotein Foam, Foam Solution, Protein Foam Concentrate, and Synthetic Foam Concentrate.

Foam Concentrate — (1) Raw chemical compound solution that is mixed with water and air to produce finished foam; may be protein, synthetic, aqueous film forming, high expansion, or alcohol types. (2) Raw foam liquid as it rests in its storage container before the introduction of water and air. *See* Aqueous Film Forming Foam, Class A Foam Concentrate, Class B Foam Concentrate, Foam, Foam Solution, and Foam System.

Foam Eductors — Type of foam proportioner used for mixing foam concentrate in proper proportions with a stream of water to produce foam solution. *See* Foam Proportioner and Foam Solution.

Foam Expansion — Result of adding air to a foam solution consisting of water and foam concentrate. Expansion creates the foam bubbles that result in finished foam or foam blanket. *See* Aeration and Expansion Ratio.

Foam Monitor — Master stream appliance used for the application of foam solution. *See* Automatic Oscillating Foam Monitor, Manual Foam Monitor, and Remote-Controlled Foam Monitor.

Foam Proportioner — Device that injects the correct amount of foam concentrate into the water stream to make the foam solution. *See* Foam Eductor and Foam Solution.

Foam Solution — Result of mixing the appropriate amount of foam concentrate with water; foam solution exists between the proportioner and the nozzle or aerating device that adds air to create finished foam. *See* Foam Concentrate, Foam Eductor, and Foam Proportioner.

Foam Stability — Relative ability of a foam to withstand spontaneous collapse or breakdown from external causes. *See* Foam Blanket.

Foam System — Extinguishing system that uses a foam such as aqueous film forming foam (AFFF) as the primary extinguishing agent; usually installed in areas where there is a risk of flammable liquid fires. *See* Aqueous Film Forming Foam, Flammable Liquid, Foam, and Foam Concentrate.

Foam Tanker — *See* Foam Tender.

Foam Tender — Apparatus that is specially designed to transport large quantities of foam concentrate to the scene of an incident; vehicle may be equipped with transfer pumps and have a tank ranging from 1,500 gallons (5 678 L) to 8,000 gallons (30 283 L). *Also known as* Foam Tanker or Mobile Water Supply Apparatus. *See* Foam Trailer and Mobile Foam Extinguishing System.

Foam Trailer — Foam concentrate tank mounted on a trailer; can be easily towed to the desired location; usually found at fixed-site facilities and used to supply master stream and subsurface injection systems. *See* Foam Tender and Mobile Foam Extinguishing System.

Foam-Water Sprinkler — Deluge-type open sprinkler that mixes water with the foam solution as it passes through the sprinkler. *See* Closed Sprinkler and Open Sprinkler.

Focal Length — Distance behind the lens where light from an object is sharply focused when the lens is set to infinity.

Foehn Wind — Wind that occurs when stable, high-pressure air is forced across and then down the lee slopes of a mountain range. The descending air is warmed and dried due to adiabatic compression; locally called by various names such as Santa Ana, Mono, or Chinook. *Also known as* Gravity Wind.

Fog Nozzle — Nozzle that can provide either a fixed or variable spray pattern; breaks the foam solution into small droplets that mix with air to form finished foam. *See* Multiagent Nozzle.

Fog Stream — Water stream of finely divided particles used for fire control.

Foil Back — Blanket or batt insulation with one surface faced with metal foil that serves as a vapor barrier and heat reflector.

Fold-A-Tank — *See* Portable Tank.

Folding Door — Door that opens and closes by folding.

Folding Jack — Common type of lifting jack. The frame of the folding jack is made of metal bars of equal lengths, fastened in the center to form Xs. This jack has limited use and is considered safe only for light loads.

Folding Ladder — Short, collapsible ladder easy to maneuver in tight places such as reaching through openings in attics and lofts.

Food Dispenser Unit — Vehicle capable of dispensing food to incident personnel.

Food Unit — Functional unit within the service branch of the logistics section of an incident management system; responsible for providing meals for personnel involved with incident.

Foot and Mouth Disease (FMD) — Acute viral disease of domestic and wild cloven-hoofed animals characterized by fever, lameness, and vesicular lesions on the feet, tongue, mouth and teats. FMD is considered to be one of the most contagious, infectious diseases known.

Footing — (1) Part of the building that rests on the bearing soil and is wider than the foundation wall. (2) Base for a column. (3) Method for securing the base of a ladder.

Foot Pads — Feet mounted on the butt of the ladder by a swivel to facilitate the placement of ladders on hard surfaces.

Footplate — A 4-inch (102 mm) metal plate that runs around the bottom edge of any railing on a balcony or elevated walkway to prevent someone's foot from slipping off such as on an elevating platform to prevent a firefighter's feet from slipping off the edge of the platform. *Also known as* Kickplate.

Force — (1) To break open, into, or through. (2) Simple measure of weight, usually expressed in pounds or kilograms.

Forced Ventilation — Any means other than natural ventilation; may involve the use of fans, blowers, smoke ejectors, and fire streams. *Also known as* Mechanical Ventilation.

Force-Vector Analysis — Graphical tool investigators can use to determine the direction of blast pressure in an explosion.

Forcible Entry — (1) Techniques used by fire personnel to gain entry into buildings, vehicles, aircraft, or other areas of confinement when normal means of entry are locked or blocked. (2) Entering a structure or vehicle by means of physical force, characterized by prying open doors and breaking windows, leaving visible indicators of illegal entry if pry marks and certain window breakage are present upon the first firefighters' arrival.

Forcing Foam Maker — *See* High Back-Pressure Foam Maker.

Fording — Ability of an apparatus to traverse a body of standing water. Apparatus specifications should list the specific water depths through which trucks must be able to drive.

Forecastle (Fo'c's'le or Fok-Sul) — Section of the upper deck located at the bow of a vessel; forward section of the main deck; a superstructure at the bow of a ship where maintenance shops, rope lockers, and paint lockers are located.

Foreign Object Damage — Damage attributed to a foreign object that can be expressed in physical or economic terms that may or may not degrade the product's required safety and/or performance characteristics.

Foreign Object Debris — Any substance, debris, or article that is alien to the vehicle or system and would potentially cause damage.

Foreman — Rank used for a company officer in some departments.

Forensic Anthropology — Science of establishing the identities of deceased victims.

Forensic Pathology — Science of determining the cause and manner of death.

Forensic Science — (1) Application of scientific procedures to the interpretation of physical events such as those that occur at a crime scene or fire scene. (2) The art of reconstructing past events and then explaining that process and one's findings to investigators and triers of fact. *Also known as* Criminalistics or Forensics.

Forensics — *See* Forensic Science.

Forensic Scientist — One who applies scientific procedures to the interpretation of physical events such as those that occur at fire scenes; one who is adept at reconstructing past events and then explaining that process and findings to investigators and triers of facts. *Also known as* Criminologist.

Forepeak — Watertight compartment at the extreme forward end of a vessel; usually used for storage. *See* Afterpeak.

Foreseeability — (1) Concept that instruction should be based not only on dangerous conditions that may exist in training but also on anticipating what firefighters might face on the job. (2) Legal concept that states that reasonable people should be able to foresee the consequences of their actions and take reasonable precautions.

Forestry Hose — Lightweight, small diameter, unlined, single-jacket hose with lightweight couplings used to combat fires in forests and in other wildland settings.

Forged Couplings — Coupling formed by pounding a hot metal pellet into a forging die, which forms the metal into the desired shape.

Fork Pockets — Transverse structural apertures (openings) in the base of the container that permit entry of forklift devices.

Formal Decontamination — *See* Technical Decontamination.

Formaldehyde (HCHO) — Colorless gas with a characteristic pungent odor produced when wood, cotton, and newspaper burn; an eye, nose, and throat irritant, and a probable carcinogen.

Formal Proposal — Written request for funding that describes the educator's organization, the problem to be solved, the solution to the problem (project plan), and the benefits of the project to the prospective donor, the target audience, and the community.

Formative Evaluation — (1) Ongoing, repeated assessment during course development and during or after instruction to determine the most effective instructional content, method, aids, and testing techniques; the evaluation of an individual presentation or evaluation of part of an overall program. (2) Evaluation of a new or revised program in order to form opinions about its effects and effectiveness as it is in the process of being developed and tested (piloted). Its purpose is to gather information to help improve the program while in progress. *Also known as* Process Evaluation. *See* Evaluation.

Former — Frame of wood or metal that is attached to the truss of the fuselage or wing of an aircraft in order to provide the required aerodynamic shape.

Formula — A mathematical computation; used frequently in the fire service primarily for applications such as determining pressures, flows, and friction loss.

Formwork — Temporary structure used to provide shape to liquid concrete while it hardens; can be made of wood, metal, or plastic. Because the formwork must be strong enough to support the weight of the wet concrete, it becomes a major structural system in itself.

Forward — Front or nose section of an aircraft or toward that area. *Also known as* Fore.

Forward Lay — Method of laying hose from the water supply to the fire scene.

Four-Step Method of Instruction — Teaching method based upon four steps: preparation, presentation, application, and evaluation. May be preceded by a pretest.

Four-Way Hydrant Valve — Device that permits a pumper to boost the pressure in a supply line connected to a hydrant without interrupting the water flow.

FPE — *See* Fire Protection Engineer.

Fragmentation — In terms of explosions, describes the process of a confining vessel losing its structural integrity and becoming shrapnel. Low-order damage involves large pieces of debris and shrapnel due to fragmentation, while high-order damage typically involves small, more widespread debris. *See* Shrapnel.

Fragmentation Effect — Process in which bomb parts and components are blown outwards by the explosion in the form of fragments, shards, or Shrapnel.

Frame — (1) Part of an opening that is constructed to support the component that closes and secures the opening such as a door or window. (2) The chassis of some automobiles. (3) Structural member of a vessel's framework that attaches perpendicularly to the keel to form the ribs of the vessel. *See* Keel.

Frangible — Breakable, fragile, or brittle.

Frangible Bulb — Small glass vial fitted into the discharge orifice of a fire sprinkler. The glass vial is partly filled with a liquid that expands as heat builds up. At a predetermined temperature, vapor pressure causes the glass bulb to break, causing water to flow.

Freeboard — Vertical distance between a vessel's lowest open deck and the water surface; measured near the center of the vessel's length where the deck is closest to the water.

Free-Burning Stage — Second stage of burning in a confined area in which the fire burns rapidly, using up oxygen and building up heat that accumulates in upper areas at temperatures that may exceed 1,300° F (700° C).

Freedom Fighters — Members of a militant organization fighting to establish a separate country or state for their nationality.

Freeflow — Continuous flow of air from the regulator, usually venting into the atmosphere.

Freelancing — Operating independently of the incident commander's command and control.

Free Play — In the context of aerial apparatus inspection, refers to the distance an activation device such as a wheel or lever will move while the system it is part of is inactive.

Free Radical — (1) Atom or group of atoms that has at least one unpaired electron and is therefore unstable and highly reactive. (2) Electrically charged, highly reactive parts of molecules released during combustion reactions.

Free Surface Effect — Tendency of a liquid within a compartment to remain level as a vessel moves, which allows the liquid to move unimpeded from side to side. Loose water anywhere in a vessel impairs stability by raising the center of gravity. *See* Center of Buoyancy, Center of Gravity, and Stability.

Freewheeling Brainstorming — Type of brainstorming in which group members speak their ideas spontaneously, and ideas are recorded on flipcharts right away; most spontaneous form of brainstorming.

Freezing Point — Temperature at which a liquid becomes a solid at normal atmospheric pressure. *See* Melting Point.

Freight Container — *See* Container (1).

Frequency — The number of cycles (360 degree coil turn) that occur within an electrical generator; measured in Hertz (Hz).

Frequency-Sharing Agreement — Written agreement between agencies that are licensed to use a communications frequency that allows the other agency to use the frequency under specified conditions.

Friction Burn — *See* Abrasion.

Friction Loss — Loss of pressure created by the turbulence of water moving against the interior walls of the hose or pipe.

Friendly Fire — Fully contained and controlled fire started for useful and nondestructive purposes.

Fringe Benefit — Employment benefit (pension, health insurance, paid holiday) granted by an employer to an employee without affecting the employee's basic wage rate; any additional benefit.

Fringe Vision — Vision surrounding central clear vision that alerts people to areas that may require attention; detects objects over a wide area, much like a wide angle lens in photography.

Front — (1) In meteorology, the boundary between two air masses of differing densities. (2) Section of the vehicle faced by the driver during normal travel or operation; generally indicated by the headlights.

Frontal Attack — Attack directed at the head of a wildland fire, from an anchor point at or near the head of the fire, which then proceeds to the flanks. *See* Attack Methods (2).

Frontal Winds — Winds generated by the movement of an air mass (front) across the earth's surface.

Front Bumper Well — Hose or tool compartment built into the front bumper of a fire apparatus.

Front-Impact Air Bags — Supplemental restraint system designed to deploy air bags to absorb passenger impacts during a collision. These air bags are activated through a system of inertia switches located forward of the passenger compartment and by microelectronic controls that may be located under the front seats or in the console between the front seats.

Front-Impact Collision — Occurs when a vehicle collides head on with another vehicle or object.

Front Member — Firefighter working at the front side of a ladder.

Front-Mount Pump — Fire pump mounted in front of the radiator of a vehicle and powered off the crankshaft.

Front of Ladder — Climbing side; the side away from a building.

Front Stringer — Stringer that supports the side of the stairs with a balustrade.

Frostbite — Local freezing and tissue damage due to prolonged exposure to extreme cold. *See* Hypothermia.

FSC — *See* Fire Standard Certified.

F-Stop — Setting on an SLR or DSLR camera that increases or decreases the camera's aperture size to adjust the amount of light entering the camera.

Fuel — Flammable and combustible substances available for a fire to consume.

Fuel Break — Wide strip or block of land on which the native vegetation has been modified (removed or widely separated) so that fires burning into them can be more readily extinguished. It may or may not have a fireline constructed in it prior to fire occurrence.

Fuel Characteristics — Factors that make up fuels such as compactness, loading, horizontal continuity, vertical arrangement, chemical content, size and shape, and moisture content.

Fuel Continuity — Degree or extent of continuous or uninterrupted distribution of fuel particles in a fuel bed, thus affecting a fire's ability to sustain combustion and spread. This applies to aerial fuels as well as surface fuels.

Fuel-Controlled — Describes a fire in which fire development is controlled by the characteristics and configuration of the fuel.

Fuel-Gas Migration — Tendency of leaking fuel gases to move through pipes, sewer systems, permeable soil, or HVAC ducts, spreading flammable gases to areas often great distances away from the source.

Fuel Load — Amount of fuel present, expressed quantitatively in terms of weight of fuel per unit area. This may be available fuel (consumable fuel) or total fuel and is usually dry weight. *Also known as* Fuel Loading.

Fuel Management — Manipulation of fuel prior to an incident to prevent the occurrence or slow the spread of wildland fire. *Also known as* Vegetation Management or Weed Abatement.

Fuel Model — Simulated fuel complex for which all fuel descriptors required for the solution of a mathematical rate-of-spread model have been specified.

Fuel Moisture — Quantity of moisture in fuel expressed as a percentage of the weight when thoroughly dried at 212° F (100° C).

Fuel Orientation — Position of the fuel (rug as a vertical wall hanging as opposed to rug on the floor, for example).

Fuel Siphoning — Unintentional release of fuel from an aircraft caused by overflow, puncture, loose cap, etc. *Also known as* Fuel Venting.

Fuel Tender — Any vehicle capable of supplying fuel to ground or airborne equipment.

Fuel-to-Air Ratio — Percentage of a fuel-gas suspended in air; ratios within the flammable range can sustain combustion when met with a competent ignition source.

Fuel Venting — *See* Fuel Siphoning.

Fuel Volume — Quantity of fuel per unit area; usually expressed in tons per acre (tonnes per hectare).

Fulcrum — Support or point of support on which a lever turns in raising or moving something.

Fulcrum-Type Stabilizer — Stabilizing device that extends at an angle down and away from the chassis of an aerial fire apparatus. *Also known as* A-Frame Stabilizer.

Full-Cycle Machine — Machine with a clutch that, when tripped, cannot be disengaged until the crankshaft has completed a full revolution and the press slide a full stroke.

Full-Duplex — Radio operating system in which two frequencies are used to communicate over one channel in a radio. This system allows operation in both directions at the same time.

Full-Facepiece Air-Purifying Respirator (FFAPR) — Filter, canister, or cartridge air-purifying respirator that covers the entire face from the forehead to the chin, providing protection to the eyes, nose, and mouth.

Full Frames — Automobile construction (also known as body-on-frame construction) consisting of a steel ladder frame that is constructed using two parallel beams that run along the long axis of the vehicle to form a chassis. Cross members are bolted and welded between these beams to provide rigidity and support. This chassis then supports the powertrain, and the vehicle body is bolted to the frame. *Also known as* Rigid Frames.

Full-Room-Involvement Pattern — Fire pattern that occurs after flashover or after a fire has burned for long periods of time, in which almost all vertical and horizontal surfaces in the compartment will show signs of damage.

Full Structural Protective Clothing — Protective clothing including helmets, self-contained breathing apparatus, coats and pants customarily worn by firefighters (turnout or bunker coats and pants), rubber boots, and gloves. It also includes covering for the neck, ears, and other parts of the head not protected by the helmet or breathing apparatus. When working with hazardous materials, bands or tape are added around the legs, arms, and waist. *See* Personal Protective Equipment (PPE).

Full Trailer — Truck trailer constructed so that all of its own weight and that of its load rests upon its own wheels; that is, it does not depend upon a truck tractor to support it. A semitrailer equipped with a truck tractor is considered a full trailer. *See* Semitrailer and Truck Tractor.

Full-Trailer Tank — Any vehicle with or without auxiliary motive power, equipped with a cargo tank mounted thereon or built as an integral part thereof, used for the transportation of flammable and combustible liquids or asphalt; constructed so that practically all of its weight and load rests on its own wheels; a trailer with axles at the front and rear of the frame capable of supporting the entire weight of the tank.

Fully Involved — When an entire area of a building is completely involved in heat and flame.

Fume — Suspension of particles that form when material from a volatilized (vapor state) solid condenses in cool air.

Fume Test — Qualitative test of a self-contained breathing apparatus (SCBA) facepiece fit in which a smoke tube is used to check for leakage around the facepiece.

Functional Fixity — Decision-making problem characterized by the tendency to use an object only for its designed purpose.

Functional Supervision — Organizational principle that allows workers to report to more than one supervisor without violating the unity of command principle; workers report to their primary supervisor for most of their activities but report to a second supervisor for activities that relate to an assigned function only, and both supervisors coordinate closely.

Funding — Fire department (or other organization) budget plus grants and in-kind contributions.

Furring — Wood strips fastened to a wall, floor, or ceiling for the purpose of attaching a finish material.

Fuse — Single-acting protective device designed to open a circuit on a predetermined overcurrent; types include Edison-based fuses and cartridge fuses.

Fused Head — Automatic sprinkler head that has operated due to exposure to heat.

Fused Sprinkler — Automatic sprinkler that has operated due to exposure to heat.

Fusee — Colored flare designed as a railway warning device used to ignite backfires and other prescribed fires.

Fuselage — Main body of an aircraft to which the wings and tail are attached. The fuselage houses the crew, passengers, and cargo.

Fusible Link — (1) Connecting link device that fuses or melts when exposed to heat. Used in sprinklers, fire doors, dampers, and ventilators. (2) Two-piece link held together with a metal that melts or fuses at a specific temperature.

Fusing System — Electrical and/or mechanical mechanism by which an explosive device is detonated. Typically composed of a power source and some kind of switch.

G

Gabled Roof — Style of pitched roof with square ends in which the end walls of the building form triangular areas beneath the roof.

Gage — See Gauge.

Gage Lines — Term used in steel construction to describe lines parallel to the length of a member on which holes for fasteners are placed. The gage distance is the normal distance between the gage line and the edge or back of the member.

Galley — (1) On an aircraft, the food storage and preparation area. (2) On a ship, the kitchen.

Gallon — Unit of liquid measure. One U.S. gallon (3.785 L) has the volume of 231 cubic inches (3 785 cubic centimeters). One imperial gallon equals 1.201 U.S. gallons (4.546 L).

Gallons per Minute (GPM) — Unit of volume measurement used for water movement.

Gambrel Roof — Style of gabled roof on which each side slopes at two different angles; often used on barns and similar structures.

Gamma Radiation — (1) Electromagnetic wave with no electrical charge. This type of radiation is extremely penetrating. (2) Very high-energy ionizing radiation composed of gamma rays. See Alpha Radiation, Beta Radiation, Ionizing Radiation, and Radiation.

Gamma Rays — (1) One of three types of radiation emitted by radioactive materials. Gamma rays have extremely short wavelengths and very high energy; they are the most penetrating and potentially lethal of the three types of radiation. (2) High-energy photon (packet of electromagnetic energy) emitted from the nucleus of an unstable (radioactive) atom. See Alpha Particle, Beta Particle, Gamma Radiation, and Radioactive Material (RAM).

Gang Nail — Form of gusset plate. These thin steel plates are punched with acutely V-shaped holes that form sharp prongs on one side that penetrate wooden members to fasten them together.

Gangrene — Local tissue death as the result of an injury or inadequate blood supply; often caused by frostbite.

Gangway — Opening in the railings on the side of a vessel for a ladder or ramp providing access to a vessel from the shore.

Gantry — Overhead cross-girder structure on which a traveling crane is mounted or from which heavy tackle is suspended. Supporting towers at each end of the structure are on wheels.

Gas — Compressible substance, with no specific volume, that tends to assume the shape of a container. Molecules move about most rapidly in this state. See Compressed Gas, Flammable Gas, and Liquefied Gas.

Gas- and Vapor-Testing System — Detection and alarm system used mainly in industry and manufacturing where there is a potential for large collections of combustible or flammable gases.

Gas/Vapor Explosion — Chemical, nonseated deflagration that occurs when a fuel-gas mixed with air in the proper ratio rapidly ignites; may reach the level of a detonation if the fuel-gas mixture ignites in a confined space, such as in a gas pipe.

Gas Chromatogram — Chart from a gas chromatograph tracing the results of analysis of volatile compounds by display in recorded peaks. *See* Gas Chromatograph.

Gas Chromatograph — Device to detect and separate small quantities of volatile liquids or gases through instrument analysis.

Gas Chromatography — Characterizing volatilities and chemical properties of compounds that evaporate enough at low temperatures (120° F or 49° C) to provide detectable quantities in the air, through the use of instrument analysis in a gas chromatograph. *See* Gas Chromatograph.

Gas-Free Certificate — Document stating that an authorized and trained person has evaluated the atmosphere of a space, tank, or container, using approved equipment and methods, and determined that the atmosphere is safe for a specific purpose. *Also known as* Certified Gas-Free or Gas Certificate.

Gaskets — Rubber seals or packings used in joints and couplings to prevent the escape or inflow of fluids (liquids and gases). For example, gaskets are used at joints in self-contained breathing apparatus to prevent the escape or inflow of gases and in fire hose couplings and pump intakes to prevent the leakage of water at connections.

Gas Mask — *See* Canister Apparatus.

Gas-Sensing Detector — Detection and alarm device that uses either a semiconductor principle or a catalytic-element principle to detect fire gases.

Gated Wye — Hose appliance with one female inlet and two or more male outlets with a gate valve on each outlet.

Gate Valve — Control valve with a solid plate operated by a handle and screw mechanism. Rotating the handle moves the plate into or out of the waterway. *See* Butterfly Valve.

Gauge — (1) Instrument used to indicate the magnitude of a variable quantity such as pressure. (2) Measurement for wire diameter. *Also known as* Gage.

GEBMO — *See* General Emergency Behavior Model.

Gelling Agents — Superabsorbent liquid polymers capable of absorbing hundreds of times their own weight in water. These gels can be used as fire suppressants and fire retardants. Gels function by entrapping water in their structure rather than air, as is the case with fire fighting foams. *Also known as* Durable Agents.

General Alarm — Larger than normal complement of firefighters and equipment assigned to an incident of large magnitude. In smaller departments this might mean that all available units are assigned to the incident.

General Aviation — All civil aviation operations other than scheduled air services and nonscheduled operations for remuneration or hire.

General Aviation Aircraft — Aircraft used for pleasure or training, business (also known as executive or corporate aircraft), or agricultural purposes.

General Emergency Behavior Model (GEBMO) — Model used to describe how hazardous materials are accidentally released from their containers and how they behave after the release. *See* Engulf (1).

General Operating Guideline (GOG) — Written guideline describing the desired outcomes to be pursued under given circumstances. A GOG allows the responsible individual more decision-making latitude than is allowed by a Standard Operating Procedure (SOP).

General Order — Standing order, usually written, that is communicated through channels to all units and remains in effect until further notice.

General Staff — Group of incident management personnel: the incident commander, operations section chief, planning section chief, logistics section chief, and finance/administrative section chief.

General Support Grant — Money given with "no strings attached"; general support grant money may be applied to any legitimate operating expense, including salaries.

General Winds — Large-scale winds caused by high- and low-pressure systems but generally influenced and modified in the lower atmosphere by terrain.

Generator — (1) Any coil of conductors that is rotated within a magnetic field. As the coil is turned in the field, a voltage is produced. (2) Auxiliary electrical power generating device. Portable generators are powered by small gasoline or diesel engines and generally have 110- and/or 220-volt capacities.

Genetic Effect — Mutations or other changes that are produced by irradiation of the germ plasma; changes produced in future generations.

Gentrification — Process of restoring rundown or deteriorated properties by more affluent people, often displacing poorer residents.

Geographic Information Systems (GIS) — Computer software application that relates physical features on the earth to a database to be used for mapping and analysis. The system captures, stores, analyzes, manages, and presents data that refers to or is linked to a location.

GHS — *See* Globally Harmonized System of Classification and Labeling of Chemicals (GHS).

Gibbs Cam — Ascender for rope climbing.

Gin Pole — Vertical lifting device that may be attached to the front or the rear of the apparatus; consists of a single pole that is attached to the apparatus at one end and has a working pulley at the other. Guy wires may also be used to stabilize the pole.

Girders — (1) Large, horizontal structural members used to support joists and beams at isolated points along their length. (2) Steel frame members in a bus that run from front to rear to strengthen and shape the roof bows. *Also known as* Stringers.

Girth Hitch — Method of attaching a piece of software to an anchor; if attached improperly, it can create a weak link in an anchor system.

GIS — *See* Geographic Information Systems.

Gladhands — Fittings for connection of air brake lines between vehicles. *Also known as* Hand Shakes, Hose Couplings, and Polarized Couplings.

Glare — Uncomfortably bright light, either direct or reflected.

Glass Door — Door consisting primarily of glass; usually set in a metal frame.

Glazier's Tool — Tool used for removing windows from their mountings.

Glazing — Glass or thermoplastic panel in a window that allows light to pass.

Globally Harmonized System of Classification and Labeling of Chemicals (GHS) — International classification and labeling system for chemicals and other hazard communication information, such as material safety data sheets.

Global Positioning System (GPS) — System for determining position on the earth's surface by calculating the difference in time for the signal from a number of satellites to reach a receiver on the ground.

Glovebox — Sealed container designed to allow a trained scientist to manipulate microorganisms while being in a different containment level than that of the agent they are manipulating; built into the sides of the glovebox are two glove ports arranged in such a way that one can place their hands into the ports and into gloves, to perform tasks inside the box without breaking the seal.

Gloves — Part of the firefighter's protective clothing ensemble necessary to protect the hands.

Glucose — Simple sugar.

Glue-Laminated Beam — (1) Wooden structural member composed of many relatively short pieces of lumber glued and laminated together under pressure to form a long, extremely strong beam. (2) Term used to describe wood members produced by joining small, flat strips of wood together with glue. *Also known as* Glued-Laminated Beam or Glulam Beam.

Goal — Broad, general, non-measurable statement of desired achievement or educational intent that usually expresses what a training organization or instructor intends to do for the learner; different from the term *objective*, which states specifically what the learner will do.

GOG — *See* General Operating Guideline.

Going Fire — Slang for a fire of such size and complexity as to be uncontrollable by initial attack units; commonly used term for large wildland fires.

Governor — Built-in pressure-regulating device to control pump discharge pressure by limiting engine rpm.

GPM — *See* Gallons Per Minute.

GPS — *See* Global Positioning System.

Gradability — Ability of a piece of apparatus to traverse various terrain configurations.

Grade — (1) Natural, unaltered ground level. (2) Surface level of pavement or stable earth.

Grade Beam — Concrete wall foundation in the form of a strong reinforced beam that rests on footings or caissons spaced at intervals.

Grade D Breathing Air — Classification of allowable contamination levels in breathing air. Compressed Gas Association (CGA) Grade D allows no more than 20 ppm carbon monoxide, 1,000 ppm carbon dioxide, and 5 mg/m³ oil vapor.

Gradient Wind — Upper-level winds caused by air movement from a high- or low-pressure system; sometimes covering as much as 300 miles (480 km), with speeds of 5 to 30 miles per hour (8 km/h to 48 km/h), and gradual shifts in direction. Gradient winds flow clockwise around high-pressure cells and counterclockwise around low-pressure cells.

Grading Schedule — Schedule of deficiency points by which insurance engineers grade the fire defenses of a community.

Grading System — System used to convert achievements to grades or class standing.

Grain Bin — Large, cylindrical tank used to store harvested grain, corn, or other similar commodities.

Grant — Gift of money to a nonprofit, tax-exempt organization or government organization.

Grantsmanship — Art of raising funds by developing grant proposals and receiving grants.

Grass Roots — Society at the local level as distinguished from the centers of political leadership.

Gravity (G) — Force acting to draw an object toward the earth's center; force is equal to the object's weight. *See* Center of Gravity.

Gravity Circle — Theoretical safety zone that surrounds the center of gravity on an aerial apparatus.

Gravity System — Water supply system that relies entirely on the force of gravity to create pressure and cause water to flow through the system. The water supply, which is often an elevated tank, is at a higher level than the system.

Gravity Tank — Elevated water storage tank for fire protection and community water service. A water level of 100 feet (30 m) provides a static pressure head of 43.4 psi (300 kPa) minus friction losses in piping when water is flowing.

Gravity Wind — *See* Foehn Wind.

Green — Area of unburned fuels, not necessarily green in color, adjacent to but not involved in a wildland fire.

Greenbelt — Landscaped and perhaps irrigated fuel break that is regularly maintained; sometimes put to an additional use, such as a golf course, park, playground, or pasture. Greenbelts may also be dedicated but unmaintained open space within or between developments.

Green Design — Term used to describe the incorporation of such environmental principles as energy efficiency and environmentally friendly building materials into design and construction.

Green Fuels — Vegetation that has a high moisture content and will not easily burn.

Grid — Column layout method used by designers to structure the parts of a page; typical grids are one-, two-, or three-column formats, with uniform margins and uniform spacing between columns.

Gridded Piping System — *See* Complex Loop.

Grid Map — Plan view of an area subdivided into a system of squares (numbered and lettered) to provide quick reference to any point.

Grid System — Water supply system that utilizes lateral feeders for improved distribution.

Grid System Water Mains — Interconnecting system of water mains in a crisscross or rectangular pattern.

Grillage Footing — Footing consisting of layers of beams placed at right angles to each other and usually encased in concrete.

Grommets — Reinforced eyelets in salvage covers through which fasteners may be passed, allowing the hanging of covers with ropes or pike poles over wall shelving and in other difficult areas.

Gross Decontamination — Quickly removing the worst surface contamination, usually by rinsing with water from handheld hoselines, emergency showers, or other water sources. *See* Decontamination.

Gross Negligence — Willful and wanton disregard. *See* Negligence.

Gross Vehicle Weight Rating (GVWR) — Maximum weight at which a vehicle can be safely operated on roadways; includes the weight of the vehicle itself plus fuel, passengers, cargo, and trailer tongue weight.

GVWR Placard — Placard that commercial vehicles are required to display in plain view.

Gross Weight — Weight of a vehicle or trailer together with the weight of its entire contents.

Ground Bus — Part of an electrical service panel where the neutral service wire is connected to the earth by a ground wire.

Ground Cover Fire — *See* Wildland Fire.

Grounded Conductor — Conductor in a branch circuit that carries the return current but that is not energized. The covering will be white or natural gray in color, and will be connected to the service neutral. *Also known as* Common Conductor or Neutral Conductor.

Ground Fault — (1) Accidental grounding of an electrical conductor. (2) Current that flows to ground outside of the normal current path, such as through a ground conductor, metal pipe, or person.

Ground Fault Circuit Interrupter (GFCI) — Electrical device designed to protect people from electrical shock by opening a circuit, thus discontinuing the flow of electricity when grounding occurs. In the event of a short circuit in the device, it prevents electrocution of people in contact with the electrical device. *Also known as* Ground Fault Indicator (GFI) Receptacle.

Ground Fire — *See* Wildland Fire.

Ground Fuel — *See* Surface Fuel.

Grounding — Reducing the difference in electrical potential between an object and the ground by the use of various conductors; similar to *bonding*.

Grounding Conductor — Conductor in a branch circuit that connects the exposed metal parts of appliances to the ground system of the service, in order to minimize the chance of electric shock. This conductor carries no current unless a fault has occurred. The conductor will be bare or have a green, or green with yellow-stripe covering.

Ground Jack — *See* Stabilizer (1).

Ground Ladder — Ladder specifically designed for fire service use that is not permanently attached (either mechanically or physically) to fire apparatus and does not require mechanical power from the apparatus for ladder use and operation.

Ground Support Unit — Functional unit within the support branch of the logistics section of an incident management system; responsible for fueling/maintaining/repairing vehicles and transporting personnel and supplies.

Group — NIMS-ICS organizational subunit responsible for a number of individual units that are assigned to perform a particular specified function (such as ventilation, salvage, water supply, extrication, transportation, or EMS) at an incident.

Group Commander — Person in charge of a group within the incident management system.

Grouping — Furniture, stock, and merchandise moved in a compact arrangement to facilitate protection by the least number of salvage covers.

Group Supervisor — Person in charge of a group within the incident command system.

Growth Ring — Layer of wood (as an annual ring) produced during a single period of growth.

Guards — Protective coverings over dangerous pieces of machinery.

Guide — (1) Document that provides direction or guiding information; does not have the force of law but may provide the basis for what is reasonable in cases of negligence. (2) Device to hold sections of an extension ladder together while allowing free movement.

Guided Discussion — Type of discussion in which a group exchanges ideas directed toward reaching a common goal or conclusion.

Gunning Fog Index — Type of readability index.

Gunwale — Raised edge along the side of a vessel that prevents loose items on deck from falling overboard. *Also known as* Fishplate or Gunnel.

Gusset Plates — Metal or wooden plates used to connect and strengthen the joints of two or more separate components (such as metal or wooden truss components or roof or floor components) into a load-bearing unit.

Guy Ropes — Ropes attached between the tip of a raised aerial device and an object on the ground to stabilize the device during high wind conditions; should be used only if approved by the manufacturer of the aerial device.

Gypsum — Hydrated calcium sulfate used for gypsum plaster and wallboard.

Gypsum Board — Widely used interior finish material; consists of a core of calcined gypsum, starch, water, and other additives that are sandwiched between two paper faces. *Also known as* Gypsum Drywall, Plasterboard, Sheetrock®, and Wallboard.

H

HAD — *See* Heat Actuated Devices.

Hailing — Technique used during physical search; involves calling out to victims and listening for responses.

Halfboard — Device used for spinal immobilization and patient removal; can be used as a lifting harness.

Half-Duplex — Radio operating system in which two frequencies are used to communicate over one channel in a radio; allows operation in both directions, but not simultaneously.

Half Hitch — Knot that is always used in conjunction with another knot; particularly useful in stabilizing tall objects that are being hoisted.

Half-Life — Time required for half the amount of a substance in or introduced into a living system or ecosystem to be eliminated or disintegrated by natural processes. For example, the period of time required for any radioactive substance to lose half of its strength or reduce by one-half its total present energy.

Halligan Tool — Prying tool with a claw at one end and a spike or point at a right angle to a wedge at the other end. *Also known as* Hooligan Tool.

Halogenated Agents — Chemical compounds that contain carbon plus one or more elements from the halogen series that were commonly used as extinguishing agents for Class B and Class C fires. *Also known as* Halogenated Hydrocarbons.

Halogenated Agent System — Extinguishing system that uses a halogenated gas as the primary extinguishing agent; usually installed to protect highly sensitive electronic equipment.

Halogenated Hydrocarbons — *See* Halogenated Agents.

Halogens — Name given to the family of elements that includes fluorine, chlorine, bromine, and iodine.

Halon — Halogenated agent; extinguishes fire by inhibiting the chemical reaction between fuel and oxygen. *See* Halogenated Agents.

Halyard — Rope used on extension ladders to extend the fly sections. *Also known as* Fly Rope.

Hand Crew — Individuals who have been organized and trained for operational assignments on an incident who primarily use hand tools to clear vegetation.

Handi-Talki — *See* Portable Radio.

Handline — (1) Fireline at a wildland fire constructed with hand tools. (2) Small hoseline (2 inch [65 mm] or less) that can be handled and maneuvered without mechanical assistance.

Handline Nozzle — Any nozzle that can be safely handled by one to three firefighters and flows less than 350 gpm (1 325 L/min).

Handrail — Top piece of a balustrade that is grasped when ascending or descending a stairway. Handrails may be attached to the wall in closed stairways.

Handsaw — Saw that is operated by hand rather than a power source. Especially useful for cutting objects that require a controlled cut but are too big to fit in the jaws of a scissors-type cutter, or unsuitable for cutting with a power saw.

Hand Shakes — *See* Gladhands.

Hand Tool — Tool that is manipulated and powered by human force.

Harbormaster — Person in charge of a port (anchorages, dock spaces, etc.) in the United Kingdom; equivalent to U.S. Coast Guard Captain of the Port.

Hard Hose — Noncollapsible hose; may be used to describe booster line (hard line) hose or hard intake/suction hose.

Hard Line — *See* Booster Hose.

Hard News — News that has a time value; must be delivered immediately or it will become stale and no longer newsworthy.

Hard Suction Hose — Flexible rubber hose reinforced with a steel core to prevent collapse from atmospheric pressure when drafting; connected between the intake of a fire pump and a water supply and must be used when drafting. *Also known as* Hard Hose, Hard Intake/Suction Hose, or Hard Sleeve.

Hard Target — Term used to define a facility or other target that is well defended or protected against a potential adversary attack; examples of hard targets include most military installations and secured government facilities.

Hardware — (1) A general term used for small equipment made of metal, such as hand tools. (2) Computer system components such as the electronic parts, keyboard, disk drive, and other physical items. (3) Ancillary equipment used in rope systems, for example, carabiners, pulleys, and figure-eight plates.

Hardy Cross Method — Iterative technique used for solving the complicated problems involving gridded water supply systems.

Hasp — Fastening device consisting of a loop, eye, or staple and a slotted hinge or bar; commonly used with a padlock.

Hatch — (1) Square or rectangular access opening in the ceiling or roof of a building, fitted with removable covers for the purpose of providing access and ventilation to the cockloft or roof. Hatches are usually locked on the inside. *Also known as* Scuttle or Scuttle Hatch. (2) Opening in the deck of a vessel that leads to a vertical space down through the various decks (hatchway); covered by a hinged or sliding hatch cover.

Hauling Prusik — Prusik attached onto a main line using a three-wrap Prusik hitch to grab the line and put it into motion. *See* Prusik.

Hauling System — Mechanical advantage system that is constructed of rope and appropriate hardware and is designed for lifting a load.

Hay Hook — *See* Bale Hook.

Hazard — Condition, substance, or device that can directly cause injury or loss; the source of a risk. *See* Fire Hazard, Hazard Assessment, Hazard Class, Hazard or Risk Analysis, Hazardous Material, or Target Hazard.

Hazard and Risk Assessment — Formal review of the hazards and risk that may be encountered while performing the functions of a firefighter or emergency responder; used to determine the appropriate level and type of personal and respiratory protection that must be worn. *See* Hazard, Hazard or Risk Analysis, Risk Management Plan, and Target Hazard.

Hazard Area — Established area from which bystanders and unneeded rescue workers are prohibited. *See* Hazard-Control Zones.

Hazard Class — Group of materials designated by the Department of Transportation (DOT) that shares a major hazardous property such as radioactivity or flammability. *See* Hazard, Hazardous Chemical, Hazardous Material, and Hazardous Substance.

Hazard-Control Zones — System of barriers surrounding designated areas at emergency scenes, intended to limit the number of persons exposed to a hazard and to facilitate its mitigation. A major incident has three zones: Restricted (Hot) Zone, Limited Access (Warm) Zone, and Support (Cold) Zone. EPA/OSHA term: Site Work Zones. *Also known as* Control Zones and Scene Control Zones. *See* Hazard Area and Initial Isolation Zone.

Hazard Identification — Process of defining and describing a hazard, including its physical characteristics, magnitude and severity, probability and frequency, causative factors, and locations or areas affected.

Hazard or Risk Analysis — Identification of hazards or risks and the determination of the appropriate response to that hazard or risk; combines the hazard assessment with risk management concepts. *See* Hazard, Hazard and Risk Assessment, and Risk Management Plan.

Hazardous Atmosphere — Any atmosphere that may or may not be immediately dangerous to life or health but that is oxygen deficient, that contains a toxic or disease-producing contaminant, or that contains a flammable or explosive vapor or gas. *See* Immediately Dangerous to Life or Health (IDLH).

Hazardous Chemical — Any chemical that is a physical hazard or health hazard to people, as defined by the Occupational Safety and Health Administration (OSHA). *See* Hazardous Material.

Hazardous Material — Any substance or material that poses an unreasonable risk to health, safety, property, and/or the environment if it is not properly controlled during handling, storage, manufacture, processing, packaging, use, disposal, or transportation. *See* Corrosive Material, Dangerous Goods (1), Hazardous Chemical, Hazardous Substance, Hazardous Waste, Material, and Product.

Hazardous Materials Company — Any piece of equipment having the capabilities, PPE, equipment, and complement of personnel as specified in the Hazardous Materials Company Types and Minimum Standards. The personnel complement shall include one member who is trained to a minimum level of Assistant Safety Officer - Hazardous Materials.

Hazardous Materials Incident — Emergency, with or without fire, that involves the release or potential release of a hazardous material. *See* Hazardous Material.

Hazardous Materials Regulations (HMR) — Regulations for the safe handling and transport of hazardous materials, developed and enforced by the U.S. Department of Transportation (DOT).

Hazardous Materials Task Force — Group of resources with common communications and a leader; may be pre-established and sent to an incident, or formed at the incident.

Hazardous Materials Technician — Individual trained to use specialized protective clothing and control equipment to control the release of a hazardous material. Hazardous materials technicians can specialize in four areas: Cargo Tank Specialty, Intermodal Tank Specialty, Marine Tank Vessel Specialty, and Tank Car Specialty.

Hazardous Materials Transportation Act (HMTA) — Law enacted in 1975 whose primary objective was to provide adequate protection against the risks to life and property inherent in the commercial transportation of hazardous material by improving the regulatory and enforcement authority of the Secretary of Transportation.

Hazardous Substance — Any substance designated under the U.S. Clean Water Act and the Comprehensive Environmental Response, Compensation and Liability Act (CERCLA) as posing a threat to waterways and the environment when released. *See* Extremely Hazardous Substance and Hazardous Material.

Hazardous Waste — Discarded material with no monetary value that can have the same hazardous properties it had before being used. Regulated by the U.S. Environmental Protection Agency (EPA) because of public health and safety concerns; regulatory authority is granted under the Resource Conservation and Recovery Act. *See* Hazardous Material.

Hazardous Waste Operations and Emergency Response (HAZWOPER) — U.S. regulations in Title 29 (Labor) *CFR* 1910.120 for cleanup operations involving hazardous substances and emergency response operations for releases of hazardous substances. *See Code of Federal Regulations (CFR)*.

Hazen-Williams Formula — Empirical formula for calculating friction loss in water systems; fire protection industry standard. To comply with most nationally recognized standards, the Hazen-Williams formula must be used.

HAZWOPER — *See* Hazardous Waste Operations and Emergency Response.

HBV — *See* Hepatitis B Virus.

Head — (1) Front and rear closure of a tank shell. (2) Alternate term for pressure, especially pressure due to elevation. For every 1-foot increase in elevation, 0.434 psi is gained (for every 1-meter increase in elevation, 9.82 kPa is gained). *Also known as* Head Pressure. (3) Top of a window or door frame. (4) Most active part of a wildland fire; the forward advancing part. *Also known as* Head of a Fire.

Head-End Power — Power developed by generators in a train's locomotive to support the energy needs of the other cars in the train consist.

Header — (1) Gathering unit portion of a combine. (2) Term used to describe the looming up of smoke from a fire. (3) Surface contact piece that collects load from uppermost area of a vertical shoring system.

Header Course — (1) Course of bricks with the ends of the bricks facing outward. (2) Masonry unit laid flat on its bed across the width of a wall, with its face perpendicular to the face of the wall; used to bond two wythes. *See* Course and Wythe.

Head Harness — Straps that hold the self-contained breathing apparatus (SCBA) facepiece in place. *Also known as* Spider Strap.

Headline — (1) Head of a newspaper story or article, usually printed in larger type, that introduces and gives the gist of the story or article that follows. (2) To publicize highly.

Head of a Fire — *See* Head.

Head-on Collision — Collision occurring when the front of a vehicle strikes either another vehicle in the front or a stationary object.

Head Pressure — Pressure exerted by a stationary column of water, directly proportional to the height of the column. *See* Head (2).

Head Protection Systems (HPS) — Air bags that deploy

from a narrow opening between the headliner and the top of the door frame to protect passengers' heads.

Headwind — Wind that is blowing in a direction toward the face of a person or the front of an aircraft. *See* Crosswind, Downwind, and Wind.

Health and Safety Officer (HSO) — Member of a fire and emergency services organization who is assigned and authorized by the administration as the manager of the health and safety program, and performs the duties, functions, and responsibilities in NFPA® 1521, *Standard for Fire Department Safety Officer*. This individual must meet the qualifications or approved equivalent of this standard.

Health Canada — Agency responsible for developing health policy, enforcing health regulations, promoting disease prevention, and enhancing healthy living in Canada.

Health Department — Governmental agency that focuses on issues related to the general health of citizens within a given region.

Health Hazard — Material that may directly affect an individual's health once it enters or comes in contact with the body. *See* Physical Hazard.

Heart — Hollow muscular organ that receives the blood from the veins, sends it through the lungs to be oxygenated, then pumps it to the arteries.

Heart Attack — *See* Acute Myocardial Infarction.

Heat — (1) Form of energy associated with the motion of atoms or molecules in solids or liquids that is transferred from one body to another as a result of a temperature difference between the bodies, such as from the sun to the earth. To signify its intensity, it is measured in degrees of temperature. (2) Form of energy associated with the motion of atoms or molecules and capable of being transmitted through solid and fluid media by conduction, through fluid media by convection, and through empty space by radiation. *See* Conduction, Convection, Heat Transfer, Pyrolysis, and Radiation.

Heat Actuated Devices (HAD) — Thermostatically controlled detection devices used to activate fire equipment, alarms, or appliances.

Heat Cramps — Heat illness resulting from prolonged exposure to high temperatures; characterized by excessive sweating, muscle cramps in the abdomen and legs, faintness, dizziness, and exhaustion. *See* Heat Exhaustion, Heat Rash, Heat Stress, and Heat Stroke.

Heat Detector — Alarm-initiating device that is designed to be responsive to a predetermined rate of temperature increase or to a predetermined temperature level.

Heat Energy Applied — Sum of the temperature of the heat source and the time of exposure.

Heat Exhaustion — Heat illness caused by exposure to excessive heat; symptoms include weakness, cold and clammy skin, heavy perspiration, rapid and shallow breathing, weak pulse, dizziness, and sometimes unconsciousness. *See* Heat Cramps, Heat Rash, Heat Stress, and Heat Stroke.

Heat Flux — Scientific measurement of how much heat is available for transfer to human skin (or any other surface). *See* Radiant Heat Flux.

Heat Flux History — Amount of heat flux exposed to materials over the duration of a fire.

Heat From Arcing — Type of electrical heating that occurs when the current flow is interrupted.

Heating Tube — Tube installed inside a tank to heat the contents. *Also known as* Fire Tube.

Heating, Ventilating, and Air Conditioning (HVAC) System — Mechanical system used to provide environmental control within a structure, and the equipment necessary to make it function; usually a single, integrated unit with a complex system of ducts throughout the building. *Also known as* Air-Handling System. *See* Mechanical System.

Heat of Combustion — Total amount of thermal energy (heat) that could be generated by the combustion (oxidation) reaction if a fuel were completely burned. The heat of combustion is measured in British Thermal Units (Btu) per pound or kilojoules per gram. *See* Combustion and Heat.

Heat of Decomposition — Release of heat from decomposing compounds, usually due to bacterial action.

Heat of Friction — Heat created by the movement of two surfaces against each other.

Heat of Hydration — During the hardening of concrete, heat is given off by the chemical process of hydration.

Heat of Ignition — Heat energy that brings about ignition; comes from various forms and usually from a specific object or source. Therefore, the heat of ignition is divided into two parts: (a) equipment involved in ignition and (b) form of heat of ignition.

Heat of Solution — Heat released by the solution of matter in a liquid.

Heat of Vaporization — Quantity of heat required to transform a liquid into a vapor.

Heat Protective Shield — Reflective shield attached around an elevating platform to protect firefighters in the platform from the effects of radiated heat.

Heat Rash — Condition that develops from continuous exposure to heat and humid air; aggravated by clothing that rubs the skin. Reduces the individual's tolerance to heat. *See* Heat Cramps, Heat Exhaustion, Heat Stress, and Heat Stroke.

Heat Release Rate (HRR) — (1) Total amount of heat produced or released to the atmosphere from the convective-lift fire phase of a fire, per unit mass of fuel consumed per unit time. (2) Measurement of the amount of heat released when a material burns as stated in kilowatts or British Thermal Units (Btu).

Heat Resistance — Foam's ability to resist the actual heat of the liquid or surface on which it is applied.

Heat Sensor Label — Label affixed to the ladder beam near the tip to provide a warning that the ladder has been subjected to excessive heat.

Heat Shadowing — Fire pattern left when an object blocks a fire's radiant heat from reaching a combustible surface behind the object. *See* Protected Area.

Heat Stratification — *See* Thermal Layering (of Gases).

Heat Stress — Combination of environmental and physical work factors that compose the heat load imposed on the body; environmental factors include air, temperature, radiant heat exchange, air movement, and water vapor pressure. Physical work contributes because of the metabolic heat in the body; clothing also has an effect. *See* Heat Cramps, Heat Exhaustion, Heat Rash, and Heat Stroke.

Heat Stroke — Heat illness caused by heat exposure, resulting in failure of the body's heat regulating mechanism; symptoms include (a) high fever of 105° to 106° F (40.5° to 41.1° C), (b) dry, red, and hot skin, (c) rapid, strong pulse, and (d) deep breaths or convulsions. May result in coma or even death. *Also known as* Sunstroke. *See* Heat Cramps, Heat Exhaustion, Heat Rash, and Heat Stress.

Heat Transfer — Flow of heat from a hot substance to a cold substance. This flow may be accomplished by convection, conduction, or radiation. *See* Conduction, Convection, Heat, and Radiation.

Heat Treatment — Controlled cooling or quenching of heated metals, in order to harden the metal; usually accomplished by immersion in a liquid quenching medium.

Heat Wave — Movement of radiated heat through space until it reaches an opaque object.

Heavy Content Fire Loading — Storing of combustible materials in high piles that are placed close together.

Heavy-Duty Appliances — Master stream equipment.

Heavy Equipment — Ground vehicles such as bulldozers, tractors, and plows used in the suppression of wildland fires and their transport vehicles. Heavy equipment does not include fire apparatus.

Heavy Equipment Transport — Any ground vehicle capable of transporting a dozer or tractor.

Heavy Fuels — Massive natural cover fuels such as logs, snags, and large limbs. Heavy fuels are not easy to ignite; once ignited, they burn slowly and hot.

Heavy Metal — Generic term referring to lead, cadmium, mercury, and other elements that are toxic in nature. The term may also be applied to compounds containing these elements. *Also known as* Toxic Element.

Heavy Rescue Vehicle — Large rescue vehicle that may be constructed on a custom or commercial chassis. Additional equipment carried by the heavy rescue unit includes A-frames or gin poles, cascade systems, larger power plants, trench and storing equipment, small pumps and foam equipment, large winches, hydraulic booms, large quantities of rope and rigging equipment, air compressors, and ladders.

Heavy Stream — *See* Master Stream.

Heavy Timber Construction — Type of construction in which the structural frame is composed of large wooden beams, columns, and trusses. *See* Type IV Construction.

Heel — (1) Base or butt end of a ground ladder. (2) To steady a ladder while it is being raised. (3) Rear portion of a wildland fire. *Also known as* Rear. (4) Angle a vessel leans to one side due to wind, waves, or turning of the vessel; measured in degrees. *See* Critical Angle of List, Heeling, and List.

Heeling — (1) Tipping or leaning to one side. (2) Causing a vessel to list (continuous lean to one side).

Heelman — Firefighter who carries the butt end of the ladder and/or who subsequently heels or secures it from slipping during operations.

Heel Plate — Metal reinforcement at the heel or butt of a ladder; generally shaped to give the ladder more stability.

Heimlich Maneuver — Technique to clear an obstruction from a patient's airway.

Helibase — Main location on an incident for parking, fueling, maintaining, and loading helicopters.

Helicopter — Rotary-wing aircraft ranging in size from small, single-seat aircraft to large transports capable of carrying up to 50 passengers. As used in fire fighting, it is capable of the delivery of firefighters, water or chemical retardants (either a fixed tank or bucket system), and internal or external cargo delivery.

Helicopter Tender — Ground service vehicle capable of supplying fuel and support equipment to helicopters.

Helispot — Temporary landing spot for helicopters.

Helitack Crew — Crew of individuals who may be assigned to support helicopter operations.

Helitanker — Air Tanker Board certified helicopter equipped with a fixed tank and capable of delivering a minimum of 1,100 gallons (4 164 L) of water, retardant, or foam.

Helmet — Protective headgear worn by firefighters that provides protection from falling objects, side blows, fire environment elements, and eye injuries.

Helmet Faceshield — *See* Faceshield.

Helmet Identification Shield — Insignia or plaque fastened to the front of the firefighter's helmet that generally displays the name of the city, and the firefighter's initials, unit, and rank.

Hematotoxic Agent — Chemical that damages the blood. *Also known as* Hemotoxin.

Hemispherical — Shaped like half of a sphere.

Hemispherical Head — End of a tank that is shaped like half of a sphere; usually found on pressure tanks such as MC-331 high-pressure tanks.

Hemispheric Release — Semicircular or dome-shaped pattern of airborne hazardous material that is still partially in contact with the ground or water. *See* Cloud, Cone, and Plume.

Hemoglobin — Oxygen-carrying component of red blood cells.

Hemorrhage — Profuse discharge of blood.

HEPA — *See* High Efficiency Particulate Air Filter.

Hepatitis B Virus (HBV) — Bloodborne virus that causes liver infection and may lead to liver failure, liver cancer, cirrhosis of the liver, or permanent scarring of the liver. Most adults can make full recovery from HBV, but children and infants are much more likely to develop a chronic infection.

Hepatotoxic Agent — Chemical that damages the liver. *Also known as* Hepatotoxin.

Herbicides — Chemicals designed to control or eliminate all or certain kinds of plants.

Herringbone Room Setup — *See* Chevron Room Setup.

Hertz (Hz) — Measurement unit of frequency. *See* Frequency.

Higbee Cut — Special cut at the beginning of the thread on a hose coupling that provides positive identification of the first thread to eliminate cross threading. *Also known as* Blunt Start.

Higbee Indicators — Notches or grooves cut into coupling lugs to identify by touch or sight the exact location of the Higbee Cut.

High Angle — Environment in which rescuers need to be secured with rope for safety. The majority of the rescue load is supported by the rope system.

High Back-Pressure Foam Maker — In-line aspirator used to deliver foam under pressure. High back-pressure aspirators supply air directly to the foam solution through a venturi action. *Also known as* Forcing Foam Maker.

High Efficiency Particulate Air (HEPA) Filter — Respiratory protection filter designed and certified to protect the user from particulates in the air; must be at least 99.97 percent efficient in removing monodisperse particles of 0.3 micrometers in diameter.

High-Expansion Foam — Foam concentrate that is mixed with air in the range of 200 parts air to 1 part foam solution (200:1) to 1,000 parts air to 1 part foam solution (1,000:1). *See* Low-Expansion Foam, Mechanical Blower, and Medium-Expansion Foam.

High Explosive — Explosive that decomposes extremely rapidly (almost instantaneously) and has a detonation velocity faster than the speed of sound. *See* Ammonium Nitrate and Fuel Oil (ANFO), Detonation, Explosive (1), and Low Explosive.

High-Hazard Training — Training that involves activities that include certain known risks and potential unknown risks. Examples include evolutions or exercises in live fire suppression, hazardous materials mitigation, above- and below-grade rescue, and the use of power tools.

High-Impact Crashes — Aircraft crashes with severe damage to the fuselage and with a significantly reduced likelihood of occupant survival.

High Mobility Multipurpose Wheeled Vehicles (HMMWV or Humvee) — Four-wheel drive military vehicle that replaced earlier Jeep and MUTT vehicles.

High-Order-Explosion Damage — Damage usually resulting from a detonation, including small shattered debris, widespread damage, and near or total destruction of the confining vessel. *See* Low-Order-Explosion Damage.

High-Pressure Air — Air pressurized to 3,000 to 5,000 psi (20 684 kPa to 34 473 kPa); used to differentiate from older air cylinders using a pressure range from 1,800 to 2,200 psi (12 411 kPa to 15 168 kPa).

High-Pressure Fog — Fog stream operated at high pressures and discharged through small diameter hose.

High-Pressure Hose — Hose leading from the air cylinder to the regulator; may be at cylinder pressure or reduced to some lower pressure.

High-Pressure Nozzle — Fire stream nozzle that is designed to be operated in excess of the 100 psi (689 kPa) to which ordinary fog nozzles are designed.

High-Pressure Tank — Cargo tank truck that carries liquefied gases. *See* Cargo Tank Truck.

High-Rack Storage — Warehousing storage of materials on high, open racks that may be as high as 100 feet (30 m).

High-Rise Building — Building that requires fire fighting on levels above the reach of the department's equipment. Various building and fire codes will also have written definitions of what is to be considered a high rise; for example, the *Uniform Building Code (UBC)* defines a high-rise building as any building of more than 75 feet (23 m) in height. *Also known as* High-Rise.

High-Rise Pack — Special kit for high-rise operations containing hose, adapters, nozzle, and spanner wrenches.

High Speed Turnoff/Taxiway — Curved or angled taxiway designed to expedite aircraft turning off the runway after landing.

High-Strength Low-Alloy (HSLA) Steel — Alloy steel developed to provide better mechanical properties or greater resistance to corrosion than carbon steel; different from other varieties of steels in that it is designed to possess specific mechanical properties.

High-Value District — Section of a city in which valuable property is concentrated and in which additional companies and apparatus are needed to combat a fire; usually the central business district of a community.

Hinged Door — *See* Swinging Door.

Hip — Junction of two sloping roof surfaces forming an exterior angle.

Hip Roof — Pitched roof that has no gables. All facets of the roof slope down from the peak to an outside wall.

Hitch — (1) Term used when a rope is wrapped around an object. If the object is removed, the hitch falls apart. (2) Connecting device at the rear of a vehicle used to pull a full trailer with provision for easy coupling. (3) Loop of rope that secures the rope but that is not a part of a standard rope knot.

HIV — *See* Human Immunodeficiency Virus.

H-Jack — *See* Box Stabilizer.

HMR — *See* Hazardous Materials Regulations.

HMTA — *See* Hazardous Materials Transportation Act.

Hog — (1) Vertical distance of a vessel's keel at amidships above a vessel's keel at the bow and stern. (2) To strain a vessel in a manner that tends to make the bow and stern lower than the middle portion, which has greater buoyancy. *Also known as* Hogging. *See* Sag and Sagging.

Hogging — *See* Hog.

Hoisting Cylinder — *See* Elevation Cylinder.

Hold-Down Locks — Locks that secure an aerial device, such as an aerial ladder, in its cradle during road travel.

Holdfast — Constructed anchor for a guy line.

Hollow Square Setup — Room arrangement in which the chairs are positioned as the outside sides of a square; similar to the U-shaped arrangement, but with this setup, the instructor/fire and life safety educator cannot walk into the center of the group.

Home Inspection — Process of educating residents about fire hazards by examining a residence for existing fire hazards and poor safety practices; also used as an evaluation instrument to determine the extent to which fire and life safety behaviors are being implemented in the community.

Home Safety Council (HSC) — U.S. non-profit organization dedicated to the prevention of home injuries.

Homogeneous — Description of a substance that has uniform structure or composition throughout.

Hook and Ladder — Old term for an aerial ladder truck.

Hooking Up — Slang for connecting a fire department pumper to a hydrant or connecting a discharge hose to the pumper.

Hooks — Curved metal devices installed on the tip end of roof ladders to secure the ladder to the highest point on the roof of a building.

Hooligan Tool — *See* Halligan Tool.

Hopcalite® — Catalytic chemical that converts carbon monoxide to carbon dioxide.

Hopper — (1) Any of various receptacles used for temporary storage of a material. (2) Tank holding a liquid and having a device for releasing its contents through a pipe. (3) Freight car with a floor sloping to one or more hinged doors for discharging bulk contents. (4) A funnel shaped bin, used for the storage of dry solid materials such as corn, which discharges from the bottom.

Hopper Window — Type of swinging window that is hinged along the bottom edge and usually designed to open inward.

Horizontal Motion — Side-to-side, swaying motion.

Horizontal Pressure Vessel — Pressurized storage tanks characterized by rounded ends; capacity may range from 500 to 40,000 gallons (1 893 L to 151 416 L). Propane, butane, ethane, and hydrogen chloride are examples of materials stored in these tanks. *See* Pressure Vessel and Spherical Pressure Vessel.

Horizontal Split-Case Pump — Centrifugal pump with the impeller shaft installed horizontally; the case in which the shaft and impeller rotates is split in the middle and can be separated, exposing the shaft, bearings, and impeller. *Also known as* Split-Case Pump.

Horizontal Storage Tank — Atmospheric storage tank that is laid horizontally and constructed of steel. *See* Atmospheric Storage Tank.

Horizontal Strut — Horizontal load-bearing timber placed between two wallplates in a horizontal shoring system.

Horizontal Ventilation — Any technique by which heat, smoke, and other products of combustion are channeled horizontally out of a structure by way of existing or created horizontal openings such as windows, doors, or other holes in walls.

Horseshoe Load — Arrangement of fire hose in a hose bed or compartment in which the hose lies on edge in the form of a horseshoe.

Hose Bed — Main hose-carrying area of a pumper or other piece of apparatus designed for carrying hose. *Also known as* Hose Body.

Hose Belt — Leather belt or nylon strap used for securing and handling charged hoselines, tools, or tying off a ladder. *See* Hose Strap or Rope Hose Tool.

Hose Bin — Tray or compartment, often located on the running board or over a hose bed, for carrying extra hose.

Hose Body — *See* Hose Bed.

Hose Bridge — Device placed alongside or astride hose that is laid across a street to permit traffic to drive over the hose without damaging it. *Also known as* Hose Ramp.

Hose Cabinet — Recessed wall cabinet that contains a wall hydrant and preconnected fire hose for incipient fire fighting. *Also known as* Hose Rack.

Hose Cap — Threaded female fitting used to cap a hoseline or a pump outlet.

Hose Clamp — Mechanical or hydraulic device used to compress fire hose to stop the flow of water.

Hose Control Device — Device used to hold a charged hoseline in a stationary position for an extended period of time.

Hose Couplings — Metal fasteners or devices attached to the ends of a length of fire hose, used to connect lengths of hose together.

Hose Dryer — Enclosed cabinet containing racks on which fire hose can be dried.

Hose Hoist — *See* Hose Roller.

Hose Jacket — (1) Outer covering of a hose. (2) Device clamped over a hose to contain water at a rupture point or to join hose with damaged or dissimilar couplings.

Hose Lay — (1) Arrangement of connected lengths of fire hose and accessories on the ground at a wildland fire, beginning at the first pumping unit and ending at the point of water delivery. (2) Connected lengths of hose from water source to pumping engine. (3) Layouts of hose from a fire pump to the place where the water needs to be.

Hose Layout, Complicated — Hose layout that includes the use of multiple lengths of unequal hoselines, unequal wyed or manifold lines, siamesed lines, or master stream devices. Such a layout requires the pump operator to perform complicated calculations in order to supply the lines properly.

Hose Layout, Simple — Hose layout that includes the use of single hoselines or multiple, wyed, siamesed, or manifold lines of equal length.

Hoseline — Flexible conduit (fire hose) used to transport water from a source of supply to a point of application, usually onto a fire. May be used to deliver water from a hydrant or other source to a pumper, from a pumper to a nozzle or other appliance, or directly from the source to the application.

Hoseline Tee — Fitting that may be installed between lengths of hose to provide an independently controlled outlet for a branch line.

Hose Load Finish — *See* Finish.

Hose Pack — Compact bundle of hose, usually bound to facilitate moving.

Hose Plug — Threaded male fitting used to cap off a pump intake.

Hose Rack — Device used to hold a length of hose preconnected to a standpipe or other source of water for incipient fire fighting. *See* Hose Cabinet.

Hose Ramp — *See* Hose Bridge.

Hose Record — Individual history of a section of hose from the time it is purchased until it is taken out of service.

Hose Reel — Cylindrical device upon which fire hose is manually or mechanically rolled for later deployment.

Hose Roller — Metal device with a roller that can be placed over a windowsill or roof's edge to protect a hose and make it easier to hoist. *Also known as* Hose Hoist.

Hose Strap — Strap or chain with a handle suitable for placing over a ladder rung; used to carry and secure a hoseline. *See* Hose Belt or Rope Hose Tool.

Hose Test Gate Valve — Special valve designed to prevent injury caused by a burst hoseline during hose testing.

Hose Tool — *See* Hose Strap.

Hose Tower — Part of a fire station or building designed so that fire hose can be hung vertically to drain and dry.

Hose Trough — *See* Hose Tube.

Hose Tube — Housing used on tank and bulk commodity trailers for the storage of cargo handling hoses. *Also known as* Hose Trough.

Hose Wringer — Device used to remove water and air from large diameter hose.

Hot Conductor — *See* Ungrounded Conductor.

Hot-Gas-Layer Pattern — Fire pattern formed by radiant heat in the hot-gas layer during a fire before flashover; these patterns are found when fires are extinguished before the fire has reached flashover.

Hotel — Subdivision of residential property classification consisting of structures or groups of structures with more than 16 sleeping units, primarily used as lodging by transients; these structures must be under single management, and meals may or may not be provided. *Also known as* Apartment Hotel, Club, Inn, Lodging House, or Motel.

Hotel Raise — Method of raising a fire department extension ladder in line with several windows so that individuals can simultaneously escape from more than one floor. *Also known as* Factory Raise.

Hotline — Telephone line and operation set up for receiving information on one particular subject, often relating to criminal behavior and given anonymously.

Hot Refuel/Defuel — Refueling or defueling of an aircraft while the engines are operating. *Also known as* Rapid Refuel/Defuel.

Hotshot Crew — Highly trained fire fighting crew used primarily in handline construction.

Hot Smoldering Phase — Phase or stage of fire in which the level of oxygen in a confined space is below that needed for flaming combustion; characterized by glowing embers, high heat at all levels of the room, and heavy smoke and fire gas production.

Hot Spot — Particularly active area of a wildland fire.

Hotspotting — Checking the spread of fire at points of more rapid spread or special threat only.

Hot Work — (1) Any operation that requires the use of tools or machines that may produce a source of ignition. (2) In maritime terms, any construction, alteration, repair, or shipbreaking operation involving riveting, welding, burning, or similar fire-producing operations.

Hourglass Pattern — Fire pattern that occurs when a smaller fire burns directly adjacent to a horizontal surface, leaving an inverted V-pattern on the wall with a traditional V-pattern above the inverted V.

House — Structure located above the main deck. *See* Superstructure.

Household Fire Warning Systems — Detection and alarm systems that include single- and multiple-station smoke detectors as well as more complicated combination systems.

House Lights — Lights throughout the fire station that are controlled from the alarm or watch desk, which makes it possible to illuminate the entire station when an alarm is received or in case of emergency.

House Line — Permanently fixed, private standpipe hoseline.

House Watch — Duty of maintaining the fire station alarm center for a prescribed period of time.

HPS — *See* Head Protection Systems.

HRR — *See* Heat Release Rate.

HSC — *See* Home Safety Council.

HSO — *See* Health and Safety Officer.

HUD — *See* Department of Housing and Urban Development.

Hull — Main structural frame or body of a vessel below the weather deck.

Human Factors — (1) Individual's attributes or characteristics that cause that individual to be involved in more accidents than others. (2) Natural desire to conserve our human resources as well as to prevent needless suffering from physical pain or emotional stress.

Human Immunodeficiency Virus (HIV) — Sexually transmitted and bloodborne virus that is the cause of AIDS.

Hunter Model of Instruction — Method of instruction that emphasizes practice or application to achieve mastery of skills; developed by Madeline Hunter of UCLA.

Hydrant Adapter — Adapter, fitting, or coupling to connect hose or pumper intake hose to a fire hydrant.

Hydrant Hose House — Small, fully enclosed structure enclosing a fire hydrant and containing some amount of fire hose and appropriate tools and appliances.

Hydrant Pressure — Amount of pressure being supplied by a hydrant without assistance.

Hydrant Wrench — Specially designed tool used to open or close a hydrant and to remove hydrant caps.

Hydration — (1) Act or process of combining with water. (2) Condition of having adequate fluid in body tissues through adequate fluid intake. (3) Chemical process in which concrete changes to a solid state and gains strength.

Hydraulic Calculations — Process of using mathematics to solve problems involving fire hydraulics.

Hydraulic Jack — Lifting jack that uses hydraulic fluid power supplied from a manually operated hand lever.

Hydraulic Pump — Positive displacement-type pump that imparts pressure on hydraulic oil within the hydraulic system.

Hydraulic Reservoir — Supplies the hydraulic fluid that is moved in and out of a hydraulic system; fluid displaced from the system flows back into the reservoir for storage before being recirculated through the system.

Hydraulics — Branch of fluid mechanics dealing with the mechanical properties of liquids and the application of these properties in engineering.

Hydraulic Shoring — Shores or jacks with movable parts that are operated by the action of hydraulic fluid.

Hydraulic System — (1) Aircraft system that transmits power by means of a fluid under pressure. (2) Aerial apparatus system that provides power to the stabilizers and aerial device.

Hydraulic Ventilation — Method of ventilating a fire building by directing a fog stream of water out a window to increase air and smoke movement.

Hydrocarbon Fuel — Petroleum-based organic compound that contains only hydrogen and carbon. *See* Liquefied Compressed Gas, Liquefied Petroleum Gas, and Polar Solvent Fuel.

Hydrocarbons — Organic compound containing only hydrogen and carbon and found primarily in petroleum products and coal.

Hydrogen Chloride (HCL) — Gas produced by the combustion of polyvinyl chlorides; when inhaled, it mixes with the moisture in the respiratory tract and forms hydrochloric acid.

Hydrogen Cyanide (HCN) — Colorless, toxic gas with a faint odor similar to bitter almonds; produced by the combustion of nitrogen-bearing substances.

Hydrogen Sulfide (H₂S) — Colorless gas with a strong rotten-egg odor produced when rubber insulation, tires, and woolen materials burn, and by the decomposition of sulfur-bearing organic material; dangerous because it quickly deactivates the sense of smell. It is commonly called *silo gas*, although it is actually one of several components of silo gas.

Hydrokinetics — Branch of hydraulics having to do with liquids (water) in motion, particularly in relation to forces created by or applied to the liquid in motion.

Hydrolyze — To cause or undergo a chemical process of decomposition involving the splitting of a bond and the addition of the element of water.

Hydrophobic — Incapable of mixing with water.

Hydroplaning — Condition in which moving tires (automobile or aircraft) are separated from pavement surfaces by steam and/or water or liquid rubber film, resulting in loss of mechanical braking effectiveness.

Hydrostatics — Branch of hydraulics dealing with the properties of liquids (water) at rest, particularly in relation to pressures resulting from or applied to the static liquid.

Hydrostatic Test — Testing method that uses water under pressure to check the integrity of pressure vessels.

Hygroscopic — Ability of a substance to absorb moisture from the air.

Hyperglycemia — Excessive sugar in the blood due to lack of insulin to metabolize the sugar. *Also known as* Diabetic Ketoacidosis.

Hypergolic — Chemical reaction between a fuel and an oxidizer that causes immediate ignition on contact, without the presence of air. An example is the contact of fuming nitric acid and UDMH (unsymmetrical dimethyl hydrazine). *See* Hypergolic Materials.

Hypergolic Materials — Materials that ignite when they come in contact with each other. The chemical reactions of hypergolic substances vary from slow reactions that may barely be visible to reactions that occur with explosive force. *See* Hypergolic.

Hypertension — High blood pressure; blood higher pressure than normal.

Hyperthermia — Abnormally high body temperature.

Hyperventilation — Rapid breathing that overoxygenates the blood.

Hypoglycemia — Potentially life-threatening condition in which the level of sugar in the blood is abnormally low.

Hypotension — Low blood pressure; blood pressure lower than normal.

Hypothermia — Abnormally low or decreased body temperature. *Also known as* Systemic Hypothermia. *See* Frostbite.

Hypothesis — Theory proposed about phenomena at a scene which requires further investigation and must be proved or disproved based upon evidence collected from the scene.

Hypovolemia — Decreased blood volume.

Hypovolemic Shock — Shock caused by loss of blood.

Hypoxia — Condition caused by a deficiency in the amount of oxygen reaching body tissues.

I

IAAI — *See* International Association of Arson Investigators.

IAFF — *See* International Association of Fire Fighters.

IAFPA — *See* International Aviation Fire Protection Association.

IAP — *See* Incident Action Plan.

IBC — (1) *See International Building Code.* (2) *See* Industrial Bulk Container. (3) *See* Intermediate Bulk Container.

I Beam — Steel or wooden structural member consisting of top and bottom flanges joined by a center web section, so that the cross section resembles a capital I.

IC — *See* Incident Commander.

ICAO — *See* International Civil Aviation Organization .

ICC — (1) *See* International Code Council. (2) *See* Interstate Commerce Commission.

ICS — *See* Incident Command System.

Ice Shrugging — Method to remove ice from an aerial device.

Identification Number — Serial number placed on each ground ladder by the manufacturer.

Identification Power — That which stems from the human tendency to follow or mimic those who are admired or respected.

Idle Thrust/RPM — Aircraft engine running at the lowest possible speed.

IDLH — *See* Immediately Dangerous to Life or Health.

IED — *See* Improvised Explosive Device.

IFR — *See* Instrument Flight Rules.

IFSAC — *See* International Fire Service Accreditation Congress.

IFSTA — *See* International Fire Service Training Association.

Ignition — Beginning of flame propagation or burning; the start of a fire. *See* Autoignition and Ignition Temperature.

Ignition Sequence — History of the fire, beginning when the ignition source and the first fuel ignited meet at the area of origin, and proceeding through the entire duration of fire spread through the scene.

Ignition Source — Mechanism or initial energy source employed to initiate combustion, such as a spark that provides a means for the initiation of self-sustained combustion. *See* Combustion, Ignition, and Ignition Temperature.

Ignition Temperature — Minimum temperature to which a fuel (other than a liquid) in air must be heated in order to start self-sustained combustion independent of the heating source. *See* Autoignition, Autoignition Temperature, Flashover, and Ignition.

Ike-O-Hook — Steel hook with an eyelet on one end; used for hanging salvage covers and other devices from pike poles or ropes.

Illegal Clandestine Lab — Laboratory established to produce or manufacture illegal or controlled substance such as drugs, chemical warfare agents, explosives, or biological agents. *See* Chemical Warfare Agent, Explosive (2), and Meth Lab.

Illegal Dump — Site where chemicals are disposed of illegally.

Illumination Unit — Portable light generating unit capable of providing 3 to 6 lights of 500 watts each with extension cords from 500 to 1000 feet (152 m to 305 m) for the purpose of providing a specified level of illumination capacity.

Illustration — Instructional method that uses the sense of sight. The instructor or educator provides information coupled with visuals such as drawings, pictures, slides, transparencies, film, models, and other visual aids to illustrate a lecture and help clarify details or processes.

ILS — *See* Instrument Landing System.

Image Stabilization (IS) — Vibration reduction feature available on some lenses and DSLR cameras. *Also known as* Optical Stabilization (OS) and Vibration Reduction (VR).

IMC — *See International Mechanical Code.*

Immediately Dangerous to Life and Health (IDLH) — Any atmosphere that poses an immediate hazard to life or produces immediate irreversible, debilitating effects on health; represents concentrations above which respiratory protection should be required. Expressed in parts per million (ppm) or milligrams per cubic meter (mg/m³); companion measurement to the permissible exposure limit (PEL). *See* Hazardous Atmosphere, Permissible Exposure Limit (PEL), Recommended Exposure Limit (REL), Short-Term Exposure Limit (STEL), and Threshold Limit Value (TLV®).

Immediate Treatment — Classification for patients with the most serious injuries at an incident, who will require packaging and movement to a health care facility as soon as possible.

Immiscible — Incapable of being mixed or blended with another substance. *See* Insoluble, Miscibility, and Soluble.

Immobilization — To hold a part firmly in place, as with a splint.

Immunity — Freedom from legal liability for an act or physical condition; opposite of *liability*. *See* Liability.

Immunization — Process or procedure by which a subject (person, animal, or plant) is rendered immune or resistant to a specific disease. This term is often used interchangeably with *vaccination* or *inoculation*, although the act of inoculation does not always result in immunity.

IMO — *See* International Maritime Organization.

IMO Type 5 — *See* Pressure Intermodal Tank.

Impact Analysis — Process used to quantify the potential negative effects of a disaster. *Also known as* Business Impact Analysis in the private sector. *See* Analysis and Cost-Benefit Analysis.

Impact Hammer — *See* Pneumatic Chisel.

Impaled — (1) Condition resulting when a patient's head or other appendage pierces a stationary object such as a windshield. (2) Condition resulting from a foreign object becoming lodged in some portion of a patient's body.

Impaled Object — Object that has caused a puncture wound and remains embedded in the wound.

Impeachment — Process of showing the judge or jury that a witness has changed his or her opinion or prior testimony.

Impeller — Vaned, circulating member of the centrifugal pump that transmits motion to the water. *See* Centrifugal Pump, Multistage Centrifugal Pump, Self-Priming Centrifugal Pump, and Single-Stage Centrifugal Pump.

Impeller Eye — Intake orifice at the center of a centrifugal pump impeller.

Impingement — *See* Flame Impingement.

Impinging Stream Nozzle — Nozzle that drives several jets of water together at a set angle in order to break water into finely divided particles.

Implosion — Rapid inward collapsing of the walls of a vessel or structure because the walls are unable to sustain a vacuum.

IM Portable Tank — *See* Nonpressure Intermodal Tank.

Impounded Water Supply — Generally used to describe an open, standing, man-made reservoir, but can be used to describe any type of standing, static water supply.

Improvised Explosive Device (IED) — Device that is categorized by its container and the way it is initiated; usually homemade, constructed for a specific target, and contained in almost anything. *See* Explosive (1) and (2).

Improvised Nuclear Device (IND) — Device that results in the formation of a nuclear-yield reaction (nuclear blast); low-yield device is called a *mininuke*. *See* Radiation (2) and Suitcase Bomb.

IMS — *See* Incident Management System.

Inappropriate Response — Reaction to a decision-making problem in which the person in charge and subordinates might try to hide their fear or revulsion by joking, getting angry, or rationalizing the problem away.

Inboard/Outboard — Refers to location with reference to the centerline of the fuselage (i.e., inboard engines are the ones closest to the fuselage, whereas outboard engines are those farthest away).

Incapacitant — Chemical agent that produces a temporary disabling condition that persists for hours to days after exposure has occurred. *See* Riot Control Agent.

Incendiarism — Deliberate setting of a fire or fires by a human being.

Incendiary — (1) An incendiary agent such as a bomb. (2) A fire deliberately set under circumstances in which the responsible party knows it should not be ignited. (3) Relating to or involving a deliberate burning of property.

Incendiary Device — (1) Contrivance designed and used to start a fire. (2) Any mechanical, electrical, or chemical device used intentionally to initiate combustion and start a fire. *Also known as* Explosive Device. *See* Incendiary Thermal Effect.

Incendiary Fire Cause — Classification referring to a fire deliberately set under circumstances in which the responsible party knows that the fire should not be ignited.

Incendiary Thermal Effect — (1) Thermal heat energy resulting from the fireball created by the burning of combustible gases or flammable vapors and ambient air at very high temperatures during an explosion. (2) Description of the brief but intense heat released during an explosion. In detonations, this heat is unlikely to ignite secondary fires; in deflagrations, this heat is more likely to ignite secondary fires.

Inches of Mercury — Scale used in measuring negative pressure; used to measure barometric pressure.

Incident — Emergency or non-emergency situation or occurrence (either human-caused or natural phenomenon) that requires action by emergency services personnel to prevent or minimize loss of life or damage to property and/or natural resources.

Incident Action Plan (IAP) — Written or unwritten plan for the disposition of an incident; contains the overall strategic goals, tactical objectives, and support requirements for a given operational period during an incident. All incidents require an action plan. On relatively small incidents, the IAP is usually not in writing; on larger, more complex incidents, a written IAP is created for each operational period, and is disseminated to units assigned to the incident. When written, the plan may have a number of forms as attachments.

Incident Base — Location at the incident where the primary logistics functions are coordinated and administered. Incident name or other designator is added to the term "base." The incident command post may be co-located with the base. There is only one base per incident. *Formerly known as* Fire Camp.

Incident Commander (IC) — Person in charge of the incident command system and responsible for the management of all incident operations during an emergency.

Incident Command Post — Location at which the incident commander and command staff direct, order, and control resources at an incident; may be co-located with the incident base.

Incident Command System (ICS) — (1) System by which facilities, equipment, personnel, procedures, and communications are organized to operate within a common organizational structure designed to aid in the management of resources at emergency incidents. (2) Management system of procedures for controlling personnel, facilities, equipment, and communications so that different agencies can work together toward a common goal in an effective and efficient manner. (3) Recommended method of establishing and maintaining command and control of an incident. It is an organized approach to incident management, adaptable to any size of type of incident. (4) Management system of procedures for establishing and maintaining command and control of an incident; developed in California in the early 1970s to address the resource management needs associated with large-scale wildland fires. *Also known as* the California FIRESCOPE Incident Command System.

Incident Investigation — Act of investigating or gathering data to determine the factors that contributed to a fatality, injury, or property loss, or to determine fire cause and origin.

Incident Management System (IMS) — (1) System described in NFPA® 1561, *Standard on Emergency Services Incident Management System*, that defines the roles, responsibilities, and standard operating procedures used to manage emergency operations. Such systems may also be referred to as Incident Command Systems (ICS). (2) Management system developed by the National Fire Service Incident Management System Consortium, combining pre-existing command systems into one.

Incident Safety Officer (ISO) — Member of the command staff responsible for monitoring and assessing safety hazards and unsafe conditions during an incident, and developing measures for ensuring personnel safety. The ISO is responsible for the enforcement of all mandated safety laws and regulations and departmental safety-related standard operating procedures. On very small incidents, the incident commander may act as the ISO.

Incipient Fire Fighting — Activities involved in fighting incipient phase fires inside or outside of buildings or other enclosed structures.

Incipient Phase — First phase of the burning process in a confined space, in which the substance being oxidized is producing some heat, but the heat has not spread to other substances nearby. During this phase, the oxygen content of the air has not been significantly reduced.

Incipient Phase Fire — Fire that is in the initial or beginning stage and that can be controlled or extinguished by portable fire extinguishers or small hoselines, without the need to wear protective clothing or breathing apparatus or to take evasive action such as crawling to avoid smoke.

Inclinometer — Instrument that measures the angle at which a vessel is leaning to one side or the other.

Increaser — Adapter used to attach a larger hoseline to a smaller one; has female threads on the smaller side and male threads on the larger side.

Incrustation — Deposit on the inner wall of a water pipe creating additional friction and loss of pressure.

Incursion — Any occurrence in the airport runway environment involving an aircraft, vehicle, person, or object on the ground that creates a collision hazard or results in a loss of required separation with an aircraft taking off, intending to take off, landing, or intending to land.

IND — *See* Improvised Nuclear Device.

Indemnify — One party agreeing to compensate another party for losses or damages that are incurred if specific actions or events occur.

Independent Learning — *See* Self-Directed Learning.

Index Gas — Commonly encountered gas, such as carbon monoxide in fires, whose concentration can be measured. In the absence of devices capable of measuring the concentrations of other gases present, the CO measurement may be assumed to indicate their concentrations as well.

Indicating Valve — Water main valve that visually shows the open or closed status of the valve.

Indicator — Visual remains at a fire scene revealing the fire's progress and action.

Indicator Action — Part of a behavioral objective that tells how a student will show a desired behavior so that it can be observed and measured.

Indictable Offense — *See* Felony.

Indictment — Formal written accusation charging the defendant with a crime.

Indirect Attack — (1) In structural fire fighting, directing fire streams toward the ceiling of a room or building in order to generate a large amount of steam. Converting the water to steam absorbs the heat of the fire and cools the area sufficiently for firefighters to safely enter and make a direct attack on the fire. *See* Attack Methods (1). (2) In wildland fire fighting, a method of controlling a fire in which a control line is constructed or located some distance from the edge of the main fire, and the fuel between the two points is burned. *See* Attack Methods (2).

Indirect Loss — Loss indirectly associated with a fire.

Individual Container — Product container used to transport materials in small quantities; includes bags, boxes, and drums. *See* Packaging (1).

Individual Emergency Conditions Breathing — Procedures or techniques performed by an individual during emergencies where SCBA malfunctions, remaining air supply is inadequate for escape, or air supply is depleted.

Individualized Instruction — Process of matching instructional methods and media with learning objectives and individual learning styles that enable a learner to achieve lesson objectives.

Induction — *See* Eduction.

Industrial — Occupancy classification whose primary objective is the manufacturing or distribution of products. *See* Occupancy Classification.

Industrial Bulk Container (IBC) — Large-capacity bulk storage container used for foam concentrate, usually in quantities of 250 to 450 gallons (946 L to 1 703 L).

Industrial Consumption — Water consumed from the water supply system by industrial facilities.

Industrial Fire Brigade — Team of employees organized within a private company, industrial facility, or plant who are assigned to respond to fires and emergencies on that property.

Industrial Fire Department — Full-time emergency response organization providing fire suppression, rescue, and related activities at a commercial, institutional, or industrial facility or facilities under the same ownership and management. While the industrial fire department is generally trained and equipped for specialized operations based on site-specific hazards present at the facility, it may also respond off-site under a mutual aid agreement.

Industrial Hose — Fire hose, usually of lighter construction than fire service hose, used by industrial fire brigades.

Industrial Occupancy — Industrial, commercial, mercantile, warehouse, utility power station, institutional or similar facilities.

Industrial Packaging — Container used to ship radioactive materials that present limited hazard to the public and the environment, such as smoke detectors. *See* Excepted Packaging, Packaging (1), Strong, Tight Container, Type A Packaging, and Type B Packaging.

Industry Standard — Set of published procedures and criteria that peer, professional, or accrediting organizations recognize as acceptable practice.

Inert Gas — Gas that does *not* normally react chemically with another substance or material; any one of six gases: helium, neon, argon, krypton, xenon, and radon. *See* Expellant Gas and Simple Asphyxiant.

Inertia — Tendency of a body to remain in motion or at rest until it is acted upon by force.

Inertia Light — Light mounted in the aircraft structure so that a sharp deceleration, such as a crash situation, will activate the light. It can also be turned on manually and removed from the mounting to be used as a portable flashlight.

Inerting — Introducing a nonflammable gas (i.e., nitrogen or carbon dioxide) to a flammable atmosphere in order to remove the oxygen and prevent an explosion.

Infectious — Transmittable; able to infect people.

Infectious Agent — Biological agent that causes disease or illness to its host. *See* Biological Attack.

Inference — Conclusion that is derived from a set of premises.

Inference Development — Development of a meaningful hypothesis, conclusion, prediction, or estimate based on the data available and the knowledge, experience, and expertise of the investigator.

Inferior — Near the feet; below.

In-Flight Emergency — Fire or other emergency that occurs when an aircraft is in-flight; includes hydraulic failure, engine failure, landing-gear malfunction, and other system malfunctions.

Inflow — Flow of grain toward the vortex of the discharge funnel in a grain bin.

Informal Proposal — In-person request for funding.

Informational Materials — Fire and life safety teaching materials that suggest an action or provide facts and figures. *Also known as* Promotional Materials.

Information Officer (IO) — *See* Public Information Officer.

Information Presentation — Lesson plan format for a presentation or delivery that covers theory and technical knowledge, such as the facts of fire growth and spread, and provides the background information (cognitive domain) that is often essential to performance skills development (psychomotor domain). *Also known as* Technical Lesson.

Information Sheet — Instructional fact sheet or type of handout used to present ideas or information that is not in printed form or otherwise available to the student to the learner. An information sheet provides additional background information on a topic, which supplements what is provided in the text or other course resources.

Infrared Analyzer — Instrument used to monitor gas and vapor exposures by measuring the infrared energy absorbed by the contaminant.

Infrared Radiation — Radiation with a wavelength outside the visible spectrum at the red end of the spectrum. Thermal radiation from free-burning fires is an example of infrared radiation.

Infrared Scanner — Device that detects radiant heat emitted by concealed materials by converting infrared energy to an electrical signal; used primarily by the fire service to detect hidden fires.

Infrared Victim Locating Device — Search device that detects heat and may be useful in locating victims.

Infrared (IR) Wave Spectrum — Wavelengths longer than visible light, lying at the red end of the spectrum. *Also known as* Infrared.

Infrastructure — Public services of a community that have a direct effect on the quality of life; includes communication technologies such as phone lines, vital services such as water supplies, and transportation systems such as airports, highways, and waterways. *See* Critical Infrastructure.

Ingestion — Taking in food or other substances through the mouth. *See* Routes of Entry.

Inhalation — Taking in materials by breathing through the nose or mouth. *See* Routes of Entry.

Inhalation Injuries — Injuries as a result of the patient inhaling products other than the normal products of respiration; dust and hazardous atmospheres are the primary concerns in structural collapse situations.

Inhalation Tube — *See* Low-Pressure Hose.

Inhalator — Mechanical device for administering breathing oxygen to an individual who is breathing.

Inhibitor — Material that is added to products that easily polymerize in order to control or prevent an undesired reaction. *See* Polymerization and Stabilizer (2)

Initial Action — *See* Initial Attack.

Initial Attack — Control efforts taken by the resources that are the first to arrive at an incident. This includes hoselines employed to prevent further extension of fire and to safeguard life and property while additional lines are being laid and other forces put in motion. *Also known as* Initial Action.

Initial Attack Apparatus — Fire apparatus whose primary purpose is to initiate a fire attack on structural and wildland fires and support associated fire department actions. *Also known as* Midi-pumper or Mini-pumper.

Initial Attack Incident — Incident that can be handled by the resources in the first-alarm assignment.

Initial Isolation Distance — Distance within which all persons are considered for evacuation in all directions from a hazardous materials incident. *See* Initial Isolation Zone, Isolation Perimeter, Protective Action Distance, and Protective Action Zone.

Initial Isolation Zone — Circular zone, with a radius equivalent to the initial isolation distance, within which persons may be exposed to dangerous concentrations upwind of the source and may be exposed to life-threatening concentrations downwind of the source. *See* Hazard-Control Zones , Initial Isolation Distance, and Isolation Perimeter.

Initiating Device — Alarm system component that transmits a signal when a change occurs; change may be the result of an action such as the activation of a manual fire alarm box, the presence of products of combustion in the atmosphere, or the automatic activation of a supervisory switch. *Also known as* Alarm-Initiating Device. *See* Fire Alarm System, Fire Detection System, and Signaling Device.

Initiators — Cylinder-shaped explosive or gas pressure devices used to create gas or mechanical pressure in order to activate another device; usually found in the seat and canopy ejection mechanism of jet military fighter aircraft.

Injection — (1) Method of proportioning foam that uses an external pump or head pressure to force foam concentrate into the fire stream at the correct ratio for the flow desired. *See* Proportioning. (2) Process of taking in materials through a puncture or break in the skin. *See* Routes of Entry.

Injector Lines — Small tubes or hoselines that inject fuel into the combustion chamber of an engine at high pressures. These pressures may be in excess of 1,200 psi (8 400 kPa).

Injury in America — Resource book for fire and life safety educators that pinpoints the effects of injury and shows how fire and burns fit into the larger picture of injuries.

Injury/Loss Statistics — Facts and figures that reflect the effects of change, are used for long-term evaluation of overall programs, and are the most reliable indicator of the success of a program.

In-Kind Contribution — Gifts of services, time, or products that do not involve money.

In-Line Eductor — Eductor that is placed along the length of a hoseline.

In-Line Proportioner — Type of foam delivery device that is located in the water supply line near the nozzle. The foam concentrate is drawn into the water line using the Venturi method. *See* Foam Proportioning, Foam Proportioner, and Venturi Principle.

In-Line Relay Valve — Valve placed along the length of a supply hose that permits a pumper to connect to the valve to boost pressure in the hose.

Inn — *See* Hotel.

Insecticides — Chemicals designed to control or eliminate certain kinds of insects.

In Service — Operational and available for an assignment.

Inside Hand or Foot — Hand or foot closest to the ladder, or closest to the other member of a two-firefighter team.

Inside Ladder Width — Distance between the inside edge of one beam and the inside edge of the opposite beam.

Insoluble — Incapable of being dissolved in a liquid (usually water). *See* Emulsion, Immiscible, Miscibility, and Soluble.

Inspection — Formal examination of an occupancy and its associated uses or processes to determine its compliance with the fire and life safety codes and standards. *See* Building Code, Code, and NFPA® 101, *Life Safety Code®*.

Inspection Holes — Small openings created by the rescuers in walls, roofs, floors, or other collapse debris; used to check for the presence of victims that may be in close proximity to where the breaching operations are progressing.

Inspector — Person who is trained and certified to perform fire prevention and life safety inspections of all types of new construction and existing occupancies. *Also known as* Code Enforcement Officer or Fire and Life Safety Inspector.

Instructional Design — *See* Curriculum Development.

Instructional Development Process — Process of designing classroom instruction that consists of three major components: analysis, design, and evaluation.

Instructional Materials — Materials that an instructor may use to ensure and/or enhance a good learning experience for students; includes lesson plans, computer-generated slide presentations, lesson outlines, and student worksheets.

Instructional Model — Series of steps that guide development of a program of instruction. It includes the steps of performing a needs analysis, planning the program, developing objectives, completing a task analysis, designing a lesson plan, and creating evaluation instruments.

Instructional Objective — *See* Behavioral Objective and Educational Objective.

Instruction Order — Organization of jobs or ideas according to learning difficulty, so that learning proceeds from the simple to the complex.

Instructor — Individual deemed qualified by the authority having jurisdiction to deliver instruction and training in fire and emergency services; charged with the responsibility to conduct the class, direct the instructional process, teach skills, impart new information, lead discussions, and cause learning to take place.

Instructor Information — Component of the lesson plan that lists lesson resources such as personnel, texts, references, sources, instructional methods, learning activities, training locations, etc. *See* Lesson Plan.

Instrument Flight Rules (IFR) — Regulations governing the operation of an aircraft in weather conditions with visibility below the minimum required for flight under visual flight rules.

Instrument Landing — Landing an aircraft by relying only on instrument data.

Instrument Landing System (ILS) — Electronic navigation system that allows aircraft to approach and land during inclement weather conditions.

Insulating Glass — Two panes of glass separated by an air space and sealed around the edge.

Insulators — Materials with atomic structures that do not allow the easy movement of electrons; opposite of *conductors*.

Insurance Institute for Highway Safety (IIHS) — Independent research organization funded by a host of well-known insurance companies; focuses on crash avoidance and the crashworthiness of vehicles.

Insurance Services Office (ISO) — Private national insurance organization that evaluates and rates fire defense for all communities through the fire-suppression rating schedule. Also serves as an advisory organization to other property-liability insurance companies. *Also known as* Rating Bureau.

In-Swinging Door — Door that swings away from someone who stands on the outside of the opening.

Intake — Inlet for water into the fire pump.

Intake Area — Area in front of and to the side of a jet engine that might be unsafe for personnel.

Intake Hose — Hose used to connect a fire department pumper or a portable pump to a nearby water source; may be soft sleeve or hard suction hose.

Intake Pressure — Pressure coming into the fire pump.

Intake Relief Valve — Valve designed to prevent damage to a pump from water hammer or any sudden pressure surge.

Intake Screen — Screen used to prevent foreign objects from entering a pump.

Integral Construction — *See* Unibody Construction.

Integral Frame — *See* Unitized Body.

Integrated Prevention Interventions — Process of combining education, technology, codes, standards, supporting incentives, and emergency response to address community risk.

Intelligence — (1) Information concerning incident management, operational security, an enemy, or an area. (2) Information about criminal or terrorist activities gathered from multiple agencies and shared to aid with investigations.

Intelligence Section — Section within an incident management system that may be activated when an incident is heavily influenced by intelligence factors, or when there is a need to manage and/or analyze a large volume of classified or highly sensitive intelligence or information. Particularly relevant to a terrorism incident for which intelligence plays a crucial role. *See* Incident Management System (IMS).

Intensity — *See* Fireline Intensity.

Intercostal Muscles — Muscles between the ribs.

Interface — Area between the fuel-rich area and the air-rich area where the two are mixing.

Interior — Internal section of a vehicle; composed of the passenger compartment and possibly a storage compartment.

Interior Access Vehicle — Fire apparatus designed to provide a raised platform for aircraft fire fighting operations that will elevate firefighters to an even level with the aircraft compartment.

Interior Exposure — Areas of a fire building that are not involved in fire but that are connected to the fire area in such a manner that may facilitate fire spread through any available openings.

Interior Finish — Exposed interior surfaces of buildings, including fixed or movable walls and partitions, columns, and ceilings. Commonly refers to finish on walls and ceilings, but not floor coverings.

Interior Structural Fire Fighting — Fire suppression and/or rescue activities within buildings or enclosed structures involving a fire that is beyond the incipient phase.

Interlocking Deadbolt — *See* Jimmy-Resistant Lock.

Intermediate Bulk Container (IBC) — Rigid (RIBC) or flexible (FIBC) portable packaging, other than a cylinder or portable tank, that is designed for mechanical handling with a maximum capacity of not more than three 3 cubic meters (3,000 L, 793 gal, or 106 ft³) and a minimum capacity of not less than 0.45 cubic meters (450 L, 119 gal, or 15.9 ft³) or a maximum net mass of not less than 400 kilograms (882 lbs). *See* Packaging (1).

Intermodal Container — Freight containers designed and constructed to be used interchangeably in two or more modes of transport. *Also known as* Intermodal Tank Container. *See* Container (2), Container Vessel, Intermodal Reporting Marks, and Refrigerated Intermodal Container.

Intermodal Reporting Marks — Series of letters and numbers stenciled on the sides of intermodal tanks that may be used to identify and verify the contents of the tank or container. *See* Intermodal Container and Railcar Initials and Numbers.

Intermodal Tank Container — *See* Intermodal Container.

Internal Floating Roof Tank — Fixed-site vertical storage tank that combines both the floating roof and the closed roof design. *Also known as* Covered Floating Roof Tank. *See* Atmospheric Storage Tank, Cone Roof Tank, External Floating Roof Tank, and Floating Roof Storage Tank.

Internal Resources — Those resources immediately available for fire department use without special arrangements; includes equipment, personnel, capabilities, and supplies.

Internal Respiration — Exchange of oxygen and carbon dioxide in the bloodstream at the cellular level.

International Air Transport Association (IATA) — Global trade organization that represents approximately 230 airlines. Its mission is to represent, lead, and serve the airline industry around the world.

International Association of Arson Investigators (IAAI) — Professional organization for fire investigators that offers training, certification, and opportunities to serve on committees to set standards for the fire investigation profession.

International Association of Fire Chiefs (IAFC) — Professional organization that provides leadership to career and volunteer chiefs, chief fire officers, and managers of emergency service organizations throughout the international community through vision, information, education, representation, and services to enhance their professionalism and capabilities.

International Association of Fire Fighters (IAFF) — Professional organization that represents career fire fighters and paramedics in labor/management relations through local labor unions. The association also gathers data on on-duty firefighter deaths and injuries.

International Aviation Fire Protection Association (IAFPA) — Professional and fraternal association of international airport, municipal, and military fire and emergency services professionals. The IAFPA was formed in 2000 by a group of airport/municipal fire service professionals and industry specialists.

International Building Code® (IBC®) — Code that is dedicated to providing safety regulations for life safety, structural, and fire protection issues that occur throughout the life of a building. *See* Building Code, Code, International Fire Code® (IFC®), and National Electrical Code® (NEC®).

International Civil Aviation Organization (ICAO) — United Nations agency responsible for developing and adopting standards and approved practices for international civil aviation that relate to aircraft rescue and fire fighting (ARFF), air navigation, preventing unlawful interference of air traffic, and facilitating border-crossing procedures.

International Code Council (ICC) — Organization that develops the *International Building Code® (IBC®)* and the *International Fire Code® (IFC®)*, for city and state adoption. Was formed by the merger of the Building Officials and Code Administrators (BOCA) International, Inc., the International Conference of Building Officials (ICBO), and the Southern Building Code Congress International (SBCCI). *See* Building Officials and Code Administrators (BOCA), *International Building Code® (IBC®)*, International Conference of Building Officials (ICBO), *International Fire Code® (IFC®)*, and Southern Building Code Congress International (SBCCI).

International Conference of Building Officials (ICBO) — Organization that provides the *Uniform Building Code (UBC)* for city and state adoption, and produces fire codes in conjunction with the Western Fire Chiefs Association. The ICBO joined with the Building Officials and Code Administrators International, Inc. (BOCA) and the Southern Building Code Congress International (SBCCI) to form the International Code Council (ICC).

International Convention for The Safety of Life at Sea (SOLAS) — International convention dealing with maritime safety; covers a wide range of measures designed to improve the safety of shipping. The first version was adopted in 1914. Since then, four more versions have been adopted. The present version was adopted in 1974 and became effective in 1980. The Protocol of 1978 and Amendments of 1990 and 1991 have since been added.

International Fire Code® (IFC®) — Code that is dedicated to ensuring public safety through the implementation of a unified set of fire protection measures and restrictions. *See* Code, *International Building Code® (IBC®)*, and *National Electrical Code® (NEC®)*.

International Fire Service Accreditation Congress (IFSAC) — Peer driven, self governing system that accredits both public fire service certification programs and higher education fire-related degree programs.

International Fire Service Training Association (IFSTA) — Nonprofit educational alliance organized to develop training materials for the fire and emergency services.

International Maritime Organization (IMO) — Specialized agency of the United Nations devoted to maritime affairs. It first met in 1959. Over the years, IMO has developed and promoted the adoption of more than 30 conventions and protocols, as well as 700 codes and recommendations dealing with maritime safety. Its main purpose is to ensure safer shipping and cleaner oceans.

International Mechanical Code (IMC) — Code that establishes minimum safeguards for heating, ventilating, and air conditioning (HVAC) systems and is published by the International Code Council (ICC). *See* Code and International Code Council (ICC).

International Plumbing Code (IPC) — Code that establishes minimum requirements for plumbing systems and is published by the International Code Council (ICC). *See* Code and International Code Council (ICC).

International Shore Connection (ISC) — Pipe flange with a standard size and bolt pattern allowing land-based fire department personnel to charge and supply a vessel's fire main.

International Society of Fire Service Instructors (ISFSI) — Professional organization for fire service instructors that provides professional development opportunities for its membership.

International Standards Organization (ISO) — World's largest developer and publisher of international standards. In relation to photography, sets the standards for film speeds; these standards have carried over to digital cameras as the ISO number, which mimics the film speed settings in film cameras.

Interoperability — Ability of two or more systems or components to exchange information and use the information that has been exchanged.

Interrogation — Formal line of questioning of an individual who is suspected of committing a crime or who may be reluctant to provide answers to the investigator's questions.

Interrupt Rating — Highest current at rated voltage that a device is intended to interrupt under standard test conditions.

Interstate Commerce Commission (ICC) — *See* Department of Transportation (DOT).

Interstitial Space — In building construction, refers to generally inaccessible spaces between layers of building materials. May be large enough to provide a potential space for fire to spread unseen to other parts of the building. *See* Attic.

Interview — Questioning an individual for the purpose of obtaining information related to an investigation.

Intravenous Fluids — Fluids administered directly into a vein or veins to maintain a patient's medications or hydration.

Intravenous Line (IV) — Catheter placed in the patient's vein to allow fluid replacement and the administration of medications.

Intrinsically Safe Equipment — Equipment designed and approved for use in flammable atmospheres that is incapable of releasing sufficient electrical energy to cause the ignition of a flammable atmospheric mixture. *Formerly known as* Explosion Proof Equipment.

Intumescent Coating — Coating or paintlike product that expands when exposed to the heat of a fire; creates an insulating barrier that protects the material that is underneath.

Inventory — Detailed, written listing of equipment and materials on hand at a given time.

Inverse Square Law — Physical law that states that the amount of radiation present is inversely proportional to the square of the distance from the source of radiation.

Inversion — (1) Increase of temperature with height in the atmosphere. Vertical motion in the atmosphere is inhibited allowing for smoke buildup. A "normal" atmosphere has temperature decreasing with height. *See* Atmospheric Stability. (2) Atmospheric phenomenon that allows smoke to rise until its temperature equals the air temperature and then spreads laterally in a horizontal layer. *Also known as* Night Inversion.

Inverted-Cone Pattern — Fire pattern formed on vertical surfaces by small fires or low-heat-release-rate fires; the pattern appears as an inverted V on the vertical surface.

Inverter — Auxiliary electrical power generating device. The inverter is a step-up transformer that converts the vehicle's 12- or 24-volt DC current into 110- or 220-volt AC current.

Investigation — The conducting of an official inquiry.

Investigative Fire Mode — Situation in which products of combustion or flames are not immediately visible to the first-arriving units, and firefighters must investigate to determine the cause of the alarm.

Involuntary Muscle — Muscle that acts without voluntary control.

Involved — Actual room, portion, or area of building involved in, or affected by fire.

Ion — Atom which has lost or gained an electron and thus has a positive or negative charge.

Ionization — (1) Process by which an object or substance gains or loses electrons, thus changing its electrical charge. (2) Process in which a charged portion of a molecule (usually an electron) is given enough energy to break away from the atom; results in the formation of two charged particles or ions: (a) a molecule with a net positive charge, and (b) a free electron with a negative charge. (3) Physical process of converting an atom or molecule into an ion by adding or removing charged particles, such as electrons or other ions.

Ionization Smoke Alarm — Type of smoke detector that uses a small amount of radioactive material to ionize air particles as they enter a sensing chamber; the ionized air particles then combine with products of combustion that enter the chamber, reducing the number of ionized particles. When the number of ionized particles falls below a given threshold, an alarm is initiated. *Also known as* Ionization Detector.

Ionizing Radiation — Radiation that has sufficient energy to remove electrons from atoms, resulting in a chemical change in the atom. *See* Nonionizing Radiation and Radiation (2).

IPC — *See International Plumbing Code.*

Ipecac Syrup — Medication used to induce vomiting.

IR — *See Infrared Wave Spectrum.*

Iris — Colored portion of the eye that surrounds the pupil.

Ironing — Flattening deformation of aerial device base rails caused by the pressure exerted when the device is extended and retracted.

Irritant — Liquid or solid that, upon contact with fire or exposure to air, gives off dangerous or intensely irritating fumes. *Also known as* Irritating Material.

Irritating Agent — *See* Riot Control Agent.

ISC — *See* International Shore Connection.

ISFSI — *See* International Society of Fire Service Instructors.

Island — Unburned area within a fire perimeter.

ISO — (1) *See* Insurance Services Office. (2) *See* International Standards Organization.

Isoamyl Acetate — Banana oil; used for an odor test of facepiece fit.

Isolate — (1) To set apart. (2) Second of three steps (locate, isolate, mitigate) in one method of sizing up an emergency situation.

Isolation Area — Predetermined area designated for temporary parking of aircraft experiencing emergencies that may adversely affect the safety of people and property.

Isolation Perimeter — Outer boundary of an incident that is controlled to prevent entrance by the public or unauthorized persons. *See* Initial Isolation Distance and Initial Isolation Zone.

ISO Setting — On a DSLR camera, changes the camera's sensitivity to light; mimics different film speeds established on film cameras.

Isotope — Atoms of a chemical element with the usual number of protons in the nucleus, but an unusual number of neutrons; has the same atomic number but a different atomic mass from normal chemical elements. *See* Radionuclide.

J

JAA — *See* Joint Aviation Authority.

Jack — Portable device used to lift heavy objects with force applied by a lever, screw, or hydraulic press.

Jacket — Metal cover that is used to protect the insulation of a tank.

Jackknife — Condition of truck tractor/semitrailer combination when their relative positions to each other form an angle of 90 degrees or less about the trailer kingpin, such as turning the tractor portion of a tractor-tiller aerial apparatus at an angle from the trailer to increase stability when the aerial device is being used.

Jack Pads — *See* Stabilizer Pad.

Jack Plates — *See* Stabilizer Pad.

Jacobs Engine Brake® — Device that mounts on, or within, the engine overhead.

Jacob's Ladder — Flexible ladder made of rope or chain but having solid rungs (wood or iron); used for boarding a vessel or scaling the sides of a vessel.

Jalousie Window — Window consisting of narrow, frameless glass panes set in metal brackets at each end that allow a limited amount of axial rotation for ventilation.

Jamb — *See* Frame.

JATO — *See* Jet-Assisted Takeoff.

Jaws — *See* Powered Hydraulic Spreaders.

Jet — Term used in England for a fire stream.

Jet-Assisted Takeoff (JATO) — Rocket or auxiliary jet used to augment normal aircraft thrust for takeoffs.

Jet Pump — Water-operated pump that creates a suction by using the Venturi Principle.

Jet Ratio Controller — Type of foam eductor that is used to supply self-educting master stream nozzles; may be located at distances up to 3,000 feet (914 m) from the nozzle.

Jet Siphon — Section of pipe or hard suction hose with a 1-inch (25 mm) discharge line inside that bolsters the flow of water through the tube. The jet siphon is used between portable tanks to maintain a maximum amount of water in the tank from which the pumper is drafting.

Jettison — To selectively discard or throw away objects or items in order to lighten a vessel's load during an emergency; for example, external fuel tanks or canopies from an aircraft or cargo from ship.

Jetway — Enclosed ramp between a terminal and an aircraft for loading and unloading passengers.

Jib — Lever used with a block and tackle to lift or lower.

JIC — *See* Joint Information Center.

Jihad — Jihad means to *strive* or *struggle* in Arabic. It encompasses a set of actions that is designed to make a person more pious, to seek perfection in the way of Allah, to expand Islam throughout the world by good example, and to defend Muslims against aggressors. Jihad may be directed against the temptations of evil, aspects of one's own self, or against a visible enemy. In the context of terrorism, radical Islamists use an extreme interpretation of jihad to justify violence against perceived enemies of Islam.

Jimmy — (1) To pry apart; usually to separate the door from its frame, allowing the latch or bolt to clear its strike. (2) A tool used to pry open locks.

Jimmy-Resistant Lock — Auxiliary lock having a bolt that interlocks with its strike, and therefore resists prying. *Also known as* Interlocking Deadbolt or Vertical Deadbolt.

JIS — *See* Joint Information System.

Job — Slang used in the Eastern U.S. fire service to describe a working fire.

Job Breakdown Sheet — Instructional sheet that lists a job and breaks it down into step-by-step procedures and required knowledge. It is designed to assist in teaching and learning a psychomotor objective. *See* Key Points.

Job Performance Requirement (JPR) — Statement that describes the performance required for a specific job.

Job Safety Analysis — Method of analyzing occupational hazards and working toward their solution.

Jockey Pump — Small-capacity, high-pressure pump used to maintain constant pressures on the fire protection system. A jockey pump is often used to prevent the main pump from starting unnecessarily. *See* Pressure Maintenance Pump.

Joiner Construction — Bulkheads that subdivide the ship into compartments but do not contribute to the structural strength of the ship. *Also known as* Nonstructural Bulkheads.

Joint Aviation Authority (JAA) — Organization representing the civil aviation regulatory authorities of various European states; it is associated with the European Civil Aviation Conference (ECAC). The purpose of the JAA is to develop and implement common aviation standards and procedures.

Joint Information Center (JIC) — Facility established to coordinate all incident-related public information activities.

Joint Information System (JIS) — Integrates incident information and public affairs into a cohesive organization designed to provide consistent, coordinated, and timely information during incident operations.

Joint Photographic Experts Group (JPEG) — Group who created the photo compression standard commonly known as the JPEG (also known as .jpg). JPEG's are RAW digital images that have been compressed to reduce their size and make them more editable and useable in digital format.

Joint Service Lightweight Integrated Suit Technology (JSLIST) — Chemical-protective, universal, lightweight, two-piece, front-opening suit that can be worn as an overgarment or as a primary uniform over underwear. The JSLIST liner consists of a non-woven front laminated to activate carbon spheres and bonded to a knitted back that absorbs chemical agents.

Joist — Horizontal supporting member composed of wood, steel or reinforced concrete that directly supports roof, ceiling, or floor assembly in a structure.

Joule (J) — Unit of work or energy in the International System of Units; the energy (or work) when unit force (1 newton) moves a body through a unit distance (1 meter). Takes the place of calorie for heat measurement (1 calorie = 4.19 J). *See* Calorie.

Journal — Book in which all activities of a fire shift are recorded. *Also known as* Day Book, Log Book, or Record Book. *See* Log.

JPR — *See* Job Performance Requirement.

JSLIST — *See* Joint Service Lightweight Integrated Suit Technology.

Judge-Made Law — *See* Judiciary Law.

Judgment — One of three requirements of evaluation; the decision-making ability of the instructor to make comparisons, discernments, or conclusions about the instructional process and learner outcomes.

Judicial System — System of courts set up to interpret and administer laws and regulations.

Judiciary Law — Law established by judicial precedent and decisions. *Also known as* Judge-Made Law or Unwritten Law. *See* Law.

Jumar — Ascender for rope climbing.

Jump Seats — Seats on a fire apparatus that are behind the front seats; usually open and facing to the rear.

Junction Box — *See* Connection Box.

Jurisdiction — (1) Legal authority to operate or function. (2) Boundaries of a legally constituted entity. *See* Authority and Authority Having Jurisdiction (AHJ).

Jury Trial — Court proceeding in which a jury acts as the trier of fact.

K

Kalamein Door — *See* Metal-Clad Door.

Kasch Step Test — Medical test used to measure cardiovascular fitness.

Keel — Principal structural member of a vessel, running fore and aft extending from bow to stern. Forms the backbone of a vessel to which frames are attached; lowest member of a vessel framework. *See* Frames.

Kelly Day — Rotating off-duty shift in addition to the normal off-duty schedule of the firefighter.

Kelly Tool — Prying tool similar to a claw tool, but with an adze blade at one end and a forked blade at the other end.

Kendrick Extrication Device (KED)® — Device used to assist with spinal immobilization and patient packaging for removal.

Kernmantle Rope — Rope that consists of a protective shield (mantle) over the load-bearing core strands (kern).

Kevlar® — Trademarked name of a lightweight, very strong, para-aramid synthetic fiber; used in many products including bicycle tires, sails, body armor, and armor components for vehicles.

Key — Device that allows a person to lock and unlock a locking mechanism. When the key is inserted into the plug of a lock it causes internal pins or disks to align in a manner that allows the plug to turn within the lock cylinder.

Key Box — *See* Key Safe.

Key-In-Knob Lock — Lock in which the lock cylinder is within the knob.

Key Plug — *See* Cylinder Plug.

Key Points — Factors that condition or influence operations within an occupation; information that must be known to perform correctly the steps in a procedure. *See* Job Breakdown Sheet.

Key Safe — Boxlike container that holds keys to the building, usually mounted on or in the front wall; requires a master key to open. *Also known as* Key Box or Knox Box (tradename).

Keystoning — Distortion of the projected transparency image that happens when the projector and screen are not perpendicular to each other.

Key Tool — Tool for manipulating an exposed lock mechanism so that the latch or deadbolt is retracted from its strike; used in conjunction with a K-Tool.

Keyway — Opening in a cylinder plug that receives the key.

Kick Panels — Vertical panel walls of a vehicle that are enclosed by several structural members.

Kickplate — *See* Footplate.

Kiln Dried — Term applied to lumber that has been dried by artificially controlled heat and humidity to a prescribed moisture content.

Kilopascal (kPa) — Metric unit of measure for pressure; 1 psi = 6.895 kPa, 1 kPa = 0.1450 psi.

Kilowatt (KW) — Measurement of rate of heat release measured in the number of Btu per second (equivalent to ten 100-watt light bulbs).

Kinematics — One branch of the study of dynamics that defines the motion of objects without addressing mass and force or the factors that lead to the motion. In terms of accidents, kinematics describe the effects of collisions on vehicles.

Kinematics of Injury — Types of injuries suffered by vehicle occupants that vary depending upon the type of collision incurred.

Kinematic Viscosity — Ratio of a fluid's absolute viscosity (lbf sec/ft^2) to its mass density (lbf sec^2/ft^4).

Kinetic Energy — Energy possessed by a moving object.

Kingpin — Attaching pin on a semitrailer that connects with pivots within the lower coupler of a truck tractor or converter dolly while coupling the two units together.

Kink — Severe bend in a hoseline that increases friction loss and reduces the flow of water through the hose.

Kink Test — Test of hose under extreme conditions to ensure performance by folding the hose over on itself, securing it to maintain the kink, and pressurizing. Pressures used vary with the type of hose tested.

Kip — Unit of weight equal to 1,000 pounds; used to express deadweight load.

Kit — Collection of tools or equipment kept in one location for a specific purpose.

Knee Bolsters — Type of antisubmarine device. *See* Antisubmarine Device.

Knee-Foot Lock — Leg position with the knee against the front of a ladder beam and the instep of the foot hooked around the rear of the butt spur on the same beam; used to secure one beam of a ladder while operating the fly section.

Kneeling — Ability of some buses to lower the front end of the bus to curb level for ease of passenger boarding.

Knock Down — Reduction of most flame and heat generation on the more vigorously burning parts of a fire edge, using an extinguishing agent such as water, in order to bring the fire to an overhaul stage.

Knot — (1) Term used for tying a rope around itself. (2) International nautical unit of speed; 1 knot = 6,076 feet or 1 nautical mile per hour (1.15 miles or 1.85 kilometers per hour).

Knowledge Change — Increase in a learner's understanding of fire and life safety practices.

Known-To-Unknown — Method of sequencing instruction so that information begins with the familiar or known and progresses to the unfamiliar or unknown while making relationships that enable learners to become familiar with the unknown.

Knox Box — *See* Key Safe.

Knurled — Having a series of small ridges or beads, as on a metal surface, to aid in gripping.

kPa — *See* Kilopascal.

Kraft Paper — Strong brown paper made of sulfate pulp.

K-Tool — V-blade tool that is designed to pull lock cylinders from a door with only minimal damage to the door itself.

Kussmaul's Respiration — Deep, rapid respirations characteristic of hyperglycemia (or diabetic ketoacidosis) that result as the body tries to eliminate excess carbon dioxide.

KW — *See* Kilowatt.

L

Label — Four-inch-square diamond-shaped marker required by federal regulations on individual shipping containers that contain hazardous materials, and are smaller than 640 cubic feet (18 m^3). *See* Marking, Package Markings, and Placard.

Labeled — Equipment, materials, or assemblies to which has been attached a label, symbol, or other identifying mark of a testing organization that indicates compliance with certain test performance standards.

Labeled Assembly — *See* Rated Assembly.

Laceration — Jagged tear or wound.

Lactic Acid — Hygroscopic organic acid normally present in tissue.

Ladder — (1) Any fire department ladder of varying length, type, or construction consisting of two rails or beams with steps or rungs spaced at intervals. Ladders are manufactured in a number of lengths and can be manually or power raised. (2) Any stairway or ladder (often nearly vertical) onboard a vessel.

Ladder Bed — Rack or racks in which ladders are carried on a ladder truck.

Ladder Belt — Belt with a hook that secures the firefighter to the ladder.

Ladder Carry — Any organized system for carrying ladders.

Ladder Company — Group of firefighters assigned to a fire department aerial apparatus equipped with a compliment of ladders; primarily responsible for search and rescue, ventilation, salvage and overhaul, forcible entry, and other fireground support functions. *Also known as* Truck Company.

Ladder Cribbing — Pieces of cribbing that have been attached to two lengths of webbing to form the appearance of a ladder.

Ladder Float — Inflated tire or inner tube fastened to a ladder and used to rescue persons from water or ice.

Ladder Fuels — Fuels that provide vertical continuity between strata, thereby allowing fire to carry from surface fuels into the crowns of trees or shrubs with relative ease. They help initiate and assure the continuation of crowning.

Ladder Gin Pole — Gin pole in which the load-supporting member is a straight ladder.

Ladder Locks — *See* Pawls.

Ladder Nesting — Positioning of different width ladders, one partially within another, for storage on apparatus.

Ladder Pipe — Master stream nozzle mounted on an aerial ladder.

Ladder Rig — Term for a simple 2:1 pulley system, used in a vertical configuration to raise and lower loads.

Ladder Spur — Spiked device that is attached to the foot of a ladder to provide good traction on soft ground.

Ladder Stop — Blocks that limit the travel of the fly sections on an extension ladder to prevent the sections from being separated.

Lading — Freight or cargo that makes up a shipment. *See* Bill of Lading and Shipping Papers.

Lagging — Heavy sheathing used in underground work to withstand earth pressure.

Lag Screw — Large wood screw with a hexagonal or square head for turning with a wrench.

Laid Rope — Rope constructed by twisting several groups of individual strands together.

Laissez-Faire Leadership — Style of leadership in which the leader shares responsibility with the group, often relying on other people for suggestions and delegating a limited amount of decision making.

Lake Test — Method of testing a salvage cover for leaks by forming a catchall to hold a small "lake" of water and observing for leakage on the underside.

Lamella Arch — Special type of arch constructed of short pieces of wood called lamellas.

Laminar Flow — Smooth, non-turbulent flow of a fluid that occurs at low velocities.

Laminated Glass — *See* Safety Glass.

Laminated Plastic — Sheet material made of lamination cloth or other fiber impregnated with plastic and brought to the desired thickness or shape with heat and/or pressure.

Lamination — (1) Bonding or impregnating superposed layers with resin and compressing under heat. (2) One of several layers of lumber making up a laminated beam.

Landing — Horizontal platform where a flight of stairs begins or ends.

Landing Gears — *See* Supports.

Landing Roll — Distance from the point of touchdown to the point where the aircraft is brought to a stop or exits the runway.

Landing Site — Area in which a helicopter will land during air medical evacuations.

Land Line — Term for a wire-connected telephone.

Lantern Roof — Roof style consisting of a high gabled roof with a vertical wall above a downward-pitched shed roof section on either side.

Lapping — Means by which fire spreads vertically from floor to floor in a multistory building. Fire issuing from a window laps up the outside of the building and enters the floor(s) above, usually through the windows. *Also known as* Autoexposure.

Lapse Rate — Change of an atmospheric variable (temperature unless specified otherwise) with height.

Large Diameter Hose (LDH) — Relay-supply hose of 3½ to 6 inches (90 mm to 150 mm) in diameter; used to move large volumes of water quickly with a minimum number of pumpers and personnel.

Large Handline — Fire hose/nozzle assembly capable of flowing up to 300 gpm (1 140 L/min).

Lash — To secure or tie anything down, or to something else, with rope or line.

Latch — Spring-loaded part of a locking mechanism that extends into a strike within the door frame.

Latch Bolt — Latch with a shim or plunger that causes the latch to operate in a manner similar to a deadbolt. The latch plunger prevents "loiding" of the latch.

Latent Heat of Vaporization — Quantity of heat absorbed by a substance at the point at which it changes from a liquid to a vapor.

Lateral — Toward the side of the human body.

Lath — (1) Closely spaced narrow strips of wood used to fasten covering material to a wall or ceiling. In older buildings, wood lath was used to support plaster finish on the walls and ceilings. (2) Used to hold salvage covers, sheeting, or tar paper in place when covering a building opening during overhaul.

Law — Rules of conduct that are adopted and enforced by an authority having jurisdiction that guide society's actions. There are three types of laws: legislative, administrative, and judiciary. *See* Administrative Law, Copyright Law, Judiciary Law, Legislative Law, Ordinance, and Statute.

Law of Association — Principle that learning comes easier when new information is related to similar things already known.

Law of Conservation of Mass — Theory that states that mass is neither created nor destroyed in any ordinary chemical reaction; mass that is lost is converted into energy in the form of heat and light.

Law of Effect — Notion that learning is more effective when a feeling of satisfaction, pleasantness, or reward accompanies or is a result of the learning process.

Law of Exercise — Idea that repetition is necessary for the proficient development of a mental or physical skill.

Law of Heat Flow — Natural law that specifies that heat tends to flow from hot substances to cold substances. This phenomenon is based on the supposition that one substance can absorb heat from another. *See* Conduction, Convection, and Radiation.

Law of Intensity — Premise that if the experience is real, there is more likely to be a change in behavior or learning.

Law of Readiness — Principle that a person learns when physically and mentally adjusted or ready to receive instruction.

Law of Recency — Principle that the more recently the reviews, warm-ups, and makeup exercises are practiced before using the skill, the more effective the performance will be.

Law of Specific Heat — (1) Measure of the heat-absorbing quality of a substance as measured in Btu's or kilojoules. (2) Relative quantity of heat required to raise the temperature of substances, or the quantity of heat that must be removed to cool a substance.

Lay — To lay out hose in a predetermined sequence for fire fighting.

Layering — Deposition of fire debris in identifiable layers, such as above or below a floor assembly, ceiling materials, or roof assembly

Layout — Distribution of hose at the scene of a fire.

Lay Testimony — *See* Fact Testimony.

LC$_{50}$ — *See* Lethal Concentration, 50 Percent Kill.

LD$_{50}$ — *See* Lethal Dose, 50 Percent Kill.

LDH — *See* Large Diameter Hose.

Leach — To pass out or through by percolation (gradual seepage).

Lead — Introductory section of a news story, typically the first few sentences.

Leader — Individual responsible for command of a crew, task force, strike team, or functional unit.

Leader's Guide — Publication of the National Safe Kids Campaign® that identifies and discusses seven fundamental steps in coalition building.

Leadership — Knack of getting other people to follow you and to do willingly the things that you want them to do.

Leading Block — Pulley or snatch block used to change the direction of the fall line in a block and tackle system. This does not affect the mechanical advantage of the system.

Leading/Trailing Edge Devices — Forward and rear edges of aircraft wings normally extended for takeoff and landings to provide additional lift at low speeds and to improve aircraft performance.

Leaf Spring Suspension — Type of suspension system consisting of several long, narrow, layers of elastic metal bracketed together.

Lean-to Collapse — Type of structural collapse where one end of a floor or roof section support fails while the other end remains secured to a wall. The floors and roof drop in large sections and form voids.

Learning — Relatively permanent change in behavior that results from learning new information, practicing skills, or developing attitudes following some form of instruction.

Learning Contract — Formal agreement between learner and instructor that establishes an amount of work that must be finished in order to successfully complete a course.

Learning Domain — Distinct sphere or area of knowledge, such as the affective, cognitive, and psychomotor domains. *See* Affective Learning Domain, Cognitive Learning Domain, and Psychomotor Learning Domain.

Learning Environment — Physical facilities where learning takes place.

Learning Objective — Description of the minimum acceptable behaviors that students must display by the end of an instructional period. *Also known as* Behavioral Objective or Educational Objective.

Learning Style — Learner's habitual manner of problem-solving, thinking, or learning, though the learner may not be conscious of his or her style and may adopt different styles for different learning tasks or circumstances.

Learn Not To Burn® Curriculum — Curriculum developed by and available from the National Fire Protection Association® in which 22 key fire safety behaviors for school children, as well as three "local option" behaviors are established.

Learn Not To Burn®: The Pre-School Program — NFPA® curriculum that addresses fire and life safety issues for preschool children.

L-E-A-S-T Method — Progressive discipline method used in the classroom; stands for leave it alone, eye contact, action, stop the class, and terminate.

Lecture — Instructional method utilizing one-way communication in which an instructor or educator provides material verbally by telling, talking, and explaining but allows no exchange of ideas or verbal feedback.

Ledge Door — Door constructed of individual boards joined within a frame. *Also known as* Batten Door.

Ledger — (1) Horizontal framework member, especially one attached to a beam side that supports the joists. (2) Book in which financial records are kept.

Lee — *See* Leeward.

Leeward — Protected side; the direction opposite from which the wind is blowing. *Also known as* Lee.

Left-Hand Door — *See* Third Door (2).

Legend — Explanatory list of symbols on a map or diagram. *See* Title Block.

Legislative Law — Law made by federal, state/province, county/parish, and city legislative bodies that have powers to make statutory laws. *See* Law and Statute.

Legislative Strategy — Compromise between what some parties want and what all parties can live with.

Legislator — An elected official who makes laws.

Legitimate Power — Power that stems from any or all of three sources: shared values, acceptance of social structure, or the sanctions of a legitimizing agent.

Leg Lock — Method of entwining a leg around a ladder rung to ensure that the individual cannot fall from the ladder, thus freeing the climber's hands for working.

Legs — *See* Supports.

LEL — *See* Lower Explosive Limit.

Lens — Clear portion of the self-contained breathing apparatus (SCBA) mask.

Lens Fogging — Condensation on the inside of the facepiece lens caused by moisture in the wearer's exhalations.

LEPC — *See* Local Emergency Planning Committee.

LERP — *See* Local Emergency Response Plan.

Lesson Plan — Teaching outline or plan for teaching that is a step-by-step guide for presenting a lesson or presentation. It contains information and instructions on what will be taught and the teaching procedures to be followed. It covers lessons that may vary in length from a few minutes to several hours. *See* Application, Evaluation (1), Instructor Information, Level of Instruction, Preparation, Presentation, Summary, and Time Frame.

Lethal — Deadly; resulting in death.

Lethal Concentration, 50 Percent Kill (LC$_{50}$) — Concentration of an inhaled substance that results in the death of 50 percent of the test population. LC$_{50}$ is an inhalation exposure expressed in parts per million (ppm), milligrams per liter (mg/liter), or milligrams per cubic meter (mg/m^3); the lower the value, the more toxic the substance. *See* Concentration (1).

Lethal Dose, 50 Percent Kill (LD$_{50}$) — Concentration of an ingested or injected substance that results in the death of 50 percent of the test population. LD$_{50}$ is an oral or dermal exposure expressed in milligrams per kilogram (mg/kg); the lower the value, the more toxic the substance. *See* Dose.

Level A Protection — Highest level of skin, respiratory, and eye protection that can be given by personal protective equipment (PPE), as specified by the U.S. Environmental Protection Agency (EPA); consists of positive-pressure self-contained breathing apparatus, totally encapsulating chemical-protective suit, inner and outer gloves, and chemical-resistant boots. *See* Chemical Protective Clothing (CPC), Personal Protective Equipment (PPE), and Special Protective Clothing.

Level B Protection — Personal protective equipment that affords the highest level of respiratory protection, but a lesser level of skin protection. Consists of positive-pressure self-contained breathing apparatus, totally encapsulating chemical-protective suit, inner and outer gloves, and chemical-resistant boots. *See* Chemical Protective Clothing (CPC), Personal Protective Equipment (PPE), and Special Protective Clothing.

Level C Protection — Personal protective equipment that affords a lesser level of respiratory and skin protection than levels A or B. Consists of full-face or half-mask APR, hooded chemical-resistant suit, inner and outer gloves, and chemical-resistant boots.

Level D Protection — Personal protective equipment that affords the lowest level of respiratory and skin protection. Consists of coveralls, gloves, and chemical-resistant boots or shoes.

Level I Staging — Used on all multiple-company emergency responses. The first-arriving vehicles of each type proceed directly to the scene, and the others stand by a block or two from the scene and await orders. Units usually stage at the last intersection on their route of travel before reaching the reported incident location.

Level II Staging — Used on large-scale incidents where a larger number of fire and emergency services companies are responding; these companies are sent to a specified remote location to await assignment. *See* Base.

Level of Learning — Lesson plan component that states the learning level that participants will reach by the end of the lesson; may be based on the taxonomy of learning domains or on performance of job requirements. *See* Lesson Plan.

Lever — Device consisting of a bar turning about a fixed point (fulcrum), using power or force applied at a second point to lift or sustain an object at a third point.

Leverage — Action or mechanical power of a lever.

Lexan® — Polycarbonate plastic used for windows; has one-half the weight of an equivalent-sized piece of glass, yet is 30 times stronger than safety glass and 250 times stronger than ordinary glass. It cannot be broken using standard forcible entry techniques.

LFL — *See* Lower Flammable Limit.

Liability — (1) All types of debts and obligations one is bound in justice to perform; a condition of being responsible for a possible or actual loss, penalty, evil, expense, or burden; a condition that creates a duty to perform an act immediately or in the future. *See* Vicarious Liability. (2) To be legally obligated or responsible for an act or physical condition; opposite of *immunity. See* Immunity.

Liaison Officer — Point of contact for assisting or coordinating agencies; member of the command staff.

Libel — Written or oral defamatory statement; the act, tort, or crime of making or publishing a libel against someone. *See* Defamation, Slander, and Tort.

Lieutenant — Rank used in some fire departments for company officers.

Life Belt — Wide, adjustable belt with a snap hook that can be fastened to the rungs of a ladder to secure a firefighter to the ladder while leaving the firefighter's hands free for working. The formal term for *life belt* is Class I Life Safety Harness.

Lifeline — Non-load-bearing rope attached to a firefighter during search operations to act as a safety line.

Life Net — Canvas device with a folding circular metal frame and spring action used to catch persons who jump from buildings; not considered safe or effective for jumps from above the fourth floor of a building.

Life of Foam — Period of time that the foam blanket remains in place until more foam must be applied.

Life Safety — Refers to the joint consideration of the life and physical well-being of individuals, both civilians and firefighters.

Life Safety Code®— *See* NFPA® 101, *Life Safety Code.*

Life Safety Harness — Harness that meets the requirements of NFPA® 1983, *Standard on Life Safety Rope and Equipment for Emergency Services. See* Class I Harness, Class II Harness, and Class III Harness.

Life Safety Rope — Rope that meets the requirements of NFPA® 1983, *Standard on Life Safety Rope and Equipment for Emergency Services*, and is dedicated solely for the purpose of constructing lines to be used for raising, lowering, or supporting people during rescue firefighting or other emergency operations, or during training. *Also known as* Lifeline.

Lift — (1) Apparatus for raising an automobile. (2) Component of the total aerodynamic force acting on an airplane or airfoil that is perpendicular to the relative wind, and that for an airplane constitutes the upward force that opposes the pull of gravity. (3) Dimension from the top of one pouring of concrete in a form to the top of the next pouring; for example, "pour concrete in 8-inch (203 mm) lifts." *See* Dependable Lift, Maximum Lift, and Theoretical Lift.

Lifter Roof Storage Tank — Atmospheric storage tank designed so that the roof floats on a slight cushion of vapor pressure. The liquid-sealed roof floats up and down with the vapor pressure. When the vapor pressure exceeds a designated limit, the roof lifts to relieve the excess pressure. *See* Atmospheric Storage Tank and Floating Roof Storage Tank.

Lift On/Lift Off (LO/LO) — Refers to a vessel capable of loading and unloading its own cargo without shoreside crane assistance.

Lift Slabs — System of concrete construction in which the floor slabs are poured in place at the ground level and then lifted to their position by hydraulic jacks working simultaneously at each column.

Lift Truck — Small truck for lifting and transporting loads. *See* EX Symbol.

Light — Visible radiation produced at the atomic level, such as a flame produced during the combustion reaction.

Light Attack Vehicle — *See* Initial Attack Apparatus or Mini-pumper.

Light Box — *See* Connection Box.

Light Detector — *See* Flame Detector.

Lighter — Large boat or barge (usually non-powered) for conveying cargo to and from vessels in harbor, transporting coal or construction materials, transporting garbage, etc. *See* Barge.

Light-Frame Construction — Method for construction of wood-frame buildings; replaced the use of heavy timber wood framing.

Light Fuels — Fast-drying fuels, with a comparatively high surface-area-to-volume ratio, that are generally less than ½ inch (6.35 mm) in diameter and have a time lag of 1 hour or less. These fuels readily ignite and are rapidly consumed by fire when dry.

Light-Gauge Steel Joist — Joist system for supporting metal decks or wood-panel flooring systems; produced from cold-rolled steel and available in several cross-sectional varieties. *See* Open-Web Joist.

Lightly Trapped — Victims who are trapped by furniture or debris within a structure that has remained standing.

Light Meter — Device used to measure the amount of light; used to determine the exposure of a photograph. DSLR cameras and other cameras often have light meters integrated in the camera that determine the exposure automatically.

Light Rescue Vehicle — Small rescue vehicle usually built on a 1-ton or 1½-ton chassis; designed to handle only basic extrication and life-support functions and carries only basic hand tools and small equipment.

Light Shaft — *See* Light Well.

Lightweight Steel Truss — Structural support made from a long steel bar that is bent at a 90-degree angle with flat or angular pieces welded to the top and bottom.

Lightweight Transparent Armor® (LTA) — Polycarbonate bulletproof glass sheets bonded together to form windows and windshields for armored vehicles and structures.

Lightweight Wood Truss — Structural supports constructed of 2 x 3-inch or 2 x 4-inch (51 mm by 76 mm or 51 mm by 102 mm) members that are connected by gusset plates.

Light Well — Vertical shaft at or near the center of a building to provide natural light and/or ventilation to offices or apartments not located on an outside wall. *Also known as* Light Shaft.

Likelihood of Survival — Determination of whether there is a greater or lesser chance of survival for victims in a collapsed structure.

Limited Access (Warm) Zone — Large geographical area between the support zone and the restricted zone, for personnel who are directly aiding rescuers in the restricted zone. This includes personnel who are handling hydraulic tool power plants, fire personnel handling standby hoselines, and so on. This zone should contain the decontamination area, the safe haven, and the Haz Mat control officer. Personnel in this zone should not get in the way of rescuers working in the restricted zone.

Line — (1) Hoseline. (2) Rope or lifeline. (3) Rope when in use, such as a main line or safety line. (4) Length of rope in use on a vessel.

Lined Hose — Fire hose composed of one or two woven outside jackets and an inside rubber lining.

Line-Item Budget — Budget that details the department's proposed expenditures line by line; the most common type of fire department budget.

Lineman's Gloves — Special gloves insulated for protection against electrical current.

Linen Hose — Fire hose made of linen or flax fabric without a rubber lining; used for standpipe cabinets and forestry operations.

Line-of-Duty — During the performance of fire department duties.

Line-of-Duty Death (LODD) — Firefighter or emergency responder death resulting from the performance of fire department duties.

Line of Sight — Generally defined as a straight path between a transmitting antenna and the receiving antenna when unobstructed by the horizon.

Line Organization — Portion of the fire department directly involved in providing fire suppression and rescue services.

Link Analysis — Method of computing, organizing, and utilizing data relating to an investigation; allows the analysis and presentation of complex data in a clear and concise manner.

Lintel — Support for masonry over an opening; usually made of steel angles or other rolled shapes, singularly or in combination.

Lipid Pneumonia — Pneumonia that may follow the aspiration of an oily substance such as mineral oil.

LIP Service — Emergency incident management priorities of **L**ife safety, **I**ncident stabilization and control, and **P**rotection of property and the environment.

Liquefied Compressed Gas — Gas that under the charging pressure is partially liquid at 70°F (21°C). *Also known as* Liquefied Gas. *See* Compressed Gas, Gas, Liquefied Natural Gas (LNG), and Liquefied Petroleum Gas (LPG).

Liquefied Flammable Gas Carrier — Tanker used to transport liquefied natural gas (LNG) and liquefied petroleum gas (LPG) (such as propane and butane); generally uses large insulated spherical tanks for product storage. *See* Tanker.

Liquefied Gas — Confined gas that at normal temperatures exists in both liquid and gaseous states. *See* Compressed Gas, Gas, Liquefied Compressed Gas, and Liquefied Petroleum Gas (LPG).

Liquefied Natural Gas (LNG) — Natural gas stored under pressure as a liquid. *See* Gas, Hydrocarbon Fuel, and Liquid Compressed Gas.

Liquefied Petroleum Gas (LPG) — Any of several petroleum products, such as propane or butane, stored under pressure as a liquid. *See* Gas, Hydrocarbon Fuel , and Liquefied Compressed Gas.

Liquid — Incompressible substance with a constant volume that assumes the shape of its container; molecules flow freely, but substantial cohesion prevents them from expanding as a gas would.

Liquid Oxygen (LOX) — Oxygen that is stored under pressure as a liquid.

Liquid Propellants — Liquids used in rockets as fuels and oxidizers.

List — Continuous lean or tilt of a vessel to one side due to an imbalance of weight within the vessel. *See* Angle of Loll, Critical Angle of List, Heel, Heeling, and Loll.

Listed — Refers to a device that has been tested by the Underwriters' Laboratories Inc. Factory Mutual System and certified as having met minimum criteria.

Listening — Process of receiving, attending to, and assigning meaning to auditory stimuli; a process of steps that gives information that listeners try to understand.

Litter — (1) Top layer of forest floor composed of loose debris of dead sticks, branches, twigs, and recently fallen leaves or needles, on top of a duff layer; decomposition does little to alter its structure. (2) Inappropriately discarded rubbish. (3) *See* Stretcher.

Live Fire Exercises — Training exercises that involve the use of an unconfined open flame or fire in a structure or other combustibles to provide a controlled burning environment. *Also known as* Live Burn Exercises.

Live Fuels — Living plants, such as trees, grasses, and shrubs, in which the seasonal moisture content cycle is controlled largely by internal physiological mechanisms rather than by external weather influences.

Live Load — (1) Items within a building that are movable but are not included as a permanent part of the structure; merchandise, stock, furnishings, occupants, firefighters, and the water used for fire suppression are examples of live loads. (2) Force placed upon a structure by the addition of people, objects, or weather. *See* Dead Load and Load.

Livestock — Cattle, horses, sheep, and other useful animals raised or kept on a ranch or farm.

LNG — *See* Liquefied Natural Gas.

Load — (1) The sum of the wattages of the various devices being served by a circuit. (2) Any effect that a structure must be designed to resist, such as gravity, wind, earthquakes, and soil pressure. *See* Dead Load and Live Load.

Load-Bearing Frame Members — Portions of the frame that provide direct support to attached members.

Load-Bearing Wall — Wall that supports itself, the weight of the roof, and/or other internal structural framing components, such as the floor beams and trusses above it. *Also known as* Bearing Wall. *See* Pony Wall.

Loading Rack — Fixed facility where either truck or railroad tank cars are bulk loaded with flammable and combustible liquids.

Loading Site — In a tanker/tender shuttle operation, the location where apparatus tanks are filled from the water supply. *See* Fill Site.

Load Line — *See* Plimsoll Mark.

Load Monitor — Device that "watches" an electrical system for added loads that may threaten to overload the system.

Load Sequencer — Device in an electrical system that turns various lights on at specified intervals, so that the start-up load for all of the devices does not occur at the same time.

Load Shedding — When an overload condition occurs, the load monitor will shut down less important electrical equipment to prevent the overload.

Load Testing — Aerial device test intended to determine whether or not the device is capable of safely carrying its rated weight capacity.

Lobby Control — In high-rise fire fighting, the individual responsible for, and the process of, taking and maintaining control of the lobby and elevators; includes establishing internal communications, coordinating the flow of personnel and equipment up interior stairways to upper levels, and coordinating with building engineering personnel.

Lobbying — Educating a person or an organization about your position on an issue or even urging the person or organization to adopt your position; more specifically, conducting activities aimed at influencing public officials, especially members of a legislative body on legislation.

Local Alarm System — *See* Protected Premises Fire Alarm System.

Local Application System — Fixed-site fire-suppression system that is required to cover a protected area with 2 feet (0.6 m) of foam depth within 2 minutes of system activation; foam supply must support the continuous operation of the system for at least 12 minutes. *See* Total Flooding System.

Local Emergency Planning Committee (LEPC) — Community organization responsible for local emergency response planning. *See* Local Emergency Response Plan (LERP).

Local Emergency Response Plan (LERP) — Plan required by U.S. Environmental Protection Agency (EPA) that is prepared by the Local Emergency Planning Committee (LEPC), detailing how local emergency response agencies will respond to community emergencies.

Local Winds — Winds that are generated over a comparatively small area, and whose speed and direction are influenced by local conditions such as topography, fires, and weather fronts. They differ from those that would be appropriate to the general pressure pattern or that possess some other peculiarity.

Locard Exchange Principle — Investigative principle that states that whenever a person comes into contact with a scene, he or she leaves something at the scene and also takes something from it.

Location Marker — Device, such as a reflective marker or flag, used to mark the location of a fire hydrant for quicker identification during a fire response.

Lock — (1) Device for fastening, joining, or engaging two or more objects together such as a door and frame. (2) *See* Pawls.

Locking In — *See* Leg Lock.

Locking Out — Process of shutting off and securing any power switches on a machine to prevent accidental or otherwise undesirable re-energization of the machine.

Lock Mechanism — Moving parts of a lock, which include the latch or bolt, lock cylinder, and articulating components.

Lockout/Tagout Device — Device used to secure any power switches on a machine to prevent accidental or otherwise undesirable re-energization of the machine.

LODD — *See* Line-of-Duty Death.

Lodging House — *See* Hotel.

Log — (1) Record book. (2) To record information in a log or record book.

Logistics — Rational calculation and reasoning used to manage the scheduling of limited materials and equipment to meet the multiple demands of training programs and instructors.

Logistics Section — Section responsible for providing facilities, services, and materials for the incident; includes the communications unit, Medical Unit, and Food Unit within the Service Branch and the Supply Unit, Facilities Unit, and Ground Support Unit within the support branch. *Also known as* Logistics.

Logroll — Method for placing a patient onto a backboard by turning the patient as a unit, first onto the side, then onto the back.

Loiding — Method of slipping or shimming a spring latch from its strike with a piece of celluloid such as a credit card.

Loll — Neutral equilibrium when vessel comes to rest within a range of stability as opposed to a point of stability; that is, instead of being stable when upright, the vessel may be stable within 1 degree to port or starboard sides, and thus will lean either port or starboard. *See* Angle of Loll and List.

LO/LO — *See* Lift-on/Lift-off.

Loma Prieta — Name given to the October 1989 earthquake in central California that occurred during the World Series baseball game in San Francisco.

Long Backboard — Board used to package a patient with suspected spinal injury.

Long-Duration Apparatus — Breathing apparatus that supplies the wearer with air for more than 30 minutes.

Longeron — Longitudinal members of the framing of an aircraft fuselage or nacelle; usually continuous across a number of bulkheads or other points of support.

Longitudinal Hose Bed — Hose bed located to the side of the main hose bed; designed to carry preconnected attack hose.

Longitudinal Stability — Ability of a vessel to return to an upright position when forced from its rest condition by pitching. *See* Stability and Static Stability.

Longshoreman — Worker who loads and unloads cargo from a vessel. *Also known as* Stevedore.

Long Ton — Unit of weight used in the marine industry; 1 long ton = 2,240 pounds or 1 tonne (1,016 kilograms). A short ton = 2,000 pounds or 0.9 tonne (907 kilograms).

Lookout — (1) Location from which fires can be detected and reported. (2) Fire crew member assigned to observe the fire from a vantage point and warn the crew when there is danger of becoming trapped.

Lookout Tower — Tower or station, usually on a high place, from which wildland fires can be detected; also used for pinpointing lightning strikes and frontal systems approaching a given area.

Loop System — Water main arranged in a complete circuit so that water will be supplied to a given point from more than one direction. *Also known as* Belt System, Circle System, or Circulating System.

Loose End — *See* Working End.

Loss Control — Practice of minimizing damage and providing customer service through effective mitigation and recovery efforts before, during, and after an incident.

Loss Control Factors — Factors that are useful in risk evaluation and that are the conditions unique to a particular scenario or location.

Loss Control Risk Analysis — Process in which specific potential risks are identified and evaluated before an incident has occurred. The goal of this process is to develop strategies to minimize the impact of these risks.

Loss Control Strategies — Actions that reduce or eliminate all or part of a loss control risk. Loss control strategies are developed by using the information from the loss control risk analysis.

Louver Cut — Rectangular exit opening cut in a roof, allowing a section of roof deck (still nailed to a center rafter) to be tilted, thus creating an opening similar to a louver. *Also known as* Center Rafter Cut.

Low Angle — Environment in which rescuers need rope for assistance. The majority of the load is on the ground, but movement would be hazardous or difficult without the aid of a rope.

Low-Density Combustible Fiberboard — Building material, often used for interior finishes, that is usually highly combustible.

Lower Airway — Portion of the respiratory system below the epiglottis.

Lower Explosive Limit (LEL) — *See* Lower Flammable Limit.

Lower Flammable (Explosive) Limit (LFL) — Lower limit at which a flammable gas or vapor will ignite and support combustion; below this limit the gas or vapor is too *lean* or *thin* to burn (too much oxygen and not enough gas). *Also known as* Lower Explosive Limit (LEL). *See* Flammable Gas, Flammable Limit, and Upper Flammable Limit (UFL).

Lower In — Procedure for positioning the tip of a ladder against a building after raising.

Lowering — Procedure for removing a ladder from the raised position.

Low-Expansion Foam — Foam concentrate that is mixed with air, in the range of less than 20 parts air to 1 part foam solution (20:1). *See* High-Expansion Foam and Medium-Expansion Foam.

Low Explosive — Explosive that decomposes or burns rapidly, but does not produce an explosive effect unless it is confined. *See* Detonation, Explosive (2), and High Explosive.

Low-Impact Crashes — Aircraft crashes that do not severely damage or break up the fuselage and are likely to have a large percentage of survivors.

Low-Order-Explosion Damage — Damage typically associated with a deflagration that includes bulging of walls, walls fallen intact away from a structure, roofs lifted and dislodged, and large debris moved only short distance.

Low-Pressure Alarm — Bell, whistle, or other audible alarm that warns the wearer when the SCBA air supply is low and needs replacement, usually when it reaches 25 percent of full container pressure.

Low-Pressure Chemical Tank Cargo tank truck designed to carry various chemicals such as flammables, corrosives, or poisons, with pressures not to exceed 40 psi (276 kPa) {2.76 bar} at 70°F (21°C). *See* Cargo Tank Truck.

Low-Pressure Hose — Hose containing pressure slightly above atmospheric pressure, leading from the regulator to the facepiece. *Also known as* Inhalation Tube.

Low-Pressure Storage Tank — Class of fixed-facility storage tanks that are designed to have an operating pressure ranging from 0.5 to 15 psi (3.45 kPa to 103 kPa) {0.03 bar to 1.03 bar}. *See* Atmospheric Storage Tank, Noded Spheroid Tank, Pressure Storage Tank, Pressure Vessel, and Spheroid Tank.

Low-Rise Elevator — Elevator that serves only the lower floors of a high-rise building.

LOX — *See* Liquid Oxygen.

LPG — *See* Liquefied Petroleum Gas.

Lugging — Condition that occurs when the throttle application is greater than necessary for a given set of conditions; may result in an excessive amount of carbon particles issuing from the exhaust, oil dilution, and additional fuel consumption. Lugging can be eliminated by using a lower gear and proper shifting techniques.

Lumber — Lengths of wood cut and prepared for use in construction.

Lungs — Paired organs of respiration that lie in the chest.

M

Machine-Guarding — Use of gates, covers, housings, deflectors, or other guards on power machinery to prevent the user from contacting moving parts or being struck by flying objects.

Machinery — All the equipment on a vessel; including but not limited to the main and auxiliary engines, pumps, deck winches, steering engine, and hoists.

Macro Lens — Camera lens that is designed for close-up photos.

Magazine — Storage facility approved by the Bureau of Alcohol, Tobacco, Firearms, and Explosives (ATF) for the storage of explosives. *See* Explosive.

Magnetic Particle Inspection — Form of nondestructive steel aerial device testing where the aerial device is magnetized and metal particles are applied. Deviances in the coating of the particles indicate flaws in the metal aerial device.

Magneto — Device used in gasoline engines that produces a periodic spark in order to maintain fuel combustion.

Main Deck — Uppermost continuous deck of a vessel that runs from bow to stern. *See* Deck.

Main Guideline — Special rope used in the United Kingdom, Australia, and New Zealand as a safety guideline to indicate a route between the entry control point and the scene of operations.

Main Line — Rope system built to support a rescuer and/or patient.

Mainline Valve — Valve that when opened lets air from the cylinder travel its normal route through the regulator to the facepiece.

Maintenance — Keeping equipment or apparatus in a state of usefulness or readiness.

Main Transverse Bulkheads — Watertight bulkheads that subdivide a vessel into watertight compartments. *See* Bulkhead (1) and Main Watertight Subdivision.

Main Watertight Subdivision — Space between two main transverse watertight bulkheads. *See* Bulkhead (1) and Main Transverse Bulkheads.

Major — Rank used by some fire departments for company officers.

Make the Fire — Order given to a specific unit to respond to a fire.

Makeup — All actions involved in connecting fire hose or apparatus to other equipment.

Making a Hydrant — Procedure for connecting to and laying hose forward from a fire hydrant.

Male Coupling — Hose coupling with external threads that fit into the threads of a female coupling of the same pitch and appropriate diameter and thread count.

Malicious — Describes a state of mind characterized by the intent to injure, vex, or annoy another person, to commit an unlawful act, or attempt to defraud; often an element of arson. Legal definitions of maliciousness vary from state to state.

Maltese Cross — Commonly used insignia of the fire service, worn on the uniform or the cap. The popular variety of the Maltese cross is actually a modification of the *cross patee* rather than the actual Maltese cross, which has eight points.

Mammalian Diving Reflex — Autonomous physiologic reaction to immersion in cold water, in which the blood and oxygen supply is shunted to the brain to keep the animal alive, although outward appearances may suggest death.

Manage — To provide direction and leadership in order to achieve organizational objectives through effective and efficient application of resources.

Management — Process of accomplishing organizational objectives through effective and efficient handling of resources; official, sanctioned leadership.

Management by Objectives (MBO) — Planning and control device used to organize resources and motivate personnel toward the fulfillment of specified objectives.

Manager — Individual who accomplishes organizational objectives through effective and efficient handling of material and human resources.

Manhole — (1) Hole through which a person may go to gain access to an underground or enclosed structure. (2) Opening usually equipped with a removable, lockable cover, that is large enough to admit a person into a tank trailer or dry bulk trailer. *Also known as* Manway.

Manifest — *See* Cargo Manifest.

Manifold — (1) Hose appliance that divides one larger hoseline into three or more small hoselines. *Also known as* Portable Hydrant. (2) Top portion of the pump casing. (3) Device used to join a number of discharge pipelines to a common outlet.

Manila Rope — Rope made from manila fiber, which is grown in Manila in the Philippines. This type of rope is not suitable for life safety applications.

Manipulative Lesson — *See* Practical Demonstration.

Manipulative-Performance Test — Practical competency-based test that measures mastery of the psychomotor objectives as they are performed in a job or evolution.

Manipulative Skills — Skills that use the psychomotor domain of learning; refers to the ability to physically manipulate an object or move the body to accomplish a task.

Manipulative Training — Lesson or exercise in a training program, in which participants handle or learn to handle equipment or materials in a coordinated or skillful manner.

Mansard Roof — Roof style with characteristics similar to both gambrel and hip roofs. Mansard roofs have slopes of two different angles, and all sides slope down to an outside wall.

Manual Foam Monitor — Foam monitor that is operated by hand; may be found mounted on apparatus, in fixed locations to protect target hazards, or as a portable unit. *See* Automatic Oscillating Foam Monitor, Foam Monitor, and Remote-Controlled Foam Monitor.

Manual on Uniform Traffic Control Devices (MUTCD) — DOT Federal Highway Administration publication that identifies the types of traffic control devices that should be used to establish work areas and identify incident scenes, as well the methods for deploying these devices.

Manual Stabilizer — Manually deployed stabilizing device for aerial apparatus that consists of an extension arm with a jack attached to the end of it.

Manufactured Home — Dwelling that is the assembly of four major components: the chassis and the floor, wall, and roof systems; although they are constructed of steel, wood, plywood, aluminum, gypsum wallboard, and other materials, they are basically frame construction. Characterized by small compartment sizes, low ceilings, and very lightweight construction throughout. *Also known as* Mobile Home.

Manufacturer's Tests — Fire pump or aerial device tests performed by the manufacturer prior to delivery of the apparatus.

Manway — *See* Manhole.

Marina — Special harbor with facilities constructed especially for yachts and other pleasure craft.

Marine Company — Personnel assigned to work on a fireboat.

Marine Unit — *See* Fire Boat.

Maritime Law — Laws relating to commerce and navigation on the high seas and other navigable waters; a court exercising jurisdiction over maritime cases. *Also known as* Admiralty Law.

Marking — Descriptive name, identification number, weight, or specification, along with instructions, cautions, or UN marks required on outer packagings of hazardous materials. *See* Label, Package Marking, and Placard.

Marrying Vehicles — Attaching two vehicles to one another in such a fashion that the two vehicles move as one stable object.

Mars Light — Single-beam, oscillating warning light; originally manufactured by the Mars Light Company.

Martial Law — System of rule that occurs when the military takes control of the administration of justice.

Mask — *See* Facepiece.

Maslow's Hierarchy of Needs — Theory put forth by psychologist Abraham Maslow stating that all human behavior is motivated by a drive to attain specific human needs in a progressive manner. The hierarchy begins with basic physiological needs and progresses through security, social, self-esteem, and self-actualization needs.

Masonry — Bricks, blocks, stones, and unreinforced and reinforced concrete products.

Mass Casualty Incident — Incident that results in a large number of casualties within a short time frame, as a result of an attack, natural disaster, aircraft crash, or other cause that is beyond the capabilities of local logistical support. *See* Multi-Casualty Incident.

Mass Communication — Rapid transmission of a warning directly to the general population.

Mass Decontamination — Conducting gross decontamination of multiple people at one time, with or without a formal decontamination corridor or line. *See* Decontamination, Decontamination Corridor, and Gross Decontamination.

Mass Media — News communications that are designed to reach a large number of people.

Mass Prophylaxis — Capability to protect the health of the population through administration of critical interventions (such as antibiotics, vaccinations, or antivirals), in order to prevent the development of disease among those who are exposed or potentially exposed to public health threats. This capability includes the provision of appropriate follow-up and monitoring of adverse events, as well as risk communication messages to address the concerns of the public.

Mass Transportation — Any mode of transportation designed to carry large numbers of people at the same time.

MAST — *See* Medical Antishock Trousers or Military Antishock Trousers.

Mast — Vertical pole, rising from the keel or deck of a vessel, that supports sailing rigging. Also used for radio antennas and signal flags.

Master — Commander of a merchant vessel. *See* Captain.

Master Stream — Large-caliber water stream usually supplied by siamesing two or more hoselines into a manifold device or by fixed piping that delivers 350 gpm (1 325 L/min) or more. *Also known as* Heavy Stream.

Master Stream Nozzle — Nozzle capable of flowing in excess of 350 gpm (1 325 L/min).

Mastery — High-level or nearly complete degree of proficiency in the performance of a skill, based on criteria stated in objectives; in training, the ability to perform at a designated skill level, which enables the learner to progress to the next designated skill level. A mastery test checks that learners have achieved the appropriate skill level (mastery). *See* Criterion-Referenced Testing.

Mastery Learning — Element of criterion-referenced or competency-based learning; outcomes of learning are expressed in minimum levels of performance for each competency.

Masthead — Printed, usually boxed section of a newspaper or periodical that gives the title and pertinent details of ownership, editorship, advertising rates, and subscription rates.

Mat Foundation — Thick slab beneath the entire area of a building; differs from a simple floor slab in its thickness and amount of reinforcement.

Matching Grant — Grant in which the funder agrees to give an amount that is equal to (or a specific ratio of) the amount that another funder gives.

Mate — *See* Chief Officer.

Material — Generic term used by first responders for a substance involved in an incident. *See* Hazardous Material and Product.

Material First Ignited — Fuel that is first set on fire by the heat of ignition. To be meaningful, both a type of material and a form of material should be identified.

Material Safety Data Sheet (MSDS) — *See* Safety Data Sheet.

Materials Needed — List of everything needed to teach a lesson, such as models, mock-ups, visual aids, equipment, handouts, and quizzes.

Matter — Anything that occupies space and has mass.

Mattress Chains — Light chains with hooks or locking devices used to bind a mattress in a roll for removal from a building.

Mattydale Hose Bed — *See* Transverse Hose Bed.

Maximum Allowable Quantity — Maximum amount of a hazardous material to be stored or used within a control area inside a building or an outdoor control area; maximum allowable quantity per control area is based on the material state (solid, liquid, or gas) and the material storage or use conditions (Source: *International Fire Code®*, 2006 edition).

Maximum Daily Consumption — Maximum total amount of water used during any 24-hour interval over a 3-year period.

Maximum Extended Length — Total length of an extension ladder with all sections fully extended and pawls engaged.

Maximum Lift — Maximum height to which any amount of water may be raised through a hard suction hose to a pump; determined by the ability of the pump to create a vacuum. *See* Lift.

May — Term used in NFPA® standards that denotes voluntary or optional compliance.

Mayday — International distress signal broadcast by voice.

Maze — Training facility with or without smoke, lighted or unlighted, in which firefighters wearing SCBA must negotiate obstacles to perform certain tasks.

MBO — *See* Management By Objectives.

MDH — *See* Medium Diameter Hose.

Mean — Term that refers to the "average" of a set of scores; calculated by adding all of the set of scores (values) and dividing by the total number of scores. For example, if a set of scores is 98, 98, 95, 92, 92, 92, 89, 88, 87, 85, 85, 79, 75, 74, and 74, the mean or average score is 91.8.

Means of Egress — (1) Safe, continuous path of travel from any point in a structure to a public way. Composed of three parts: exit access, exit, and exit discharge. (2) Continuous and unobstructed way of exit travel from any point in a building or structure to a public way, consisting of three separate and distinct parts: exit access, exit, and exit discharge. (Source: NFPA® 101, *Life Safety Code®*). *See* Egress, Exit, Exit Access, Exit Discharge, Public Way, and Travel Distance.

Mechanical Advantage — (1) Gain in force, when levering, by moving the fulcrum closer to the object. (2) Used in rope rescue and to lift heavy objects, this refers to the advantage created when levers, pulleys, and tools are used to make work easier. (3) The ratio of the force applied by a simple machine, such as a lever or block and tackle, to the force applied to the machine by the user.

Mechanical Blower — High-expansion foam generator that uses a fan to inject the air into the foam solution as it passes through the unit. *See* High-Expansion Foam.

Mechanical Explosion — Explosion that is the result of an increase in pressure in a confined container; may or may not be a result of additional heat. *See* Boiling Liquid Expanding Vapor Explosion (BLEVE).

Mechanical Filter — Air-purification component that physically separates the greatest part of water, oil, and other contaminants from compressed air. May also refer to the filter on a negative-pressure respirator that performs the same task.

Mechanical Foam — Foam produced by a physical agitation of a mixture of foam concentrate, water, and air. *See* Chemical Foam.

Mechanical Heat Energy — Heat that is generated by friction or compression. Moving parts on machines, such as belts and bearings, are a source of mechanical heating.

Mechanical Shoe Seal — Fabric seal that is anchored to the top of the roof and rides on the inside of a large fuel storage tank wall. The actual mechanical shoe, also known as a pantograph, is attached below the fabric seal to keep the roof properly aligned within the tank. *Also known as* Pantograph Seal.

Mechanical System — Large equipment system within a building that may include climate-control systems; smoke, dust, and vapor removal systems; trash collection systems; and automated mail systems. Does not include general utility systems such as electric, gas, and water. *See* Heating, Ventilating, and Air-Conditioning (HVAC) System.

Mechanical Trauma — Injury, such as an abrasion, puncture, or laceration, resulting from direct contact with a fragment or a whole container.

Mechanical Ventilation — *See* Forced Ventilation.

Mechanism of injury — Forces placed on the victim's body by collapse or collision.

Media — *See* Medium.

Media Advisory — Advisory of specific event or program to be held in the future; in contrast, a *news release* discusses something that has already happened.

Media Kit — Packet containing information about the public fire and life safety educator's own organization.

Medial — Toward the midline of the body.

Median — Middle score in a set of scores (values) that are arranged or ranked in size (order) from high to low. For example, if a set of scores is 98, 98, 95, 92, 92, 92, 89, 88, 87, 85, 85, 79, 75, 74, and 74, the median or middle score is 88.

Media Release — Prepared statement distributed to provide the media with information in a ready-to-use news story format. *Also known as* Press Release.

Medical Antishock Trousers (MAST) — Inflatable trousers used to counteract the effects of heavy blood loss. *Also known as* Military Antishock Trousers.

Medic-Alert® Bracelet (or Necklace) — *See* Medical Identification Bracelet (or Necklace).

Medical Evaluation — Annual evaluation performed by a physician or professional health-care provider to ensure that a fire and emergency services responder is physically fit to perform the duties assigned; required before a responder uses respiratory protection.

Medical Examination — Complete medical examination by a physician or professional health-care provider for entry-level emergency personnel and periodically for all personnel during their service careers; mandatory for personnel who will be using respiratory protection equipment.

Medical Examiner — Medically qualified government officer whose duty is to investigate deaths and injuries that occur under unusual or suspicious circumstances, to perform post-mortem examinations, and in some jurisdictions to initiate inquests. *Also known as* Coroner.

Medical Identification Bracelet (or Necklace) — Medical identification worn by individuals having an illness that requires certain care and treatment. *Also known as* Medic-Alert® Bracelet (or Necklace).

Medical Unit — Functional unit within the service branch of the logistics section of an incident command system; responsible for providing emergency medical treatment for emergency personnel. This unit does not provide treatment for civilians.

Medic Unit — (1) Ambulance staffed by paramedics. (2) Nonpatient transport vehicle used by paramedics to respond to emergencies. *Also known as* Paramedic Unit.

Medium — Vehicle for sending a message; the plural for the term is *media*. *Also known as* Communications Vehicle.

Medium Diameter Hose (MDH) — 2½- or 3-inch (65 mm or 77 mm) hose that is used for both fire fighting attack and relay-supply purposes.

Medium-Duty-Chassis Ambulance — Ambulance built upon a medium truck chassis rated at over 15,000 pounds to under 32,000 pounds gross vehicle weight.

Medium-Expansion Foam — Foam concentrate that is mixed with air in the range of 20 parts air to 1 part foam solution (20:1) to 200 parts air to 1 part foam solution (200:1). *See* High-Expansion Foam and Low-Expansion Foam.

Medium Fuels — Material available to burn in a geographic area that is in the midrange of size such as various brush species; generally excludes short grasses and large trees.

Medium-Pressure Air — Air pressurized from 2,000 to 3,000 psi (13 790 kPa to 20 684 kPa); used to distinguish specific types of breathing-air cylinders.

Medium Rescue Vehicle — Rescue vehicle somewhat larger and better equipped than a light rescue vehicle; may carry powered hydraulic spreading tools and cutters, air bag lifting systems, power saws, oxyacetylene cutting equipment, ropes and rigging equipment, as well as basic hand equipment.

Megapixel — One million pixels; used as the reference for the number of pixels in a digital image. Also refers to the number of image sensor elements that a digital camera can display, which in turn describes the largest photograph that can be taken with that camera.

Megawatt (MW) — Measurement of rate of heat release equal to 1,000 kilowatts (equivalent to ten thousand 100-watt bulbs).

Melting Point — Temperature at which a solid substance changes to a liquid state at normal atmospheric pressure. *See* Freezing Point.

Member Organization — Organization formed to represent the collective and individual rights and interests of the fire and emergency services organization, such as a labor union or fraternal organization.

Membrane — Thin sheath or layer of pliable material.

Membrane Ceiling — Usually refers to a suspended, insulating ceiling tile system.

Membrane Roof — Roof consisting of a single membrane laid in sheets on a roof deck, and attached using adhesives, gravel ballasts, mechanical fasteners, or heating the roof side of the membrane. Can be applied over existing roofs. *Also known as* Single-Ply Membrane Roof.

Membrane Structure — (1) Structure with an enclosing surface of a thin stretched flexible material. Examples include a simple tent or an air-supported structure. (2) Weather-resistant, flexible or semiflexible covering consisting of layers of materials over a supporting framework.

Mentor — Trusted and friendly adviser or guide for someone who is new to a particular role.

Mentoring — Instructional method in which an individual, as trusted and friendly advisor or guide, sets tasks, coaches activities, and supervises progress of individuals in new learning experiences or job positions.

Mercantile — Occupancy Classification whose primary objective is the wholesale purchase and retail sale of goods for profit. *See* Occupancy Classification.

Message — Information, ideas, attitude, or opinion that is transmitted and received.

Metabolism — Conversion of food into energy and waste products.

Metacenter (m) — Point through which the force of buoyancy works; point of intersection of the vertical through the center of buoyancy of a floating body with the vertical through the new center of buoyancy when the body is displaced. *See* Center of Buoyancy and Metacentric Height.

Metacentric Height (gm) — Measure of a vessel's initial stability; distance of the metacenter above the center of gravity of a floating body. *See* Center of Buoyancy, Center of Gravity, and Metacenter.

Metal-Clad Door — Door with a metal exterior; may be flush type or panel type. *Also known as* Kalamein Door.

Meter Booting — The addition of insulators to an electrical meter by the utility company.

Meth Lab — Illegal clandestine laboratory established to produce illegal methamphetamine (meth). *See* Illegal Clandestine Lab.

Method of Instruction — Procedure, technique, or manner of instructing others that is determined by the type of learning to take place. Typical examples are lecture, demonstration, or group discussion.

Microanalysis — Examination of items such as damaged electrical wiring, tool marks, and impressions from tires and shoes found at a fire scene; also involves the analysis of broken glass, smoking materials and matches, and hair or fibers found at the scene or on a suspect.

Micron — Unit of length equal to one-millionth of a meter.

Micro Siemen — One millionth of a siemen; a siemen is a Standard International (SI) unit of measurement of electrical conductance.

Microwave — Term applied to radio waves in the frequency range of 1000 mhz and above.

Middle-of-the-Road Leader — Leadership style characterized by a leader who is moderately concerned with both production and relationships.

Midi-pumper — Apparatus sized between a mini-pumper and a full-sized fire department pumper, usually with a gross vehicle weight of 12,000 pounds (5 443 kg) or greater. The midi-pumper has a fire pump with a rated capacity generally not greater than 1,000 gpm (3 785 L/min). *See* Initial Attack Apparatus.

Midship Pump — Fire pumps mounted at the center of the fire apparatus.

Mil — One thousandth of an inch (0.001 inch [0.0254 mm]).

Military Antishock Trousers (MAST) — *See* Medical Antishock Trousers.

Military Aviation Aircraft — Cargo, fighter, bomber, trainer, and special-mission aircraft.

Military Fire Department — Fire prevention/suppression unit operated by the U.S. Department of Defense (DoD); jurisdiction is usually limited to the confines of a military base or installation.

Military Specifications (MILSPECS) — Specifications developed by the U.S. Department of Defense (DoD) for the purchase of materials and equipment.

Mill — One thousandth of an inch (.001 inch [.0254 mm]).

Miller Board — Board used to package a patient with suspected spinal injury; may also be used with a harness for lifting the patient.

Millwork — Woodwork such as doors and trim.

MILSPECS — *See* Military Specifications.

Mineral Soil — Soil containing little or no combustible material.

Mine Rescue Drill — Special drill, operated by the mine emergency division of the U.S. Mine Safety and Health Administration, that can drill a 24-inch diameter (0.6 m) shaft through 50 feet (15 m) of solid limestone in one day.

Mine Resistant Ambush Protected (MRAP) Vehicles — Series of armored fighting vehicles designed to survive ambushes and improvised explosive device (IED) attacks.

Mine Safety and Health Administration (MSHA) — U.S. government organization that regulates mine safety.

Minimum Acceptable Standard — Lowest acceptable level of student performance.

Mininuke — *See* Improvised Nuclear Device (IND).

Mini-pumper — Small fire apparatus mounted on a pickup-truck-sized chassis, usually with a pump having a rated capacity less than 500 gpm (2 000 L/min). Its primary advantage is speed and mobility, which enables it to respond to fires more rapidly than larger apparatus. *Also known as* Light Attack Vehicle. *See* Initial Attack Apparatus.

Minor Treatment — Classification for patients with minor injuries; they may simply require first aid and may even be able to be transported to medical facilities in private vehicles without the care of EMS staff.

Miosis — Abnormal contraction of the pupils, resulting in a pinpoint appearance.

Miranda Warning — Rights read to suspects in the U.S.; based upon the Supreme Court decision *Miranda vs. Arizona*. Miranda language may vary among U.S. states.

Miscibility — Two or more liquids' capability to mix together. *See* Immiscible, Insoluble, and Soluble.

Miscible — Materials that are capable of being mixed.

Misdemeanor — Lesser crime usually punishable by a fine or a term of less than one year in jail or prison.

Mist — Finely divided liquid suspended in the atmosphere; generated by liquids condensing from a vapor back to a liquid, or by breaking up a liquid into a dispersed state by splashing, foaming, or atomizing. *See* Aerosol.

Mitigate — (1) To cause to become less harsh or hostile; to make less severe, intense or painful; to alleviate. (2) Third of three steps (locate, isolate, mitigate) in one method of sizing up an emergency situation.

Mixed Occupancy — Where two or more types or classes of occupancy exist in the same building or structure. Separate requirements are often impractical so the most restrictive fire and life safety requirements apply.

Mixture — Substance containing two or more materials not chemically united.

Mobile Attack — In wildland fire fighting, suppressing fire along a fire edge by driving mobile apparatus along the perimeter and simultaneously applying fire streams to knock down the fire. *Also known as* Pump and Roll.

Mobile Communications Unit — Unit designed and constructed for the purpose of providing specified level of incident radio communications capacity and personnel.

Mobile Data Communications System (MDCS) — Allows for data exchange and private communications between other mobile data terminal (MDT) units.

Mobile Data Terminal (MDT) — Mobile computer that communicates with other computers on a radio system.

Mobile Foam Apparatus — *See* Mobile Foam Extinguishing System.

Mobile Foam Extinguishing System — Foam delivery system that is mounted on a fire apparatus or trailer. *See* Foam Tender and Foam Trailer.

Mobile Home — *See* Manufactured Home.

Mobile Kitchen Unit — Unit designed and constructed for the purpose of dispensing food for incident personnel, providing specified level of capacity.

Mobile Radio — (1) Radio service between a radio station at a fixed location and one or more mobile stations, or between mobile stations. (2) Radio mounted on an apparatus.

Mobile Water Supply Apparatus — Fire apparatus with a water tank of 1,000 gallons (3 785 L) or larger whose primary purpose is transporting water; may also carry a pump, some hose, and other equipment. *Also known as* Tanker or Tender.

Mock Incident — Simulated emergency that allows responders to test their skills under realistic conditions. *Also known as* Staged Incident.

Mock-Up — Working model for realistic training and drilling.

Mode — (1) Phase, step, or progression of applying fireground strategy. (2) Most frequent score (value) in a set of scores. For example, if a set of scores is 98, 98, 95, 92, 92, 92, 89, 88, 87, 85, 85, 79, 75, 74, and 74, the mode or most frequent score is 92.

Modem — Device that converts digital data from a computer to an analog signal that can be transmitted on a telephone line.

Modular Building — Building assembled at the factory in two or more all inclusive sections. All utilities and millwork are also installed at the factory, and connected when the building is delivered to a site.

Moist Adiabatic Lapse Rate — Rate of decrease in temperature with increasing height of an air mass.

Moisture Barrier — (1) Liner within a piece of protective clothing that is designed to keep water out. (2) Backing found on building insulation that prevents moisture from entering the structure.

Moisture Content — Amount of moisture that is available in the environment.

Molecular Sieve — Air-purification component that chemically absorbs water from compressed air.

Molotov Cocktail — Crude bomb made of a breakable container, such as a bottle filled with a flammable liquid; usually fitted with a wick that is ignited just before the bottle is hurled, creating a fire bomb.

Monitor — (1) To measure radioactive emissions from a substance with monitoring device. (2) To closely follow radio communications. (3) To observe and record the activities of an individual performing a function. (4) Individual assigned to supervise an evacuation process for a specified area within a structure, such as a ward monitor or floor monitor.

Monitor Appliance — Master stream appliance whose stream direction can be changed while water is being discharged; can be fixed, portable, or a combination. *Also known as* Monitor.

Monitor Roof — Roof style similar to an exaggerated lantern roof, with a raised section along the ridge line, providing additional natural light and ventilation.

Monitor Valve — Multidirectional valve used to control the flow of hydraulic oil through a hydraulic system.

Monitor Vent — Structure, usually rectangular in shape, which penetrates the highest point of a roof to provide additional natural light and/or ventilation. May have metal, glass, wired glass, or louvered sides, which are counterweighted, hinged, and designed to stay in place when held shut with a fusible link; this type of monitor vent is designed to ventilate an area when heat fuses the link. *Also known as* Monitor.

Monocoque — Construction technique in which an object's external skin supports the structural load of the object.

Monopropellant — Chemical or mixture of chemicals that is stable under specific storage conditions, but reacts very rapidly under other conditions to produce large amounts of energetic (hot) gasses. Monopropellants, such as hydrazine, are commonly used in aircraft emergency power units.

Moody Diagram — Diagram used with the Darcy-Weisbach friction loss computation technique in fluid flow; relates the Reynolds number, pipe size, and roughness to a friction factor.

Mooring — (1) Permanent anchoring equipment (attached by a chain to a buoy) to which a vessel may connect a line, wire, or chain, eliminating the need to use the vessel's anchor. (2) Act of securing a vessel. (3) Location where a vessel is berthed. *See* Anchorage, Berth, and Berthing Area.

Mop-Up — (1) Overhaul of a fire or hazardous material scene. (2) In wildland fire fighting, the act of making a fire safe after it is controlled by extinguishing or removing burning material along or near the control line, felling dead trees (snags), and trenching logs to prevent rolling.

Mortar — Cement-like liquid material that hardens and bonds individual masonry units into a solid mass.

Mortise — (1) Notch, hole, or space cut into a door to receive a lock case, which contains the lock mechanism. (2) Hole, groove, or slot cut into a wooden ladder beam to receive a rung tenon. (3) Notch, hole, or space cut into a piece of timber to receive the projecting part (tenon) of another piece of timber.

Mortise Cylinder — Lock cylinder for a mortise lock.

Mortise Lock — Lock mortised into a door. *Also known as* Box Lock.

Motel — *See* Hotel.

Motivation — Internal process, arousal and maintenance of behavior, in which energy is produced by needs or expended in the direction of goals. Motivation usually occurs in someone who is interested in achieving a goal. *See* Preparation Step.

Motive Power Unit — Engine, locomotive, or other power unit that provides power to move a train.

Motor Nerves — Nerves that carry impulses from the brain to the muscles.

Motor Vehicle Accident (MVA) — Term used when one vehicle hits a stationary object or another vehicle.

Mouse — To tightly wrap or cover the open end of a hook with a material to prevent an object from slipping off the hook. Mousing the hook prevents the hook from accidentally slipping off its intended anchor point.

Mouth-to-Mouth Breathing — Form of resuscitation that involves placing one's mouth over the patient's mouth, then breathing into the patient. *Also known as* Mouth-to-Mouth Resuscitation.

Mouth-to-Mouth Resuscitation — *See* Mouth-to-Mouth Breathing.

Movement Area — Runways, taxiways, and other areas of an airport that are used for taxiing, hover taxiing, air taxiing, takeoff, and landing of aircraft; does not include loading ramps and aircraft parking areas.

Move-Up — Procedure where uncommitted apparatus are relocated to stations emptied by apparatus committed to a long-term incident.

Moving Pivot — Method for positioning a ladder parallel to the objective while raising it.

MSDS — *See* Safety Data Sheet.

MSHA — *See* Mine Safety and Health Administration.

MT — Prefix to the name of a tank vessel powered by diesel machinery.

Mucous Membrane — Membrane that lines many organs of the body and contains mucus-secreting glands.

Mullion — Vertical division between multiple windows or a double door opening.

Multiagent Nozzle — Device that is capable of simultaneously applying any two of the following: foam, halon substitute, or dry chemical extinguishing agents. *See* Fog Nozzle.

Multibolt Lock — High security lock that uses metal rods to secure the door on all sides.

Multi-Casualty Incident — Emergency incident involving 20 or more transportable patients; may be classified as Extended, Major, or Catastrophic. *Also known as* Multiple-Casualty Incident. *See* Mass Casualty Incident.

Multigas Detector — Personal device that checks air quality against a wide range of harmful gases.

Multi-Jurisdictional Incident — Incident that involves or threatens to involve property in more than one jurisdiction; for example, a fire or other emergency in an industrial complex that may threaten to spread into an adjacent municipality and/or a navigable waterway.

Multiloop — Preferred method of software to attach to an anchor point.

Multiple Alarm — Additional alarm, such as second or third, that is a call for additional assistance or response.

Multiple Jacket Hose — Type of hose construction consisting of a combination of two separately woven jackets (double jackets), or two or more interwoven jackets, and lined with an inner rubber tube.

Multiple Patient Incident (MPI) — Incident where the emergency response resources are not overtaxed by the number of patients involved.

Multiple Points of Origin — Two or more separate points of fire origin discovered at a fire scene; indicates a strong possibility of arson.

Multipurpose Fire Extinguisher — Portable fire extinguisher that is rated for Class A, Class B, and Class C fires. *Also known as* A:B:C Extinguisher.

Multistage Centrifugal Pump — Centrifugal fire pump having more than one impeller. *See* Centrifugal Pump, Impeller, Self-Priming Centrifugal Pump, and Single-Stage Centrifugal Pump.

Multiversal — Master stream appliance that may be removed from the pumper and anchored on the ground for use.

Munitions Loaders — Military vehicles used to transport and load/off-load bombs and other munitions from military aircraft.

Muntin — Small members dividing the glass panes in a window sash.

Muscle Cars — High performance American cars made from 1964 to 1974, or modeled on cars built during that time; usually 2-door, rear wheel drive, mid-sized vehicles with oversized, V8 engines.

Mushroom Capital — Flaring conical head on a concrete column.

Mushrooming — Tendency of heat, smoke, and other products of combustion to rise until they encounter a horizontal obstruction; at this point they will spread laterally until they encounter vertical obstructions and begin to bank downward.

Muster List — List of crew members/passengers and their duty/emergency stations on a vessel.

Mutagen — Material that causes changes in the genetic system of a cell, in ways that can be transmitted during cell division. The effects of a mutagen may be hereditary.

MUTCD — *See Manual on Uniform Traffic Control Devices.*

Mutual Aid — Reciprocal assistance from one fire and emergency services agency to another during an emergency, based upon a prearranged agreement; generally made upon the request of the receiving agency.

Mutual Aid Agreement — Written agreement between agencies and/or jurisdictions that they will assist one another on request by furnishing personnel, equipment, and/or expertise in a specified manner.

Mutual Company — Insurance company that is run to benefit the insured, and in which any revenue above operating expenses is returned to policyholders as dividends.

MV — Prefix to the name of a vessel powered by diesel machinery.

MVA — *See* Motor Vehicle Accident.

Mystery Nozzle — Older style, variable gallonage, adjustable fog stream nozzle.

N

Nacelle — Housing of an externally mounted aircraft engine.

Nader Pin — Bolt on a vehicle's door frame that the door latches onto in order to close.

Nader Safety Lock — Vehicle door safety lock; required by law on all passenger vehicles built since 1973.

NAFI — *See* National Association of Fire Investigators.

Nailable — Construction term for the ability of a material to accept nails.

Nasal Cannula — Small tubular prong that fits into the patient's nostril to provide supplemental oxygen; usually there are two, one for each nostril.

National Association of Fire Investigators (NAFI) — Nonprofit association of fire investigators dedicated to the education of fire investigators worldwide; offers training and certification.

National Cave Rescue Commission — Division of the National Speleological Society that specializes in cave rescue.

National Crime Information Center (NCIC) — Computerized index of criminal justice information available to federal, state, and local law enforcement and other criminal justice agencies. NCIC is operational 24 hours a day, 365 days a year.

National Defense Area (NDA) — Temporary establishment of "federal areas" for the protection or security of U.S. Department of Defense (DoD) resources. Normally, NDAs are established for emergency situations, such as accidents; NDAs may be established or discontinued, or have their boundaries changed as necessary to provide protection or security of DoD resources.

National Electrical Code® (NEC®) — NFPA® 70, *National Electrical Code®*, is the standard for electrical activity; contains basic minimum provisions considered necessary to safeguard persons and buildings. It was prepared by the NFPA® National Electrical Code Committee.

National Fire Academy (NFA) — Division of the U.S. Fire Administration that provides training and certification to members of the fire and emergency services, public and private, across the U.S.

National Fire Codes® (NFC®) — Series of codes and standards pertaining to fire protection adopted and published by the National Fire Protection Association® and periodically revised by various committees.

National Fire Danger Rating System (NFDRS) — Multiple index matrix designed to provide fire-control and land-management personnel with a systematic means of assessing various aspects of fire danger on a day-to-day basis. The system is used to classify wildland fuels based on similar burning characteristics.

National Fire Incident Reporting System (NFIRS) — One of the main sources of information (data, statistics) about fires in the U.S. Under NFIRS, local fire departments collect fire incident data and send these to a state coordinator, who compiles statewide fire incident data and forwards the information to the USFA.

National Fire Protection Association® (NFPA®) — U.S. nonprofit educational and technical association devoted to protecting life and property from fire by developing fire protection standards and educating the public. Located in Quincy, Massachusetts. *See* NFPA® 704 Labeling System and NFPA® 704 Placard.

National Fire Sprinkler Association (NFSA) — U.S.-based non-profit organization that champions the cause of widespread acceptance of fire sprinklers for fire protection.

National Highway Traffic Safety Administration (NHTSA) — Agency within the U.S. Department of Transportation (DOT) that publishes annual summary reports of fatal highway accidents.

National Incident Management System - Incident Command System (NIMS-ICS) — The U.S. mandated incident management system that creates a unified structure for federal, state, and local lines of government for incident response. NIMS-ICS defines the roles, responsibilities, and standard operating procedures used to manage emergency operations.

National Institute For Occupational Safety And Health (NIOSH) — U.S. government agency that helps ensure that the workplace and associated equipment are safe; investigates workplaces, recommends safety measures and reports of on-the-job fire injuries. Operates as part of the Centers for Disease Control and Prevention, within the U.S. Department of Health and Human Services.

National Professional Qualifications Board (Pro Board) — Nonprofit organization that provides accreditation to organizations that certify uniform members of public fire departments, both career and volunteer.

National Research Council (NRC) — Canada's publicly funded premier organization for scientific research and development.

National Response Center — U.S. federal organization charged with coordinating the response of numerous agencies to emergency incidents involving the release of significant amounts of hazardous materials.

National Response Framework (NRF) — U.S. document that provides guidance on how communities, states, the federal government, and private-sector and nongovernmental partners conduct all-hazards emergency response.

National Safe Kids® Campaign — Nationwide coalition with the goal of reducing preventable injuries to children.

National Standard Thread (NST) — Screw thread of specific dimensions for fire service use as specified in NFPA® 1963, *Standard for Screw Threads and Gaskets for Fire Hose Connections*.

National Transportation Safety Board (NTSB) — Agency within the U.S. Department of Transportation (DOT) that maintains a fire-related database on aircraft and railway accidents, as well as highway accidents involving hazardous materials injuries.

National Wildland Fire Coordinating Group (NWCG) — Multiagency group that coordinates programs of the participating wildfire management agencies, in order to avoid duplication, increase effectiveness, and provide a means of constructively working together. NWCG provides a forum to discuss, recommend action, or resolve substantive issues and problems; it is also the certifying body for all courses in the National Fire Curriculum. Curerntly participating agencies are the Department of Agriculture Forest Service (FS); the U.S. Fire Administration (USFA); state forestry agencies through the National Association of State Foresters (NASF); and four Department of the Interior agencies - Bureau of Land Management (BLM), National Park Service (NPS), Bureau of Indian Affairs (BIA), and the Fish and Wildlife Service (FWS).

Natural Barrier — Area where the lack of flammable material obstructs the spread of wildland fires.

Natural Cover Fire — *See* Wildland Fire.

Natural Fire Cause — Classification referring to fires where human intervention has not been involved in the ignition process; examples include fires caused by lightning, storms, or floods.

Natural Ventilation — Techniques that use the wind, convection currents, and other natural phenomena to ventilate a structure without the use of fans, blowers, or other mechanical devices.

Naval Architecture — Branch of knowledge concerned with the design and construction of things that float, such as vessels, submarines, docks, or yachts.

Navigable — Term for any body of water suitable for navigation by any particular vessel, although not necessarily all vessels.

NBIE — *See* National Burn Information Exchange.

NCIC — *See* National Crime Information Center.

Neat Cement — Pure cement uncut by a sand mixture.

Needs Analysis — Assessment of training needs that identifies the gap between what exists and what should exist; study of a selected group's needs for the purpose of providing appropriate training or equipment to satisfy those needs.

Needs Assessment — Analysis identifying life-support and critical infrastructure requirements.

Negative — Clear text radio response for "no."

Negative Buoyancy — Tendency to sink.

Negative Heat Balance — Condition that occurs in a fire when heat is dissipated faster than it is generated and, therefore, will not sustain combustion. *See* Positive Heat Balance.

Negative Pressure — Air pressure less than that of the surrounding atmosphere; a partial vacuum.

Negative-Pressure Phase — Portion of an explosion in which air rushes back toward the center; caused by the low pressure created from the positive-pressure phase.

Negative-Pressure Ventilation — Technique using smoke ejectors to develop artificial circulation and to pull smoke out of a structure. Smoke ejectors are placed in windows, doors, or roof vent holes to pull the smoke, heat, and gases from inside the building and eject them to the exterior.

Negligence — Breach of duty where there is a responsibility to perform or conduct that fails to meet the standard of care required by the law, or that would be expected of a reasonable and prudent person under like circumstances. *See* Gross Negligence, Proximate Cause, Standard of Care, and Tort.

Nephrotoxic Agent — Chemical that damages the kidneys. *Also known as* Nephrotoxin.

Nerve Agent — Toxic agent that attacks the nervous system by affecting the transmission of impulses. *See* Chemical Warfare Agent.

Nesting — *See* Ladder Nesting.

Net Pressure — *See* Net Pump Discharge Pressure.

Net Pump Discharge Pressure (NPDP) — Actual amount of pressure being produced by the pump; difference between the intake pressure and the discharge pressure. *Also known as* Engine Pressure or Net Pressure.

Network — Informal group of persons with a mutual interest who communicate with each other to share ideas, information, and resources.

Networking — Communicating and creating linkages between people and clusters of people.

Neurotoxic Agent — Chemical that damages the central nervous system. *Also known as* Neurotoxin.

Neutral Conductor — *See* Grounded Conductor.

Neutral Pressure Plane — Point within a building, especially a high-rise, where the interior pressure equals the atmospheric pressure outside. This plane will move up or down, depending on variables of temperature and wind.

Neutron — Part of the nucleus of an atom that has a neutral electrical charge yet produces highly penetrating radiation; ultrahigh energy particle that has a physical mass like alpha or beta radiation but has no electrical charge. *See* Radiation (2).

Newel — Outer posts of balustrades and the stiffening posts at the angle and platform of stairways.

NFA — *See* National Fire Academy.

NFC — *See* National Fire Codes.

NFDRS — *See* National Fire Danger Rating System.

NFIRS — *See* National Fire Incident Reporting System.

NFPA® — *See* National Fire Protection Association.

NFPA® 101, *Life Safety Code* — Widely used building standard that addresses the life safety aspects of building design in order to protect lives in the event of a fire. Formerly known as *Code for Safety to Life from Fire in Buildings and Structures.*

NFPA® 704 Labeling System — Labeling system derived from NFPA® 704, *Standard System for the Identification of the Hazards of Materials for Emergency Response.* This labeling system is intended to aid in identifying hazardous materials in fixed facilities; its color-coded, symbol-specific placard is divided into sections that identify the degree of hazard with respect to health, flammability, reactivity, and special hazards. *See* NFPA® 704 Placard.

NFPA® 704 Placard — Color-coded, symbol-specific placard affixed to a structure to inform of fire hazards, life hazards, special hazards, and reactivity potential. The placard is divided into sections that identify the degree of hazard according to health, flammability, reactivity, and special hazards. *See* NFPA® 704 Labeling System.

NFPA® Fire Department Survey — Annual survey in which the NFPA® gathers data and statistics about fires in the U.S.

NFSA — *See* National Fire Sprinkler Association.

NHTSA — *See* National Highway Traffic Safety Administration.

Niells-Robertson Stretcher — Stretcher that immobilizes a patient, prevents further spinal damage, and protects the head; excellent for cave and confined-space rescues.

Night Inversion — *See* Inversion.

Night Latch — Button on a rim lock that prevents retracting the latch from the outside.

Night Order Book — Written instructions, special orders, or reminders from the captain or master for each officer taking night watch; placed in the chart room before the captain or master retires for the night.

9-1-1 — Universal emergency number used to summon police, fire, or medical assistance throughout the U.S. The *Omnibus Crime Control and Safe Streets Act of 1968* authorized and designated its use.

NIMS-ICS — *See* National Incident Management System - Incident Command System.

NIOSH — *See* National Institute for Occupational Safety and Health.

Nitrogen — Inert gas that is commonly used as a propellant in portable fire extinguishers.

Nitrogen-Bearing Substances — Substances that produce hydrogen cyanide; found in synthetic fibers such as nylon and polyurethane foam, some plastics (particularly in aircraft), and natural fibers such as wool, rubber, and paper.

Nitrogen Oxides — Group of gases consisting of nitrogen and oxygen and commonly given off as a by-product of the combustion process.

Nitroglycerin — Viscous liquid used in the production of dynamite and other explosives; toxic and highly sensitive to heat and shock. Also used medically as a drug to treat angina pectoris, usually taken under the tongue.

Noded Spheroid Tank — Low-pressure fixed facility storage tank held together by a series of internal ties and supports that reduce stress on the external shell. *See* Low-Pressure Storage Tank, Pressure Storage Tank, and Spheroid Tank.

NOMEX® Fire-Resistant Material — Flame-resistant fabric used to construct firefighter's personal protective equipment.

NOMEX® Hood — *See* Protective Hood.

Nomograph — Chart in which a straight line is drawn between two scales intersecting a third scale which satisfies an equation. Often used based on the Hazen-Williams formula, to assist in the determination of fire flows.

Nonaspirating Foam Nozzle — Nozzle that does not draw air into the foam solution stream. The foam solution is agitated by the nozzle design, causing air to mix with the solution after it has exited the nozzle. *See* Air-Aspirating Foam Nozzle.

Nonbearing Wall — *See* Non-Load-Bearing Wall.

Nonbulk Packaging — Package that has the following characteristics: (a) maximum capacity of 119 gallons (450 L) or less as a receptacle for a liquid, (b) maximum net mass of 882 pounds (400 kg) or less and a maximum capacity of 119 gallons (450 L) or less as a receptacle for a solid, and (c) water capacity of 1,000 pounds (454 kg) or less as a receptacle for a gas. *See* Bulk Packaging and Packaging (1).

Noncombustible — Incapable of supporting combustion under normal circumstances. *See* Combustion and Nonflammable.

Nonconforming Apparatus — Apparatus that does not conform to NFPA® standards.

Nondestructive Testing — Method of testing metal objects that does not subject them to stress-related damage.

Nondiked Area — Any location where flammable or combustible liquids might be spilled but not contained within a system of predesigned barriers. *See* Diked Area.

Nondirectional Anchor — Anchor that is capable of supporting a load in any direction.

Nonflammable — Incapable of combustion under normal circumstances; normally used when referring to liquids or gases. *See* Flammable and Noncombustible.

Nonflammable Gas — Compressed gas not classfied as flammable. *See* Compressed Gas, Flammable Gas, and Gas.

Nonintervention Mode *See* Nonintervention Strategy.

Nonintervention Operations — Operations in which responders take no direct actions on the actual problem. *See* Defensive Operations and Offensive Operations.

Nonintervention Strategy — Strategy for handling fires involving hazardous materials, in which the fire is allowed to burn until all of the fuel is consumed. *Also known as* Nonintervention Mode. *See* Defensive Strategy, Offensive Strategy, and Strategy.

Nonionizing Radiation Series of energy waves composed of oscillating electric and magnetic fields traveling at the speed of light; examples include ultraviolet radiation, visible light, infrared radiation, microwaves, radio waves, and extremely low frequency radiation. *See* Ionizing Radiation and Radiation (2).

Non-Lifeline Rope — Rope that does not meet the requirements set forth in NFPA® 1983, *Standard on Life Safety Rope and Equipment for Emergency Services*.

Nonliquefied Gas — Gas, other than a gas in a solution, that under the charging pressure is entirely gaseous at 70°F (21°C). *See* Gas and Liquefied Compressed Gas.

Non-Load-Bearing Wall — Wall, usually interior, that supports only its own weight. These walls can be breached or removed without compromising the structural integrity of the building. *Also known as* Nonbearing Wall.

Nonmetallic (NM) Shielded Cable — Factory assemblies with two or more wires that have a nonmetallic outer sheath which is moisture resistant and fire retardant.

Nonpersistent Agent — Chemical agent that generally vaporizes and disperses quickly (in less than 10 minutes). *See* Persistent Agent and Vapor Pressure.

Nonpressure Intermodal Tank — Portable tank that transports liquids or solids at a maximum pressure of 100 psi (689 kPa) {6.9 bar}. *Also known as* IM Portable Tank. *See* Intermodal Container and Pressure Intermodal Tank.

Nonpressure Liquid Tank Cargo tank truck used to carry flammable liquids (such as gasoline and alcohol), combustible liquids (such as fuel oil), Division 6.1 poisons, and liquid food products. *See* Cargo Tank Truck.

Nonpressure Storage Tank — *See* Atmospheric Storage Tank.

Nonprofit — Legal status that the U.S. Internal Revenue Service (IRS) may give to an organization; nonprofit, tax-exempt organizations are sometimes called 501(c) organizations, after the section of the Internal Revenue Code that describes them. Designation as a nonprofit requires the submission of a written application to the IRS for review.

Nonrated Concentrate — Foam concentrate that has not been tested or certified by Underwriters Laboratories Inc. *See* Foam Concentrate and Rated Concentrate.

Non-Rebreather Mask — Device used to deliver a high concentration of oxygen through the mouth and nose to injured or ill patients.

Nonseated Explosion — Explosion having no identifiable epicenter or seat; typically deflagrations in fuel-air mixtures and dust clouds. *See* Seated Explosion.

Nonthreaded Coupling — Coupling with no distinct male or female components. *Also known as* Sexless Coupling or Storz Coupling.

Nonverbal Cues — Messages without words; often transmitted in gestures, posture or body language, eye contact, facial expression, tone of voice, or appearance.

Normal Operating Pressure — Amount of pressure that is expected to be available from a hydrant, prior to pumping. *See* Static Pressure.

Normal Path of Travel — *See* Common Path of Travel.

Norm-Referenced Testing — Assessment or measurement of student performance in which a student's test performance is compared with the performance of other students, and his or her grade is dependent on the average performance and variability of performance among those other students. *See* Test.

Nosecup — Device inside a facepiece that directs the wearer's exhalations away from the facepiece lens, thus preventing internal fogging of the lens.

Nosing — Usually rounded edge of a stair tread that projects over a riser.

Noxious — Physically harmful or destructive to living beings; unwanted or troublesome.

Nozzle — Appliance on the discharge end of a hoseline that forms a fire stream of definite shape, volume, and direction.

Nozzleperson — Individual assigned to operate a fire department nozzle. *Also known as* Nozzleman.

Nozzle Pressure — Velocity pressure at which water is discharged from the nozzle.

Nozzle Reaction — Counterforce directed against a person holding a nozzle or a device holding a nozzle by the velocity of water being discharged.

NRC — (1) *See* National Response Center. (2) *See* Nuclear Regulatory Commission. (3) *See* National Research Council.

NRF — *See* National Response Framework.

NST — *See* National Standard Thread.

NTSB — *See* National Transportation Safety Board.

Nuclear Heat Energy — Creation of heat through the splitting apart or combining of atoms.

Nuclear Radiation — Emission of alpha, beta, and gamma radiation resulting from the decay of an atomic nucleus.

Nuclear Regulatory Commission (NRC) — U.S. agency that regulates commercial nuclear power plants and the civilian use of nuclear materials, as well as the possession, use, storage, and transfer of radioactive materials.

Nurse Tanker — Very large water tanker (generally 4,000 gallons [15 140 L] or larger) that is stationed at the fire scene and serves as a portable reservoir rather than as a shuttle tanker. *Also known as* Nurse Tender.

NWCG — *See* National Wildland Fire Coordinating Group.

O

Objective — (1) Purpose to be achieved by tactical units at an emergency. (2) Specific, measurable, achievable statement of intended accomplishment. (3) Purpose or educational goal of a presentation or program; a step necessary to achieve a stated goal. (4) Unbiased; dealing with facts of interpreting results without the distortion of personal feelings, prejudices, or interpretations. *See* Behavioral Objective, Enabling Objective, and Performance Objective.

Objective Test — Test or test items designed so that all qualified test developers agree on the correct answer. Test items and their answers are based on course objectives that were developed from some selected criterion or standard. Types of objective tests include multiple-choice, matching, true-false, and short answer/completion. *See* Test.

Observation — Actually seeing or watching a person's behavior in a natural setting. As a means of evaluation, direct observation provides very reliable information on the effects of programs.

Occlusive Dressing — Watertight dressing for a wound.

Occupancy — (1) General fire and emergency services term for a building, structure, or residency. (2) Building code classification based on the use to which owners or tenants put buildings or portions of buildings. Regulated by the various building and fire codes. *Also known as* Occupancy Classification.

Occupancy Classification — Classifications given to structures by the model code used in that jurisdiction based on the intended use for the structure. *See* Assembly, Building Code, Industrial, Mercantile, and Occupancy.

Occupant — Person who lives in, uses, occupies, or has other possession of an apartment, house, or other premise. *See* Occupancy (1) and Occupant Load.

Occupant Load — Total number of people who may occupy a building or portion of a building at any given time. *See* Occupant.

Occupant Services Unit — Sector/Group designated to provide information and support services to the victims of a fire. Among the services provided may be assistance in contacting relatives, public agencies, and/or charitable institutions for transportation, temporary shelter, and other basic needs.

Occupational Analysis — Method of gathering information about an occupation and developing a description of qualifications, conditions for performance, and an orderly list of duties.

Occupational Safety And Health Administration (OSHA) — Division of the U.S. Department of Labor (DOL) that develops and enforces standards and regulations for occupational safety in the workplace.

Odor Test — Qualitative test of facepiece fit.

ODP — *See* Office for Domestic Preparedness.

Offensive Fire Attack — Aggressive, usually interior fire attack that is intended to stop the fire at its current location. *Also known as* Offensive Mode Attack.

Offensive Fire Fighting — Fire control activities intended to reduce the size of a fire and extinguish it.

Offensive Mode — *See* Offensive Strategy.

Offensive Mode Attack — *See* Offensive Fire Attack.

Offensive Operations Operations in which responders take aggressive, direct action on the material, container, or process equipment involved in an incident. *See* Defensive Operations and Nonintervention Operations.

Offensive Strategy — (1) In wildland fire fighting, generally refers to direct attack on the fire perimeter by crews, engines, aircraft, or an aggressive indirect attack such as backfiring. (2) Overall plan for incident control established by the incident commander (IC) in which responders take aggressive, direct action on the material, container, or process equipment involved in an incident. *See* Defensive Strategy, Nonintervention Strategy, and Strategy.

Office for Domestic Preparedness (ODP) — Former U.S. agency under the Department of Homeland Security that issued federal emergency responder guidelines for events involving weapons of mass destruction.

Officer — Any member of the fire and emergency services with supervisory responsibilities; company officer level and above.

Off-Gassing — Emission of toxic gases; the release of chemicals from non-metallic substances under ambient or greater pressure conditions.

Ohm — Basic unit of measurement of electrical resistance, symbolized either by Ω or R. One ohm is the resistance between two points in a conductor when one volt produces one ampere of current.

Ohmmeter — Device designed to measure electrical resistance in a circuit.

Ohm's Law — Mathematical relationship between a circuit's voltage (V), current (I), and resistance (R): $V = IR$.

OI — *See* Predetermined Procedures.

Oil Tanker — Tank vessel specially designed for the bulk transport of petroleum products by sea. *Also known as* Tanker.

OJT — *See* On-the-Job Training.

Olfactory Fatigue — Gradual inability of a person to detect odors after initial exposure; may be extremely rapid in the case of some toxins, such as hydrogen sulfide.

One- and Two-Family Dwellings — Subdivision of residential property classification consisting of structures that have one or two dwelling units; each is occupied by members of a single family, with as many as three non-family-members living in rented rooms.

One-Compartment Subdivision — Subdivision of a vessel by bulkheads that will result in a vessel remaining afloat with any one compartment flooded under certain conditions. *See* Compartmentation.

On-the-Job Training (OJT) — System of training firefighters that makes full use of personal contact between firefighters and their immediate supervisor; trains firefighters both physically and psychologically for the position they will perform.

Opacity — Capacity to obstruct the transmission of radiant energy-like heat.

Open-Circuit Airline Equipment — Airline breathing equipment that allows exhaled air to be discharged to the open atmosphere.

Open-Circuit Self-Contained Breathing Apparatus — SCBA that allows the wearer's exhaled air to be discharged or vented into the atmosphere.

Open-Ended Question — Question that requires more than a yes or no answer.

Open-Head System — *See* Deluge Sprinkler System.

Opening — Beginning or motivational part of a fire and life safety educator's presentation.

Open Learning — Form of distance learning designed so that participants attend a minimum number of classes and complete reading and writing assignments that are turned in or mailed to the instructor. *See* Distance Learning.

Open Sprinkler — Sprinkler that lacks a heat-sensitive element and is open at all times; used on a deluge-type sprinkler system. *See* Closed Sprinkler and Foam-Water Sprinkler.

Open Stringer — Stringer that is notched to follow the lines of the treads and risers of a stairway.

Open-Top Floating Roof Tank — *See* External Floating Roof Tank.

Open Up — To ventilate a building or other confined space.

Open Web Joist — Joist with a web composed of materials that do not fill the entire web space. Examples include steel bars or tubes.

Open Web Truss — Structural assembly consisting of a top chord and a bottom chord connected by a triangulated series of web components such as bars or tubes.

Operating Budget — Budget intended to fund the day-to-day operations of the department or agency; usually includes the costs of salaries and benefits, utility bills, fuel, and preventive maintenance.

Operating Instruction (OI) — *See* Standard Operating Procedure (SOP).

Operation — One step in performing a job skill within an occupation. Operations are listed in the order in which they are performed.

Operational Level — Level of training established by the National Fire Protection Administration® allowing first responders to take defensive actions at hazardous materials incidents. *See* Awareness Level and Operations Plus.

Operational Period — Period of time scheduled for execution of a specified set of operational goals and objectives as identified in the incident action plan (IAP). An operational period may be 12 hours, 24 hours, or any other arbitrary amount of time. A new IAP is created for each operational period.

Operational Readiness — Ready for or in condition to undertake a destined or predetermined function.

Operational Strategy — Overall plan for incident attack and control.

Operational Tactics — Methods of employing equipment and personnel to obtain optimum results in carrying out operational strategies.

Operational Tests — Tests designed to ensure that the aerial device controls operate the aerial device in the intended manner.

Operation School Burning — Series of fire tests in Los Angeles that analyzed the physiological effects of fire in schools and determined tenability.

Operations Plus — Level of training allowing first responders to take defensive actions at all hazardous materials incidents, plus offensive actions when dealing with gasoline, diesel fuel, natural gas, and liquefied petroleum gas (LPG).

Operations Section — Incident command system section responsible for all tactical operations at the incident. The Operations Section includes branches, divisions and/or groups, task forces, strike teams, single resources, and staging areas. *Also known as* Ops Section.

Operations Section Chief — Person responsible to the incident commander for managing all tactical operations directly applicable to accomplishing the incident objectives. *Also known as* Ops Chief or Ops Section Chief.

Operations Security (OPSEC) — Process of identifying critical information that hostile intelligence systems might obtain and use, and the process of selecting and executing measures that eliminate or reduce vulnerabilities that could be exploited to gain such information.

Opinion Testimony — When a credentialed expert takes the stand to present not just factual information, but interpretation of those facts based upon his or her area of expertise.

OPSEC — *See* Operations Security.

Optical Stabilization (OS) — *See* Image Stabilization (IS).

Optimum Ratio — *See* Stoichiometric Ratio.

Oral Airway — Device inserted in the patient's upper airway to keep the tongue from blocking the airway.

Oral Test — Type of test or form of assessment in which candidates are tested, usually individually, in face-to-face discussion with an examiner or group of examiners. Candidates are usually assessed individually, and often in conjunction with written and/or skill testing. *See* Test.

Order — Specific rule, regulation, or authoritative direction.

Ordinance — Local or municipal law that applies to persons and things of the local jurisdiction; a local agency act that has the force of a statute. Different from law that is enacted by federal or state/provincial legislatures. *See* Law.

Ordnance — Bombs, rockets, ammunition, and other explosive devices carried on most military aircraft, ships, and combat vehicles

Organic Peroxide — Any of several organic derivatives of the inorganic compound hydrogen peroxide.

Organic Vapor/Acid Gas Cartridge — Device in respiratory protection equipment that absorbs harmful vapors and gases from breathable air, preventing harmful gases from being inhaled. Each cartridge is a one-time use item and will last 8 to 10 hours.

Organophosphate Pesticides — Group of chemicals used to kill insects by disrupting their brains and nervous systems; these chemicals inactivate acetylcholinesterase, an enzyme which is essential to nerve function in insects, humans, and many other animals.

Orientation — (1) Direction in which a building faces. (2) Relating blueprints to the actual structure with respect to direction. (3) Location or position relative to the points of the compass.

Oriented Strand Board (OSB) — Construction material made of many small wooden pieces (strands) bonded together to form sheets, similar to plywood.

Orifice — Opening, usually circular, through which water is discharged.

Orifice Plate Meter — Device used for measuring water flow that is similar in principle to a Venturi meter. The change of water velocity is accomplished by using a plate with an orifice that is smaller than the diameter of the pipe in which it is placed.

Origin — *See* Point of Origin.

O-Ring — Circular gasket with rounded edges used for sealing between two machined surfaces; usually made of rubber or silicone.

ORM-D — Other Regulated Material – Domestic. *See* Other Regulated Material.

Orthopedic Injuries — Injuries to the bones, mainly the extremities.

OSHA — *See* Occupational Safety and Health Administration.

OS&Y Valve — Outside stem and yoke valve; a type of control valve for a sprinkler system in which the position of the center screw indicates whether the valve is open or closed. *Also known as* Outside Screw and Yoke Valve.

Other Regulated Material — Material, such as a consumer commodity, that does not meet the definition of a hazardous material and is not included in any other hazard class but possesses enough hazardous characteristics that it requires some regulation; presents limited hazard during transportation because of its form, quantity, and packaging.

Outage — Difference between the full or rated capacity of a tank or tank car as compared to actual content.

Outboard — Anything that is on the seaside of a vessel; anything mounted outside the hull.

Outcome Objective — Desired student performance resulting from a lesson or presentation.

Outer Shell — Outer fabric of protective clothing.

Outlet Valve — Valve farthest downstream to which a discharge hose is attached in a tank piping system.

Out-of-Service — Unit that is not available for assignment to a response.

Out-of-Service Resources — Resources, such as companies or crews, assigned to an incident but unable to respond for mechanical, rest, or personnel reasons.

Outreach Activity — Method the public fire and life safety educator uses to reach an audience, generally a direct presentation.

Outrigger — *See* Stabilizer.

Outside Aid — Assistance from agencies, industries, or fire departments that are not part of the agency having jurisdiction over the incident.

Outside Hand or Foot — Hand or foot furthest from the ladder and furthest from the other member of a two-firefighter team.

Outside Sprinkler — System with open sprinklers, automatically or manually operated, to protect a structure or window openings against a severe exposure hazard.

Outside Standpipe — Standpipe riser that is on the exterior of a building and is equipped with a fire department siamese connection.

Outside Width — Dimension from the outside surface of one ladder beam to the outside surface of the opposite ladder beam, or the widest point of a ladder including staypoles when provided, whichever is greater.

Overburden — Loose earth covering a building site.

Overcurrent — Any current that is in excess of the rated current of equipment or the ampacity of a conductor, and may be caused by an overload, short circuit, or ground fault.

Overfiring — Overheating of a solid-fuel room heater by heating the unit and its connections until they glow a dull red, thus subjecting the unit and surrounding materials to higher-than-expected heat.

Overhand Safety Knot — Knot used in conjunction with other knots to eliminate the danger of the running end of the rope slipping back through a knot, causing the knot to fail.

Overhaul — Operations conducted once the main body of fire has been extinguished; consists of searching for and extinguishing hidden or remaining fire, placing the building and its contents in a safe condition, determining the cause of the fire, and recognizing and preserving evidence of arson.

Overhead — (1) Underside of a deck; ceiling of a vessel's compartment. *Also known as* Deckhead. (2) *See* Transparency.

Overhead Door — Door that opens and closes above a large opening, such as in a warehouse or garage, and is usually of the rolling, hinged-panel, or slab type.

Overhead Expenses — Expenses necessary for routine administration of a project, program, or department.

Overhead Hazards — Identified during recon, these include problems with overhead utilities as well as loose debris on the structure, damaged chimneys, and the weight or movement of unorganized rescuers above the recon team.

Overhead Question — Type of question or questioning method in which an instructor asks a question of the whole group rather than just one person, and to which anyone is free to respond.

Overlapping Rotation — Tactic used during prolonged rescue operations. In order to maintain effectiveness of rescue operations, personnel should be rotated in and out of an assignment in an overlap fashion so that not all personnel are rotated at the same time.

Overload — Operation of equipment or a conductor in excess of its rated ampacity. If continued for a sufficient length of time, overheating to the point of damage may occur.

Overpressure — Increase in pressure above normal or atmospheric pressure.

Override Collision — Occurs when a striking vehicle collides with another vehicle and comes to rest on top of the vehicle being struck.

Overrun — Area beyond the end of the runway that has been cleared of nonfrangible obstacles and strengthened to allow overruns without serious damage to the aircraft. *Also known as* Clearway.

Overrun Area — *See* Stopway Area.

Overt — Not secret; in the open.

Overthrottling — Process of injecting or supplying the diesel engine with more fuel than can be burned.

Overturn Protection — Structural component that provides protection for fittings on top of a tank in case of rollover. May be combined with flashing rail or flashing box.

Oxidation — Chemical process that occurs when a substance combines with oxygen; a common example is the formation of rust on metal. *See* Decomposition and Pyrolysis.

Oxides of Nitrogen — Nitrogen oxide (NO_2) and nitric oxide (NO); can mix with moisture in the air and respiratory tract and form nitric and nitrous acids that can burn the lungs.

Oxidizer — Any substance or material that yields oxygen readily and may stimulate the combustion of organic and inorganic matter. *See* Combustion, Prilled Oxidizer, and Strong Oxidizer.

Oxidizing Agent — Substance that oxidizes another substance; can cause other materials to combust more readily or make fires burn more strongly. *Also known as* Oxidizer.

Oxyacetylene Cutting Torch — Commonly used torch that burns oxygen and acetylene to produce a very hot flame. Used as a forcible entry cutting tool for penetrating metal enclosures that are resistant to more conventional forcible entry equipment.

Oxygen (O_2) — A chemical element. Colorless, odorless, tasteless gas constituting 21 percent of the atmosphere.

Oxygenator — Simplified, convenient oxygen administration system for home use when prolonged administration is necessary.

Oxygen-Deficient Atmosphere — Any atmosphere containing less than the normal 21 percent oxygen found in atmospheric air. At least 16 percent oxygen is needed for flame production and human life.

Oxygen-Enriched Atmosphere — Area in which the concentration of oxygen is in excess of 21 percent by volume or 21.3 kPa; typically 23.5 percent for confined spaces, as defined by the Occupational Safety and Health Administration (OSHA).

Oxygen-Generating Apparatus — SCBA that chemically generates oxygen for breathing by the wearer. This apparatus is no longer acceptable within the fire service.

Oxygen-Generating Canister — Container of chemicals that generate oxygen when mixed with the moisture of an individual's breath.

Oxygen Mask — Device that fits over a patient's nose and mouth and is used to administer supplemental oxygen.

Oxygen Therapy — Administration of oxygen through a mask or tube in the nose to increase the amount of oxygen in the patient's blood.

Oxyhemoglobin — Combination of oxygen and hemoglobin.

P

Package Markings — Descriptive name, instructions, cautions, weight, and specification marks required on the outside of hazardous materials containers. *See* Label, Marking, and Placard.

Packaging — (1) Broad term the U.S. Department of Transportation uses to describe shipping containers and their markings, labels, and/or placards. *See* Bulk Packaging, Combination Packaging, Composite Packaging, Excepted Packaging, Individual Container, Industrial Packaging, Intermediate Bulk Container (IBC), Nonbulk Packaging, Strong, Tight Container, Type A Packaging, and Type B Packaging. (2) Readying a victim for transport.

Padlock — Detachable, portable lock with a hinged or sliding shackle.

Pager — Compact radio receiver used for providing one-way communications

Paid-on-Call Firefighter — Firefighter who receives reimbursement for each call that he or she attends. *Also known as* Call Firefighter.

Pancake Collapse — Situation where the weakening or destruction of bearing walls cause the floors or the roof to collapse, which allows the debris to fall as far as the lower floor or basement. Typically, there will be little void space with these types of collapse. *Also known as* Pancake.

Pandemic — Epidemic occurring over a very wide area (several countries or continents) and usually affecting a large proportion of the population.

Panelboard — Single or multiple panels that contain conductive bus bars and automatic overcurrent protection devices such as circuit breakers or fuses. These panels may also contain manually operated switches.

Panel Cutter — Chisel-like tool used with a mallet or hammer to cut through sheet metal.

Panel Door — Door inset with panels, which are usually made of wood, metal, glass, or plastic.

Panel Points — Points where the load of roof panels is transferred to trusses.

Panic — Sudden and excessive feeling of alarm or fear, usually affecting a body of persons; originates in some real or supposed danger that is vaguely apprehended. May lead to extravagant and injudicious efforts to secure safety.

Panic Hardware — Hardware mounted on exit doors in public buildings that unlocks from the inside and enables doors to be opened when pressure is applied to the release mechanism. *Also known as* Exit Device.

Pantograph — Mechanical linkage device which maintains electrical contact with a contact wire and transfers power from the wire to the traction unit of electric buses, locomotives, and trams.

Pantograph Seal — *See* Mechanical Shoe Seal.

PAPR — *See* Powered Air-Purifying Respirator.

PAR — *See* Personnel Accountability Report

Paracargo — Anything intentionally dropped or intended for dropping from any aircraft by parachute, other retarding devices, or free fall.

Paradoxical Movement — Motion of an injured section of a flail chest; opposite to the normal movement of the chest wall.

Parallel Attack — Constructing a fireline parallel to a wildland fire's edge. After the line is constructed, the fuel inside the line is burned out.

Parallel Circuit — Circuit configuration in which different components in the circuit receive current from different pathways, which allows individual components in the circuit to continue to function even if another component fails.

Parallel Method — Constructing, with hand tools, a fire line parallel to a wildland fire's edge. After the line is constructed, the fuel inside the line is burned out.

Parallel Operation — Operation of a multistage pump in which each of its impellers receives water from a common source. Water flowing through the pump is divided among the stages or impellers and contributes volume directly to the discharge. *Also known as* Volume Operation.

Paramedic — Professional level of certification for emergency medical personnel who are trained in advanced life support procedures.

Paramedic Engine — Fire engine company that carries firefighter/paramedics and paramedic equipment.

Paramedic Unit — *See* Medic Unit (1).

Parapet — (1) Portion of the exterior walls of a building that extends above the roof. A low wall at the edge of a roof. (2) Any required fire walls surrounding or dividing a roof or surrounding roof openings such as light/ventilation shafts.

Parapet Wall — Vertical extension of an exterior wall, and sometimes an interior fire wall, above the roofline of a building.

Park — Rest position of a ladder with one beam resting on the ground and the rungs vertical and perpendicular to the ground.

Parquet Flooring — Flooring, usually of wood, laid in an alternating or inlaid pattern to form various designs. Flooring strips may be glued together to make square units.

Participative Leadership — *See* Democratic Leadership.

Particulate — Very small solid, such as dust, that is suspended in the atmosphere.

Particulate Air Filter — Portion of respiratory protective equipment that traps particulates from the air before they can be inhaled.

Partition Wall — Interior non-load-bearing wall that separates a space into rooms.

Part-Paid Firefighter — Firefighters paid on the basis of time that they are used.

Parts Per Million (ppm) — Method of expressing the concentration of very dilute solutions of one substance in another, normally a liquid or gas, based on volume; expressed as a ratio of the volume of contaminants (parts) compared to the volume of air (million parts).

Party Wall — Dividing wall that stands between two adjoining buildings or units, often on the property line, and is common to both buildings. A party wall is almost always a load-bearing wall and usually serves as a fire wall.

Pascal's Law — Law of physical science that states that pressure acts in all directions and not simply downward.

PASS — *See* Personal Alert Safety System.

Passageway — Any interior walkway, corridor, or hallway in a vessel.

Passenger Side — Side of a vehicle that is opposite of the steering wheel.

Passive-Sentence Index — Index that measures the readability of a passage of text by determining the percentage of passive sentences it contains.

Pathogens — Organisms that cause infection, such as viruses and bacteria.

Patient — Person who is receiving medical care.

Patient Assessment — Process of examining a patient to determine injuries or illness.

Patient Decontamination — Removing contamination from injured patients or victims. *See* Decontamination.

Patio Door — Sliding glass door that is commonly placed in an opening that accesses the patio or rear of a residence.

Patrol — (1) To travel over a given route to prevent, detect, and suppress fires. (2) In wildland fire fighting, to go back and forth vigilantly over a length of control line during and/or after construction, in order to prevent slopovers, suppress spot fires, and extinguish overlooked hot spots.

Pattern — (1) Shape of the water stream as it is discharged from a fog nozzle. (2) Distinctive markings left on a structure or contents after a fire.

Pawls — Devices attached to the inside of the beams on fly sections; used to hold the fly section in place after it has been extended. *Also known as* Dogs or Ladder Locks.

PC — Personal Computer.

PCB — *See* Polychlorinated Biphenyl.

PDP — *See* Pump Discharge Pressure.

Peak Hourly Consumption — Maximum amount of water used in a water distribution system during any hour of a day.

Pedestal — *See* Control Pedestal.

Peer Assistance — Situation in which learners assist their peers in the learning process.

Peer Pressure — Decision-making problem; the tendency of a decision maker to bow to the will of the group rather than to lead the group.

PEL — *See* Permissible Exposure Limit.

PEL-C — *See* Permissible Exposure Limit/Ceiling Limit.

Pendant Sprinkler — Automatic sprinkler designed for placement and operation with the head pointing downward from the piping.

Penetrant — Water with added chemicals called wetting agents that increase water's spreading and penetrating properties due to a reduction in surface tension. *Also known as* Wet Water.

Penetration — Process in which a hazardous material enters an opening or puncture in a protective material. *See* Routes of Entry.

Penthouse — (1) Structure on the roof of a building that may be used as a living space, to enclose mechanical equipment, or to provide roof access from an interior stairway. (2) Room or building built on the roof, which usually covers stairways or houses elevator machinery, and contains water tanks and/or heating and cooling equipment. *Also known as* Bulkhead.

Per Capita — Per unit of population.

Percentage Score — Way of interpreting evaluation results by expressing a part of a whole in hundredths.

Performance — Part of an educational objective that tells what learners must do to show what they have learned. *Also known as* Behavior.

Performance-Based Learning — *See* Competency-Based Learning.

Performance Bond — Binding financial agreement that ensures that the manufacturer will build the apparatus to the desired specifications. Usually, the amount of the bond is equal to the difference that would be required to have another manufacturer build the apparatus specified.

Performance Budget — Form of program budgeting in which the cost of each unit of performance (fire call, EMS call, code enforcement inspection, plan review, etc.) is identified, and total funding is based on projected performance levels.

Performance Evaluation — Evaluation of an individual's job performance as measured against one or more objective performance criteria.

Performance Levels — Desired level of ability required to perform a particular job as specified in a behavioral objective.

Performance Objective — Explicitly worded statement that specifies learners' behaviors (actions or performances), the conditions by which they will perform (what is given to them to perform), and the criteria they will meet (standards or similar measurable requirements). The objective states that the activity will be performed in some observable and measurable form. *See* Behavioral Objective, Learning Objective, and Objective (1).

Performance Requirements — Written list of expected capabilities for new apparatus. The list is produced by the purchaser and presented to the manufacturer as a guide for what is expected.

Performance Standards — Minimum level of knowledge and/or skill that a student must demonstrate to successfully complete a training or education session.

Performance Test — Test that measures a learner's ability and proficiency in performing a job or evolution by requiring that he or she handle equipment or materials in a coordinated, step-by-step process; measures learner or employee achievement of a psychomotor objective and holds the test-taker to either a speed standard (timed performance), a quality standard (minimum acceptable product or process standard), or both. Typically given at the end of instruction to measure final performance. *Also known as* Skills Test. *See* Test.

Perimeter — (1) Outer boundary of a fire or other incident scene established to secure the area, ensure safety, examine a scene, protect civilians, and/or collect evidence. (2) The perimeter of a wildland fire is the boundary of the fire; the total length of the outer edge of the burning or burned area.

Perimeter Control — Establishing and maintaining control of the outer edge or boundary of an incident scene.

Periphery-Deflected Fire Streams — Fire streams produced by deflecting water from the periphery of an inside circular stem in a fog nozzle against the exterior barrel of the nozzle.

Perjury — Lying under oath in a court or legal proceeding.

Permanent Deformation — Deformation remaining in any part of a ladder or its components after all test loads have been removed.

Permeation — Process in which a chemical passes through a protective material on a molecular level.

Permissible Exposure Limit (PEL) — Maximum time-weighted concentration at which 95 percent of exposed, healthy adults suffer no adverse effects over a 40-hour work week; an 8-hour time-weighted average unless otherwise noted. PELs are expressed in either parts per million (ppm) or milligrams per cubic meter (mg/m³). They are commonly used by OSHA and are found in the NIOSH *Pocket Guide to Chemical Hazards*. *See* Immediately Dangerous to Life or Health (IDLH), Permissible Exposure Limit/Ceiling Limit (PEL-C), Recommended Exposure Limit (REL), Short-Term Exposure Limit (STEL), and Threshold Limit Value (TLV®).

Permissible Exposure Limit/Ceiling Limit (PEL-C) — Maximum concentration to which an employee may be exposed at any time, even instantaneously, as established by Occupational Safety and Health Administration (OSHA). *See* Permissible Exposure Limit (PEL).

Peroxidizable Compound Material apt to undergo spontaneous reaction with oxygen at room temperature and form peroxides and other products.

Persistence — Length of time a chemical agent remains effective without dispersing. *See* Dispersion, Nonpersistent Agent, and Persistent Agent.

Persistent Agent — Chemical agent that remains effective in the open (at the point of dispersion) for a considerable period of time (more than 10 minutes). *See* Dispersion, Nonpersistent Agent, and Persistence.

Person-Borne Improvised Explosives Device (PBIED) — Improvised explosive device carried by a person; employed by suicide bombers as well as individuals coerced into carrying the bomb against their will. *See* Explosion, High Explosive, and Improvised Explosive Device.

Personal Alert Device (PAD) — *See* Personal Alert Safety System.

Personal Alert Safety System (PASS) — Electronic lack-of-motion sensor that sounds a loud tone when a firefighter becomes motionless. It can also be manually triggered to operate. *Also known as* Personal Alert Device. *See* Personal Protective Equipment.

Personal Line — Short, 20-foot (6 m) rope used in the United Kingdom, Australia, and New Zealand by an SCBA team member to maintain contact with another team member or the main guideline.

Personal Protective Clothing — Garments emergency responders must wear to protect themselves while fighting fires, mitigating hazardous materials incidents, performing rescues, and delivering emergency medical services.

Personal Protective Equipment (PPE) — General term for the equipment worn by fire and emergency services responders; includes helmets, coats, pants, boots, eye protection, hearing protection, gloves, protective hoods, self-contained breathing apparatus (SCBA), personal alert safety system (PASS) devices, and chemical protective clothing. When working with hazardous materials, bands or tape are added around the legs, arms, and waist. *Also known as* Bunker Clothes, Chemical Protective Clothing, Full Structural Protective Clothing, Protective Clothing, Turnout Clothing, or Turnout Gear. *See* Chemical Protective Clothing (CPC) and Special Protective Clothing (1).

Personnel Accountability Report (PAR) — Roll call of all units (crews, teams, groups, companies, sectors) assigned to an incident. The supervisor of each unit reports the status of the personnel within the unit at that time, usually by radio. A PAR may be required by standard operating procedures at specific intervals during an incident, or may be requested at any time by the incident commander or the incident safety officer.

Personnel Accountability System — Method for identifying which emergency responders are working on an incident scene.

Personnel Carriers — Armored fighting vehicles designed to transport infantry to a battlefield.

Personnel Management — Decision-making concerning the effective use of human resources within an organization so that organizational and individual goals are met.

Personnel Record — Account of an individual employee's work history; includes personal data (such as name, address, date of employment, or job classification), citations, commendations, promotions, performance evaluations, letters of reprimand or other disciplinary documentation, and medical history.

Pesticides — Chemicals designed and used to control or eliminate undesirable forms of life, such as plants and animal pests.

Petroleum Carrier — Tank vessel that transports crude or finished petroleum products. *See* Tanker.

pH — Measure of acidity of an acid or the level of alkaline in a base. *See* Acid, Alalki, and Base.

Phantom Box — Predetermined fire department response assignment to a given location that is not equipped with a fire alarm box.

Phase — Distinguishable part in a course, development, or cycle; aspect or part under consideration.

Phase I Operation — Emergency operating mode for elevators. Phase I operation recalls the car to a certain floor and opens the doors.

Phase II Operation — Emergency elevator operating mode that allows emergency use of the elevator with certain safeguards and special functions.

Phobia — Abnormal and persistent fear of a specific object or situation.

Phonetic Alphabet — Alphabet devised by the International Civil Aviation Organization for use in radio-telephone conversations. Words are used phonetically in place of letters; for example, A is alpha, B is bravo, etc.

Phosgene (COCl$_2$) — Toxic gas produced when refrigerants, such as freon, plastics containing polyvinyl chloride (PVC), or electrical wiring insulation, contact flames; may be absorbed through the skin as well as through the lungs.

Photoelectric Cell — Light-sensitive device used in some fire detectors. Cell initiates an alarm signal when light strikes it or is kept from striking it, depending upon the particular design.

Photoelectric Smoke Detector — Type of smoke detector that uses a small light source, either an incandescent bulb or a light-emitting diode (LED), to detect smoke by shining light through the detector's chamber. Smoke particles reflect the light into a light-sensitive device called a photocell.

Photo Log — Assembled group of photographs with numerical references and descriptions of the photos.

Photon — Packet of electromagnetic energy.

Physical Change — When a substance remains chemically the same but changes in size, shape, or appearance.

Physical Hazard — Material that presents a threat to health because of its physical properties. *See* Health Hazard and Physical Properties.

Physically Fit — As determined by a qualified physician, an individual who has no known physical or medical limitations that would interfere with the performance of sustained heavy work or the use of self-contained breathing apparatus (SCBA) that may be required during emergency operations.

Physical Properties — Properties that do not involve a change in the chemical identity of the substance, but affect the physical behavior of the material inside and outside the container, which involves the change of the state of the material. Examples include boiling point, specific gravity, vapor density, and water solubility. *See* Boiling Point, Chemical Properties, Specific Gravity, Vapor Density, and Water Solubility.

Physical Science — Study of the physical world around us; includes the sciences of chemistry and physics.

Physical Search — Performed by rescuers without outside search-specific resources; involves an organized approach to checking all areas of the structure. This is the most easily implemented type of search, as it can be done with available resources.

Physiological — (1) Of or relating to an organism's healthy and normal functioning. (2) First and most basic group of needs in Maslow's Hierarchy of Needs; needs such as food, water, and shelter, which are related to personal survival and are essential to sustain life. Maslow's physiological needs also include escaping from a situation, such as a fire, that is immediately life-threatening.

Physiological Stress — Stress caused by physical exertion.

Picket — Steel rod or wooden stake driven into the ground to create an anchor, such as for a guy line.

Pick-Head Axe — Forcible entry tool that has a chopping blade on one side of the head and a sharp pick on the other side.

Pick-Up Plate — Sloped plate and structure of a trailer, which is located forward of the kingpin and designed to facilitate engagement of fifth wheel to kingpin.

Pickup Tube — Solid or flexible tube used to transfer foam concentrate from a storage container to the in-line eductor or proportioner.

Pictogram — Drawing or symbol that indicates information.

Pier — (1) Supporting section of a wall between two openings. (2) Short masonry column. (3) Load-supporting member constructed by drilling or digging a shaft, then filling the shaft with concrete. (4) Elevated working platform, usually made of wood or masonry, that extends outward from the shore into a standing body of water for use as a landing place for vessels; supported on pilings and open underneath, allowing the berthing of vessels alongside. *See* Wharf.

Piercing Nozzle — Nozzle with an angled, case-hardened steel tip that can be driven through a wall, roof, or ceiling to extinguish hidden fire. *Also known as* Piercing Applicator Nozzle or Puncture Nozzle.

Piezometer Tube — Device that uses the heights of liquid columns to illustrate the pressures existing in hydraulic systems.

Piggyback Transport — *See* Trailer-On-Flatcar (TOFC).

Pig Rig — Term used for a simple 3:1 mechanical advantage pulley system. Used in a horizontal configuration to attach to a main line or directly to a load; more versatile than a simple 3:1 Z-pulley system.

Pike Pole — Sharp prong and hook of steel, on a wood, metal, fiberglass, or plastic handle of varying length, used for pulling, dragging, and probing.

Pilaster — Rectangular masonry pillar that extends from the face of a wall to provide additional support for the wall; may also be for decorative use only, in which case it does not provide any support.

Piles — Wooden or steel beams used to support loads; piles are driven into the ground and develop their load-carrying ability either through friction with the surrounding soil or by being driven into contact with rock or a load-bearing soil layer.

Pilot — Person knowledgeable of the local waters who meets vessels and steers them safely into and out of port.

Piloted Ignition — Moment when a mixture of fuel and oxygen encounters an external heat (ignition) source with sufficient heat energy to start the combustion reaction.

PIN — *See* Product Identification Number.

PIO — *See* Public Information Officer.

Pincer Attack — Simultaneous attack on two or more sides of a wildland fireline. Similar to a wildland flank attack. *See* Attack Methods (2).

Pinch Point — Any point, other than the point of operation, at which it is possible for a part of the body to be caught between the moving parts of the machine or between a moving part and a stationary part where the user could receive a crushing injury to a portion of the body.

Pin Lug Couplings — Hose couplings with round lugs in the shape of a pin.

Pipe Chase — Concealed vertical channel in which pipes and other utility conduits are housed. Pipe chases that are not properly protected can be major contributors to the vertical spread of smoke and fire in a building. *Also known as* Chase.

Pipe Plugs and Caps — Devices used to stop broken water lines in order to minimize water damage.

Piston Pump — Positive-displacement pump using one or more reciprocating pistons to force water from the pump chambers.

Piston Valve — Valve with an internal piston that moves within a cylinder to control the flow of water through the valve.

Pitch — (1) In steel construction, the spacing between rivet centers. (2) Slope of a roof expressed as a ratio of rise to span. (3) Resin present in certain woods. (4) Asphaltic, tarlike liquid used to repair blacktopped streets. (5) Angle between horizontal and a ladder positioned for use.

Pitched Roof — Roof, other than a flat or arched roof, that has one or more pitched or sloping surfaces.

Pitot Gauge — Instrument that is inserted into a flowing stream of water to measure the velocity pressure of the stream; commonly used to measure flow. Functions by converting the velocity energy to pressure energy that can then be measured by a pressure gauge that reads in units of pounds per square inch (psi) or kilopascals (kPa).

PIV — *See* Post Indicator Valve.

PIVA — *See* Post Indicator Valve Assembly.

Pivot — Method for turning a ladder on one beam when the ladder has been raised to a near vertical position.

Pivoting Deadbolt — Lock having a deadbolt that pivots 90 degrees, designed to fit a narrow-entry, stiled door.

Pivoting Window — Window that opens and closes either horizontally or vertically on pivoting hardware.

Pixel — Smallest item of information in a digital image; can be used to define the size of a digital image, the printing capabilities of a digital printer, or the screen resolution of high definition televisions and computer monitors.

Placard — Diamond-shaped sign that is affixed to each side of a structure or a vehicle transporting hazardous materials to inform responders of fire hazards, life hazards, special hazards, and reactivity potential. The placard indicates the primary class of the material and, in some cases, the exact material being transported; required on containers that are 640 cubic feet (18 m³) or larger. *See* Label, Marking, NFPA® 704 Placard, Package Marking, and Packaging.

Plagiarism — To present as an original idea without crediting the source.

Plancier — Board that forms the underside of an eave or cornice.

Plane of Weakness — Area created by the rescuers in a wall or floor that is weaker than the surrounding structural material.

Planning Meeting — Meeting held as needed at any point during an incident, in order to select specific strategies and tactics for incident control operations and for service and support planning.

Planning Model — Organized procedure that includes the steps of analyzing, designing, developing, implementing, and evaluating instruction; a systematic approach to the design, production, evaluation, and use of a system of instruction.

Planning Section — Incident command system section responsible for collection, evaluation, dissemination, and use of information about the development of the incident and the status of resources; includes the situation status, resource status, documentation, and demobilization units, as well as technical specialists.

Plan of Operations — Clearly identified strategic goal and the tactical objectives necessary to achieve that goal; includes assignments, authority, responsibility, and safety considerations.

Plans Review — Process of reviewing building plans and specifications to determine the safety characteristics of a proposed building; generally done before permission is granted to begin construction.

Plan View — Drawing containing the two-dimensional view of a building as seen from directly above the area. *See* Detailed View, Elevation View, and Sectional View.

Plasterboard — *See* Wallboard.

Plaster Hook — Barbed collapsible hook on a pole used to puncture and pull down materials.

Plat — Drawing of a parcel of land that gives its legal description.

Plate — Top (top plate) or bottom (soleplate) horizontal structural member of a frame wall or partition.

Plate Glass — Sheet glass that is ground, polished, and clear.

Platform — (1) Intermediate landing between floors to change the direction of a stairway or to break up excessively long flights. (2) Main deck of an offshore drilling rig. (3) Horizontal surface extending partway through a vessel, usually in the cargo space. (4) Any flat-topped vessel capable of providing a working area for personnel or vehicles.

Platform Frame Construction — Type of framing in which each floor is built as a separate platform, and the studs are not continuous beyond each floor. *Also known as* Western Frame Construction.

Platoon — Entire shift of a fire department; may indicate those who are on or off duty.

Plat Plan — *See* Plat.

Play a Stream — To direct a stream of water at the fire.

Playpipe — Base part of a three-part nozzle that extends from the hose coupling to the shutoff.

Plimsoll Mark — Symbol placed on the sides of a vessel's hull at amidships, indicating the maximum allowable draft of the vessel. *Also known as* Load Line.

Plot Plan — Architectural drawing showing the overall project layout of building areas, driveways, fences, fire hydrants, and landscape features for a given plot of land; view is from directly above. *See* Construction Plan, Floor Plan, and Site Plan.

Plug — (1) Fire hydrant. (2) Wooden peg used to stop a hole in a container. (3) Safety device that grounds a tank vehicle or rail tank car during the loading and unloading process and prevents static electricity buildup. (4) Patch to seal a small leak in a container.

Plug Pressure — *See* Flow Pressure.

Plume — Irregularly shaped pattern of an airborne hazardous material where wind and/or topography influence the downrange course from the point of release. *See* Cloud, Cone, and Hemispheric Release.

Plume-Generated Pattern — Any of a number of fire patterns created as a result of the plume of hot gases rising above an individual fire. *See* Circular-Shaped Pattern, Hourglass Pattern, Inverted-Cone Pattern, U-Pattern, and V-Pattern.

Plymetal Panels — Railcar floor panels constructed of plywood sheets covered by sheets of metal, usually aluminum.

Plywood — Wood sheet product made from several thin veneer layers that are sliced from logs and glued together.

PMP — Prusik minding pulley. A specially designed pulley to work with tandem Prusiks in rope rescue systems.

Pneumatic — Operated by air or compressed air.

Pneumatic Chisel — Tool designed to operate at air pressures between 100 and 150 psi (700 kPa and 1 050 kPa); during periods of normal consumption, it will use about 4 to 5 cubic feet (113 L to 142 L) of air per minute. It is useful for extrication work. *Also known as* Air Chisel, Impact Hammer, or Pneumatic Hammer.

Pneumatic Lifting Bag — Inflatable, envelope-type device that can be placed between the ground and an object and then inflated to lift the object; it can also be used to separate objects. Depending on the size of the bag, it may have lifting capabilities in excess of 75 tons (68 040 kg).

Pneumatic Power — Power derived by using the properties of compressed air at rest or in motion; generally used with a pressure regulator.

Pneumatic Shoring — Shores or jacks with movable parts that are operated by the action of a compressed gas.

Pneumatic Tools — Tools that receive their operating energy from compressed air.

Pneumothorax — Accumulation of air in the pleural cavity, usually after a wound or injury that penetrates the chest wall or lacerates the lungs.

Point and Cut Off — Attacking several heads or fingers of a wildfire at the same time and then connecting the short line segments.

Pointer Pattern — Fire pattern created when structural components such as wood studs or trim are exposed to flame; sharp edges of the component are often burned away on the side of the component that faces the heat source. Also refers to a series of burned components that indicate a longer duration on one end of the series to shorter duration on the other.

Point of No Return — Point at which the remaining operation time of the SCBA is equal to the time necessary to return safely to a nonhazardous atmosphere.

Point of Operation — Location at which the intended work is being done.

Point of Origin — Exact physical location where the heat source and fuel come into contact with each other, causing a fire.

Poison — Any material that is injurious to health when taken into the body. *See* Convulsant and Toxin.

Poke-Through — Opening in a floor, ceiling, or wall through which ducting, plumbing, or electrical conduits pass. If these openings are not properly caulked or sealed, they can contribute significantly to the spread of smoke and fire in a building.

Polarized Couplings — *See* Gladhands.

Polar Solvent Fuel — (1) Flammable liquids that have an attraction for water, much like a positive magnetic pole attracts a negative pole; examples include alcohol, ketone, and lacquer. *See* Flammable Liquid and Hydrocarbon Fuel. (2) A liquid having a molecule in which the positive and negative charges are permanently separated, resulting in their ability to ionize in solution and create electrical conductivity; examples include water, alcohol, and sulfuric acid.

Pole — (1) Sliding pole from upper stories to the apparatus area of a fire station. (2) Ladder poles to assist in raising large ground ladders. (3) Pike pole.

Pole Ladder — Large extension ladder that requires tormentor poles to steady the ladder as it is raised and lowered. *Also known as* Bangor Ladder.

Police Power — (1) Authority that may be given to an inspector to arrest, issue summons, or issue citations for fire code violations. (2) Constitutional right of the government to impose laws, statutes, and ordinances, including zoning ordinances and building and fire codes, in order to protect the health, safety, morals, and general welfare of the public.

Polychlorinated Biphenyl (PCB) — Toxic compound found in some older oil-filled electric transformers.

Polyethylene Membrane — Type of plastic sheet used for waterproofing.

Polymerization — Reactions in which two or more molecules chemically combine to form larger molecules; this reaction can often be violent. *See* Inhibitor.

Polyvinyl Chloride (PVC) — Synthetic chemical used in the manufacture of plastics and single-ply membrane roofs.

Pompier Belt — *See* Class I Harness.

Pompier Ladder — Scaling ladder with a single beam and a large curved metal hook that can be put over windowsills for climbing.

Pony Wall — Non-load-bearing wall that is less than 36 inches (914 mm) high. *See* Load-Bearing Wall.

Poop Deck — Partial deck above main deck at stern. *See* Deck.

Porcelainize — To coat with a ceramic material.

Port — (1) General area of a shore establishment having facilities for the landing, loading/unloading, and maintenance of vessels; a harbor with piers. (2) Left-hand side of a vessel as a person faces forward. *Also known as* Port Side.

Portable Basin — *See* Portable Tank.

Portable Equipment — Items carried on the fire or rescue apparatus that are not permanently attached to or a part of the apparatus.

Portable Fire Extinguisher — *See* Fire Extinguisher.

Portable Foam Extinguishing System — Foam extinguishing system that can be carried by hand, such as a handheld foam fire extinguisher. *See* Fixed Foam Extinguishing System and Semifixed Foam Extinguishing System.

Portable Hydrant — *See* Manifold.

Portable Ladder Pipe — Portable, elevated master stream device clamped to the top two rungs of the aerial ladder when needed and supplied by a 3- or 3½-inch (77 mm or 90 mm) fire hose.

Portable Pump — (1) Small fire pump, available in several volume and pressure ratings, that can be removed from the apparatus and taken to a water supply inaccessible to the main pumper. (2) In marine fire fighting, a small gasoline-driven pump used in emergencies to deliver water to a fire independent of a vessel's fire main system.

Portable Radio — Hand-held, self-contained transceiver radio used by personnel to communicate with each other when away from the vehicle radio. A portable radio draws upon power from its own battery and uses its case along with an antenna to make up the antenna assembly. Portable radios do not have much power; they generally transmit 1 to 5 watts and have limited coverage areas. Duration of battery and duty cycles depends on their power source. *Also known as* Handi-Talki.

Portable Source — Water that is mobile and may be taken directly to the location where it is needed; may be a fire department tanker or some other vehicle that is capable of hauling a large quantity of water.

Portable Tank — Collapsible storage tank used during a relay or shuttle operation to hold water from water tanks or hydrants; this water can then be used to supply attack apparatus. *Also known as* Catch Basin, Fold-a-Tank, Porta-Tank, or Portable Basin.

Porta-Power — Manually operated hydraulic tool that has been adapted from the auto body business to the rescue service. This device has a variety of tool accessories that allows it to be used in numerous applications.

Port Authority — Agency entrusted with the duty or power of constructing, improving, managing, or maintaining a harbor or port. *Also known as* Harbor Authority, Harbor Board, Port Commission, or Port Trust.

Porthole — Circular window in the side of a vessel.

Portland Cement — Most commonly used cement, consisting chiefly of calcium and aluminum silicate. It is mixed with water to form a paste that hardens, and is therefore known as a hydraulic cement.

Port of Registry — Port in which a vessel is registered. *Also known as* Home Port.

Port State — Nation in which a port is located.

Port State Authority — Government agency having authority over port operations.

Position — (1) Specific assignment during a fire operation. (2) To spot an apparatus for maximum effective use.

Position Description — Written description of a specific employee position that spells out the expectations of the job, the activities that are needed to meet those expectations, and the qualifications needed to fill the job.

Positive Buoyancy — Tendency to float.

Positive Displacement Pumps — Self-priming pump that utilizes a piston or interlocking rotors to move a given amount of fluid through the pump chamber with each stroke of the piston or rotation of the rotors. Used for hydraulic pumps on aerial devices' hydraulic systems and for priming pumps on centrifugal fire pumps.

Positive Heat Balance — Situation that occurs when heat is fed back to the fuel; a positive heat balance is required to maintain combustion. *See* Negative Heat Balance.

Positive Pressure — Air pressure greater than that of the surrounding atmosphere.

Positive-Pressure Phase — Portion of an explosion in which gases are expanding outward from the center.

Positive-Pressure SCBA — Protective breathing apparatus that maintains a slight positive pressure inside the mask.

Positive-Pressure Test — Test to verify that there is positive pressure within a facepiece; after donning the facepiece, the wearer pulls the sealing surface of the facepiece away from the skin, allowing air to escape.

Positive-Pressure Ventilation (PPV) — Method of ventilating a confined space by mechanically blowing in fresh air in sufficient volume to create a slight positive pressure within, thereby forcing the contaminated atmosphere out the exit opening. *See* Ventilation.

Possible — Legal classification for an occurrence that is less likely than 50 percent.

Posterior — At or toward the back.

Post-Fire Operations — Overhaul after knockdown. Includes searching for and extinguishing hidden fire, determining the fire cause, identifying and preserving evidence of arson, and making the building and area safe for occupation; may also include returning to quarters, preparing equipment for future response, and writing incident reports.

Post-Incident Analysis — General overview and critique of the incident by members of all responding agencies (including dispatchers) that should take place within two weeks of the actual incident.

Post-Incident Loss Control Activities — Those preparations needed in order to turn the property back over to the owner or occupant.

Post-Incident Stress — Psychological stress that affects emergency responders after returning from a stressful emergency incident.

Post Indicator Valve (PIV) — Type of valve used to control underground water mains that provides a visual means for indicating "open" or "shut" positions; found on the supply main of installed fire protection systems. The operating stem of the valve extends above ground through a "post," and a visual means is provided at the top of the post for indicating "open" or "shut." *See* Wall Post Indicator Valve.

Post Indicator Valve Assembly (PIVA) — Similar to a post indicator valve (PIV), except that the valve used is of the butterfly type; in contrast, the PIV and the wall post indicator valve (WPIV) use a gate valve.

Post-Tensioned Reinforcing — Technique used in post-tensioned concrete; reinforcing steel in the concrete is tensioned after the concrete has hardened.

Post-Traumatic Incident Debriefing — Counseling designed to minimize the effects of post-incident trauma. *Also known as* Critical Incident Stress Debriefing.

Post-Traumatic Stress Disorder (PTSD) — Disorder caused when persons have been exposed to a traumatic event in which they have experienced, witnessed, or been confronted with an event or events that involve actual death, threatened death, serious injury, or the threat of physical injury to self or others. *Also known as* Critical Incident Stress (CIS) and Post-Traumatic Stress Syndrome.

Potassium Iodide — Drug used as a blocking agent to prevent the human thyroid gland from absorbing radioactive iodine.

Potential Energy — Stored energy possessed by an object that can be released in the future to perform work.

Pot Metals — Slang term for alloys consisting of inexpensive, low-melting point metals that are normally used for inexpensive castings; examples include zinc, lead, copper, and aluminum.

Pounds Per Square Inch (psi) — Unit for measuring pressure in the English or Customary System. Its International System equivalents are kilopascals (kPa) and bar.

Pounds Per Square Inch - Absolute (psia) — Unit for measuring pressure in the English or Customary System; its International System equivalents are kilopascals (kPa) and bar. Absolute pressure equals atmospheric pressure (14.7 psi) plus the gauge pressure; at 100 psig, absolute pressure equals 114.7 psia.

Pounds Per Square Inch — Gauge (psig) — Pressure indicated on a gauge that does not include atmospheric pressure; at sea level, 0 psig is equal to 14.7 psia.

Power — Amount of energy delivered over a given period of time.

Powered Air-Purifying Respirator (PAPR) — Motorized respirator system that uses a filter to clean surrounding air before delivering to the wearer to breathe; typically includes a blower/battery box worn on the belt, a headpiece, and a breathing tube.

Powered Hydraulic Shears — Large rescue tool whose two blades open and close by the use of hydraulic power supplied through hydraulic hoses from a power unit.

Powered Hydraulic Spreaders — Large rescue tool whose two arms open and close by the use of hydraulic power supplied through hydraulic hoses from a power unit; capable of exerting in excess of 20,000 pounds (9 072 kg) of force at its tips. *Also known as* Jaws.

Power Plant — *See* Apparatus Engine.

Power Take-Off (PTO) — Rotating shaft that transfers power from the engine to auxiliary equipment. All farm tractors are designed to operate the PTO shaft at either 540 or 1,000 revolutions per minute.

Power Tool — Tool that acquires its power from a mechanical device, such as a motor or pump.

Power Train — (1) Includes all of the parts that create and transfer power to the surface being traversed. *Also known as* Drive Train. (2) Means of transferring power from an engine to a pump; includes all power-transmitting components.

PPE — *See* Personal Protective Equipment.

ppm — *See* Parts Per Million.

PPV — *See* Positive-Pressure Ventilation.

Practical Demonstration — Method of teaching psychomotor skills, such as installing a smoke detector or using a portable fire extinguisher safely. *Also known as* Manipulative Lesson.

Practical Training Evolution — *See* Evolution.

Preaction Sprinkler System — Fire-suppression system that consists of closed sprinkler heads attached to a piping system that contains air under pressure and a secondary detection system; both must operate before the extinguishing agent is released into the system. Similar to a dry-pipe sprinkler system. *See* Deluge Sprinkler System, Dry-Pipe Sprinkler System, and Wet-Pipe Sprinkler System.

Preassembled Lock — Lock designed to be installed as a complete unit, requiring no assembly, within a door. *Also known as* Unit Lock.

Preattack Planning — *See* Pre-Incident Planning.

Precast Concrete — Method of building construction where the concrete building member is poured and set according to specification in a controlled environment and is then shipped to the construction site for use.

Precipitation — Any or all forms of water particles, liquid or solid, that fall from the atmosphere.

Preconnect — (1) Attack hose connected to a discharge when the hose is loaded; this shortens the time it takes to deploy the hose for fire fighting. (2) Soft-sleeve intake hose that is carried connected to the pump intake. (3) Hard suction hose or discharge hose carried connected to a pump, eliminating delay when hose and nozzles must be connected and attached at a fire.

Predischarge Alarm — Alarm that sounds before a total flooding fire extinguishing system is about to discharge; this gives occupants the opportunity to leave the area.

Predetermined Procedures — *See* Standard Operating Procedure (SOP).

Prefabricated Construction — Method of building construction in which the walls, floors, and ceilings are manufactured complete with plumbing, electrical wiring, and millwork (woodwork such as doors and trim). Once delivered to the site, the entire assembly is erected. *Also known as* Panelized Construction.

Prefire Inspection — *See* Pre-Incident Planning.

Prefire Planning — *See* Pre-Incident Planning.

Pre-Incident Inspection — Thorough and systematic inspection of a building for the purpose of identifying significant structural and/or occupancy characteristics to assist in the development of a pre-incident plan for that building. *See* Pre-Incident Planning.

Pre-Incident Plan — Document, developed during pre-incident planning that contains the operational plan or set procedures for the safe and efficient handling of emergency situations at a given location, such as a specific building or occupancy. *Also known as* Preplan.

Pre-Incident Planning — Act of preparing to manage an incident at a particular location or a particular type of incident before an incident occurs. *Also known as* Prefire Inspection, Prefire Planning, Pre-Incident Inspection, Pre-Incident Survey, or Preplanning.

Pre-Incident Survey — Survey of a facility or location made before an emergency occurs in order to prepare for an appropriate emergency response. *Also known as* Preplan.

Preliminary Hearing — Court proceeding in which the prosecution must establish that a crime has been committed and that there is probable cause to believe the defendant committed the crime.

Premise — Proposition from which inferences may be drawn to reach conclusions about a question or problem.

Premixing — Mixing pre-measured portions of water and foam concentrate in a container. Typically, the premix method is used with portable extinguishers, wheeled extinguishers, skid-mounted twin-agent units, and vehicle-mounted tank systems. *See* Batch Mixing.

Preparation Step — First step in conducting a lesson, in which the job or topic to be taught is identified, a teaching base is developed, and students are motivated to learn.

Preparedness — Activities to ensure that people are ready for a disaster and respond to it effectively; includes determining what will be done if essential services are lost, developing a plan for contingencies, and practicing the plan.

Preplan — *See* Pre-Incident Plan and Pre-Incident Survey.

Preponderance of Evidence — In civil proceedings, a collection of evidence that proves that an alleged civil wrong is probable to have occurred.

Prerequisite — (1) Something that is necessary to an end or to carrying out a function; knowledge or skill required before the learner can acquire additional or more complex knowledge or skill. (2) Entry-level knowledge or abilities that a learner must have prior to starting a particular course or qualifying for a certain job or promotion. *See* Requisite.

Prescribed Burning — (1) Controlled application of fire to wildland fuels in either their natural or modified state, under specified environmental conditions, that allows the fire to be confined to a predetermined area and produces the fire behavior and fire characteristics required to attain planned fire treatment and resource-management objectives. (2) A written plan that describes specifically planned results and specific conditions as part of a vegetation-management program.

Prescriptive Test — Test given at the beginning of instruction to determine what the individual or audience already knows; alternatively, a test that is given remedially. *Also known as* Pretest.

Prescriptive Training — Instructional approach that uses the four-step teaching method in a different order: evaluation, preparation, presentation, application, and reevaluation.

Presentation — (1) Second of the four teaching steps in which the educator teaches a class or individual and transfers facts and ideas. (2) Lesson plan component in which an instructor provides to, shares with, demonstrates to, and involves the participants in the lesson information. *See* Lesson Plan. (3) Single delivery of fire and life safety information. *Also known as* Lesson or Delivery.

Presentation Step — Second step in conducting a lesson, at which point new information and skills are presented to the learners.

Preservice Tests — Tests performed on fire pumps or aerial devices before they are placed into service; these tests consist of manufacturers' tests, certification tests, and acceptance tests.

Press Conference — Scheduled event intended for presenting prepared information to the media; may or may not include a question and answer section.

Press Release — *See* Media Release.

Pressure — Force per unit area exerted by a liquid or gas measured in pounds per square inch (psi) or kilopascals (kPa).

Pressure-Demand Device — Self-contained breathing apparatus (SCBA) that may be operated in either positive-pressure or demand mode. This type of SCBA is presently being phased out and replaced with positive-pressure-only apparatus.

Pressure Differential — Effect of altering the atmospheric pressure within a confined space by mechanical means. When air is exhausted from within the space, a low-pressure environment is created and replacement air will be drawn in; when air is blown into the space, a high-pressure environment is created and air within will move to the outside.

Pressure Gauge — Device for indicating pressure; the most common pressure gauges use a dial face to indicate pressures, such as the pump discharge pressure.

Pressure Governor — Pressure control device that controls engine speed, eliminating hazardous conditions that result from excessive pressures.

Pressure Intermodal Tank — Liquefied gas container designed for working pressures of 100 to 500 psig (689 kPa to 3 447 kPa) {6.9 bar to 34.5 bar}. *Also known as* Spec 51, or internationally as IMO Type 5. *See* Intermodal Container and Nonpressure Intermodal Tank.

Pressure Maintenance Pump — Pump used to maintain pressure on a fire protection system in order to prevent false starts at the fire pump.

Pressure Operation — Operation of a two- (or more) stage centrifugal pump in which water passes consecutively through each stage (or impeller) to provide high pressures at a reduced volume. *Also known as* Series Operation.

Pressure Point — Point over an artery where the pulse may be felt; pressure on the point often helps to stop the flow of blood from a wound beyond that point.

Pressure-Reducing Valve — Valve installed at standpipe connection that is designed to reduce the amount of water pressure at that discharge to a specific pressure, usually 100 psi (700 kPa). *See* Standpipe System.

Pressure Regulator — Device used to maintain a constant pressure within a pump while operating.

Pressure-Relief Device — Automatic device designed to release excess pressure from a container.

Pressure Storage Tank — Class of fixed facility storage tanks divided into two categories: low-pressure storage tanks and pressure vessels. *See* Atmospheric Storage Tank, Low-Pressure Storage Tank, and Pressure Vessel.

Pressure Tank — Water storage receptacle that uses compressed-air pressure to propel the water into the distribution system. Pressure tanks are generally small and provide only a limited amount of water for fire protection.

Pressure Tank Railcar — Tank railcars that carry flammable and nonflammable liquefied gases, poisons, and other hazardous materials. They are recognizable by the valve enclosure at the top of the car and the lack of bottom unloading piping.

Pressure Vessel — Fixed-facility storage tanks with operating pressures above 15 psi (103 kPa) {1.03 bar}. *See* Low-Pressure Storage Tank, Pressure Storage Tank, and Spherical Pressure Vessel.

Prestressing — Compressive force induced in the concrete before the load is applied by placing the reinforcing bars in concrete beams in tension before the concrete is poured, so that the member will develop greater strength after the concrete has set. This "pre" stress is applied by tightening or "pre" loading the reinforcing steel; the preloading of the steel creates compressive stresses in the concrete that counteract the tensile stresses, which result when loads are applied.

Pre-Suppression — Activities in advance of fire occurrence to ensure effective suppression action.

Pretensioned Reinforcing — Reinforcing method used with pretensioned concrete. Steel strands are stretched between anchors producing a tensile force in the steel; concrete is then placed around the steel strands and allowed to harden.

Pretest/Posttest — Prescriptive evaluation instrument administered to students and used to compare knowledge or skills either before (pretest) or after (posttest) a presentation or program. Pretests check entry-level knowledge or abilities; pretest scores are compared with posttest scores to determine learners' progress. *See* Test.

Pretreating — Exposure protection tactic in which water, foam, or retardant is applied to unburned materials near the fire; this soaks the material, making it less likely to ignite.

Prevention — Actions to avoid, prevent, or intervene to stop an incident from occurring; predetermined action or process employed to deter, obstruct, negate, forestall, hinder, impede, or preclude the occurrence of a potential loss.

Prevention Intervention — Reducing risk through education, technology, fire codes, standards, supporting incentives, or emergency response.

Preventive Maintenance — Scheduled, ongoing, routine inspection and maintenance that is intended to prolong the life and to prevent the breakdown of apparatus, equipment, and facilities; does not involve repairing or replacing damaged or worn-out components.

Prill — Spherical pellets.

Prilled Oxidizer — Solid material such as ammonium nitrate that is formed into spherical pellets through a process that involves spraying the material in liquid form and allowing the drops to solidify. *See* Oxidizer.

Primary Damage — Damage caused by a fire itself and not by actions taken to fight the fire.

Primary Explosive — High explosive that is easily initiated and highly sensitive to heat; often used as a detonator.

Primary Feeder — Large pipes (mains), with relatively widespread spacing, that convey large quantities of water to various points of the system for local distribution to the smaller mains.

Primary Label — Label placed on the container of a hazardous material to indicate the primary hazard. *See* Subsidiary Label.

Prime — To create a vacuum in a pump by removing air from the pump housing and intake hose, which permits the drafting of water.

Primer — *See* Priming Device.

Primer Fluid Tank — Tank of fluid used to seal and lubricate the priming pump.

Primer Oil Tank — Tank of oil used to seal and lubricate the priming pump.

Priming Device — Any device, usually a positive-displacement pump, used to exhaust the air from inside a centrifugal pump and the attached hard suction; this creates a partial vacuum, allowing atmospheric pressure to force water from a static source through the suction hose into the centrifugal pump. *Also known as* Primer.

Priority Traffic — *See* Emergency Traffic.

Privacy Law — Federal and state/provincial statue that prohibits an invasion of a person's right to be left alone and also restricts access to personal information.

Private Branch Exchange (PBX) — Telephone switching system found in large businesses or organizations that allows many users to be reached by dialing a seven-digit number. Internal users of a PBX system can use special features such as hold, conference calling, or transfer; many times these systems are marketed under trade names such as Centrex.

Private Connection — Connections to water supplies other than the standard municipal water supply system; may include connection within a large industrial facility, a farm, or a private housing development.

Private Hydrant — Hydrant provided on private property or on private water systems to protect private property. *Also known as* Yard Hydrant.

Private Law — Portion of the law that defines, regulates, enforces, and administers relationships among individuals, associations, and corporations. *See* Public Law.

Probable — Legal classification that means *more likely than not* or at least 50.1 percent accurate.

Probable Cause — Sufficient information or facts to believe that it is probable (more likely than not) that a certain party is responsible for committing a felony (indictable offense).

Proceed With Caution — Order for incoming units to discontinue responding at an emergency rate; after the order has been given, units should turn off warning devices and follow routine traffic regulations. *Also known as* Reduce Speed.

Process Alarm — Device which monitors the activity of industrial equipment to alert workers to critical failures in machinery; may also deactivate or de-energize equipment in order to to prevent a fire.

Process Evaluation — *See* Formative Evaluation.

Procurement Unit — Functional unit within the finance section of an incident command system; responsible for financial matters involving vendors.

Product — Generic term used in industry to describe a substance that is used or produced in an industrial process. *See* Hazardous Material and Material.

Product Identification Number (PIN) — Number assigned by the United Nations and used in the *Emergency Response Guidebook (ERG)* to identify specific product names.

Production Order — Order in which jobs must be done; more difficult jobs may have to be done first.

Products of Combustion — Materials produced and released during burning.

Program — Comprehensive strategy that addresses fire and life safety issues via educational means.

Program Budget — Budgetary system in which each major program (such as administration, suppression, prevention, EMS, or training) is funded independently of other departmental programs. The overall department budget is a composite of the individual program budgets.

Progress Chart — Chart designed to record the progress of an individual or group during a course of study.

Progressive Hose Lay — Method used when fire apparatus cannot drive along a wildland fire's edge, making a mobile attack impossible. Consists of laying hose from a fire pump to the fire's edge, extinguishing fire in that area, connecting another section, advancing, extinguishing fire as far as the hose will reach, and repeating this process until the fire is extinguished.

Progressive Line Construction — System of organizing workers to build a fireline in which they advance without changing relative positions in line.

Progressive Method — Progressive method of constructing a fire line. Each member of a hand crew takes a few strokes to clear fuel or widen the break, advances a specified distance, takes a few strokes, and advances; this process is repeated until the fire is extinguished.

Progress Test — Diagnostic device to measure the progress or improvement of learners throughout a course; helps guide instructors and participants in deciding which areas need more emphasis or learning time. Typically called a quiz and may be written or oral. *See* Test.

Projected Window — Type of swinging window that is hinged at the top and swings either outward or inward.

Project Grant — Money given for a very specific activity or for very specific expenses, such as the purchase of fire safety educational videotapes for use in community schools.

Promotional Materials — *See* Awareness Materials and Informational Materials.

Prone — Position of lying face downward.

Prop — Object used during a fire and life safety presentation that the audience can see, touch, smell, or hear; for example, a burned remnant from a home fire, a piece of melted glass, a manual fire alarm pull station, or a smoke detector.

Propagation — Spread of combustion through a solid, gas, or vapor, or the spread of fire from one combustible to another.

Proper Seal — Result of the facepiece fitting snugly against the bare skin, preventing the entry of smoke, fumes, or gases.

Proportional Directional Control Valve — Valve that controls the flow of hydraulic fluid through a hydraulic system.

Proportioner — Device used to introduce the correct amount of agent, especially foam and wetting agents, into streams of water. *See* Foam Proportioner.

Proportioning — Mixing water with an appropriate amount of foam concentrate in order to form a foam solution.

Proportioning Valve — Foam system valve that is used to balance or divide the air supply between the aeration system and the discharge manifold.

Proposal — Document or request that describes the accomplishments an applicant promises to achieve in return for the investment of the sponsor's funds.

Proprietary Alarm System — Fire protection system owned and operated by the property owner.

Props — *See* Supports.

Prop Wash — Current of air created by the rotation of a propeller.

Prospect — Local business or other resource that may be a possible source of funding.

Protected Area — Undamaged surface within an otherwise fire damaged area, possibly resulting from objects shielding the surface from the effects of the fire; generally used to refer the fire investigator to where large objects such as furniture were positioned before the fire. *See* Heat Shadowing.

Protected Corridor — Corridor with code required fire-rated walls; intended to protect occupants as they make their way to an exit.

Protected Premises Fire Alarm System — (1) Alarm system that alerts and notifies only occupants on the premises of the existence of a fire so that they can safely exit the building and call the fire department. If a response by a public safety agency (police or fire department) is required, an occupant hearing the alarm must notify the agency. (2) Combination of alarm components designed to detect a fire and transmit an alarm on the immediate premises. *Also known as* Local Alarm System.

Protected Stair Enclosure — Stair with code required fire-rated enclosure construction; intended to protect occupants as they make their way through the stair enclosure.

Protected Steel — Steel beams that are covered with either spray-on fireproofing (an insulating barrier) or fully encased in an Underwriters Laboratories Inc. (UL) designed system.

Protection Factor — Ratio of contaminants in the atmosphere outside the facepiece to the contaminants inside the facepiece; determined by quantitative fit testing from the manufacturer.

Protection Plates — Plates fastened to a ladder to prevent wear at points where it comes in contact with mounting brackets.

Protective Action Distance — Downwind distance from a hazardous materials incident within which protective actions should be implemented. *See* Initial Isolation Distance, Protective Action Zone, and Protective Actions.

Protective Actions — Steps taken to preserve health and safety of emergency responders and the public. *See* Protective Action Distance and Protective Action Zone.

Protective Action Zone — Area immediately adjacent to and downwind from the initial isolation zone, which is in imminent danger of being contaminated by airborne vapors within 30 minutes of material release. *See* Initial Isolation Zone, Protective Action Distance, and Protective Actions.

Protective Clothing — Includes the helmet, protective coat, protective trousers, protective hood, boots, gloves, self-contained breathing apparatus, and eye protection where applicable. *See* Personal Protective Equipment.

Protective Coat — Coat worn during fire fighting, rescue, and extrication operations.

Protective Hood — Hood designed to protect the firefighter's ears, neck, and face from exposure to extreme heat; typically made of Nomex®, Kevlar®, or PBI®, and available in long or short styles.

Protective Signaling Systems — Detection and alarm systems that transfer information from a specific place in a fire-involved building to some remote monitoring station.

Protective Trousers — Pants worn during fire fighting operations. *Also known as* Bunker Pants, Night Hitches, or Turnout Pants.

Protein Foam Concentrate — Foam concentrate that consists of a protein hydrolysate plus additives to prevent the concentrate from freezing, prevent corrosions on equipment and containers, prevent bacterial decomposition of the concentrate during storage, and control viscosity. *See* Foam Concentrate.

Proton — Part of an atom that possesses a positive charge.

Proximal — Located near the trunk of the body.

Proximate Cause — That which (an act), in a natural and continuous sequence unbroken by any intervening cause, produces injury, and without which (the act) the result would not have occurred. *See* Negligence.

Proximity Clothing — Special personal protective equipment with a reflective exterior that is designed to protect the firefighter from conductive, convective, and radiant heat while working in close proximity to the fire. *Also known as* Proximity Suit.

Prusik — Length of low stretch Kernmantle rope, six to eight millimeters in diameter, tied with a double overhand bend into a loop.

Prusik Hitch — Prusik loop wrapped three times around a line, forming a hitch that can slip along the rope or seize the rope and hold it.

Prusik Knot — Special knot used to assist a person climbing a rope.

Pry — To raise, move, or force with a prying tool.

Prying Tools — Hand tools that use the principle of leverage to allow the rescuer to exert more force than would be possible without the tool; typically long, slender, and constructed of hardened steel.

psi — *See* Pounds Per Square Inch.

psig — *See* Pounds Per Square Inch Gauge.

Psychological Stress — Mental stress.

Psychomotor Learning Domain — Learning that involves physical, hands-on activities, or actions that a students must be able to do or perform. *See* Learning Domain.

PTO — *See* Power Take-Off.

PTSD — *See* Post-Traumatic Stress Disorder.

Public-Duty Doctrine — States that a government entity (such as a state or municipality) cannot be held liable for an individual plaintiff's injury that results from a governmental officer or employee's breach of a duty that is owed to the general public, rather than to the individual plaintiff.

Public Information Officer (PIO) — Member of the command staff responsible for interfacing with the media, public, or other agencies requiring information direct from the incident scene. *Also known as* Information Officer (IO). *See* Incident Management System (IMS).

Public Law — Classification of law consisting of constitutional, administrative, criminal, and international law. *See* Private Law.

Public Safety Answering Point (PSAP) — Facility or location at which 9-1-1 calls are answered, either by direct calling, rerouting, or diversion.

Public Safety Department — Organization that combines the administrative, financial, and technical service and support for functions such as fire and rescue services, police, ambulance and emergency medical services, and emergency communications.

Public Service — (1) Slang used over the radio to have someone make a call by telephone. (2) Service rendered in the public interest.

Public Way — Parcel of land such as a street or sidewalk that is essentially open to the outside and is used by the public to move from one location to another. *See* Means of Egress.

Pull Box — Manual fire alarm activator.

Pulley — (1) Small, grooved wheel through which the halyard is drawn on an extension ladder. (2) Wheel used to transmit power by means of a band, belt, cord, rope, or chain passing over its rim. (3) Steel or aluminum rollers used to change direction and reduce friction in rope rescue systems.

Pulling Line — *See* Fall Line.

Pull-In Point — Rotating portion of a machine that is capable of entangling a victim if a body part or piece of clothing comes into contact with it.

Pull Line — *See* Fall Line.

Pulmonary Artery — Major artery leading from the right ventricle to the lungs.

Pulmonary Edema — Accumulation of fluids in the lungs.

Pulmonary Resuscitation — *See* Artificial Respiration.

Pulmonary Veins — Veins that carry oxygenated blood from the lungs to the left atrium.

Pulse — Rhythmic throbbing caused by expansion and contraction of arterial walls as blood passes through them.

Pump — (1) A device that imparts pressure to water. (2) To supply water to hoselines. (3) Apparatus in a two-piece engine company that positions as the attack apparatus at the fire scene.

Pump and Roll — Ability of an apparatus to pump water while the vehicle is in motion. *See* Mobile Attack.

Pump Apparatus — Fire department apparatus that has the primary responsibility to pump water.

Pump Can — Water-filled pump-type extinguisher. *Also known as* Pump Tank.

Pump Capacity Rating — Maximum amount of water a pump will deliver at the indicated pressure.

Pump Charts — Charts carried on a fire apparatus to aid the pump operator in determining the proper pump discharge pressure when supplying hoselines.

Pump Discharge Pressure (PDP) — Actual pressure of the water as it leaves the pump and enters the hoseline; total amount of pressure being discharged by a pump. In mathematical terms, it is the pump intake pressure plus the net pump discharge pressure. Measured in pounds per square inch.

Pump Drain — Drain located at the lowest part of the pump to help remove all water from the pump; this eliminates the danger of damage due to freezing.

Pumper, Class A — Pumper that delivers its rated capacity of at least 750 gpm (3 000 L/min) at 150 psi (1 000 kPa) net pump pressure at a lift of not more than 10 feet (3 m) with a motor speed of not more than 80 percent of the certified peak of the brake horsepower curve. Will deliver 70 percent of rated capacity at 200 psi (1 350 kPa) and 50 percent of rated capacity at 250 psi (1 700 kPa).

Pumper, Class B — Pumper that delivers its rated capacity at 120 psi (800 kPa) net pump pressure at a lift of not more than 10 feet (3 m) with a motor speed of not more than 80 percent of the certified peak of the brake horsepower curve. Will deliver 50 percent of its rated capacity at 200 psi (1 350 kPa) and 33 1/3 percent of its rated capacity at 250 psi (1 700 kPa). Class B pumps have not been manufactured since the mid-1950s.

Pumper Outlet Nozzle — Fire hydrant outlet that is 4 inches (102 mm) in diameter or larger.

Pumper/Tender — Mobile water supply apparatus equipped with a fire pump. In some jurisdictions, this term is used to differentiate a fire pump equipped mobile water supply apparatus whose main purpose is to attack the fire. *Formerly known as* Pumper/Tanker.

Pumping Apparatus — Fire department apparatus that has the primary responsibility to pump water.

Pump-Off Line — Pipeline that usually runs from the tank discharge openings to the front of the trailer; most pumps are mounted on the tractor.

Pump Operator — Firefighter charged with operating the pump and determining the pressures required to operate it efficiently.

Pump Panel — Instrument and control panel located on the pumper.

Pump Room — Compartment in tank vessels where the pumping plant for handling cargo is installed; pumps are placed as low as possible in order to facilitate draining. In oil tankers over 400 feet (122 m) long, two pump rooms are provided, along with a ballast pump in some cases.

Pump Tank — *See* Pump Can.

Punch Press — Large, heavy piece of industrial machinery used to cold-form sheet metal.

Puncture Nozzle — *See* Piercing Nozzle.

Purging — Freeing from impurities by introducing fresh air; for example, ventilating a contaminated space.

Purification System — Series of mechanical and chemical filters through which compressed breathing air is passed to remove moisture, oil, carbon monoxide, and other contaminants.

Purlin — Horizontal member between trusses that support the roof.

PVC — *See* Polyvinyl Chloride.

Pyro — *See* Pyromaniac.

Pyrolysis — Thermal or chemical decomposition of fuel (matter) because of heat, generally resulting in the lowered ignition temperature of the material; the pre-ignition combustion phase of burning during which heat energy is absorbed by the fuel, which in turn gives off flammable tars, pitches, and gases. Pyrolysis of wood releases combustible gases and leaves a charred surface. *Also known as* Pyrolysis Process or Sublimation. *See* Decomposition, Heat, and Oxidation.

Pyromania — Psychological disorder in which the sufferer has an uncontrollable impulse to set fires, either to relieve tension or produce a feeling of euphoria.

Pyromaniac — Person with an uncontrollable impulse to set fires, or who enjoys setting fires. *See* Pyromania.

Pyrometer — Device used to measure temperatures by wavelength or electrical generation; pyrometers connected to thermocouples record the heat at various points.

Pyrophoric — Material that ignites spontaneously when exposed to air. *Also known as* Air-Reactive Material.

Pyrophoric Liquids — Liquids that ignite spontaneously in dry or moist air at or below 130°F (54°C).

Pyrophoric Materials — Elements that react and ignite on contact with air.

Pyrotechnics — Fireworks.

Pyroxylin Plastic — Nitrocellulose plastic that is extremely combustible and susceptible to deterioration and self-ignition; produces toxic fumes when burned.

Q

Q — Slang for a Federal Q_2B Mechanical Coaster Siren.

Qassam Rocket — Improvised or homemade steel rocket filled with explosives that is produced by Hamas. Qassam rockets have no guidance system, and their warheads are typically filled with TNT and urea nitrate.

Quad — Four-way combination fire apparatus; combines the water tank, pump, and hose of a pumper with the ground ladder complement of a truck company. *Also known as* Quadruple Combination.

Quadrant — One of the four regions into which the abdomen may be divided for purposes of physical diagnosis.

Qualitative Evaluation — Assessment method that does not use numbers and that relies on the fire and life safety educator's experience, judgment, and interpretation.

Qualitative Test — Test of facepiece fit in which the wearer's sense of smell or taste is used to determine whether a facepiece fits properly; examples are the irritant fume test, odor test, and taste test.

Quantitative Evaluation — Assessment method that uses numbers to compare different materials and methods, is likely to be more sophisticated than qualitative methods, and involves formal testing.

Quantitative Test — Test of facepiece fit in which instruments determine the amount of contaminants inside the facepiece.

Quarantine — State of enforced isolation; restraint upon the activities or communication of persons or the transport of goods, designed to prevent the spread of disease or pests.

Quarter Drain Time — *See* Quarter-Life.

Quarter-Life — Time required, in minutes, for one-fourth of the total liquid solution to drain from a foam blanket. *Also known as* 25 Percent Drain Time and Quarter Drain Time. *See* Drainage Time.

Quarter Panels — Rear sections of the vehicle's body shell, including the rear fender and the C-post.

Quarters — Fire station or office.

Quarter-Turn Coupling — Nonthreaded (sexless) coupling with two hooklike lugs that slip over a ring on the opposite coupling and then rotate 90 degrees clockwise to lock.

Quench — To extinguish a fire by cooling.

Quick-Fill® System — Mine Safety Appliances Company (MSA) system that can be used as an emergency breathing system connection or that can be used to refill self-contained breathing apparatus (SCBA) cylinders during nonemergency conditions.

Quintuple Combination Pumper (Quint) — Apparatus that serves as an engine and as a ladder truck; equipped with a fire pump, water tank, ground ladders, hose bed, and aerial device.

R

R — *See* Roentgen.

Rabbet — Groove cut in the surface or on the edge of a board to receive another member.

Rabbeted Jamb — Jamb into which a shoulder has been milled to permit the door to close against the provided shoulder.

Rabbit Tool — Hydraulic spreading tool that is specially designed to open doors that swing inward.

Races — (1) Sliding channels between two sections of the aerial device. (2) Interior of a box-beam construction aerial device.

Rack — (1) Framework used to support ladders while being carried on fire apparatus. (2) Act of placing a ladder on an apparatus.

rad — *See* Radiation Absorbed Dose.

Radial Artery — One of the major arteries of the forearm, located where the pulse can be felt at the base of the thumb.

Radial Engines — Internal-combustion, piston-driven aircraft engines with cylinders arranged in a circle.

Radiant Heat — *See* Radiation.

Radiant Heat Flux — Measure of the rate of heat transfer to a surface, expressed in kilowatts/m².

Radiated Heat — *See* Radiation.

Radiation — (1) Transmission or transfer of heat energy from one body to another body at a lower temperature through intervening space by electromagnetic waves, such as infrared thermal waves, radio waves, or X-rays. *Also known as* Radiated Heat. (2) Energy from a radioactive source emitted in the form of waves or particles, as a result of the decay of an atomic nucleus; process known as *radioactivity. Also known as* Nuclear Radiation. *See* Alpha Radiation, Beta Radiation, Gamma Radiation, Ionizing Radiation, Nonionizing Radiation, Radiation Absorbed Dose (rad), Radioactive Material (RAM), and Radioactive Particles.

Radiation Absorbed Dose (rad) — English System unit used to measure the amount of radiation energy absorbed by a material; its International System equivalent is gray (Gy). *See* Radiation (2) and Radioactive Material (RAM).

Radiation detector — Device for detecting the presence and sometimes the amount of radiation.

Radiation-Emitting Device (RED) — Powerful gamma-emitting radiation source used as a weapon.

Radiative Feedback — Radiant heat from the combustion process that provides energy for the continued vaporization of the fuel. *See* Vaporization.

Radiator Fill Line — Small waterline leading from the fire pump to the radiator of the apparatus; used to refill the radiator during pumping at a fire scene.

Radioactive Material (RAM) — Material whose atomic nucleus spontaneously decays or disintegrates, emitting radiation. *See* Becquerel (Bq), Curie (Ci), and Radiation (2).

Radioactive Particles — Particles emitted during the process of radioactive decay. There are three types of radioactive particles: alpha, beta, and gamma. *See* Alpha Particle, Beta Particle, Gamma Rays, and Radiation (2).

Radioactivity — *See* Radiation (2).

Radio Channel — Band of frequencies of a width sufficient to permit its use for radio communication.

Radiography — Process of making a picture on a sensitive surface by a form of radiation other than light.

Radioisotope — Unstable or radioactive isotope (form) of an element that can change into another element by giving off radiation. *See* Radionuclide.

Radiological Dispersal Device (RDD) — Device that spreads radioactive contamination over the widest possible area by detonating conventional high explosives wrapped with radioactive material. *Also known as* Dirty Bomb.

Radiological Dispersal Weapons (RDW) — Devices that spread radioactive contamination without using explosives; instead, radioactive contamination is spread using pressurized containers, building ventilation systems, fans, and mechanical devices.

Radionuclide — Any radioactive isotope (form) of any element. *See* Radioisotope.

Radiopharmaceutical — Radioactive drug used for diagnostic or therapeutic purposes.

Radio Repeater — Combination of a radio receiver and a radio transmitter that receives a weak or low-level signal and retransmits it at a higher level or higher power, so that the signal can cover longer distances without degradation.

Radio Systems Regulations — Federal Communications Commission (FCC) rules that govern the operation of radio systems.

Radio Transmitter — Device for producing radio frequency power for purposes of radio transmission.

Radius — Half the diameter of a circle; line or distance from the center of a circle to any point on its circumference.

Rafter — Inclined beam that supports a roof, runs parallel to the slope of the roof, and to which the roof decking is attached.

Rafter Cut — *See* Louver Cut.

Ragged Left — Format in a written text in which every line ends the same distance from the right-hand edge of the page or column.

Rail — (1) Horizontal member of a window sash. (2) Metal portion of a railroad track upon which the car wheels ride. *See* Beam.

Railcar Initials and Numbers — Combination of letters and numbers stenciled on rail tank cars that may be used to get information about the car's contents from the railroad's computer or the shipper. *Also known as* Reporting Marks. *See* Intermodal Reporting Marks.

Rail Tank Car — Railroad car that is designed to carry liquids in pressurized or unpressurized cylinders; may be constructed of steel, stainless steel, or aluminum.

Rain-Down Application Method — Foam application method that directs the stream into the air above the unignited or ignited spill or fire, allowing the foam to float gently down onto the surface of the fuel. *See* Bank-Down Application Method and Roll-On Application Method.

Rain Roof — Second roof constructed over an existing roof.

Raise — Any of several accepted methods of raising and placing ground ladders into service; for example the two-firefighter raise.

Raker — Diagonal strut which collects load delivered by the wallplate in a raker shoring system, such as an angled timber bearing the load exerted on a raking shore.

Raker Shore — Shore footed on a horizontal surface used to brace a vertical surface.

Ram — *See* Extension Ram.

RAM — *See* Radioactive Material.

Ramp — (1) Area at airports intended to accommodate aircraft for purposes of loading or unloading passengers or cargo, refueling, parking, or maintenance. (2) Parking space between the fire station garage doors and the street. (3) Movable stairway or enclosure for loading and unloading passengers.

Ranking of Scores — Process of arranging a number of scores (values) in order from high to low, making it easy to determine median and mode.

Rapid Intervention Crew (RIC) — Two or more fully equipped and immediately available firefighters designated to stand by outside the hazard zone to enter and effect rescue of firefighters inside, if necessary. *Also known as* Rapid Intervention Team (RIT).

Rapid Intervention Team (RIT) — *See* Rapid Intervention Crew.

Rapid Intervention Vehicle (RIV) — Type of mobile foam apparatus that is used to provide a rapid attack on an aircraft crash incident for quick extinguishment and rescue.

Rapid Relief — Fast release of a pressurized hazardous material through properly operating safety devices caused by damaged valves, piping, or attachments or holes in the container.

Rappel — To slide or descend down a rope in a controlled manner using a friction device. *Also known as* Sliding Rope.

Rappelling — Technique of sliding or descending down a rope in a controlled manner using a friction device, such as descending down the side of a building or cliff, or landing firefighters from helicopters in hover during wildland fire fighting operations.

Ratchet-Lever Jack — Type of lifting jack that uses the principles of leverage to operate. It is capable of lifting moderately heavy loads but tends to be unstable; generally recognized as the most dangerous of all jacks.

Rate Compensated Heat Detector — Temperature-sensitive device that sounds an alarm at a preset temperature, regardless of how fast temperatures change.

Rated Assembly — Assemblies of building components such as doors, walls, roofs, and other structural features that may be, because of the occupancy, required by code to have a minimum fire-resistance rating from an independent testing agency. *Also known as* Labeled Assembly.

Rated Concentrate — Foam concentrate that has been tested and certified by Underwriters Laboratories Inc. *See* Foam Concentrate and Nonrated Concentrate.

Rated Fire Barrier Assembly — Continuous membrane, such as a wall or floor assembly, that is designed and constructed to limit the spread of fire and restrict the spread of smoke; must achieve a specified fire-resistance rating and meet the test performance requirements of an independent testing organization.

Rated Fire Door Assembly — Door, frame, and hardware assembly that has a fire-resistive rating from an independent testing agency.

Rated Smoke Barrier Assembly — Continuous membrane, such as a wall, floor, or ceiling assembly, that is designed and constructed to restrict the spread of smoke, and meets certain performance testing requirements, typically from an independent testing organization.

Rate Meter — Nuclear radiation detection device.

Rate-of-Raise Alarm System — System that detects fire by an abnormal rate of heat increase; operates when a normal amount of air in a pneumatic tube or chamber expands rapidly when heated, exerting pressure on a diaphragm.

Rate-of-Rise Heat Detector — Temperature-sensitive device that sounds an alarm when the temperature rises at a preset value, such as a 12-15°F (7-8°C) increase per minute.

Rate of Spread (ROS) — Relative activity of a fire in extending its horizontal dimensions. Expressed as rate of increase of the total perimeter of a fire, as rate of forward spread of the fire front, or as rate of increase in area, depending on the intended use of the information; usually expressed in chains or acres (hectares) per hour for a specific period in the fire's history.

Rate of Vaporization — Speed at which a liquid evaporates or vaporizes. *See* Vaporization.

Rating Bureau — *See* Insurance Services Office.

Raw Image — Digital image that has undergone no compression.

Raw Score — Score on a test that has not yet been statistically processed to make it comparable with other scores. For example, an individual who received 38 points on a test of 40 questions has a raw score of 38; to compare the score to 100 percent, divide the raw score (38) by the total number of possible points (40) to get the percentage score of 95. Raw scores and the percent scores can be compared to other learner scores (norm-referenced), or scores can be assigned to a selected mastery level based on a standard or job performance requirement (criterion-referenced); for example, 85 percent is considered mastery.

Razor Ribbon — Coil of lightweight, flexible metallic ribbon with extremely sharp edges; often installed on parapet walls and on fence tops to discourage trespassers.

RDD — *See* Radiological Dispersal Device.

Reaction Distance — *See* Driver Reaction Distance.

Reactive Material — Substance capable of chemically reacting with other substances; for example, material that reacts violently when combined with air or water. *See* Air-Reactive Material, Reactivity, and Water-Reactive Material.

Reactivity — Ability of two or more chemicals to react and release energy, and the ease with which this reaction takes place. *See* Chemical Reaction and Reactive Material.

Readability Index — System for measuring how easy or difficult a passage is to read.

Reading a Roof — Process of observing the surface and other important features of a roof from a point of safety, in order to assess the roof's condition before stepping onto it.

Rear — (1) Part of a wildland fire opposite the head; the slowest burning part of the fire. *See* Heel. (2) Opposite end of the vehicle from the front; usually indicated by the taillights.

Rear-End Collision — Type of collision in which a vehicle is struck from behind.

Rear-Impact Collision — Collision in which one vehicle is struck in the rear by another vehicle, or in which a vehicle backs into an object.

Rear of Ladder — Side closest to the objective; the nonclimbing side.

Reasonable Accommodation — Legal requirement (under Title VII of the *Civil Rights Act of 1964*) that employers make reasonable adjustments to an employee's work schedule or other job requirements to accommodate employee differences, such as religion, gender, and/or physical or mental disability.

Rebar — Steel bars that are placed inside concrete structural elements to reinforce and strengthen the element.

Rebreather — Closed-circuit breathing apparatus.

Reburn — Burning of an area that has been previously burned but that contains flammable fuel that ignites when burning conditions are more favorable; area that has reburned.

Recall — (1) To call off-duty firefighters back to duty. (2) To order units responding to or on the scene of an emergency to return to their quarters.

Receiver — (1) Part of an automatic switching system that receives signals from a calling device or other source for interpretation and action. (2) Person or persons to whom a message is directed in the communications process. *Also known as* Audience.

RECEO Model — One of many models for prioritizing activities at an emergency incident: Rescue, Exposures, Confine, Extinguish, and Overhaul.

RECEO V/S Model — One of many models for prioritizing activities at an emergency incident: Rescue, Exposures, Confine, Extinguish, Overhaul, Ventilation, and Salvage.

Reciprocating Engine — Internal-combustion engine with cylinders arranged in opposition, and in in which the back and forth movement of the pistons causes the rotation of a crank shaft.

Reciprocating Saw — Electric saw that uses a short, straight blade that moves back and forth.

Recommended Exposure Limit (REL) — Recommended value expressing the maximum time-weighted dose or concentration to which workers should be exposed over a 10-hour period, as established by National Institute for Occupational Safety and Health (NIOSH). *See* Permissible Exposure Limit (PEL), Short-Term Exposure Limit (STEL), and Threshold Limit Value (TLV®).

Reconnaissance — Process of examining an area to obtain information about the current specific situation, probable fire behavior, and other information related to fire-suppression.

Reconstruction — Portion of an investigation in which the investigator attempts to determine the original position of the contents at the scene.

Record Book — *See* Journal.

Recovery — (1) Situation where the victim is most probably dead, and the goal of the operation is to recover the body. (2) Process of restoring normal public or utility services following a disaster; activities necessary to rebuild after a disaster, such as rebuilding homes and businesses, clearing debris, repairing roads and bridges, and restoring water and other essential services.

RED — *See* Radiation-Emitting Device.

Red Blood Cells — Cellular components of the blood that transport oxygen from the lungs to body tissues and carbon dioxide from the tissues to the lungs.

Red Line — *See* Booster Hose.

Reducer — Adapter used to attach a smaller hose to a larger hose; the female end has the larger threads, while the male end has the smaller threads. *See* Adapter, Fitting, and Increaser.

Reduce Speed — *See* Proceed With Caution.

Reducing Agent — Fuel that is being oxidized or burned during combustion. *See* Fuel.

Reducing Wye — Wye that has two outlets smaller in diameter than the inlet valve. *Also known as* Leader Line Wye.

Redundancy — Secondary or backup systems that allow for uninterrupted use in the event of failure or damage to the primary system.

Reefer — *See* Refrigerated Intermodal Container.

Reefer Container — Cargo container having its own refrigeration unit. *See* Container and Container Terminal.

Reference — Method by which an authority having jurisdiction (AHJ) refers to a code in a regulation and states that the code is legally enforceable.

Reel Load — Arrangement of fire hose, especially large diameter hose, on a reel.

Reeves Stretcher — Device used to package a patient for removal from a confined environment.

Reeving — Threading rope or cable through a block.

References — Citations, bibliographies, and resources used in developing, planning, and researching course or lesson information.

Reformulated Gasoline — *See* Blended Gasoline.

Refractive Index — Measurement of the amount by which the speed of light (or other waves such as sound waves) is reduced inside a medium such as a finished foam solution.

Refractometer — Device used to measure the amount of foam concentrate in the solution; operates on the principle of measuring the velocity of light that travels through the foam solution.

Refrigerant — Substance used within a refrigeration system to provide the cooling action.

Refrigerated Intermodal Container — Cargo container having its own refrigeration unit. *Also known as* Reefer. *See* Container Vessel and Intermodal Container.

Refrigerated Liquids — *See* Cryogens.

Refrigerated Vessel — Vessel specially designed and equipped for the transportation of food products (such as meat, fruit, fish, butter, or eggs) under cold storage; cargo space is insulated for this purpose.

Refrigerating Plant — Installation of machinery for the purposes of cooling designated spaces aboard a vessel and manufacturing ice.

Refrigeration Unit — Cooling equipment used to maintain a constant temperature within a given space.

Refuse Chute — Vertical shaft with a self-closing access door on every floor; usually extending from the basement or ground floor to the top floor of multistory buildings.

Regenerative Braking — Mechanical system that reduces the speed of a vehicle by converting part of the vehicle's kinetic energy into another type of energy that can be fed back into a power system or stored for future use.

Reglet — Flat, narrow molding that forms a water seal for roofing in a parapet wall.

Regulations — Rules or directives of administrative agencies that have authorization to issue and enforce them. *See* Code and Standard.

Regulator — Device between the facepiece and air cylinder of the SCBA that reduces the pressure of the air coming from the cylinder.

Regulator Breathing — Emergency procedure in which the firefighter breathes directly from the regulator outlet if the low-pressure hose or facepiece is damaged.

Regulator Gauge — Gauge connected to the regulator of an SCBA that indicates the pressure of the air reaching the regulator; used as an indication of the air pressure in the air cylinder.

Rehab — *See* Rehabilitation.

Rehabilitation — (1) Activities necessary to repair environmental damage or disturbance caused by wildland fire or the fire-suppression activity. (2) Allowing firefighters or rescuers to rest, rehydrate, and recover during an incident; also refers to a station at an incident where personnel can rest, rehydrate, and recover. *Also known as* Rehab.

Reinforced Concrete — Concrete that is internally fortified with steel reinforcement bars or mesh placed within the concrete before it hardens. Reinforcement allows the concrete to resist tensile forces.

Rekindle — Reignition of a fire because of latent heat, sparks, or smoldering embers; can be prevented by proper overhaul.

REL — *See* Recommended Exposure Limit.

Relative Humidity — Measure of the moisture content (water quantity expressed in a percentage) in both the air and solid fuels.

Relay — (1) Use of two or more pumpers to move water distances that would require excessive pressures if only one pumper was employed. (2) To shuttle water between a source and an emergency scene using mobile water supply apparatus.

Relay Emergency Valve — Combination valve in an air brake system that controls brake application and provides for automatic emergency brake application should a trailer become disconnected from the towing vehicle.

Relay Operation — Using two or more pumpers to move water over a long distance by operating them in series; water discharged from one pumper flows through hoses to the inlet of the next pumper, and so on. *Also known as* Relay Pumping.

Relay Pumping — *See* Relay Operation.

Relay Question — Type of question in which an instructor or educator returns or redirects a question from the audience back to the individual who asked the question, or to the group, to answer.

Relay-Supply Hose — Hose between the water source and the attack pumper, laid to provide large volumes of water at low pressure. *Also known as* Feeder Line or Supply Hose.

Relay Valve — Pressure-relief device on the supply side of the pump designed to protect the hose and pump from damaging pressure surges common in relay pumping operations.

Relay Valve (In-Line) — Special valve that is inserted in the middle of a long relay hose; allows an additional pumper to connect to the line to boost pressure without having to interrupt the current flow of water.

Reliability — A condition of validity; the extent to which a test or test item consistently and accurately produces the same results or scores when given to a set of learners on different occasions, marked by different assessors, or marked by the same assessors on different occasions.

Relief Cut — Cut made to reduce resistance and to facilitate the bending of a portion of a car or other object.

Relief Valve — Pressure control device designed to eliminate hazardous conditions resulting from excessive pressures by allowing this pressure to bypass to the intake side of the pump.

rem — *See* Roentgen Equivalent in Man.

Remote-Controlled Foam Monitor — Large-capacity foam system that is operated by a remote control located away from the monitor; usually found on aircraft rescue apparatus, fire fighting apparatus, and fireboats. *See* Automatic Oscillating Foam Monitor, Foam Monitor, and Manual Foam Monitor.

Remote Power Outlet (RPO) — AC power receptacle mounted on or in a vehicle and powered by an inverter from the vehicle's DC electrical system.

Remote Pressure Gauge — Pressure gauge that is not mounted on the regulator but can be seen by the SCBA wearer; commonly found on SCBA that have facepiece-mounted regulators.

Remote Station Alarm System — System in which alarm signals from the protected premises are transmitted over a leased telephone line to a remote receiving station with a 24-hour staff; usually the municipal fire department's telecommunications center.

Repair — To restore or put together something that has become inoperable or out of place.

Repeater System — System in which a radio message is received on one frequency (input) and then rebroadcast at a high energy level on another frequency (output); this enables two lower power field units to speak to each other without having to be nearby. Repeaters can be mounted in cars or be part of a complex network of other repeaters to provide adequate coverage.

Reporting Locations — Any one of six facilities/locations where incident-assigned resources may check in. The locations are: incident command post - resources status unit (RESTAT), base, camp, staging area, helibase, and division supervisor for direct line assignments.

Reporting Marks — *See* Railcar Initials and Numbers.

Request for Proposal — Document that defines the specific requirements for an item that an organization intends to purchase through the bid process.

Requisite — Fundamental knowledge or essential skill one must have in order to perform a specific task. *See* Prerequisite.

Rescue — Saving a life from fire or accident; removing a victim from an untenable or unhealthy atmosphere.

Rescue Breathing — *See* Artificial Respiration.

Rescue Company — Specialized unit of people and equipment dedicated to performing rescue and extrication operations at the scene of an emergency. *Also known as* Rescue Squad or Rescue Truck.

Rescue Eight — Device used to create friction for rappelling or for lowering a load and as a collection point. *Also known as* Figure-Eight Plates, Rescue Eight with Ears, or Figure-Eight Descenders.

Rescue Knot — Knot that is easy to tie, easy to inspect visually, easy to untie after loading, and that remains tied and will not untie itself or loosen during use. Causes minimal loss in rope strength when tied.

Rescue Load — Normally considered to be 450 pounds (204 kg), or one fully equipped rescuer and patient.

Rescue Officer — Officer in charge of the rescue company.

Rescue Pumper — Specially designed apparatus that combines the functions of both a rescue vehicle and a fire department pumper.

Rescue Rope — Term used interchangeably with life safety rope.

Research and Special Programs Administration (RSPA) — U.S. Department of Transportation agency that carries out and enforces the hazardous materials regulations (HMR) through a program of regulation, enforcement, emergency response education and training, and data collection and analysis.

Reserve Apparatus — Apparatus not scheduled to respond to fires in normal or first-line duty but available for emergencies or replacing first-line equipment.

Reset — (1) To restore fire protection or detection equipment to original standby condition after operation. (2) To reactivate an inoperable fire alarm box or sprinkler system.

Residential Board and Care Facility — Subdivision of residential property classification consisting of a structure or part of a structure used for boarding or lodging four or more residents who are not related to the operators or owners, in order to provide personal care services

Residential Occupancy — Occupancy that provides sleeping accommodations for routine residential purposes; includes all structures designed for providing sleeping accommodations.

Residential Sprinkler System — Wet- or dry-pipe fire suppression system that is built into a residential structure; activation of a sprinkler causes the extinguishing agent to flow from the open sprinkler.

Residual Pressure — Pressure at the test hydrant while water is flowing; represents the pressure remaining in the water supply system while the test water is flowing and is that part of the total pressure that is not used to overcome friction or gravity while forcing water through fire hose, pipe, fittings, and adapters.

Resistance — Opposition to the flow of an electric current in a conductor or component; measured in ohms (Ω).

Resistance Heating — Heat generated by passing an electrical current through a conductor, such as a wire or an appliance.

Resistance to Freezing — Foam concentrate's usefulness after it has frozen and thawed; most can be freeze protected, but some concentrates freeze at lower temperatures than others.

Resources — (1) All of the immediate or supportive assistance available, or potentially available, for assignment to help control an incident; includes personnel, equipment, control agents, agencies, and printed emergency guides. (2) Locations that provide instructional training materials and support.

Resource Status Unit (RESTAT) — Functional unit within the planning section of an incident command system; responsible for recording and evaluating the status of resources committed to the incident, the impact that additional responding resources will have on the incident, and the anticipated resource needs.

Respiration — Act of breathing; the exchange of oxygen and carbon dioxide in the body tissues and lungs.

Respirator — Device designed to protect the wearer from inhaling harmful air contaminants. There are two main categories of respirators are air-purifying respirators, which use cartridges or filters to remove contaminants, and air-supplied respirators, such as SCBAs and airline respirators, which provide an alternate supply of fresh air.

Respiratory Arrest — Cessation of breathing.

Respiratory Hazards — Any exposure to products of combustion, superheated atmospheres, toxic gases, vapors, dust, potentially explosive or oxygen-deficient atmospheres, or any other condition that creates a hazard to the respiratory system.

Respiratory Protection Program — Systematic and comprehensive program of training in the use and maintenance of respiratory protection devices and related equipment.

Respiratory Protection Specialist School — School that provides 25 to 60 hours of additional or advanced training in the use of respiratory protection equipment. *Also known as* Smoke Divers School.

Respiratory System — System of organs that serve the function of respiration; consists of lungs, their nervous and circulatory supply, and the channels by which these are continuous with the outer air.

Responder Unit — Emergency medical unit that carries first aid and/or advanced life support equipment but is not equipped for patient transport.

Responding — Clear text radio term given when a unit is en route to an assignment.

Response — Call to respond.

Response District — Geographical area to which a particular apparatus is assigned to be first due on a fire or other emergency incident. *Also known as* District.

Response Time — Time between when a fire company is dispatched and when it arrives at the scene of an emergency.

Response Time Index (RTI) — Numerical value representing the speed and sensitivity with which a heat responsive fire protection device, such as a fusible link, responds.

Responsibility — Act or duty for which someone is clearly accountable.

Rest — Position of a ladder when both beams are resting on and parallel to the ground.

Restricted Grant — *See* Project Grant.

Restricted (Hot) Zone — (1) In a hazmat incident, the area of the incident including the product, its container, and the immediate area exposed to gases, vapors, mist, dust, smoke, or runoff. (2) In a rescue or extrication operation, the area where the extrication is taking place. Only personnel who are attending directly to the victims should be in this zone; this avoids crowding and confusion among rescuers.

Resuscitation — Act of reviving an unconscious patient. *See* Artificial Respiration.

Retardant — *See* Fire Retardant.

Retardant Drop — Fire retardant cascaded from an air tanker or helicopter.

Retard Chamber — Chamber that that catches and slows the excess water that may be sent through the alarm valve of an automatic sprinkler system during momentary water pressure surges; this reduces the chance of false alarm activation. The retard chamber is installed between the alarm check valve and alarm signaling equipment.

Retention — Characteristic of Class A foam and foam solution; its ability to remain on and in the fuel, reduce the fuel temperature, and increase the fuel moisture content.

Return-Air Plenum — Unoccupied space within a building through which air flows back to the heating, ventilating, and air-conditioning (HVAC) system; normally immediately above a ceiling and below an insulated roof or the floor above. *See* Heating, Ventilating, and Air-Conditioning (HVAC) System.

Returning — Clear text radio term used when a company is leaving the scene of an incident.

Reverse Curl — Method of returning a one-firefighter ladder to a flat rest position on the ground.

Reverse Hose Lay — *See* Reverse Lay.

Reverse Lay — Method of laying hose from the fire scene to the water supply.

Revolving Door — Door made of three or four sections, or wings, arranged on a central pivot that operates by rotating within a cylindrical housing.

Reward Power — Power based on the subordinate's perception of the leader's ability to grant rewards, such as salary increases, promotions, and bigger budgets.

Reynolds Number (Re) — Mathematically calculated factor that determines the state of flow (laminar or turbulent) of a fluid.

Rhetorical Question — Question designed to stimulate thinking or motivate participants rather than to seek a correct answer; an answer is not necessarily required or expected.

Rhythm — Handling and climbing ladders with smooth motion.

Ribbon — Narrow strip of board cut to fit into the edge of studding to help support joists.

RIBC — *See* Rigid Intermediate Bulk Container.

Rib Cage — Skeletal framework of the chest; composed of the sternum, ribs, and thoracic vertebrae.

RIC — *See* Rapid Intervention Crew.

Rickettsia — Specialized bacteria that live and multiply in the gastrointestinal tract of arthropod carriers, such as ticks and fleas. *See* Bacteria and Virus.

Ridge — Peak or sharp edge along the very top of a pitched roof of a building. *Also known as* Ridge Beam, Ridge Board, or Ridge Pole.

Ridge Beam — Highest horizontal member in a pitched roof to which the upper ends of the rafters attach. *Also known as* Ridge Board or Ridgepole. *See* Ridge.

Rig — Any piece of fire apparatus.

Rigging — Ropes or cables used with lifting or pulling devices such as block and tackle.

Righting Arm — Moment that tends to return a vessel to the upright position after any small rotational displacement. *Also known as* Righting Moment or Restoring Moment.

Right Justified — *See* Ragged Left.

Right of Entry — Legal access to private property obtained in one of five ways: exigent circumstances, consent, administrative search warrant, criminal search warrant, or contractual entry agreement.

Right of Privacy — Concept that means that an individual's records are confidential. *See Family Education Rights and Privacy Act of 1974.*

Rigid Conduit — Nonflexible steel tubing used for the passage of electrical conductors.

Rigid Intermediate Bulk Container (RIBC) — *See* Intermediate Bulk Container (IBC)

Rim Cylinder — Lock cylinder for a rim lock.

Rim Lock — Type of auxiliary lock mounted on the surface of a door.

Ring Stiffener — Circumferential tank shell stiffener that helps to maintain the tank cross section.

Riot Control Agent — Chemical compound that temporarily makes people unable to function, by causing immediate irritation to the eyes, mouth, throat, lungs, and skin. *Also known as* Irritating Agent or Tear Gas. *See* Incapacitant.

Rise — Vertical distance between the treads of a stairway, or the height of the entire stairway.

Riser — (1) Vertical part of a stair step. (2) Vertical water pipe used to carry water for fire protection systems above ground, such as a standpipe riser or sprinkler riser. (3) Pipe leading from the fire main to the fire station (hydrants) on upper deck levels of a vessel. *See* Automatic Sprinkler System and Standpipe System.

Risk — (1) Likelihood of suffering harm from a hazard; exposure to a hazard. The potential for failure or loss. (2) Estimated effect that a hazard would have on people, services, facilities, and structures in a community; likelihood of a hazard event resulting in an adverse condition that causes injury or damage. Often expressed as *high, moderate,* or *low* or in terms of potential monetary losses associated with the intensity of the hazard.

Risk Analysis — *See* Hazard or Risk Analysis.

Risk Assessment — (1) Determining the risk level or seriousness of a risk. (2) Process for evaluating risk associated with a specific hazard defined in terms of probability and frequency of occurrence, magnitude and severity, exposure, and consequences. *Also known as* Risk Evaluation.

Risk Identification — Stage of loss control risk analysis where planners identify risks, in addition to common risks, that are specific to a certain facility, occupancy, or area.

Risk Level — Seriousness of a risk, which is determined by considering how often it may occur (frequency) and how bad it is when it occurs (severity).

Risk Management — Process of identifying and analyzing the exposure to hazards, selecting appropriate risk management techniques to handle exposures, implementing chosen techniques, and monitoring the results of those risk management techniques.

Risk Management Plan — Written plan that identifies and analyzes the exposure to hazards, selects appropriate risk management techniques to handle exposures, implements of chosen techniques, and monitors of the results of those risk management techniques. *See* Hazard Assessment or and Hazard Risk Analysis.

RIT — *See* Rapid Intervention Team.

Rivet Construction — Multi-piece metal structure (aerial device) fastened together by rivets.

Road Performance Test — Series of tests required to determine the performance ability of fire apparatus.

Roadside — Side of the trailer farthest from the curb when trailer is traveling in a normal forward direction (left-hand side); opposite to "curbside."

Road Tests — Pre-service apparatus maneuverability tests designed to determine the road-worthiness of a new vehicle.

Rocker Panels — Narrow body panels on each side of an automobile, below the doors and between the kick panel and the quarter panel; usually rounded in shape.

Rocket-Propelled Grenade (RPG) — Common anti-tank projectile launched from a handheld tube.

Roentgen (R) — English System unit used to measure radiation exposure, applied only to gamma and X-ray radiation; the unit used on most U.S. dosimeters. *See* Gamma Radiation, Radiation (2), Radiation Absorbed Dose (rad), Radioactive Material (RAM), and Roentgen Equivalent in Man (rem).

Roentgen Equivalent in Man (rem) — English System unit used to express the radiation absorbed dose (rad) equivalence as pertaining to a human body; used to set radiation dose limits for emergency responders. Applied to all types of radiation. *See* Radiation (2), Radiation Absorbed Dose (rad), Radioactive Material (RAM), and Roentgen.

Role — Socio-psychological concept that says the role or status someone has in a building determines that person's response to a fire or other emergency.

Role Model — Individual to whom others look to as an example while learning or adopting a new role or job; the part an instructor plays, the image an instructor portrays, and the actions an instructor demonstrates to learners or program participants who look to their instructor as an example.

Role-Playing — Discussion in which a group acts out various scenarios. *See* Discussion.

Rolled Shape — Structural steel member made by passing a hot steel billet between shaped rollers until it reaches the required shape and dimensions.

Roll-On Application Method — Method of foam application in which the foam stream is directed at the ground at the front edge of the unignited or ignited liquid fuel spill; foam then spreads across the surface of the liquid. *Also known as* Bounce. *See* Bank-Down Application Method and Rain-Down Application Method.

Roll On/Roll Off Cargo (RO/RO) — Form of cargo handling using a vessel designed to carry vehicles that are loaded and unloaded by driving them onto/off the vessel by means of ramps.

Roll-On/Roll-Off Vessel (RO/RO Vessel) — Ship with large stern and side ramp structures that are lowered to allow vehicles to be driven on and off the vessel; for example, a vehicle ferry. *See* Cargo Vessel.

Rollover — (1) Condition in which unburned combustible gases are released in a confined space (such as a room or aircraft cabin) during the incipient or early steady-state phase and accumulate at the ceiling level. These superheated gases are pushed, under pressure, away from the fire area and into uninvolved areas where they mix with oxygen. When their flammable range is reached and additional oxygen is supplied by opening doors and/or applying fog streams, they ignite and a fire front develops, expanding very rapidly in a rolling action across the ceiling. *See* Backdraft, Flashover, and Incipient Phase. (2) Involves a vehicle rolling sideways onto its side and possibly continuing onto its top, then the opposite side.

Rollover Protection — Roll bars and roll cages within automobiles that protect passengers in the event of a rollover.

Romax™ — Trade name for nonmetallic-shielded cable.

Roof — (1) Outside top covering of a building. (2) Vehicle body component above the passengers' heads that encloses the passenger compartment.

Roof Bows — Steel frame members that run horizontally from side to side.

Roof Covering — Final outside cover that is placed on top of a roof deck assembly; common roof coverings include composition or wood shake shingles, tile, slate, tin, or asphaltic tar paper. *See* Roof Deck.

Roof Deck — Bottom components of the roof assembly that support the roof covering; the roof deck may be constructed of such components as plywood, wood studs (2 inches by 4 inches [50mm by 100 mm] or larger), lath strips, and other materials.

Roof Decking — *See* Sheathing.

Roof Ladder — Straight ladder with folding hooks at the top end; the hooks anchor the ladder over the roof ridge.

Rookie Academy — Special school to indoctrinate newly appointed firefighters in the rudiments of all fire service subjects.

Rooming House — Subdivision of residential property classification consisting of structures with sleeping accommodations for up to 16 persons on either a temporary or permanent basis, where meals may or may not be provided, but lacking separate cooking facilities for each occupant.

Rope Hose Tool — Piece of rope spliced to form a loop through the eye of a metal hook; used to secure hose to ladders or other objects. *See* Hose Belt and Hose Strap.

Rope Rescue — Use of rope and related equipment to perform rescue.

RO/RO — *See* Roll On/Roll Off Cargo and Roll On/Roll Off Vessel.

ROS — *See* Rate of Spread.

Rotary Gauge — Gauge for determining the liquid level in a pressurized tank.

Rotary Gear Positive Displacement Pump — Type of positive displacement pump commonly used in hydraulic systems. The pump imparts pressure on the hydraulic fluid by having two intermeshing rotary gears that force the supply of hydraulic oil into the pump casing chamber.

Rotary Rescue Saw — *See* Circular Saw.

Rotary Vane Pump — Type of positive displacement pump commonly used in hydraulic systems. A rotor with attached vanes is mounted off-center inside the pump housing; pressure is imparted on the water as the space between the rotor and the pump housing wall decreases.

Rotational Collisions — Collisions caused by off center front or side impacts that forcefully turn the impacted vehicle horizontally, causing one or both of the vehicles to spin.

Rotational Locks — Locking mechanisms that prevent the aerial device turntable from rotating unexpectedly.

Rotor — Rotating airfoil assemblies that provide lift for helicopters and other rotary-wing aircraft.

Rotor Blast — Air turbulence occurring under and around the rotors of an operating helicopter. *Also known as* Rotor Downwash from the main rotor.

Rotor Downwash — *See* Rotor Blast.

Round-Robin Brainstorming — Method of brainstorming in which each member of a group offers an idea in turn, with participants electing to pass on any round, until everyone has passed a turn; ideas are recorded as soon as they are stated.

Round Turn — Element of a knot that consists of further bending one side of a loop.

Routes of Entry — Pathways by which hazardous materials get into (or affect) the human body; common routes are inhalation, ingestion, skin contact, injection, absorption, and penetration (for radiation). *See* Permeation and Radiation (2).

RPG — *See* Rocket-Propelled Grenade.

rpm — Revolutions Per Minute.

RSPA — *See* Research and Special Programs Administration.

Rub Rail — Sixteen-gauge steel W-shaped rails placed the full length of the sidewalls on a bus; they are intended to minimize penetration during collision.

Rudder — Upright movable part of the aircraft tail assembly that assists in the directional control of the aircraft. *Also known as* Vertical Stabilizer.

Run — (1) Response to a fire or alarm. (2) The horizontal measurement of a stair tread or the distance of the entire stair length.

Run Block — *See* Truss Block.

Rung — Step portion of a ladder running from beam to beam.

Rung Block — *See* Truss Block.

Rungs Away — Position of a raised truss ladder when the rungs are on the side furthest from the objective.

Rungs Down — Position of a truss ladder at rest when the rungs are on the side closest to the ground.

Rung Side — Front or climbing side of a ladder; the side away from the building or objective.

Rungs Up — Position of a truss ladder at rest when the rungs are on the side furthest from the ground.

Running Block — In a block and tackle system, the block attached to the load that is to be moved.

Running Fire — (1) Wildland fire that spreads rapidly. (2) Behavior of a fire spreading rapidly with a well-defined head.

Running Part — Part of the rope that is to be used for work such as hoisting, pulling, or belaying.

Runway — Defined rectangular area on airports prepared for the takeoff or landing of aircraft along its length.

Runway Threshold — Beginning or end of a runway that is usable for landing or takeoff.

Rupture Disk — Formed, thin metal membrane or diaphragm designed to burst at a predetermined pressure and temperature in order to prevent overpressurization of the attached vessel or container; a pressure-relief device. *See* Emergency-Relief Device.

S

Saddle — Depression or pass in a ridgeline; low area on a ridgeline between two higher points.

Saddle Burn — Saddle-shaped fire pattern that is the result of fire burning downward through the floor surface above the joist.

SAE — *See* the Society of Automotive Engineers.

Safe Refuge — *See* Safety Zone.

Safety — (1) Extra hitch tied in the end of a knot to prevent the end from being pulled through the knot. (2) Device designed to prevent an inadvertent or hazardous operation. (3) To insert locking pins into appropriate openings on ejection seats in military aircraft to render the seats safe to work on or around.

Safety Bar — Hinged bar designed to protect firefighters from falling out of the open jump seat area of a fire apparatus.

Safety Belt — Life safety harness.

Safety Can — Flammable liquid container, usually five gallons (19 L) or less, that has a self-closing spout and has been approved by a suitable testing agency.

Safety Chain — Chain connecting two vehicles to prevent separation in the event the primary towing connection breaks.

Safety Data Sheet (SDS) — Form provided by the manufacturer and blender of chemicals that contains information about chemical composition, physical and chemical properties, health and safety hazards, emergency response procedures, and waste disposal procedures of a specified material. *Formerly known as* Material Safety Data Sheet (MSDS).

Safety Gates — Protective guards that are placed over the apparatus jump seat opening to prevent firefighters from falling off the apparatus.

Safety Glass — Type of glass composed of two sheets of glass that are laminated to a sheet of plastic sandwiched between them under high temperature and pressure; primarily used for automobile windshields and some rear windows. *Also known as* Laminated Glass.

Safety Glasses — *See* Safety Goggles.

Safety Goggles — Enclosed, but adequately ventilated goggles that have impact- and shatter-resistant lenses to protect the eyes from dusts, chips, and other small particles; should be OSHA approved. *Also known as* Safety Glasses.

Safety Guidelines — Rules, regulations, or policies created and/or adopted by an organization that list steps or procedures to follow that will aid in reducing, if not eliminating, accident or injury. *Also known as* Safety Plan.

Safety Island — *See* Safety Zone.

Safety Line — (1) Extra rope tied to the main hauling rope in a rope rescue operation. (2) System built to protect a rescuer and/or patient.

Safety Net — Net used to protect firefighters in the event of a fall during aboveground rope training evolutions.

Safety Officer — (1) Fire officer whose primary function is to administrate safety within the entire scope of fire department operations. *Also known as* Health and Safety Officer. (2) Member of the IMS command staff responsible to the incident commander for monitoring and assessing hazardous and unsafe conditions and developing measures for assessing personnel safety on an incident. *Also known as* Incident Safety Officer.

Safety Policy — Written policy that is designed to promote safety to departmental members.

Safety Program — Program that sets standards, policies, procedures, and precautions regarding the safe purchase, operation, and maintenance of the department's equipment, and educates employees on how to protect themselves from personal injury.

Safety Relief Valve — Device on cargo tanks with an operating part held in place by a spring; the valve opens at preset pressures to relieve excess pressure and prevent failure of the vessel.

Safety Shoes — (1) Rubber or neoprene foot plates, usually of the swivel type, attached to the butt end of the beams of a ground ladder. (2) Protective footwear meeting OSHA requirements.

Safety Zone — Recently burned area or one cleared of vegetation, used for escape in the event a line is outflanked or a spot fire outside a control line renders the line unsafe. In firing operations, crews progress so as to maintain a safety zone close at hand, allowing the fuels inside the control line to be consumed before going ahead. *Also known as* Safe Refuge or Safety Island.

Sag — (1) The vertical distance of the ship's keel at amidships below the ship's keel at the bow and stern. (2) To curve downward in the middle as a result of improper loading. *Also known as* Sagging. *See* Hog.

Sagging — *See* Sag.

Sail Area — Area of a vessel, when viewed from the side, that is above the waterline and is subject to the force of the wind.

Salamander — Portable heating device; generally found on construction sites.

Salvage — Methods and operating procedures by which firefighters attempt to save property and reduce further damage from water, smoke, heat, and exposure during or immediately after a fire; may be accomplished by removing property from a fire area, by covering it, or by other means.

Salvage Cover — Waterproof cover made of cotton duck, plastic, or other material used by fire departments to protect unaffected furniture and building areas from heat, smoke, and water damage; a tarpaulin. *Also known as* Tarp.

Salvage Kit — Assortment of tools and appliances used for a specific purpose during salvage.

Salvo Drop — Air tanker dropping its entire load of fire retardant at one time.

Sampling Error — Measure of the error created because estimates are based on a sampling of fire losses rather than on a complete census of the fire problem. *Also known as* Standard Error.

Sanction — Notice or punishment attached to a violation for the purpose of enforcing a law or regulation. *See* Citation and Violation.

Sandshoe — Flat, steel plate that serves as ground contact on the supports of a trailer; used instead of wheels, particularly where the ground surface is expected to be soft.

Sanitary Sewer — Underground pipe used to carry waste from toilets (water closets) and from other drains.

Sanitary Tee — Soil pipe fitting with a side outlet to form a tee shape; the side outlet has a smooth radius to permit unhampered flow in the fitting.

Sanitize — To make free from dirt or microorganisms that endanger health.

Saponification — Phenomenon that occurs when mixtures of alkaline based chemicals and certain cooking oils come into contact, resulting in the formation of a soapy film.

SAR — *See* Supplied Air Respirator.

SARA — *See* Superfund Amendments and Reauthorization Act.

Sarin (GB) — Fluorinated phosphinate chemical warfare agent classified as a nerve agent.

Sash — Framework in which panes of glass are set in a window or door.

Sash Cord — Cotton cord, usually ¼ inch (6.35 mm) in diameter, that is used for securing tiebacks, guy lines, hose bundles, or salvage covers by lacing through grommets.

Saturation Tactics — Practice of having a person (usually a child) who has played with fire repeat an act (such as lighting a match) until the person's curiosity is satisfied and the act becomes boring; no longer a recommended practice.

Save — Life that has been saved as a direct result of a public fire and life safety education program.

Sawtooth Roof — Roof style characterized by a series of alternating vertical walls and sloping roofs that resembles the teeth of a saw; this type of roof is most often found on older industrial buildings to provide light and ventilation.

Scald — Burn to the human body caused by contact with hot fluids or steam; or, to cause such a burn.

Scantlings — Dimensions of the various parts of a vessel (frames, girders, plating, etc.).

Scare Tactics — Practice of frightening a child who has played with fire by showing the child pictures of injured or dead children, pets, or burned toys, or by threatening the child with punishment, hospitalization, or painful treatment. Not a recommended practice.

Scarf Joint — Connection between two parts made by the cutting of overlapping mating parts and securing them by glue or fasteners so that the joint is not enlarged and the patterns are complementary.

SCBA — *See* Self-Contained Breathing Apparatus.

Scene Assessment — Initial observation and evaluation of an emergency scene; related more to incident stabilization than to problem mitigation.

Scene Control Zones — *See* Hazard-Control Zones.

Scene Management — Those elements of incident management that include keeping those not involved in the incident from entering unsafe areas and protecting those in potentially unsafe areas through evacuation or sheltering in place.

scf — *See* Standard Cubic Foot.

scfm — *See* Standard Cubic Feet Per Minute.

Schedule — Table or chart on plans that contains information relating to doors, windows, hardware, and room finishes. *See* Door/Window Schedule.

Schema — Refers to conceptual or knowledge structure (a mental map) in our memory system that we use to interpret information that is presented to our senses by the external environment. When our senses are presented with a new object or situation, we match it against our existing knowledge or schema and act upon it based on our experience. If we don't have the appropriate knowledge or experience, we change the schema or develop additional ones. We develop more sophisticated and differentiated schemata as we gain new knowledge and encounter more experiences. The plural form is *schemata*.

Scene Control Zones — *See* Hazard-Control Zones.

School Bus — As defined by U.S. Federal Motor Vehicle Safety Standards, a passenger motor vehicle designed to carry more than 10 passengers, in addition to the driver, and which the Secretary of Transportation determines is to be used for the purpose of transporting preschool, primary, and secondary school students to or from such schools or school-related events.

Scientific Method — Widely accepted, systematic approach to examining evidence in order to create hypotheses and draw conclusions about phenomena at a fire or explosion scene.

Scissor Stairs — Two sets of crisscrossing stairs in a common shaft. Each set serves every floor but on alternately opposite sides of the stair shaft; for example, one set would serve the west wing on even-numbered floors and the east wing odd-numbered floors, while the other set would serve floors opposite to the first set.

Sclera — White outer coat enclosing the eyeball, except the part covered by the cornea.

Scoop Stretcher — Device used to package patient for removal from a confined environment; may be placed around the patient without lifting the patient.

Scratch Line — Unfinished preliminary control line, hastily established or constructed as an emergency measure to check the spread of fire.

Screed — Two or more strips set at a desired elevation so that concrete may be leveled by drawing a leveling device over their surface; also the straightedge.

Screw-In Expander Method — Method of attaching threaded couplings to rubber-jacket booster hose with expanders that are screwed into place.

Screw Jacks — Long, nonhydraulic jacks that can be extended or retracted by turning a collar on a threaded shaft.

Scrub Area — Area within the span of reach of an aerial device.

SCUBA — *See* Self-Contained Underwater Breathing Apparatus.

Scupper — (1) Form of drain opening provided in outer walls at floor or roof level to remove water to the exterior of a building in order to reduce water damage. (2) Opening in the side of a vessel to allow water falling on deck to drain overboard.

Scuttle — Opening in the roof or ceiling that provides access to the roof or attic; fitted with removable covers that may be used for access or ventilation. *See* Hatch.

SDS — *See* Safety Data Sheet.

Sea Chest — (1) Enclosure attached to the inside of a vessel's underwater shell open to the sea and fitted with a portable strainer plate; passes seawater into the vessel for cooling, fire fighting, or sanitary purposes. (2) Storage chest for mariner's personal property.

Sealed, Pneumatic, Line-Type Heat Detector — Heat-sensitive device that depends on the presence of normal pressure at normal temperatures.

Search — Techniques that allow the rescuer to identify the location of victims and to determine access to those victims in order to remove them to a safe area.

Search and Rescue Boat — Watercraft designed and equipped to carry personnel during search and rescue operations such as boating accidents, flood evacuations, and dive rescues.

Search and Rescue Operation — Emergency incident operation consisting of an organized search for the occupants of a structure or for those lost in the outdoors, and the rescue of those in need.

Search Assessment — Search assessment and findings performed by search personnel.

Search Warrant — Written order, in the name of the People, State, Province, Territory, or Commonwealth, signed by a magistrate, that commands a peace officer to search for personal property or other evidence and return it to the magistrate.

Seat Belt Pretensioners — Protective devices designed to tighten the belts as the front-impact air bags deploy.

Seat Catapult — Device for catapulting the seat from an aircraft in case of emergency.

Seated Explosion — Explosion with a clearly defined epicenter or seat, often a crater; typically associated with boiling liquid expanding vapor explosions (BLEVEs) and high explosives. *See* Nonseated Explosion.

Seat of Fire — Area in which the main body of fire is located.

Seaworthy — In fit condition to go safely to sea.

Secondary Collapse — Collapse that occurs after the initial collapse of a structure: common causes include aftershock (earthquake), weather conditions, and the movement of structural members.

Secondary Contamination — Contamination of people, equipment, or the environment outside the hot zone without contacting the primary source of contamination. *Also known as* Cross Contamination. *See* Contamination, Decontamination, and Hazard-Control Zones.

Secondary Damage — Damage caused by or resulting from those actions taken to fight a fire and leaving the property unprotected.

Secondary Decontamination — Taking a shower after having completed a technical decontamination process. *See* Decontamination and Technical Decontamination.

Secondary Device — Bomb or other weapon placed at the scene of an ongoing emergency response that is intended to cause casualties among responders; secondary explosive devices are designed to explode after a primary explosion or other major emergency response event has attracted large numbers of responders to the scene.

Secondary Duties — Actions required to restore the emergency scene to a safe condition.

Secondary Explosion — Explosion occurring as a direct result of an initial explosion or previous explosion.

Secondary Explosive — High explosive that is designed to detonate only under specific circumstances.

Secondary Feeder — Network of intermediate-sized pipes that reinforce the grid within the loops of the primary feeder system and aid in providing the required fire flow at any given point in a sprinkler system.

Secondary Line — Any fireline that is constructed at a distance from the fire perimeter, concurrently with or after a line has already been constructed on or near the perimeter of the fire; generally constructed as an insurance measure in case a fire escapes control by the primary line.

Second-Degree Burn — Burn to the human body that penetrates beneath the superficial skin layers to the dermis; produces edema, skin blisters, and possible scarring.

Section — Organizational level of an incident command system; has functional responsibility for primary segments of incident operations such as Operations, Planning, Logistics, and Finance/Administrative. This section level is organizationally between branch and incident commander.

Sectional View — Vertical view of a building as if it were cut into two parts; the purpose of a sectional view is to show the internal construction of each assembly. *See* Detailed View, Elevation View, and Plan View.

Sector — Either a geographic or function-based subdivision or assignment within the Fireground Command System or National Fire Service Incident Management System; may take the place of either a division, a group, or both.

Secure — (1) To make fast; for example, to secure a line to a cleat or other stationary object. (2) To close in a manner that prevents accidental opening or operation.

Security — Second need in Maslow's Hierarchy of Needs, concerned with personal safety and future physical comfort; similar to physiological needs, but encompassing long-term dangers or dangers that are not immediately threatening.

Security Window — Window designed to prevent illegal entrance to a building.

Sediment — Dirt and other foreign debris that may fall out of a fluid and collect in fluid-moving equipment.

Seismic Effect — Movement of a shock wave through the ground or structure after a large detonation; may cause additional damage to surrounding structures.

Seismic Forces — Forces produced by earthquakes; they are the most complex forces that can be exerted on a building.

Seismic Victim Locating Device — Device that detects minute vibrations and movement within a collapsed structure in order to help identify a victim's location.

Selective Routing (SR) — Enhanced 9-1-1 feature that allows 9-1-1 calls to be routed to the appropriate public safety answering point (PSAP); this system allows for more than one PSAP to be located in an area where jurisdictions share the same central telephone office.

Selector Valve — Three-way valve on a fire department aerial apparatus that directs oil to either stabilizer control valves or the aerial device control valves. *Also known as* Diverter Valve.

Self-Actualization — Highest need in Maslow's Hierarchy of Needs; the need to realize one's full potential.

Self-Closing Door — (1) Door equipped with a door closer. (2) On a ship, an installation in which watertight doors are remotely operated by a hydraulic pressure system, allowing them to be closed simultaneously from the bridge or separately at the doors from either side of the bulkhead. *See* Door Closer.

Self-Contained Breathing Apparatus (SCBA) — Respirator worn by the user that supplies a breathable atmosphere that is either carried in or generated by the apparatus and is independent of the ambient atmosphere. Respiratory protection is worn in all atmospheres that are considered to be Immediately Dangerous to Life and Health (IDLH). *Also known as* Air Mask or Air Pack. *See* Supplied Air Respirator (SAR).

Self-Contained Underwater Breathing Apparatus (SCUBA) — Protective breathing apparatus designed to be used underwater by divers to allow the exploration of underwater environments. *Also known as* SCUBA Gear or Underwater Breathing Gear.

Self-Directed Learning — Method of instruction in which an individual either is given or selects a set of objectives to complete through his or her own method of learning, at his or her own pace; based on an instructor's determination of the content. Learners are responsible for how much they learn and how they learn it, but this type of instruction does not relieve the instructor of the responsibility of ensuring that the learner accomplishes the intended tasks and skills in appropriate formats. *Also known as* Independent Learning.

Self-Educting Master Stream Foam Nozzle — Large-capacity nozzle with built-in foam eductor.

Self-Educting Nozzle — Handline nozzle that has the foam eductor built into it.

Self-Esteem — Second highest need in Maslow's Hierarchy of Needs; the need to have self-respect and respect for others, to have social status within the group, and to be recognized for one's worth or value.

Self-Heating — Form of chemical heat energy that occurs when a material increases in temperature without the addition of external heat. *Also known as* Spontaneous Heating.

Self-Presenters — Individuals who have not gone through victim registration processes at the incident scene.

Self-Priming Centrifugal Pump — Centrifugal pump that uses an air-water mixture to reach a fully primed pumping condition. *See* Centrifugal Pump, Multistage Centrifugal Pump, and Single-Stage Centrifugal Pump.

Self-Sustained Chemical Reaction — One of the four sides of the fire tetrahedron representing a process occurring during a fire: Vapors or gases are distilled from flammable materials during initial burning; atoms and molecules are released from these vapors and combine with other radicals to form new compounds. These compounds are again disturbed by the heat, releasing more atoms and radicals that again form new compounds, restarting the chain reaction. Interrupting the chain will stop the overall reaction; this is the extinguishing mechanism utilized by several extinguishing agents. *Also known as* Chemical Chain Reaction.

Semantics — Study of meaning in words and symbols; refers to language, word meanings, and meaning changes due to context, all of which may be affected by an individual's background, knowledge, and experience.

Semiconductor — Material that is neither a good electrical conductor nor a good insulator, and therefore may be used as either in some applications. *See* Conductor and Thermistor.

Semifixed Foam Extinguishing System — Foam system that is designed to provide fire-extinguishing capabilities to an area but is not automatic in operation and depends on human intervention to place it into operation. *See* Fixed Foam Extinguishing System and Portable Foam Extinguishing System.

Semisubsurface Injection — Application method that discharges foam through a flexible hose that rises from the bottom of a storage tank, up through the fuel, and to the surface of the fuel; foam then blankets the surface of the fuel. *See* Direct Injection and Subsurface Injection.

Semitrailer — Freight trailer that when attached is supported at its forward end by the fifth wheel device of the truck tractor; occasionally used to refer to a trucking rig made up of a tractor and a semitrailer. *See* Fifth Wheel.

Semitrailer Tank — Any vehicle with or without auxiliary motive power, equipped with a cargo tank mounted thereon or built as an integral part thereof, that is used for the transportation of flammable and combustible liquids or asphalt; constructed so that when drawn by a tractor by means of a fifth-wheel connection, some part of its load and weight rests upon the towing vehicle.

Sender — Person who sends or transmits a message in the communications process. *Also known as* Source.

Senior Facility Manager — Individual with overall responsibility for a particular commercial, institutional, or industrial facility.

Sensitizer — *See* Allergen.

Separating — Act of creating a barrier between the fuel and the fire.

Sequential Training — Preferred training method, in which the student is taken step by step from simple to complex exercises when learning to use equipment such as a self-contained breathing apparatus (SCBA).

Sergeant — Rank used by some fire departments for company officers or fire apparatus driver/operators.

Series Circuit — Circuit configuration in which the current flows through all the components.

Series Operation — *See* Pressure Operation.

Serology — Science of analyzing bodily fluids such as saliva, blood, urine, or semen.

Serrated — Notched or toothed edge.

Service Branch — Branch within the logistics section of an incident command system; responsible for service activities at an incident. Components include the communications unit, medical unit, and foods unit.

Service Learning — Educational trend that tries to connect young people to the community in which they live through community service projects.

Service Records — Detailed description of maintenance and repair work for a particular apparatus or piece of equipment.

Service Test — Series of tests performed on apparatus and equipment in order to ensure operational readiness of the unit; should be performed at least yearly, or whenever a piece of apparatus or equipment has undergone extensive repair.

Session Guide — Plan for using a group of lesson plans or instructional materials during a predetermined period of instruction.

Set — (1) Individual incendiary fire. (2) Point or points of origin of an incendiary fire. (3) Material left to ignite an incendiary fire at a later time. (4) Individual lightning or railroad fires, especially when several are started within a short time. (5) Burning material at the points deliberately ignited for backfiring, slash burning, prescribed burning, and other purposes. *See* Permanent Deformation (1).

Setback — Distance from the street line to the front of a building.

SETIQ — *See* the Emergency Transportation System for the Chemical Industry (Mexico).

Sewer Drain Guard — Strainer to prevent debris from getting into the sewer system; used when utilizing soil pipes to remove water during salvage operations.

Sexless Coupling — *See* Nonthreaded Coupling.

Sexual Harassment — Unwanted and unwelcome sexual behavior toward a worker by someone who has the power to reward or punish the worker.

Shackle — (1) Hinged part of a padlock. (2) A U-shaped metal device that is secured with a pin or bolt across the device's opening. (3) A hinged metal loop that is secured with a quick-release locking pin mechanism.

Shaft — Any vertical enclosure within a building; for example, a stairwell or elevator hoistway.

Shaft Alley — Narrow, watertight compartment between the engine room and the stern of a vessel that houses the propeller shaft. *Also known as* Shaft Tunnel.

Shaftway — Tunnel or alleyway through which the drive shaft or rudder shaft passes.

Shall — Common verb used in NFPA® standards denoting compulsory compliance. When used in codes, "shall" denotes a mandatory provision.

Shank — Portion of a coupling that serves as a point of attachment to the hose.

Shaped Charge — (1) Concave metal hemisphere (known as a liner) backed by a high explosive, seated in a steel or aluminum casing; when the high explosive is detonated, the metal liner is compressed and squeezed forward, forming a jet of superheated liquid metal whose tip may travel many times faster than the speed of sound. (2) An explosive that has been designed (or shaped) to direct the energy of the explosion in a single direction.

Shear Line — Space between the shell and the plug of a lock cylinder that is obstructed by tumblers in the locked position.

Shear Point — Hazard created by a reciprocal (sliding) movement of a mechanical component past a stationary point on a machine.

Shears — Powered hydraulic cutting tool that will cut most metals, other than case-hardened steel.

Shear Strength — Ability of a building component or assembly to resist lateral or shear forces.

Shear Stress — Stress resulting when two forces act on a body in opposite directions in parallel adjacent planes.

Sheathing — (1) Covering applied to the framing of a building to which siding is applied. (2) First layer of roof covering laid directly over the rafters or other roof supports; may be plywood, chipboard sheets, or planks that are butted together or spaced about 1 inch (25 mm) apart. *Also known as* Decking or Roof Decking.

Shed Roof — Pitched roof with a single sloping aspect, resembling half of a gabled roof.

Sheet Bend — *See* Becket Bend.

Sheeting — Wood planks and wood panels that support trench walls when held in place with shoring.

Sheetrock® — Brand name often used to describe any gypsum wallboard. *See* Wallboard.

Shelf Angles — Brackets fastened to the face of a building at or near floor levels to support masonry or wall facing materials.

Shell — (1) Outer component of a screw-in expander coupling. (2) Outer layer of fabric on personal protective clothing.

Shell Structure — Rigid, three-dimensional structure having an outer "skin" thickness that is small compared to other dimensions.

Shelter and Thermal Control — Process of protecting patients and rescuers from inclement weather and extreme temperatures.

Shelter in Place — Having occupants remain in a structure or vehicle in order to provide protection from a rapidly approaching hazard. *See* Evacuation.

Shims — Wedges used in pairs to tighten up a shoring system.

Shiplap Siding — Horizontal siding boards lapped over each other to provide a water shedding effect.

Shipping Papers — Shipping orders, bills of lading, manifests, waybills, or other shipping documents issued by the carrier. *See* Air Bill, Bill of Lading, Consist, Lading, and Waybill.

Shock — Failure of the circulatory system to produce sufficient blood to all parts of the body; results in depression of bodily functions, and eventually death if not controlled.

Shock Front — Boundary between the pressure disturbance created by an explosion (in air, water, or earth) and the ambient atmosphere, water, or earth.

Shock Loading — Loads that involve motion; includes the forces arising from wind, moving vehicles, earthquakes, vibration, falling objects, or the addition of a moving load force to an aerial device or structure. *Also known as* Dynamic Load.

Shock Wave — Blast pressure front moving faster than the speed of sound; becomes an amplitude wave that travels through solid objects and the ground.

Shoe — Metal plate used at the bottom of heavy timber columns.

S-Hook — S-shaped steel hook frequently used in salvage operations by placing through grommet holes when hanging salvage covers; also used to hang covers for drying after cleanup.

Shop — Fire department maintenance or repair area.

Shoring — General term used for lengths of timber, screw jacks, hydraulic and pneumatic jacks, and other devices that can be used as temporary support for formwork or structural components or used to hold sheeting against trench walls. Individual supports are called shores, cross braces, and struts. *See* Cribbing (2).

Shoring Block — Shim for a jack.

Shoring Timbers — Heavy timbers used to support bulkheads damaged by collision or to secure cargo; also any props or supports placed against or beneath anything to prevent sinking or sagging.

Short Circuit — Abnormal, low-resistance path between conductors that allows a high current flow that normally leads to an overcurrent condition.

Short-Jacking — Setting the stabilizers on one side of an apparatus shorter than the stabilizers on the other side; usually done when access for full stabilization is restricted.

Short-Term Exposure Limit (STEL) — Fifteen-minute time-weighted average that should not be exceeded at any time during a workday; exposures should not last longer than 15 minutes and should not be repeated more than four times per day with at least 60 minutes between exposures. *See* Immediately Dangerous to Life or Health (IDLH), Permissible Exposure Limit (PEL), Recommended Exposure Limit (REL), and Threshold Limit Value (TLV®).

Shoulder Carry — Procedure of carrying fire hose or a ground ladder on the shoulder.

Shove Knife — Tool for opening a latch on a lock.

Shrapnel — Descriptor of debris, large and small, carried by the blast-pressure front of an explosion.

Shrapnel Fragmentation — Small pieces of debris thrown from a container or structure that ruptures from containment or restricted blast pressure.

Shutoff Nozzle — Type of nozzle that has a valve or other device for controlling the water supply; firefighters use it to control water supply at the nozzle rather than at the source of supply.

Siamese — Hose appliance used to combine two or more hoselines into one; usually has female inlets and a male outlet and is commonly used to supply the hose leading to a ladder pipe.

Side-Impact Collision — (1) Collision in which a vehicle is struck along its side by another vehicle. *Also known as* Broadside Collision or T-Bone Collision. (2) Collision in which a vehicle slides sideways into another object.

Side-Impact Protection Systems (SIPS) — Air bag systems designed to protect passengers during side-impact collisions; may be operated mechanically or powered by the vehicle's electrical system.

Side Rails — Upper and lower side rails, which are the main longitudinal frame members of a tank used to connect the upper and lower corner fittings, respectively. *See* Beam.

Sidewall Sprinkler — Sprinkler designed to be positioned at the wall of a room rather than in the center of a room; has a special deflector that creates a fan-shaped pattern of water that is projected into the room, away from the wall. *Also known as* Wall Sprinkler.

Signaling Device — System component that generates an audible, visual, or motion signal intended to alert humans to the activation of an alarm-initiating device. *See* Fire Alarm System, Fire Detection System, and Initiating Device.

Significant New Alternatives Policy (SNAP) — EPA-mandated program for identifying and evaluating new alternative agents to replace ozone-depleting substances such as halon.

Silage — Contents of a silo.

Silent Alarm — *See* Still Alarm.

Sill — (1) Bottom rough structural member that rests on the foundation. (2) Bottom exterior member of a window or door or the masonry below.

Siliceous Aggregate — Coarse material such as gravel, broken stone, or sand, with which silica, cement, and water are mixed to form concrete.

Silo — Tall, round structure found on farms, at grain elevators, and at mills; used to store feed for livestock, and grain during shipment to and upon arrival at the mills.

Silo Gas — Collection of gases produced during the spoilage of crops in a silo; includes methane, carbon dioxide, nitrogen dioxide, and hydrogen sulfide.

Simple Asphyxiant Any inert gas that displaces or dilutes oxygen below the level needed by the human body. *See* Asphyxiant and Inert Gas.

Simple Fracture — Fracture in which the skin overlaying the broken bone is intact.

Simple Loop — Loop in which there is exactly one inflow point and one outflow point, and exactly two paths between the inflow and outflow points.

Simple Tackle — One or more blocks reeved with a single rope.

Simple-To-Complex — Method of sequencing instruction so that information begins with the basic or simple information, or beginning steps, and progresses to the more difficult or complex information and processes.

Simple Triage and Rapid Treatment (START) — Triage evaluation method for checking respiratory, circulatory and neurological function, with the intention of categorizing patients in one of the four care categories: Immediate, Delayed, Minor, and Dead/Non-salvageable. The START method is recommended for use by first-arriving responders for initial and secondary field triage.

Simplex — Radio operating system in which one frequency is used to communicate between radio units or stations; communication can only take place in one direction at a time, otherwise transmissions become unreadable and garbled.

Single-Acting Hydraulic Cylinder — Hydraulic cylinder capable of transmitting force in only one direction.

Single-Edge Snap Throw — Method of spreading a salvage cover with a snap action; intended for spreading covers in narrow spaces.

Single-Issue Leader — Leader who is very concerned about either production needs or worker needs.

Single-Issue Leadership — Leadership style that is characterized by an overriding concern for either production or people.

Single-Jacket Hose — Type of hose construction consisting of one woven jacket; usually lined with an inner rubber tube.

Single Ladder — *See* Straight Ladder.

Single-Lens Reflex (SLR) Camera — Film camera that uses a semi-automatic moving mirror system that allows the photographer to see exactly what will be captured on the film.

Single Loop — Method of attaching software to an anchor.

Single-Ply Membrane Roof — *See* Membrane Roof.

Single Resource — Individual company or crew.

Single-Stage Centrifugal Pump — Centrifugal pump with only one impeller. *See* Centrifugal Pump, Multistage Centrifugal Pump, and Self-Priming Centrifugal Pump.

Sinkhole — Natural depression in a land surface formed by the collapse of a cavern roof; generally occurs in limestone regions.

Siphon — (1) Section of hard suction hose or piece of pipe used to maintain an equal level of water in two or more portable tanks. (2) A method of utilizing atmospheric pressure to transfer a liquid over a small elevation from an upper level to a lower level.

Siphon Eductor — Water removal device that utilizes venturi action to evacuate water from basements, sumps, or low areas.

SIPS — *See* Side-Impact Protection Systems.

Siren — Audible warning device that makes a high-pitched or an alternating high- and low-pitched wailing sound when used by emergency vehicles.

Sisal Rope — Rope made from sisal fiber; most common substitute for manila rope. Sisal is a hard fiber with about three-fourths the tensile strength of manila; its most common use is in binder's twine, but it is sometimes used in larger ropes.

Site — Term used to indicate the location of a building, construction site, or an incident.

Site Plan — Drawing that provides a view of the proposed construction in relation to existing conditions. Includes survey information and information on contours and grades; generally the first sheet on a set of drawings. *See* Construction Plan, Floor Plan, and Plot Plan.

Site-Specific Hazard — Hazard that sometimes or always exists at the facility for which the fire brigade is responsible, but does not exist in most other occupancies.

Site Work Zones — *See* Hazard-Control Zones.

Situation Status Unit (SITSTAT) — Functional unit within the planning section of an incident command system; responsible for analysis of situation as it progresses. Reports to the planning section chief.

Situational Awareness — An individual's perception and comprehension of the details of his or her surrounding environment, and the understanding of how events occurring in the moment may affect the future.

Size-Up — Ongoing mental evaluation process performed by the operational officer in charge of an incident; assessment of all influential factors in order to develop objectives, strategy, and tactics for fire suppression, before committing personnel and equipment to a course of action. Size-up results in a plan of action that may be adjusted as the situation changes; it includes such factors as time, location, nature of occupancy, life hazard, exposures, property involved, weather, nature and extent of fire, and fire fighting facilities.

SKED® — Compact device for patient removal from a confined space with spinal immobilization; may be used as a lifting device with a harness.

Skeleton Key — Key for a warded lock.

Skid Load — System of loading fire hose so that the top layer can be pulled off at the fire.

Skid Unit — Fire fighting system or systems built on a frame that can be mounted in the bed of a pickup truck or larger vehicle.

Skills Test — Evaluation instrument used to assess an individual's ability to perform a specific physical behavior. *Also known as* Performance Test.

Skin — (1) Outer covering of the body, and the largest organ of the body. Consists of the dermis and the epidermis, and contains various sensory and regulatory mechanisms. (2) Outer covering of an aircraft, which includes the covering of wings, fuselage, and control surfaces.

Skin Contact — Occurrence in which a chemical or hazardous material (in any state — solid, liquid, or gas) contacts the skin or exposed surface of the body, such as the mucous membranes of the eyes, nose, or mouth. *See* Routes of Entry.

Skin Penetrating Agent Applicator Tool® (SPAAT) — Penetrating nozzle used on aircraft fires.

Skip Breathing — Emergency procedure in which the firefighter inhales normally, holds the inhalation for as long as it would take to exhale, takes another breath, and then exhales; used only when the firefighter is stationary and must wait for help.

Skip Shoring — Procedure for supporting trench walls with uprights and shores at spaced intervals.

Skull — Bony structure surrounding the brain; consists of the cranial bones, the facial bones, and the teeth.

Skylights — Roof structures or devices intended to increase natural illumination within buildings, either in rooms or over stairways and other vertical shafts that extend to the roof.

Slab — (1) Heavy steel plate used under a steel column. (2) Reinforced concrete floor. (3) Reinforced wall section in tilt-slab construction.

Slab and Beam Frame — Construction technique using concrete slabs supported by concrete beams.

Slab Door — Door that appears to be made of a single piece (slab) of wood; there are two types, hollow core and solid core.

Slag — Hot molten metal that is a byproduct of welding or torch cutting operations.

Slander — False and defamatory oral statement about a person that damages his or her reputation. Definitions vary among states/provinces; may require proof or the presence of other factors. *See* Defamation, Libel, and Tort.

Slash — Debris left after logging, pruning, thinning, or brush cutting; includes logs, chunks, bark, branches, stumps, and broken understory trees or brush.

Sleeper — Compartment built into or behind the cab of a large truck, to be used by the driver for rest and relaxation.

Sleeve — Tube or pipe extending through a floor slab to provide openings for the passage of plumbing and heating pipes to be installed later.

Slide Pole — Brass or stainless steel pole that allows firefighters to quickly slide down to the apparatus bay from the floor above.

Sliding Door — Door that opens and closes by sliding across its opening, usually on rollers.

Sliding Fifth Wheel — Fifth-wheel assembly capable of being moved forward or backward on the truck tractor, in order to vary load distribution and adjust the overall length of combination.

Sliding Rope — *See* Rappel.

Sling — Assembly that connects the load to the material handling equipment. There are four common types of slings: chain, wire rope, synthetic round, and synthetic web.

Sling Psychrometer — Meteorological instrument used to determine relative humidity.

Slip Brainstorming — Type of brainstorming in which each person in the group independently and anonymously writes ideas on a slip of paper, and the slips are then collected and organized.

Slip Hook — Hook used on a chain that is designed to be fastened by slipping it over a link in the chain.

Slope — Natural or artificial topographic incline; degree of deviation from horizontal.

Slope Winds — Small-scale convective winds that occur due to local heating and cooling of a natural incline of the ground.

Slopover — (1) Fire edge that crosses a control line at a wildland fire. *Also known as* Breakover. (2) Situation that occurs when burning oil that is stored in a tank is forced over the edge of the tank by water that is heated to the boiling point and has accumulated under the surface of the oil.

SLR — *See* Single-Lens Reflex Camera.

Slump Test — Method of evaluating the moisture content of wet concrete by measuring the amount that a small, cone-shaped sample of the concrete settles or "slumps" after it is removed from a standard-sized test mold.

Slurry — (1) Watery mixture of insoluble matter such as mud, lime, or Plaster of Paris. (2) Thick mixture formed when a fire-retardant chemical is mixed with water and a viscosity agent. (3) Suspension formed by a quantity of powder mixed into a liquid in which the solid is only slightly soluble.

Small Diameter Hose (SDH) — Hose of ¾ to 2 inches (20 mm to 50 mm) in diameter; used for fire fighting purposes. *Also known as* Small Line.

Small Line — *See* Small Diameter Hose.

Smallpox — Serious, contagious, and sometimes fatal infectious disease; there is no specific treatment, and the only prevention is vaccination.

Smoke — Visible products of combustion resulting from the incomplete combustion of carbonaceous materials; composed of small particles of carbon, tarry particles, and condensed water vapor suspended in the atmosphere, which vary in color and density depending on the types of material burning and the amount of oxygen.

Smoke Alarm — Device designed to sound an alarm when the products of combustion are present in the room where the device is installed. The alarm is built into the device rather than being a separate system.

Smoke Building — *See* Smokehouse.

Smoke-Control System — Engineered system designed to control smoke by using mechanical fans to produce airflows and pressure differences across smoke barriers, in order to limit and direct smoke movement.

Smoke Curtains — Salvage covers placed in stairways, halls, or doors to prevent movement of smoke into clear areas.

Smoke Damper — Device installed in air ducts that penetrate a vertical or horizontal assembly such as a wall, floor, or ceiling; designed and constructed to restrict the movement of smoke between compartments. *See* Duct and Fire Damper.

Smoke Detector — Alarm-initiating device designed to actuate when visible or invisible products of combustion (other than fire gases) are present in the room or space where the unit is installed.

Smoke Diver — Highly trained user of a self-contained breathing apparatus (SCBA).

Smoke Diver School — School that provides the firefighter with 25 to 30 hours of sequential training in self-contained breathing apparatus use.

Smoke Ejector — Blower device (ducted fan) used primarily to expel smoke from burning buildings; sometimes used to blow fresh air into a building to assist in purging smoke or other contaminants. Powered by gasoline, electricity, or hydraulics; may be used in conjunction with a flexible duct.

Smoke Explosion — Form of fire gas ignition; the ignition of accumulated flammable products of combustion.

Smokehouse — (1) Specially designed fire training building that is filled with smoke to simulate working under live fire conditions; used for SCBA and search and rescue training. *Also known as* Smoke Building. (2) A building used for the smoking of meat.

Smoke Jumpers — Wildland firefighters who are deployed into remote wildland fires and other emergencies by parachuting from aircraft.

Smoke Management System — System that limits the exposure of building occupants to smoke; may include elements such as compartmentation, control of smoke migration from the affected area, and a means of removing smoke to the exterior of the building.

Smoke Obscuration — Act of being hidden by smoke.

Smokeproof Enclosures — Stairways that are designed to limit the penetration of smoke, heat, and toxic gases from a fire on a floor of a building into the stairway, and that serve as part of a means of egress. *See* Means of Egress.

Smoke Room — Enclosed area into which mechanically generated smoke is introduced and in which firefighters perform training exercises while wearing SCBA.

Smoke Shaft — Fire resistive shaft or tower, with or without an exhaust fan at the top, for the purpose of removing smoke directly to the outside from any of the floors served that may become involved in a fire. Smoke shafts are often used in conjunction with a smokeproof enclosure.

Smoke Tower — Fully enclosed escape stairway that exits directly onto a public way; these enclosures are either mechanically pressurized or they require the user to exit the building onto an outside balcony before entering the stairway. *Also known as* Smokeproof Enclosure or Smokeproof Stairway.

Smoke Tube — Device containing stannic or titanium tetrachloride used to produce nontoxic smoke for testing a facepiece seal.

Smoldering — Fire burning without flame and barely spreading.

Smoldering Phase — *See* Hot Smoldering Phase.

Smothering — Act of excluding oxygen from a fuel.

Snag — Standing dead tree or part of a dead tree from which at least the leaves and smaller branches have fallen.

Snap Coupling — Coupling set with nonthreaded male and female components; when a connection is made, two spring-loaded hooks on the female coupling engage a raised ring around the shank of the male coupling.

Snap Link — *See* Carabiner.

Social Need — Middle need in Maslow's Hierarchy of Needs; the need to belong to a group or to have some means of identification.

Society of Automotive Engineers (SAE) — Organization of engineers in the automotive industry; the initials SAE coupled with a number (e.g. SAE 30) are used to indicate the viscosity of motor oil.

Sodium Saccharin — Chemical substance used in qualitative facepiece fit taste tests.

Soffit — Lower horizontal surface such as the undersurface of eaves or cornices.

Soft Sleeve Hose — Large diameter, collapsible piece of hose used to connect a fire pump to a pressurized water supply source; sometimes incorrectly referred to as *soft suction hose.*

Soft Target — Term used to define a facility or other target that is undefended or unprotected against attack from a potential adversary; examples include most public assembly areas such as churches, schools, bus stations, and shopping districts.

Soft Tissue Injury — Damage to human tissue that encloses bones or joints, such as muscles, tendons, or ligaments.

Software — (1) Computer program that performs a specific function or set of functions. (2) In rope rescue, refers to nylon webbing, rope, and harnesses.

SOG — *See* Standard Operating Guideline and Standard Operating Procedure.

Soil Stack — Vertical pipe which runs from the horizontal soil pipe to the house drain to carry waste, including that from water closets.

Solar Heat Energy — Energy transmitted from the sun in the form of electromagnetic radiation.

SOLAS — *See* International Convention for the Safety of Life at Sea.

Sole — Horizontal wooden member that rests on the top of a foundation wall of a building; the vertical framing of the exterior walls and the first-floor wooden floor joists are supported by these members. *Also known as* Sill.

Sole Plate — (1) Member against which the vertical load of a shore is ultimately exerted. (2) Surface contact piece that distributes loads delivered by struts.

Solicit — To approach with a request.

Solid — Substance that has a definite shape and size; the molecules of a solid generally have very little mobility.

Solid Core Door — Door whose entire core is filled with solid material.

Solid Stream — Hose stream that stays together as a solid mass, as opposed to a fog or spray stream; a solid stream is produced by a smooth bore nozzle and should not be confused with a straight stream.

Solubility — Degree to which a solid, liquid, or gas dissolves in a solvent (usually water).

Soluble — Capable of being dissolved in a liquid (usually water). *See* Immiscible, Insoluble, Miscibility, and Water Solubility.

Somatic — Pertaining to all tissues other than reproductive cells.

SOP — *See* Standard Operating Procedure.

Sorbent — Material, compound, or system that holds contaminants by adsorption or absorption. In *adsorption,* the contaminant molecule is retained on the surface of the sorbent granule by physical attraction; in *absorption*, a solid or liquid is taken up or absorbed into the sorbent material.

Sorption — Method of removing contaminants; used in vapor- and gas-removing respirators.

Sounding — (1) Process of testing structural integrity of a roof or floor of a building, or of locating underlying supporting members, by striking the surface of the assembly with the blunt end of a hand tool. (2) Name of the measurement of the depth of water in which a vessel is floating.

Source — *See* Sender.

Southern Building Code Congress International (SBCCI) — Organization that provided the *Standard Building Code* along with mechanical, plumbing, and fire prevention codes for city and state adoption. SBCCI was found mostly in the southern states. It has joined with the Building Officials and Code Administrators International, Inc. (BOCA) and the International Conference of Building Officials (ICBO) to form the International Code Council (ICC).

SPAAT — *See* Skin Penetrating Agent Applicator Tool®.

Space frames — Aluminum skeletons that are similar to aircraft frames, upon which the aluminum, plastic, or composite skin of the vehicle's body is attached; the internal structure of these space frames provides the structural support for the vehicle, while the skin provides aerodynamics, styling, and protection from the elements.

Spacer — Length of timber that keeps a breast timber from shifting vertically.

Spalling — Expansion of excess moisture within concrete due to exposure to the heat of a fire, resulting in tensile forces within the concrete, causing it to break apart. The expansion causes sections of the concrete surface to violently disintegrate, resulting in explosive pitting or chipping destruction of the material's surface.

Spandrel — Part of a wall between the head of a window and the sill of the window above it.

Spanish Windlass — Tool, such as a stick or dowel, used for post-tensioning lines by twisting.

Spanner Wrench — Small tool primarily used to tighten or loosen hose couplings; can also be used as a prying tool or a gas key.

Span of Control — Maximum number of subordinates that that one individual can effectively supervise; ranges from three to seven individuals or functions, with five generally established as optimum.

Spar — Principal, span-wide aircraft structural member of an airfoil or control surface.

Spark — (1) *See* Buff. (2) Small bit of solid material heated to incandescence.

Speaking Diaphragm — Device on some SCBA facepieces that aids oral communication.

Spec 51 — *See* Pressure Intermodal Tank.

Spec Building — Building built without a tenant or occupant. *Spec* is short for *speculation.*

Special Duty — Type of obligation that an inspector assumes by providing expert advice or assistance to a person; this obligation may make the inspector liable if it creates a situation in which a person moves from a position of safety to a position of danger by relying upon the expertise of the inspector.

Special Fire Hazard — Fire hazard arising from processes or operations that are peculiar to the individual occupancy.

Special Police — *See* Fire Police.

Special Protective Clothing — (1) Chemical protective clothing specially designed to protect against a specific hazard or corrosive substance. *See* Chemical Protective Clothing (CPC) and Personal Protective Equipment (PPE). (2) High-temperature protective clothing, including approach, proximity, and fire entry suits.

Special Rescue Technician — *See* Technical Rescuer.

Special Service — Fire company's assignment to a special detail, such as removing water from a basement or directing traffic.

Special Service Unit — *See* Emergency Truck.

Specification Marking — Stencil on the exterior of tank cars indicating the standards to which the tank car was built; may also be found on intermodal containers and cargo tank trucks.

Specifications — (1) Detailed information provided by a manufacturer on the function, care, and maintenance of equipment or apparatus. (2) Detailed list of requirements prepared by a purchaser and presented to a manufacturer or distributor when purchasing equipment or apparatus.

Specific Gravity — Weight of a substance compared to the weight of an equal volume of water at a given temperature. A specific gravity less than1 indicates a substance lighter than water; a specific gravity greater than 1 indicates a substance heavier than water. *See* Physical Properties and Vapor Density.

Specific Heat — Amount of heat required to raise the temperature of a specified quantity of a material, and the amount of heat necessary to raise the temperature of an identical amount of water by the same number of degrees.

Spectrochemical Analysis — Test method by which contaminants suspended in oil can be detected; typically expresses contaminant level in parts per million (ppm).

Speed Brakes — *See* Spoilers.

Speedometer — Dashboard gauge that measures the speed at which the vehicle is traveling.

Spherical Pressure Vessel — Round-shaped fixed facility pressure vessel. *See* Pressure Vessel.

Spheroid Tank — Round- or oval-shaped fixed facility low-pressure storage tank. *See* Low-Pressure Storage Tank, Noded Spheroid Tank, and Pressure Storage Tank.

Sphygmomanometer — Device for measuring blood pressure; blood pressure cuff.

Spice — Attention-getter or energizer that gets the audience's attention during a fire and life safety presentation.

Spider Strap — *See* Head Harness.

Spinal Column — Flexible bony structure that supports the central part of the body and encloses the spinal cord.

Spinal Cord — Part of the central nervous system contained within the spinal column, extending from the base of the brain to the coccyx.

Spinal Immobilization — Stabilizing the patient's cervical spine (neck and back) to prevent severing of the spinal cord under the assumption, based on mechanism of injury or actual findings, that the patient has an injury. *Also known as* Spinal Precautions.

Spinal Precautions — *See* Spinal Immobilization.

Spirometer Test — Medical test used to measure pulmonary capacity.

Splash Guard — Deflecting shield sometimes installed on tank trailers to protect meters, valves, and other components.

Splash Pattern — Characteristic pattern left on a wall by an accelerant splashed there; usually in the shape of an inverted V.

Splice — (1) To join two ropes or cables by weaving the strands together. (2) Process of joining two covers into a larger or longer one with a leakproof seal.

Splint — Support used to immobilize a fracture or restrict movement of a body part.

Split Drop — Two retardant drops made from one compartment at a time, from an air tanker with a multicompartment tank.

Split Lay — Hose lay deployed by two pumpers, one making a forward lay and the other making a reverse lay from the same point.

Split-Sash — Two-piece window split horizontally in the middle.

Splitter Valve — Valve installed to divide the pipeline manifold.

Spoilage — Decomposition of grain or other perishable items.

Spoilers — Movable aerodynamic devices or plates on aircraft, which extend into the airstream to break up the smoothness of flow and thus increase drag and decrease lift. This process results in reduced airspeed during descent and assists in slowing the aircraft after landing. *Also known as* Speed Brakes.

Spoliation — Term which refers to evidence that is destroyed, damaged, altered, or otherwise not preserved by someone who has responsibility for the evidence.

Spontaneous Combustion — *See* Spontaneous Ignition.

Spontaneous Heating — Heating resulting from chemical or bacterial action in combustible materials that may lead to spontaneous ignition. *See* Spontaneous Ignition.

Spontaneous Ignition — Combustion of a material initiated by an internal chemical or biological reaction producing enough heat to cause the material to ignite. *Also known as* Spontaneous Combustion.

Spores — Airborne reproductive particles produced by plants that may or may not be airborne.

Spot Fire — Wildland fire started outside the perimeter of a main fire; typically caused by flying sparks or embers landing outside the main fire area. *See* Spotting.

Spotter — (1) Experienced firefighter who guides and directs bulldozer operations for wildland fire fighting operations. (2) Firefighter who walks behind a backing apparatus to provide guidance for the driver/operator. *Also known as* Swamper.

Spotting — (1) Positioning the apparatus in a location that provides the utmost efficiency for operating on the fireground. (2) Positioning a ladder to reach an object or person. (3) Behavior of a wildland fire that produces sparks or embers that are carried by the wind to start new fires beyond the main fire. *See* Spot Fire.

Spray — Application of water through specially designed nozzles in the form of finely divided particles.

Spray Curtain Nozzle — Fog nozzle mounted to the underside of an elevating platform to provide a protective shield against convected heat for firefighters operating in the platform.

Sprinkler — Water flow discharge device in a sprinkler system; consists of a threaded intake nipple, a discharge orifice, a heat-actuated plug, and a deflector that creates an effective fire stream pattern that is suitable for fire control. *See* Automatic Sprinkler System.

Sprinkler Block — *See* Sprinkler Wedge.

Sprinkler Connection — *See* Fire Department Connection.

Sprinkler Kit — Collection of sprinklers, wedges, tongs, and wrenches used to close or replace open sprinklers.

Sprinkler Riser — Vertical pipe used to carry water to the sprinkler system.

Sprinkler System — Fixed piping system that is designed to discharge water in the event of a fire. *See* Automatic Sprinkler System.

Sprinkler System Supervision Systems — *See* Waterflow Alarm.

Sprinkler Tongs — Tool used to stop the flow of water from a sprinkler.

Sprinkler Wedge — Wedge-shaped piece of wood used to stop the flow of water from individual sprinklers. *Also known as* Sprinkler Block.

Sprinkler Wrench — Special wrench designed for tightening or loosening sprinklers.

Spurs — Metal points at the end of a ladder or staypole.

Squad — *See* Rescue Company.

Squeegee — Rubber-edged broomlike device used in salvage to assist in the removal of water from floors; used by pushing the water to a drain, disposal area, or collection place.

S/S — Prefix to the name of a vessel with a steam propulsion plant.

Stability — Tendency of a floating vessel to return to an upright position when inclined from the vertical by an external force, such as winds or waves. When a vessel returns to or remains at rest after being acted upon, it is either in stable or neutral equilibrium; if it continues to move unchecked in reaction to the external force, it is in unstable equilibrium. If an unstable vessel does not find a point of stable or neutral stability, it continues to incline until it capsizes. *See* Free Surface Effect, Longitudinal Stability, and Static Stability.

Stabilization — (1) Process of providing additional support to key places between an object of entrapment and the ground or other solid anchor points, in order to prevent unwanted movement. (2) Stage of an incident when the immediate problem or emergency has been controlled, contained, or extinguished.

Stabilizer — (1) Device that transfers the center of gravity of an apparatus and prevents it from tipping as the aerial device, hydraulic lifting boom, gin pole, or A-frame is extended away from the centerline of the chassis. *Also known as* Outrigger or Stabilizing Jack. (2) Chemical added to an unstable substance to prevent a violent reaction. *Also known as* Inhibitor. (3) Airfoil on an airplane, used to provide stability; for example, the aft horizontal surface to which the elevators are hinged (horizontal stabilizer), and the fixed vertical surface to which the rudder is hinged (vertical stabilizer).

Stabilizer Foot — Flat metal plate attached to the bottom of the aerial apparatus stabilizer to provide firm footing on the stabilizing surface. *Also known as* Stabilizer Boot.

Stabilizer Pad — Unattached flat metal plate that is larger in area than the stabilizer foot; placed on the ground beneath the intended resting point of the stabilizer foot, in order to provide better weight distribution. *Also known as* Jack Pad or Jack Plate.

Stable Atmosphere — Condition of the atmosphere in which the temperature decrease with increasing altitude is less than the dry adiabatic lapse rate; in this condition, the atmosphere tends to suppress large-scale vertical motion.

Stack — Ducting through which exhaust gases and often supply gas are routed; a chimney. *See* Economizer and Fiddley.

Stack Action — See Stack Effect.

Stack Effect — (1) Tendency of any vertical shaft within a tall building to act as a chimney or "smokestack", by channeling heat, smoke, and other products of combustion upward due to convection. *Also known as* Stack Action. (2) Phenomenon of a strong air draft moving from ground level to the roof level of a building; affected by building height, configuration, and temperature differences between inside and outside air. *Also known as* Chimney Effect.

Stack Valve — Type of multidirectional valve used in an aerial device hydraulic system.

Staff Organization — Portion of the fire department that supports the line organization.

Staged Incident — *See* Mock Incident.

Staging — (1) Standardized process or procedure by which available resources responding to a fire or other emergency incident are held in reserve at a location away from the incident while awaiting assignment. (2) In high-rise fire fighting, the incident management system (IMS) term for the area within the building where relief crews are assembled and spare equipment is stockpiled, usually established two floors below the fire floor. Staging may also include a first-aid station and rehab.

Staging Area — Prearranged, temporary strategic location, away from the emergency scene, where units assemble and wait until they are assigned a position on the emergency scene; these resources (personnel, apparatus, tools, and equipment) must then be able to respond within three minutes of being assigned. Staging area managers report to the incident commander or operations section chief, if one has been established.

Staging Area Manager — Company officer of the first-arriving company at the staging who takes command of the area and is responsible for communicating available resources and resource needs to the operations section chief.

Stair Nosing — Plate that wraps around the front edge of the stair.

Stair Pressurization System — System that enables a stairwell to have separate air-handling controls that can be adjusted to increase the air pressure in the stairway so that the smoke, heat, and other products of combustion on the fire floor will not enter the stairwell.

Standard — (1) Criterion documents that are developed to serve as models or examples of desired performance or behaviors, and that contain requirements and specifications outlining minimum levels of performance, protection, or construction. No one is required to meet the requirements set forth in standards unless those standards are legally adopted by the authority having jurisdiction, in which case they become law. *See* Code and Regulations. (2) That part of an educational objective that describes the minimum level of performance that a learner must meet in accomplishing the performance/behavior.

Standard Apparatus — Apparatus that conforms to the standards set forth by the National Fire Protection Association® standards on fire apparatus design.

Standard Cubic Feet Per Minute (SCFM) — Volume of material based on the standard cubic foot flowing past or through a specified measuring point.

Standard Cubic Foot (scf) — Amount of air in a cubic foot at 14.7 psia and 60 degrees Fahrenheit.

Standard Deviation — Average of the degree to which the scores in a test deviate from the mean.

Standard Error — *See* Sampling Error.

Standard of Care — Degree of care that a reasonably prudent person should exercise in the same or similar circumstances; an important consideration in legal matters concerning negligence. *See* Negligence.

Standard Operating Guideline (SOG) — *See* Standard Operating Procedure (SOP).

Standard Operating Procedure (SOP) — Predetermined method or rule that an organization uses to perform routine functions, in addition to operating actions used to perform at every possible type of emergency incident. Usually these procedures are written in a policies and procedures handbook, and all firefighters should be well versed in their content. An SOP may specify the functional limitations of fire brigade members in performing emergency operations. *Also known as* Operating Instruction (OI), Predetermined Procedures, or Standard Operating Guideline (SOG).

Standard Response — Predetermined amount of resources that will be dispatched to the report of an emergency.

Standard Thread — National Standard hose threads.

Standard Time-Temperature Curve — Plot on a graph of temperature versus time used in structural fire tests. *Also known as* Time-Temperature Curve.

Standard Transportation Commodity Code — Numerical code on the waybill used by the rail industry to identify the commodity. *Also known as* STCC Number.

Stand By — (1) To remain immediately available. (2) To relocate to another fire station and cover that district for additional emergencies in the area. (3) To clear the airwaves for a broadcast.

Standardization — Process of making or creating things that meet an established criteria.

Standing Block — Block, in a block and tackle system, that is attached to a solid support and from which the fall line leads.

Standing Part — Part of a rope between the working end and the running part.

Standpipe Hose — Single-jacket lined hose that is preconnected to a standpipe; used primarily by building occupants to mount a quick attack on an incipient fire.

Standpipe System — Wet or dry system of pipes in a large single-story or multistory building, with fire hose outlets installed in different areas or on different levels of a building to be used by firefighters and/or building occupants. Allows for the quick deployment of hoselines during fire fighting operations. *See* Dry Standpipe System, Riser, and Wet Standpipe System.

Starboard — Right-hand side of a vessel as a person faces forward. *Also known as* Starboard Side.

Static — (1) Stationary; without movement. (2) Refers to the amount of stretch built into a rope. Static ropes have relatively little stretch; they are ideal for rescue work where stretch becomes a hazard and a nuisance, but should not be used where long falls could be anticipated before being stopped by the rope.

Static Electricity — Accumulation of electrical charges on opposing surfaces, created by the separation of unlike materials or by the movement of surfaces.

Static Load — Load that is steady, motionless, constant, or applied gradually.

Static Pressure — (1) Potential energy that is available to force water through pipes and fittings, fire hose, and adapters. (2) Pressure at a given point in a water system when no water is flowing. *See* Normal Operating Pressure.

Static Rope — Rope that will stretch a relatively short distance under load.

Static Source — Body of water that is not under pressure (other than atmospheric) or in a supply piping system, and must be drafted from in order to be used. Static sources include ponds, lakes, rivers, wells, etc.

Static Stability — Ability of a vessel to initially resist heeling from the upright position. Initial stability characteristics hold true only for relatively small angles of inclination; at larger angles (over 10 degrees), the ability of a vessel to resist inclining moments is determined by its overall stability characteristics. *Also known* as Initial Stability. *See* Longitudinal Stability and Stability.

Static Stress — Stress imposed on the aerial device when it is at rest.

Static Water Supply — Supply of water at rest that does not provide a pressure head for fire suppression but may be employed as a suction source for fire pumps; for example, water in a reservoir, pond, or cistern.

Statistics — Numerical data.

Station Bill — List of all crew members showing where they should be for the various operations involved in operating a vessel; shows the duty stations and duties of the crew, by rank.

Statute — Federal or state/provincial legislative act that becomes law; prescribes conduct, defines crimes, and promotes public good and welfare. *Also known as* Statutory Law. *See* Copyright Law, Law, and Legislative Law.

Staypole — Pole attached to long extension ladders to assist in raising and steadying the ladder; some poles are permanently attached, and some are removable. *Also known as* Tormentor Pole.

STCC Number — *See* Standard Transportation Commodity Code.

Steady-State Burning Phase — (1) Phase of the fire in which sufficient oxygen and fuel are available for fire growth and open burning, to a point where total involvement is possible. (2) Phase of the fire in which the rate of heat release is constant with respect to time.

Steam Conversion — Physical changing of water from a liquid to a gaseous form; water expands in size 1,700 times when it converts to steam.

Steamer Connection — Large-diameter outlet, usually 4½ inches (115 mm), at a hydrant or at the base of an elevated water storage container.

Steeple Raise — *See* Auditorium Raise.

Steering Gear — All the apparatus by which a vessel is steered; includes the wheel, rudder, and any ropes or chains connected to them.

Steiner Tunnel — Test apparatus used in the determination of flame spread ratings; consists of a horizontal test furnace 25 feet (7.6 m) long, 17½ inches (445 mm) wide, and 12 inches (305 mm) high that is used to observe flame travel. A 5,000 Btu (5 270 kJ) flame is produced in the tunnel, and the extent of flame travel across the surface of the test material is observed through ports in the side of the furnace.

Steiner Tunnel Test — Test to determine the flame-spread ratings of various materials. The test apparatus consists of a horizontal furnace 25 feet (7.6 m) long, 17½ inches (445 mm) wide, and 12 inches (305 mm) high; a 5,000 Btu (5 270 kJ) flame is produced in the tunnel, and the extent of flame travel across the surface of the test material is observed through ports in the side of the furnace. *See* Flame Spread Rating.

STEL — *See* Short-Term Exposure Limit.

Stem — (1) Part of a lock cylinder that activates the bolt or latch as the key is turned. *Also known as* Tailpiece. (2) Rod-type portion of a hydrant, between the operating nut and the valve. (3) Introductory statement in a multiple-choice test item.

Stem Light — Elevating floodlighting tower.

Stem Wall — In platform frame construction, an exterior wall between the foundation and the first floor of a building.

Step Block — Piece of cribbing with a tapered end, specially designed for stabilization of automobiles. *Also known as* Step Chock.

Step Chock — *See* Step Block.

Stern — Back end or rear of a vessel.

Stevedore — *See* Longshoreman.

Stile — Vertical member of a window sash.

Still Alarm — Response to an emergency in which no audible alarm is sounded at dispatch; usually a one- or two-company response. *Also known as* Silent Alarm.

Stimsonite® Markers — Raised reflective marker typically used as a roadway safety device; blue-colored markers are used by the fire service to mark hydrant locations.

Stinger — Bright, one-directional, moving warning light.

Stoichiometric ratio — Ideal fuel-to-air ratio at which complete combustion of fuels occurs without byproducts of combustion; does not naturally occur. *Also known as* Optimum Ratio.

Stokes Basket — Wire or plastic basket-type litter suitable for transporting patients from locations where a standard litter would not be easily secured, such as a pile of rubble, a structural collapse, or the upper floor of a building; may be used with a harness for lifting.

Stoma — Small opening, especially an artificially created opening.

Stop, Drop, and Roll — Fire and life safety behavior to be performed when one's clothing or hair catches fire.

Stops — Wood or metal pieces that prevent the fly section of a ladder from being extended too far.

Stopway Area — Area beyond the runway end capable of supporting aircraft that overshoot the runway on aborted takeoff or landing without causing structural damage to the aircraft. *Also known as* Overrun Area.

Storage Tank — Storage vessel that is larger than 60 gallons (227 L) and is located in a fixed location.

Story — Space in a building between two adjacent floor levels, or between a floor and the roof.

Storz Coupling — Nonthreaded (sexless) coupling commonly found on large-diameter hose.

Straight Jack — Stabilizing device that extends straight down from the chassis.

Straight Ladder — One-section ladder. *Also known as* Single Ladder.

Straight Lay — Hose laid from the hydrant or water source to the fire.

Straight Stream — Most compact discharge pattern that a fog nozzle can produce; similar to but not as compact as a solid stream.

Strainers — Wire or other metal guards used to prevent debris from clogging the intake hose of fire pumps.

Straining Piece — Length of timber that keeps pressure on the breast timbers of a flying shore.

Strap — Metal piece used to hold together joints in heavy timber construction.

Straps — Strips of webbing with buckles for securing ladders, improvising step ladders, and other tying purposes.

Strategic Goals — Broad statements of desired achievement to control an incident; achieved by the completion of tactical objectives. *See* Strategy, Tactical Objectives, and Tactics.

Strategic Planning — Process for identifying long-term goals and objectives for a program or department, usually for a period of five years.

Strategy — Overall plan for incident attack and control established by the incident commander (IC). *See* Defensive Strategy, Nonintervention Strategy, Offensive Strategy, and Tactics.

Stratification — Formation of smoke into layers as a result of differences in density with respect to height, with low density layers on the top and high density layers on the bottom.

Stratum — Sheet-like layer of rock or earth; numerous other layers, each with different characteristics, are typically found above and below.

Stress — (1) Factors that work against the strength of any piece of apparatus or equipment. (2) State of tension put on a shipping container by internal or external chemical, mechanical, or thermal change. (3) Any condition causing bodily or mental tension. *See* Critical Incident Stress (CIS), Physiological Stress, Post-Traumatic Stress Disorder (PTSD), and Psychological Stress.

Stressed Skin — Outer surface of a structure when it provides lateral support.

Stress Test — Test in which a person's vital functions are monitored while the person labors.

Stretcher — Portable device that allows two or more persons to move the sick or injured, by carrying or rolling, while keeping the patient immobile.

Stretch Hose — To lay out hose as a line or advance it into a building.

Strike — Metal plate mounted in the door frame that receives the latch or deadbolt.

Strike Team — Specified combinations of the same kind and type of resources with common communications and a leader; usually composed of either engines, hand crews, or bulldozers, but may be composed of any resource of the same kind and type. Exception — *see* Enhanced Strike Team.

Striking Tools — Tools characterized by large, weighted heads on handles; includes axes, battering rams, ram bars, punches, mallets, hammers, sledgehammers or mauls, chisels, automatic center punches, and picks.

Stringer — (1) Horizontal structural member supporting joists and resting on vertical supports. (2) General construction term referring to the member on each side of a stair that supports the treads and risers. *See* Girders and Longeron.

Stripped Territory — Area that has been completely depleted of fire protection apparatus and staffing.

Strip Ventilation — *See* Trench Ventilation or Trenching (2).

Strobe — High-intensity flashing light.

Strong Oxidizer — Material that encourages a strong reaction (by readily accepting electrons) from a reducing agent (fuel). *See* Oxidizer.

Strong, Tight Container — Packaging used to ship materials of low radioactivity. *See* Excepted Packaging, Industrial Packaging, Packaging (1), Type A Packaging, and Type B Packaging.

Structural Abuse — Using or changing a building beyond its originally designed capabilities.

Structural Engineer — Licensed professional engineer trained in structural stability.

Structural Instability — Degree to which a specific structure has lost its integrity.

Structural Triage — Process of inspecting and classifying structures according to their defensibility/indefensibility, based on their situation, their construction, and the immediately adjacent fuels.

Structure — Constructed object; usually a building standing free and aboveground.

Structure Fire — Fire that involves a building, enclosed structure, vehicle, vessel, aircraft, or like property.

Structure Hazard Assessment — Assessment performed by a structural engineer and hazardous materials specialist to determine the current condition of the structure.

Structure Protection Group/Sector Supervisor — Individual responsible for supervising assigned strike teams, firefighters, or single resources in the defense of structures from wildland fire.

Strut — (1) Aircraft structural components designed to absorb or distribute abrupt compression or tension, such as the landing gear forces. (2) In a shore, any member that holds either a vertical or horizontal compression load.

Stud — Vertical structural member within a wall in frame buildings; most are made of wood, but some are made of light-gauge metal.

Student — Any person involved in a formal learning process; the most important member of any class, in that all the activities and efforts are directed toward enabling him or her to learn.

Study Session — Formal, open meeting of a legislative body to study the merits of proposed legislation, and to ask questions of the fire and life safety code official and the public regarding the provisions of the proposed code. *See* Code.

Study Sheet — Instructional document designed to generate student interest in a topic and explain to students the specific areas to study.

Subbasement — Basement below the level of a first basement.

Subcutaneous Layer — Bottom layer of skin, consisting of fatty tissues that insulate the body and store excess calories.

Subhead — Headline that is subordinate to or of lesser importance than the main headline; generally printed in smaller type than the main headline.

Subjective Test — Type of test in which a learner is free to organize, analyze, revise, redesign, or evaluate a problem based on his or her perceptions and understanding; measures higher cognitive levels than other types. Common types of subjective tests are essays and term papers. Different but equally qualified assessors will judge the quality and characteristics of a learner's work differently (subjectivity) and may therefore award different scores. The results may be influenced by the subject being tested, the test itself, the tester, or other outside factors. *See* Test.

Sublimation — Vaporization of a material from the solid to vapor state without passing through the liquid state.

Submersible Pump — Pump capable of operating when placed underwater.

Subsidence — Sinking or settling of land due to various natural and human-caused factors, such as the removal of underground water or oil.

Subsidiary Label — Label indicating a secondary hazard associated with a material. *See* Primary Label.

Subsonic — Slower than the speed of sound.

Substance Abuse — Uncontrolled or excessive use of a drug by an individual.

Substrate — Layer of material between a roof deck and the roof covering that may or may not be bonded to the roof covering; the most common substrate is roofing felt or tar paper.

Subsurface Fire — Fire that consumes the organic material beneath the ground, such as a peat fire or burning roots.

Subsurface Fuel — All combustible materials below the surface litter that normally support smoldering combustion without flame; examples include tree or shrub roots, peat, and sawdust.

Subsurface Injection — Application method where foam is pumped into the bottom of a burning fuel storage tank and allowed to float to the top to form a foam blanket on the surface of the fuel. *See* Direct Injection and Semisubsurface Injection.

Sucking Chest Wound — Wound in which the chest wall is penetrated, causing air to accumulate in the pleural cavity.

Suction — (1) Misnomer used to describe the drafting process. (2) Inlet side of the pump that is better referred to as the *Intake*. (3) *See* Hard Suction Hose.

Suffocate — To die from being unable to breathe; to be deprived of air or to stop respiration, as by strangulation or asphyxiation.

Suitcase Bomb — Small, suitcase-or backpack-sized nuclear weapon. *See* Improvised Nuclear Device.

Sulfur Dioxide (SO$_2$) — Colorless gas produced when sulfur-containing materials burn; its pervasive, highly irritating rotten-egg odor makes it detectable below its IDLH level of 100 ppm.

Summary — Lesson plan component in which an instructor restates or reemphasizes key points with the learners; this is accomplished by methods such as asking questions, guiding review, and having learners recall relationships, make comparisons, or draw conclusions. *See* Lesson Plan.

Summary Offense — Lowest form of offense in most legal systems; minor infractions of laws or local ordinances. Offender is typically served a citation on the spot where the violation occurred.

Summative Evaluation — (1) Comprehensive approach to evaluation by using test results, instructor observations, and the course critique to determine total course effectiveness. (2) Evaluation that sums up the effects and effectiveness of a program or teaching activity at the conclusion of a training course or session. *Also known as* Posttest. *See* Evaluation (2).

Sump — (1) Low point of a tank at which the emergency valve or outlet valve is attached. (2) Area in the air-purification system that receives drainage.

Sump Basin — Pit or reservoir, often connected to a drain, that serves as a receptacle for water; can be improvised from salvage covers, ladders, and pike poles.

Sunset Provision — Clause in a law or ordinance that stipulates the periodic review of government agencies and programs in order to continue their existence. *See* Ordinance.

Sunshine Laws — Local, state, or provincial laws that require public notification and open attendance of government meetings.

Sunstroke — *See* Heat Stroke.

Super Bus — School bus with an extra-large carrying capacity; may carry up to 84 people seated and over 100 people if standing is permissible.

Superfund Amendments and Reauthorization Act (SARA) — U.S. law that reauthorized the Comprehensive Environmental Response, Compensation and Liability Act (CERCLA) to continue cleanup activities around the country; included several site-specific amendments, definition clarifications, and technical requirements. Enacted in 1986.

Superplasticizer — Admixture used with concrete or mortar mix to make it workable, pliable, and soft while using relatively little water.

Superior — Near the head; above.

Supersonic — Faster than the speed of sound.

Superstructure — Enclosed structure built above the main deck that extends from one side of a vessel to the other. *See* House.

Supervise — To oversee the work of others or another.

Supervised Circuit — Alarm circuit on which a minute electrical current is constantly flowing; when this current is shorted or interrupted, an alarm or trouble signal is initiated.

Supervisor — (1) A person who is responsible for directing the performance of other people or employees. (2) IMS term for the individual responsible for command of a division, group, or sector.

Supervisory Circuit — Electronic circuit within a fire protection system that monitors the system's readiness and transmits a signal when there is a problem with the system.

Supine — Lying horizontal in a face upward position.

Supplemental Pumping — Pumping water from a stronger point in the water system to the units at the fire, or pumping it back into the water system where it is weak. Used when a large fire overwhelms the water supply system.

Supplied Air Respirator (SAR) — Atmosphere-supplying respirator for which the source of breathing air is not designed to be carried by the user; not certified for fire fighting operations. *Also known as* Airline Respirator System. *See* Self-Contained Breathing Apparatus (SCBA).

Supply/Exhaust Ventilation — Combined supply and exhaust system of mechanical ventilation that is generally used in the ventilation of passenger quarters. *See* Ventilation.

Supply Hose — Hose between the water source and the attack pumper, laid to provide large volumes of water at low pressure. *Also known as* Feeder Line or Relay-Supply Hose.

Supply Unit — Functional unit within the support branch of the logistics section of an incident command system; responsible for ordering equipment/supplies required for incident operations.

Support Branch — Branch within the logistics section of an incident command system; responsible for providing the personnel, equipment, and supplies to support incident operations. Components include the supply unit, facilities unit, and ground support units.

Supported Tip — Operation of an aerial device with the tip of the device or the platform resting on another object, such as a window ledge or roofline.

Supports — Devices, generally adjustable in height, that are used to support the front end of a semitrailer in an approximately level position when disconnected from the towing vehicle. *Formerly known as* Dollies, Landing Fears, Legs, and Props.

Support (Cold) Zone — Area that surrounds the limited access (warm) zone and is restricted to emergency response personnel who are not working in either the restricted (hot) zone or the limited access (warm) zone. This zone may include the portable equipment and personnel staging areas and the command post; the outer boundary of this area should be cordoned off to the public.

Suppressant — *See* Fire Suppressant.

Suppressing — Preventing the release of flammable vapors, to reduce the possibility of ignition or reignition.

Suppression — *See* Fire Suppression.

Suppression-Generated Pattern — Fire pattern left as a result of the way the fire was extinguished during fire-suppression efforts.

Suppression System — System designed to act directly upon the hazard to mitigate or eliminate it, not simply to detect its presence and/or initiate an alarm.

Surface Application — Application method where finished foam is applied directly onto the surface of the burning fuel or unignited fuel spill.

Surface Bolt — Sliding bolt installed on the surface of a door.

Surface-Burning Characteristic — Speed at which flame will spread over the surface of a material.

Surface Contamination Contamination that is limited to the surface of a material. *See* Contaminant, Contamination, and Decontamination.

Surface Fire — Wildland fire that burns loose and includes dead branches, fallen leaves, needles, duff, stubble, grass, and low vegetation.

Surface Fuel — Fuel that contacts the surface of the ground; consists of duff, leaf and needle litter, dead branch material, downed logs, bark, tree cones, and low-stature living plants. These are the materials normally scraped away to construct a fireline. *Also known as* Ground Fuel.

Surface Hazards — Class of hazards that includes debris on the ground, trip hazards, and unstable footing.

Surface Systems — System of construction in which the building consists primarily of an enclosing surface, and in which the stresses resulting from the applied loads occur within the surface-bearing wall structures.

Surface Tension — (1) Force minimizing a liquid surface's area. (2) The effect of a surfactant on the water/concentrate solution; allows the water to spread more rapidly over the surface of Class A fuels and to penetrate organic fuels.

Surface-To-Mass Ratio — Ratio of the surface area of the fuel to the mass of the fuel.

Surface Victims — Victims not trapped by the structure, usually found on top of structural debris; may have been injured by falling debris or by falling down.

Surfactant — Chemical that lowers the surface tension of a liquid; allows water to spread more rapidly over the surface of Class A fuels and penetrate organic fuels. *See* Surface Tension.

Surveillance — Close watch kept over someone or something.

Surveillance Systems — Ongoing, systematic collection and analysis of data; may lead to actions taken to prevent and control an infectious disease. *See* Surveillance.

Survey — Evaluation instrument used to identify the behavior and/or attitude of an individual or audience, both before and after a presentation.

Survey Meter — Nuclear-radiation detection instrument.

Suspended Ceiling — Very common ceiling system composed of a metal framework suspended, by wires, from the underside of the roof or the floor above; the framework supports panels that constitute the finish of the ceiling. Typically found in office buildings and in the common areas of apartment buildings and hotels.

Suspension Harness — Web suspension network that supports the helmet on the firefighter's head and prevents the shell from striking the head when hit.

Suspicious Fires — Fires that may be incendiary or caused by arson.

Sustained Attack — Continuing fire-suppression action until the fire is under control.

S/V — Prefix to the name of a vessel propelled by sail.

Swamper — *See* Spotter (2).

Swash Plates — Metal plates in the lower part of tanks that prevent the surging of liquids with the motion of a vessel.

Sweep Pattern — Effective lateral range of an elevated master stream nozzle.

Sweetener — Component (generally charcoal) in an air-purification system that removes odors and tastes from the compressed breathing air.

Swinging Door — Door that opens and closes by swinging from one side of its opening, usually on hinges. *Also known as* Hinged Door.

Swiss Seat — Harness that keeps a person's center of gravity near normal while rappelling.

Switchable Regulator — Positive-pressure breathing apparatus regulator that has a switch to accommodate donning.

Switch List — List of railroad cars on a track and instructions as to where those cars go within the yard.

Swivel — Free-turning ring on all Storz fire hose couplings, and on the female coupling of threaded couplings.

Symptom — Sensation or awareness of a disturbance of a bodily function, as reported by the patient.

Syndromic Surveillance — Surveillance using health-related data that precede diagnosis and signal a sufficient probability of a case or an outbreak to warrant further public health response. *See* Surveillance.

Synergistic Effect — Phenomenon in which the combined properties of substances have an effect greater than their simple arithmetical sum of effects.

Synthesis — Process of combining elements to make a compound.

Synthetic Foam Concentrate — Foam concentrate that is composed of a synthetically produced material, such as a fluorochemical or hydrocarbon surfactant, that forms a foam blanket across a liquid; performs similarly to a protein-based foam concentrate. Examples include aqueous film-forming foam and alcohol-resistant aqueous film-forming foam. *See* Foam Concentrate.

Synthetic Nylon — Artificial material that has replaced natural fiber in rope construction, due to its superior strength and durability.

Synthetic Stucco — *See* Exterior Insulation and Finish Systems.

System — Total combination of hardware, software, and anchors to create a main line or a safety line.

Systemic Effect Something that affects an entire system rather than a single location or entity.

Systemic Hypothermia — *See* Hypothermia.

Systole — Rhythmic contraction of the heart by which blood is pumped throughout the body.

T

Tachometer — Instrument that indicates the rotational speed of a shaft in revolutions per minute (rpm); usually used to indicate engine speed.

Tactical Box — Reduced assignment to a fire alarm.

Tactical Objectives — Specific operations that must be accomplished to achieve strategic goals; objectives must be both specific and measurable. *See* Strategic Goals and Tactics.

Tactics — Methods of employing equipment and personnel on an incident to accomplish specific tactical objectives, in order to achieve established strategic goals. *See* Strategic Goals, Strategy, and Tactical Objectives.

Tag Line — (1) Non-load-bearing rope attached to an object to help steer it in a desired direction, prevent it from spinning or snagging on obstructions, or act as a safety line. (2) As used in anchors, a length of rope or webbing used to extend anchor points closer to the actual rescue work site.

Tailboard — Back step of fire apparatus.

Tailpiece — Part of a lock cylinder that activates the bolt or latch as the key is turned. *Also known as* Stem.

Talk Group — Group of mobile radio units that are addressed as a single entity by a radio system; functionally equivalent to a conventional repeater channel.

Tally — Rectangular plastic identification tag used for entry control in the United Kingdom, Australia, and New Zealand.

Tandem — (1) Two-axle suspension or support. (2) Two or more units of any kind working one in front of the other

to accomplish a specific fire-suppression job; this term can be applied to combinations of hand crews, engines, bulldozers, or aircraft.

Tandem Attack — Attack on a wildland fire using multiple resources, including apparatus, hand crews, or aircraft. *See* Attack Methods (2).

Tandem Prusik — Two Prusiks, one made from 65 inches (1.65 meters) of line and one made from 53 inches (1.35 meters) of line, to form a long and a short matched pair of Prusiks. Used together, attached to a line with a Prusik hitch, they form a braking device on a main line or safety line.

Tandem Pumping — Short relay operation in which the pumper taking water from the supply source pumps into the intake of the second pumper; the second pumper then boosts the pressure of the water even higher. This method is used when pressures higher than the capability of a single pump are required.

Tanker — (1) Mobile water supply fire apparatus that carries at least 1,500 gallons (6 000 L) of water and is used to supply water to fire scenes that lack fire hydrants. *Also known as* Tender in ICS terms. (2) In the ICS, tanker refers to a water-transporting fixed-wing aircraft. (3) Vessel (ship) that exclusively carries liquid products in bulk. *Also known as* Tank Vessel. *See* Chemical Carrier, Liquefied Flammable Gas Carrier, Oil Tanker, and Petroleum Carrier.

Tankerman — Person qualified and certified to perform all duties included in the handling of bulk liquid cargoes (petroleum products). *See* Oil Tanker.

Tanker/Pumper — Mobile water supply apparatus equipped with a fire pump. In some jurisdictions, this term is used to differentiate a fire pump equipped mobile water supply apparatus whose main purpose is to shuttle water.

Tanker Shuttle Operation — Method of supplying water to a fire scene; tankers carry water between a water source and the pumping engines, generally in a rotating order. *See* Water Shuttle Operation.

Tank Motor Vehicle — *See* Cargo Tank Truck.

Tank Top — Lowest deck; top plate of the bottom tanks. *See* Deck.

Tank Truck — Single self-propelled motor vehicle equipped with a cargo tank mounted thereon, and used for the transportation of flammable and combustible liquids or asphalt; a tank truck with two or three axles on which the tank is permanently affixed. *See* Cargo Tank Truck.

Tank Vehicle — Any tank truck, full-trailer tank, or tractor and semitrailer tank combination.

Tank Vessel — *See* Tanker.

Tape — (1) Tape recording of calls received and dispatched during telecommunications center operations. (2) The paper printout of code signals on some types of alarm systems.

Tapped Out — *See* Under Control.

Tar and Gravel Roof — *See* Built-Up Roof.

Tare — Weight of an empty vehicle or container; subtracted from gross weight to ascertain net weight.

Target Audience — Group of people who will receive the fire and life safety education presentation. This may not always be the group of people identified as a high-risk group; rather, it may be those who influence or control the high-risk group.

Target Hazard — Facility in which there is a great potential likelihood of life or property loss in the event of an attack or natural disaster. *See* Hazard and Hazard Assessment.

Tarp — *See* Salvage Cover.

Task — Duty or job in an occupation that is performed regularly and requires psychomotor skills and technical information to meet occupational requirements.

Task Analysis — Systematic analysis of duties for a specific job or jobs, which identifies and describes all component tasks of that job; enables program developers to design appropriate training for personnel and trainees who must learn certain tasks to perform a job.

Task Force — (1) Group of individuals convened to analyze, investigate, or solve a particular problem. (2) Group of resources, with common communications and a leader, temporarily assembled for a specific mission. An example would be a group of firefighters and equipment assigned to a special task, such as backfiring; consists of three engines, a dozer, a hand crew, and a task force leader. (3) Any combination of single resources, within a reasonable span of control, assembled for a particular tactical need with common communications and a leader.

Tax-Exempt — *See* Nonprofit.

Taxiway — Specially designated and prepared surface on an airport for aircraft to taxi to and from runways, hangars, and parking areas.

Taxonomy — Classification system in which each separate class of items is given a name, and items within a class are more like one another than like items in other classes. Examples are the Dewey Decimal System and Bloom's Taxonomy of Objectives for the Cognitive Domain.

T-Bone Collision — *See* Side-Impact Collision.

TC — *See* Transport Canada.

Teaching — Method of giving instruction through various forms of communicating knowledge and demonstrating skill; successful teaching causes an observable change in behavior through activities that provide opportunities for learners to demonstrate knowledge and skill, and to receive feedback on progress toward expected behavior change.

Teaching Aids — *See* Instructional Materials.

Team Emergency Conditions Breathing — Procedures or techniques performed by a team of two individuals during emergencies when one person's SCBA malfunctions or does not have adequate air supply. *Also known as* Buddy Breathing.

Team Teaching — Instructional method in which a group of two or more instructors work together, combining their individual content, techniques, and materials in order to present information, demonstrate skills, and supervise practice of a class or several classes. The instructor with the expertise in a particular topic teaches that particular topic; remaining instructors share the responsibilities of assisting with instructional details and supervising practice of skills. A lead instructor organizes and coordinates the activities of all instructors.

Tear Gas — *See* Riot Control Agent.

Technical Assistance — Personnel, agencies, or printed materials that provide technical information on handling hazardous materials or other special problems.

Technical Decontamination — Using chemical or physical methods to thoroughly remove contaminants from responders (primarily entry team personnel) and their equipment; usually conducted within a formal decontamination line or corridor following gross decontamination. *Also known as* Formal Decontamination. *See* Decontamination, Decontamination Corridor, and Gross Decontamination.

Technical Lesson — *See* Information Presentation.

Technical Rescue — Application of special knowledge, skills and equipment to safely resolve unique and/or complex rescue situations. This term has often been used interchangeably with rope rescue; however, it can refer to other disciplines, such as trench or confined space rescue, which require advanced knowledge to perform.

Technical Rescuer — Individual who has been trained to perform or direct a variety of unique and/or complex rescue situations, such as rope rescues (low- and high-angle), confined space, trench and excavation, structural collapse, mine and tunnel, and other rescue types. *Also known as* Special Rescue Technician or Technical Rescue Specialist.

Technical Rescue Specialist — *See* Technical Rescuer.

Technical Search — Use of specialized equipment to locate victims; examples of this equipment include seismic, acoustic, fiber-optic, and infrared devices.

Technical Skills — Skills involving manipulative aptitude.

Technical Specialists — Personnel with special skills that are activated only when needed; may be needed in the areas of fire behavior, water resources, environmental concerns, resource use, and training. Technical specialists report initially to the planning section of an incident management system but may be assigned anywhere within the organizational structure as needed.

Telecommunications Center — Facility (a building or portion of a building) that is specifically configured for the primary purpose of providing emergency communication services or public safety answering point (PSAP) services to one or more public safety agencies under the authority or authorities having jurisdiction. Serves as the point through which nearly all information flows, is processed, and is acted upon. *Also known as* Alarm Center, Comm Center, Communications Center, or Dispatch Center.

Telecommunications Device for the Deaf (TDD) — Special type of phone used by hearing-impaired individuals that sends text messages. Letters are transmitted in a specific code, to be decoded by another similar device at the telecommunications center. The *Americans with Disabilities Act of 1990* requires that all public safety telecommunications centers have one available for use.

Telecommunicator — Person who works in the telecommunications center and processes information from the public and from emergency responders. *Formerly known as* Dispatcher. *Also known as* Emergency Communications Technician.

Telephone Alarm Box — Public fire alarm station with a telephone that provides a direct line to the telecommunicator. *Also known as* Call Box.

Telephoto Lens — Fixed focal length lens with a long focal length and a shallow depth of field.

Telephone Tree — Passing information by means of people calling other people, who in turn call others; this process is repeated until all persons on the tree have been contacted.

Telescoping Aerial Platform Apparatus — Aerial apparatus equipped with an elevating platform, as well as piping systems and nozzles for elevated master stream operations. These apparatus are not meant to be climbed and are equipped with a small ladder that is to be used only for escape from the platform in emergency situations.

Telescoping Boom — Aerial device raised and extended via sections that slide within each other.

Teletype (TTY) — Similar to a TDD device in which messages are sent over phone lines; however, teletype machines usually use dedicated phone lines and have other features, such as the ability to send messages to many users at once, query certain databases, or provide a secure network.

Temperature — Measure of a material's ability to transfer heat energy to other objects; the greater the energy, the higher the temperature. Measure of the average kinetic energy of the particles in a sample of matter, expressed in terms of units or degrees designated on a standard scale. *See* Celsius Scale and Fahrenheit Scale.

Temperature Bar — Reinforcing bar within concrete used to counteract stresses caused by temperature changes.

Temperature-Compensated Conductivity Meter — Device designed to measure the conductivity of a solution and adjust for conductivity variances at different temperatures.

Temperature Gradient — Measure of the change in temperature as a function of distance from a particular location, typically expressed in units of temperature per a measure of distance.

Temperature Inversion — Meteorological condition in which the temperature of the air some distance above the earth's surface is higher than the temperature of the air at the surface; normally, air temperatures decrease as altitude increases. An air inversion traps air, gases, and vapors near the surface, and impedes their dispersion.

Tempered Glass — Type of glass specially treated to become harder and more break-resistant than plate glass or a single sheet of laminated glass; most commonly used in side windows and some rear windows.

Temporal Artery — Any one of three arteries located on each side of the head, above and in front of the upper portion of the ear; supplies blood to the scalp.

Temporary Deformation — Alteration of form or shape that disappears entirely after a load has been removed.

Tenability — Determination of whether or not people can remain unhurt or escape a fire area without serious injury.

Tenable Atmosphere — Atmosphere capable of maintaining human life.

Tender — Term used within the incident command system for a mobile piece of apparatus that has the primary function of supporting another operation; examples include a water tender that supplies water to pumpers, or a fuel tender that supplies fuel to other vehicles. *See* Mobile Water Supply Apparatus and Tanker (1).

Tenement — *See* Apartment.

Tenon — Projecting member in a piece of wood or other material for insertion into a mortise to make a joint.

Tensile — Force of pulling apart or stretching.

Tensile Stress — Stress in a structural member that tends to stretch the member or pull it apart; often used to denote the greatest amount of tensile force a component can withstand without failure.

Tension — Vertical or horizontal forces that tend to pull things apart; for example, the force exerted on the bottom chord of a truss.

Tension Ring Method — Method used to attach a coupling to large diameter hose using a tension ring and contractual sleeve.

Tepee Cut — *See* Triangular Cut.

Teratogen — Chemicals that interfere with the normal growth of an embryo, causing malformations in the developing fetus.

TERC — See Transportation Emergency Rescue Committee.

Terminal — *See* Break Bulk Terminal, Bulk Terminal, Car Terminal, Container Terminal, and Dry Bulk Terminal.

Terne Coated Steel — Cold rolled sheet steel that was hot-dip coated with a lead-tin alloy; this dull gray coating provides corrosion protection from contact with petroleum fuels.

Terrazzo — Mixture of a liquid and chipped marble that is poured as a floor; hardens to form a durable, long-lasting floor.

Territory — Specific geographical area to be covered by a responding company.

Terrorism — Unlawful use of force or violence against persons or property for the purpose of intimidating or coercing a government, the civilian population or any segment thereof, in furtherance of political or social objectives; defined by the U.S. Federal Bureau of Investigation (FBI). *See* Biological Attack, Chemical Attack, and Improvised Explosive Device.

Test — Any means by which the absence, presence, amount, or nature of some learner quality or ability is observed or inferred and appraised or measured. *See* Comprehensive Test, Criterion-Referenced Testing, Norm-Referenced Test, Objective Test, Oral Test, Performance Test, Pretest/Posttest, Progress Test, Subjective Test, and Written Test.

Test Hydrant — Fire hydrant used during a fire-flow test to read the static and residual pressures. *See* Flow Hydrant.

Test Item Analysis — Process that shows how difficult a test is, how much it discriminates between high and low scorers, and whether the alternatives used for distracters truly work.

Test Planning — Steps to determine the purpose and type of test, identify and define the learning objectives, prepare the test specifications, and construct the test items.

Test Planning Sheet — Planning form that lists and specifies the number of test items to be written and at what levels of learning in each content area. This planning sheet aids the test developer in ensuring that necessary numbers of questions are included for each objective or learning level in order to appropriately measure learning.

Tetrahedron — (1) Four-sided solid geometric figure that resembles a pyramid. (2) In fire science, a tetrahedron is used to represent the flaming mode of combustion consisting of fuel, heat, oxygen, and the uninhibited chain reaction. *See* Fire Tetrahedron. (3) A hollow four-sided object mounted on a central pivot used to indicate wind direction at some airports.

Theoretical Lift — Theoretical, scientific height that a column of water may be lifted by atmospheric pressure in a true vacuum; at sea level, this height is 33.8 feet (10 m). The height will decrease as elevation increases. *See* Lift.

Theoretical Mechanical Advantage — Advantage gained if all friction could be removed from a system; can never be attained in actuality.

Theory X — Style of leadership in which the leader believes that the average worker prefers to be directed and will avoid responsibility due to a general lack of ambition.

Theory Y — Style of leadership in which the leader believes that the average worker enjoys work, performs well with minimal supervision, will both seek and accept responsibility if given the opportunity, and will subscribe to organizational objectives if he associates those objectives with direct rewards.

Theory Z — Management style based on the belief that involved workers are the key to increased productivity and that there is a mutual loyalty between the company and the workers that often translates into lifetime employment and a close relationship between work and social life.

Thermal Balance — *See* Thermal Layering (of Gases).

Thermal Barrier — Heat protective barrier within protective clothing.

Thermal Belt — Elevation on a mountainous slope that typically experiences the least variation in diurnal temperatures and has the highest average temperatures and, thus, the lowest relative humidity. Its presence is most evident during clear weather with light wind.

Thermal Blocking — Phenomenon that occurs when a concealed hot spot contains enough heat to turn small amounts of penetrating water into steam, thereby preventing the water from cooling the material thoroughly.

Thermal Burns — Burns caused by contact with flames, hot objects, and hot fluids; examples include scalds and steam burns.

Thermal Column — Updraft of heated air, fire gases, and smoke directly above the involved fire area. *Also known as* Convection Column.

Thermal Conductivity — Ability of a substance to conduct heat.

Thermal Expansion — Elongation or expansion of materials, such as steel, when exposed to heat.

Thermal Layering (of Gases) — Outcome of combustion in a confined space; gases tend to form into layers according to temperature, with the hottest gases found on the ceiling and the coolest gases at floor level. *Also known as* Heat Stratification or Thermal Balance.

Thermal Protective Performance (TPP) — Rating given to protective clothing to indicate the level of heat protection it affords the wearer.

Thermal Radiation — Transmission or transfer of heat energy, from one body to another body at a lower temperature, through intervening space by electromagnetic waves similar to radio waves or X-rays.

Thermal Updraft — Convection column of hot gases, smoke, and flames rising above a high-intensity fire; can create unsafe operating conditions for aircraft and reduce the effectiveness of finished foam.

Thermistor — Semiconductor made of substances whose resistance varies rapidly and predictably with temperature. *See* Semiconductor.

Thermocouple — Device for measuring temperature in which two electrical conductors of dissimilar metals, such as copper and iron, are joined at the point where the heat is to be applied. *See* Conductor.

Thermoelectric-Effect Heat Detector — Heat-sensitive device that measures electrical resistance changes that correspond with temperature changes.

Thermoplastic — Plastic that softens with an increase of temperature and hardens with a decrease of temperature but does not undergo any chemical change. Synthetic material made from the polymerization of organic compounds that become soft when heated and hard when cooled.

Thermoplastic Glazing — Plastic glazing made of acrylic, butyrate, or polycarbonate plastic; known for its resistance to breakage.

Thermosetting Plastics — Plastics that are hardened into a permanent shape in the manufacturing process and are not subject to softening when heated again.

Third-Degree Burn — Full-thickness burn that penetrates the epidermis, dermis, and underlying tissue, leaving skin charred or white and leathery, and accompanied by an initial loss of pain or sensation to the area because of destroyed nerve cells.

Third Door — (1) Automobile extrication technique used to free people who are trapped in the rear seat of a two-door vehicle. (2) An additional emergency exit door that may be found on the left side of some school buses, depending on local requirements. *Also known as* Left-Hand Door.

Third-Party Testing Agency — Independent agency hired to perform nonbiased testing on a specific piece of apparatus.

Third Rail — Electrically charged rail used to convey power to electrically powered trains; usually a contact shoe rides along the third rail to provide electrical pickup.

Threaded Coupling — Male or female coupling with a spiral thread.

Thread Gauge Device — Device that is screwed onto the discharge of a hydrant to check the condition of the threads and ensure that they are not damaged.

Thready Pulse — Pulse that is very weak; characteristic of a person in shock.

Three-Ply Process — Process of producing rubber-covered hose in which a nitrile rubber is vulcanized to the interior surface of a woven polyester tube.

Three Bight — Method of attaching a software loop to an anchor.

Threshold Limit Value (TLV®) — Maximum concentration of a given material in parts per million (ppm) that may be tolerated for an 8-hour exposure during a regular workweek without ill effects. *See* Permissible Exposure Limit (PEL), Recommended Exposure Limit (REL), Short-Term Exposure Limit (STEL), Threshold Limit Value/Ceiling (TLV®/C), Threshold Limit Value/Short-Term Exposure Limit (TLV®/STEL), and Threshold Limit Value/Time Weighted Average (TLV®/TWA).

Threshold Limit Value/Ceiling (TLV®/C) — Maximum concentration of a given material in parts per million (ppm) that should not be exceeded, even instantaneously. *See* Permissible Exposure Limit (PEL), Recommended Exposure Limit (REL), Short-Term Exposure Limit (STEL), Threshold Limit Value (TLV®), Threshold Limit Value/Short-Term Exposure Limit (TLV®/STEL), and Threshold Limit Value/Time Weighted Average (TLV®/TWA).

Threshold Limit Value/Short-Term Exposure Limit (TLV®/STEL) — Fifteen-minute time-weighted average exposure. It should not be exceeded at any time nor repeated more than four times daily, with a 60-minute rest period required between each STEL exposure. These short-term exposures can be tolerated without suffering from irritation, chronic or irreversible tissue damage, or narcosis of a sufficient degree to increase the likelihood of accidental injury, impair self-rescue, or materially reduce worker efficiency. TLV/STELs are expressed in parts per million (ppm) and milligrams per cubic meter (mg/m^3). *See* Permissible Exposure Limit (PEL), Recommended

Exposure Limit (REL), Short-Term Exposure Limit (STEL), Threshold Limit Value (TLV®), Threshold Limit Value/Ceiling (TLV®/C), and Threshold Limit Value/Time Weighted Average (TLV®/TWA).

Threshold Limit Value/Time-Weighted Average (TLV®/TWA) — Maximum airborne concentration of a material to which an average, healthy person may be exposed repeatedly for 8 hours each day, 40 hours per week without suffering adverse effects. Based upon current available data and adjusted on an annual basis. *See* Permissible Exposure Limit (PEL), Recommended Exposure Limit (REL), Short-Term Exposure Limit (STEL), Threshold Limit Value (TLV®), Threshold Limit Value/Ceiling (TLV®/C), and Threshold Limit Value/Short-Term Exposure Limit (TLV®/STEL).

Throttle Control — Device that controls the engine speed.

Through the Roof — Description of a fire that has gained sufficient headway and vented itself by burning a hole through the roof.

Throw a Ladder — Raise a ladder quickly.

Throwing Salvage Covers — To spread salvage covers by throwing them.

Thrust — Pushing or pulling force developed by an aircraft engine.

Thrust Reverser — Device or apparatus for diverting jet engine thrust in order to slow or stop the aircraft.

Thumbturn — Part of the lock, other than the key or knob, used to lock and unlock the door.

TIC — *See* Toxic Industrial Chemical.

Tie — (1) Metal strip used to tie masonry wall to the wood sheathing. (2) Device used to tie the two sides of a form together.

Tied-Back Anchor — Method of building a strong anchor system from a weak or inadequate anchor point.

Tie In — (1) Securing oneself to a ladder; accomplished by using a rope hose tool or belt or by inserting one leg between the rungs. (2) Securing a ladder to a building or object.

Tier — (1) Horizontal division of a multistory building, usually the stories in a steel-frame building. (2) Layer of hose loaded in the hose bed of a fire apparatus.

Tie Rods — Metal rods running from one beam to the other.

TIH — *See* Toxic Inhalation Hazard.

Tiller — Rear steering mechanism on a tractor-trailer aerial ladder truck.

Tillered Truck — *See* Tractor-Drawn Apparatus.

Tillerman — *See* Tiller Operator.

Tiller Operator — Driver/operator of the trailer section of a tractor-tiller aerial ladder apparatus. *Also known as* Tillerman.

Tilting Joint — Joint that allows movement in a tilt steering wheel.

Tilt-Up Construction — Type of construction in which concrete wall sections (slabs) are cast on the concrete floor of the building, then tilted up into the vertical position. *Also known as* Tilt-Slab Construction.

Tilt-Up Wall — Precast concrete wall that is raised or tipped up into position with a crane.

TIM — *See* Toxic Industrial Material.

Time Frame — Lesson plan component that lists the estimated time it will take to teach a lesson. *See* Lesson Plan.

Time-Temperature Curve — *See* Standard Time-Temperature Curve.

Time Unit — Functional unit within the finance/administrative section; responsible for record keeping of time for personnel working at an incident.

Tin-Clad Door — Similar to a metal-clad door, except covered with a lighter-gauge metal.

Tip — (1) Extreme top of a ladder. *Also known as* Top. (2) Slang for a nozzle.

Title Block — Small information section on the face of every plan drawing; contains such information as name of project, title of the particular drawing, the scale used, and date of drawing and/or revisions. *See* Legend.

Title VII — Part of the *Civil Rights Act of 1964* that prohibits discrimination based on race, color, religion, national origin, or gender.

TLV® — *See* Threshold Limit Value.

TLV®/C — *See* Threshold Limit Value/Ceiling.

TLV®/STEL — *See* Threshold Limit Value/Short-Term Exposure Limit.

TLV®/TWA — *See* Threshold Limit Value/Time-Weighted Average.

TOFC — *See* Trailer-on-Flatcar.

Toggle — (1) Hinge device by which a staypole is attached to a ladder. (2) Piece or device for holding or securing rope or chain by twisting. (3) Type of joint consisting of two levers joined at the end that exert outward pressure when a force is applied to straighten them.

Ton Container — Pressurized tank with a capacity of 1 short ton or approximately 2,000 pounds (907 kg or 0.9 tonne).

Tone Out — To dispatch by activating pagers or station-alerting equipment using radio tones.

Tones — Radio signals that activate pagers or station-alerting systems.

Tongue — Rib on the edge of a ladder beam that fits into a corresponding groove or channel attached to the edge of another ladder beam; its purpose is to hold the two sections together while allowing the sections to move up and down.

Tongue and Groove — Projection on the edge of a board that fits into a recess in an adjacent board.

Tonnage — Amount of internal volume of the vessel, where 100 cubic feet (2.8 m³) = one ton, used for determining port and canal charges.

TOPOFF Exercise — National-level, multiagency, multijurisdictional, real-time, and limited-notice weapons of mass destruction (WMD) response exercise designed to better prepare senior government officials to effectively respond to an actual terrorist attack.

Topography — Physical configuration of the land or terrain; often depicted using contour lines.

Topside — General term referring to the weather decks as opposed to belowdeck.

Top Ventilation — *See* Vertical Ventilation.

Torch — Professional firesetter, often for hire, who deliberately and maliciously sets fire to property.

Torching — (1) Burning of fuel at the end of the exhaust pipe or stacks of an aircraft engine due to excessive richness of the fuel/air mixture. (2) Vertical phenomenon in which a surface fire ignites the foliage of a tree or bush that becomes entirely involved in fire very quickly. A torching fire may or may not initiate a crown fire.

Tormentor Poles — *See* Staypole.

Torque — (1) Force that tends to create a rotational or twisting motion. (2) Measurement of engine shaft output. (3) Force that produces or tends to produce a twisting or rotational action.

Torque Box — Structural housing that contains the rotational system for the aerial device between the apparatus chassis frame rails and the turntable.

Torque Wrench — Specially designed wrench that may be set to produce a particular amount of torque on a bolt.

Torsional Load — Load offset from the center of the cross section of the member and at an angle to or in the same plane as the cross section; produces a twisting effect that creates shear stresses in a material.

Tort — Private or civil wrong or injury, including action for bad faith breach of contract, resulting from breach of duty that is based on society's expectations regarding interpersonal conduct; a violation of a duty imposed by general law upon all persons in a relationship that involves a given transaction. *See* Civil Wrong, Libel, Negligence, and Slander.

Tort Liability — Liability for a civil wrong or injury; noncriminal acts or failures to act that result in physical and/or monetary damages.

Total Energy — Total energy at any point in a system; the sum of the potential energy and kinetic energy at that point.

Total Flooding System — Fire-suppression system designed to protect hazards within enclosed structures; foam is released into a compartment or area and fills it completely, extinguishing the fire. *See* Local Application System.

Total Pressure — Total amount of pressure at any point in a system, including static pressure and velocity pressure.

Total Station — Surveying equipment attached to a computer-imaging system, used to create computer models of incident scenes.

Total Stopping Distance — Sum of the driver reaction distance and the vehicle braking distance.

Touch Off — Term for setting a fire or for describing a fire that firefighters believe has been purposely set.

Touring Bus — *See* Commercial Motor Coach.

Tourniquet — Any wide, flat material wrapped tightly around a limb to stop bleeding; used only for severe, life-threatening hemorrhage that cannot be controlled by other means.

Tow Bar — Device used to maintain the distance between a towed vehicle and the towing vehicle.

Towboat — *See* Tugboat.

Tower — *See* Drill Tower.

Tower Ladder — Telescoping aerial platform fire apparatus.

Toxic — Poisonous.

Toxic Atmosphere — Any area, inside or outside a structure, where the air is contaminated by a poisonous substance that may be harmful to human life or health if it is inhaled, swallowed, or absorbed through the skin. *See* Toxic Gas.

Toxic Element — *See* Heavy Metal.

Toxic Gas — Gas that contains poisons or toxins that are hazardous to life. Many gaseous products of combustion are poisonous; toxic materials generally emit poisonous vapors when exposed to an intensely heated environment. *See* Gas, Toxic Material, and Toxin.

Toxicity — Ability of a substance to do harm within the body. *See* Toxic Inhalation Hazard (TIH), Toxic Material, and Toxin.

Toxic Industrial Chemical (TIC) — *See* Toxic Industrial Material (TIM).

Toxic Industrial Material (TIM) — Industrial chemical that is toxic at a certain concentration and is produced in quantities exceeding 30 tons per year at any one production facility; readily available and could be used by terrorists to deliberately kill, injure, or incapacitate people. *Also known as* Toxic Industrial Chemical (TIC). *See* Chemical Attack and Terrorism.

Toxic Inhalation Hazard (TIH) — Liquid or gas known to be a severe hazard to human health during transportation.

Toxic Material — Substance classified as a poison, asphyxiant, irritant, or anesthetic that can damage the environment or cause severe illness, poisoning, birth defects, disease, or death when ingested, inhaled, or absorbed by living organisms. *See* Asphyxiant, Toxic Gas, Toxic Inhalation Hazard (TIH), Toxicity, and Toxin.

Toxic Substances Control Act (TSCA) — Law giving the Environmental Protection Agency (EPA) the ability to track the 75,000 industrial chemicals currently produced or imported into the U.S.; enacted in 1976.

Toxin — Substance that has the property of being poisonous. *See* Biological Toxin, Poison, Toxic Gas, Toxicity, and Toxic Material.

TPP — *See* Thermal Protective Performance.

Trace Evidence — Evidence that generally requires laboratory analysis; examples include fingerprints, DNA, or fibers.

Traction — (1) Act of exerting a pulling force. (2) The friction between a wheel and the surface on which it is rolling that permits the wheel to move forward and exert a pulling force.

Tractor-Drawn Apparatus — Truck equipped with steerable rear wheels on its trailer. *Also known as* Tillered Truck.

Tractor-Plow — Tractor with a plow for exposing mineral soil.

Tractor-Tiller Aerial Ladder — Aerial ladder apparatus that consists of a tractor power unit and trailer (tiller) section that contains the aerial ladder, ground ladders, and equipment storage areas. The trailer section is steered independently of the tractor by the tiller operator.

Trade Secret — Formula, practice, process, design, instrument, pattern, or compilation of information used by a business to obtain an advantage over competitors or customers.

Traffic Control — Important function of scene management that helps to control scene access and vehicular traffic in and out of the area. This function is generally handled by law enforcement personnel.

Traffic Control Device — Mechanical device that automatically changes traffic signal lights to favor the path of responding emergency apparatus.

Traffic Pattern — Traffic flow that is prescribed for aircraft landing or taking off from an airport.

Trail Drop — Dropping fire suppressant sequentially from tanks in aircraft; generally used with light fuels.

Trailer — (1) Combustible material, such as rolled rags, blankets, newspapers, or flammable liquid, often used in intentionally set fires to connect remote fuel packages (such as pools of ignitable liquid and other combustible materials) in order to spread fire from one point or area to other points or areas; frequently used in conjunction with an incendiary device. (2) Fire pattern left behind after the combustible material has burned. (3) Highway or industrial-plant vehicle designed to be hauled/pulled by a tractor.

Trailer-on-Flatcar (TOFC) — Rail flatcar used to transport highway trailers. *Also known as* Piggyback Transport.

Trailing Edge Devices — Rear edges of aircraft wings; normally extended for takeoff and landing to provide additional lift at low speeds and to improve aircraft performance.

Train Consist — *See* Consist.

Training — Supervised activity or process for achieving and maintaining proficiency through instruction and hands-on practice in the operation of equipment and systems that are expected to be used in the performance of assigned duties. *Also known as* Drilling.

Training Aids — Broad term referring to any audiovisual aids, reprinted materials, training props, or equipment used to supplement instruction.

Training Concentrates — Foam concentrates that are specially designed for hydrocarbon fuel fire training; generally reproduce the white color, appearance, expansion ratio, and drain time of AFFF.

Training Officer — Individual responsible for running a fire department's training program, to include the administration of all training activities; typically reports directly to the fire chief. *Also known as* Chief of Training or Drillmaster.

Transcription — Method by which an authority having jurisdiction (AHJ) adopts a code in whole to become a new regulation.

Transfer — (1) To move a firefighter to a different unit. (2) The movement of companies or apparatus.

Transfer of Learning — Process of applying what has been learned in one situation to a new situation.

Transfer Valve — Valve used for placing multistage centrifugal pumps in either volume or pressure mode operation.

Transfilling System — Self-contained breathing apparatus designed so that two SCBAs can be connected by a hose, allowing the air pressure of the two SCBA cylinders to equalize; used as an EBSS to equalize air pressure of one cylinder with an adequate air supply and another cylinder with depleted or inadequate air supply.

Transformer — Device that uses coils and magnetic fields to increase (step-up) or decrease (step-down) incoming voltages.

Transit Bus — Vehicle designed to move a large number of people over relatively short distances; most commonly found in urban or metropolitan areas that operate a mass transit system.

Transit Time — Time that it takes a foam solution to pass from the proportioner to the nozzle.

Transition — (1) Passage from one state, stage, subject, or place to another. (2) Section of a tank that joins two unequal cross-sections.

Transmission of Heat — Flow of heat by conduction, convection, or radiation.

Transmit — To send out an alarm by vocal, visual, or audible means.

Transmit Site — Assembly of elements capable of functioning together to transmit signal waves.

Transmitter — Device for sending or transmitting codes or signals over alarm circuits when operated by any one of a group of actuating devices or for sending voice communications over the air.

Transparency — Educational visual aid printed on acetate or mylar and projected onto a screen for common viewing. *Also known as* Overhead.

Transparent armor — Ballistic protection materials used as windows for vehicles.

Transportation Area — Location where accident casualties are held after receiving medical care or triage before being transported to medical facilities.

Transportation Emergency Rescue Committee (TERC) — Organization founded in 1986 that serves as a competent source of guidance and information on transportation emergencies for those involved in providing emergency services; members share their vehicle extrication expertise by conducting schools, seminars, and competitive exercises.

Transportation Group — Group within the incident command system responsible for seeing that all patients are transported to the appropriate medical facility.

Transportation Security Administration (TSA) — U.S. Department of Homeland Security (DHS) agency that is responsible for the security of the national transportation systems (highways, buses, railroads, mass transit systems, ports, and airports); established following the events of September 11, 2001.

Transport Canada (TC) — Canadian agency responsible for developing and administering policies, regulations, and programs for a safe, efficient, and environmentally friendly transportation system; contributing to Canada's economic growth and social development; and protecting the physical environment.

Transport Index — Number placed on the label of a package expressing the maximum allowable radiation level in millirem per hour at 1 meter (3.3 feet) from the external surface of the package.

Transshipment — Transfer of cargo from one vessel to another before the place of destination has been reached.

Transverse — Athwartship (side to side) dimensions of a vessel.

Transverse Hose Bed — Hose bed that lies across the pumper body at a right angle to the main hose bed; designed to deploy preconnected attack hose to the sides of the pumper. *Also known as* Mattydale Hose Bed.

Trash Line — Small diameter, preconnected hoseline intended to be used for trash or other small, exterior fires.

Trauma Kit — Well-stocked medical first-aid kit.

Travel Corridors — Areas inside a building that are designed and used for travel by occupants; includes hallways, stairwells, access ramps, and elevator shafts.

Travel Distance — Distance from any given area in a structure to the nearest exit or to a fire extinguisher. *See* Exit and Means of Egress.

Tread — Horizontal face of a step.

Treatment Group — Group within the incident command system responsible for triage and the initial treatment of patients.

Tree System — Water supply piping system that uses a single, central feeder main to supply branches on either side of the main.

Tremie — Chute used to deliver concrete to the bottom of a caisson.

Trench — Temporary excavation in which the length of the bottom exceeds the width of the bottom; generally limited to excavations that are less than 15 feet (4.6 m) wide at the bottom and less than 20 feet (6 m) deep.

Trenching — (1) In wildland fire fighting, digging a trench in a slope to catch any burning, rolling material that could cross the control line. (2) In strip or trench ventilation, the process of opening a roof area the width of the building, with a 2 foot (0.6 m) wide opening, to channel out fire and heat.

Trench Jack — Jack used to keep sheeting or wales apart for the insertion of a breast timber in a trenching operation; also a jack that is used as a breast timber.

Trench Lip — Edge of a trench.

Trench Ventilation — Defensive tactic that involves cutting an exit opening in the roof of a burning building, extending from one outside wall to the other, to create an opening at which a spreading fire may be cut off. *Also known as* Strip Vent. *See* Trenching (2).

Triage — (1) System used for sorting and classifying accident casualties to determine the priority for medical treatment and transportation. (2) *See* Structural Triage.

Triage Tagging — Method used to identify accident casualties as to extent of injury.

Triangular Cut — Triangular opening cut in a roll-up or tilt-slab door to provide access into the building or a means of egress for those inside. *Also known as* Tepee Cut.

Trier of Fact — Party that determines the facts in a legal case. In a jury trial, the jury is the trier of fact; in a bench (non-jury) trial, the judge is the trier of fact.

Trim — (1) Relation of a vessel's floating attitude to the water or to the longitudinal angle of a vessel; the difference between forward and aft draft readings. (2) To cause a vessel to assume a desirable position in the water by arrangement of ballast, cargo, or passengers. *See* Ballast and Trimming Tank.

Trimming Tank — Tank located near the ends of a vessel used to change the trim of a vessel by admitting or discharging water ballast. *See* Ballast Tank and Trim.

Trip Curve — Relationship between current and time that determines when circuit protective devices operate.

Triple-Combination Pumper — Fire department pumper that carries a fire pump, hose, and a water tank.

Triple Hydrant — Fire hydrant having three outlets, usually two 2½-inch (65 mm) outlets and one 4½-inch (115 mm) outlet.

Trouble Signal — Signal given by a fixed fire protection alerting system when a power failure or other system malfunction occurs.

Truck — (1) Self-propelled vehicle carrying its load on its wheels; primarily designed for transportation of property rather than passengers. (2) Slang term for an aerial apparatus such as a ladder truck.

Truck Company — Group of firefighters assigned to a fire department aerial apparatus equipped with a compliment of ladders; primarily responsible for search and rescue, ventilation, salvage and overhaul, forcible entry, and other fireground support functions. *Also known as* Ladder Company.

Truck Tractor — Powered motor vehicle designed to pull a truck trailer. *See* Truck Trailer.

Truck Trailer — Vehicle without motor power; primarily designed for transportation of property rather than passengers and drawn by a truck or truck tractor. *See* Full Trailer.

Trumpets — Symbolic insignia of rank used throughout the fire service; originated during the time when fire officers gave commands through speaking trumpets.

Trunked Radio System — Radio system designed to use available frequencies more efficiently by use of a computerized radio controller. The radio controller assigns a group of radios to a certain frequency to allow communications when one of the radios transmits; the system then simultaneously switches all radios on that channel or talk group to the assigned frequency to listen to the transmission. These systems are typically very complex and can cover entire states and regions.

Trunnion — In a hydraulic cylinder, the pivoting end of the piston rod that is connected to the anchor ear by the heel pin.

Truss — (1) Structural member used to form a roof or floor framework; trusses form triangles or combinations of triangles to provide maximum load-bearing capacity with a minimum amount of material. Often rendered dangerous by exposure to intense heat, which weakens gusset plate attachment. (2) Beams consisting of one tensile chord, one compression chord, and truss blocks or spaces between the two.

Truss Block — Block used to separate the beams of a truss beam ladder. *Also known as* Beam Block and Run Block.

Truss Construction Ladder — Aerial device boom or ladder sections that are constructed by trussed metal pieces.

Trussed Rafter — Roof truss that serves to support the roof and ceiling construction.

TSA — *See* Transportation Security Administration.

TSCA — *See* Toxic Substances Control Act.

Tube Seal — Type of seal used on a floating roof fuel storage tank; the seal is constructed of urethane foam that is contained within an envelope, and is connected to the edge of the roof around the entire circumference of the tank. A secondary weather shield is usually installed above the main seal.

Tube Trailer — *See* Compressed Gas Tube Trailer.

Tubular Deadbolt — Deadbolting bored lock. *Also known as* Auxiliary Deadbolt.

Tubular Truss-Beam Construction — Similar in design to the truss construction of aerial ladders; tubular steel is welded to form a box shape, using cantilever or triangular truss design.

Tug — See Aircraft Tug.

Tugboat — Strongly built, powerful boat used for towing and pushing in harbors and inland waterways. *Also known as* Towboat.

Tumbler — Pin in the tumbler type of lock cylinder.

Turbojet — Jet engine employing a turbine-driven compressor to compress the intake air, or an aircraft with this type of engine. Also known as a gas turbine.

Turbulence — (1) Irregular motion of the atmosphere usually produced when air flows over a comparatively uneven surface such as the surface of the earth; when two currents of air flow past or over each other in different directions or at different speeds. (2) In terms of explosions, the changes in shape of the blast-pressure front as the expanding pressure is forced around objects and/or toward areas of ventilation; occurs in deflagrations but not in detonations.

Turbulent State — Fluid flow is in the turbulent state at higher velocities where there is no definite pattern to the direction of the water particles. Turbulent flow is reflected by a calculated Reynolds number in excess of 2,100.

Turn Out — Alerting of a fire company for a response.

Turnaround Maintenance Tag — Tag attached to the valve on the oxygen tank of closed-circuit self-contained breathing apparatus that tells when the unit was last serviced, lists what services were performed, and indicates that the unit is ready to perform.

Turnout Gear — Term used to describe personal protective clothing made of fire resistant materials that includes coats, pants, and boots. *Also known as* Turnout Boots, Turnout Clothing, Turnout Coat, Turnout Pants, Turnouts, or Bunker Gear. *See* Personal Protective Equipment.

Turntable — Rotational structural component of the aerial device. Its primary function is to provide continuous rotation on a horizontal plane.

Turret/Turret Nozzle — Large, pre-plumbed master stream appliance connected directly to a pump that is mounted on a pumper, a trailer, and some airport rescue and fire fighting apparatus, and is capable of sweeping from side to side and designed to deliver large volumes of foam or water. *Also known as* Deck Gun, Deck Pipe, or Turret Pipe.

Turret Pipe — *See* Turret/Turret Nozzle.

Tween Deck — Intermediate deck between the main deck and the bottom of a cargo hold; designed to support cargo so that the cargo at the bottom of the hold is not crushed by the weight of cargo above it. *See* Deck.

25 Percent Drain Time — *See* Quarter-Life.

Twist Lock — (1) Mechanically operated device located on the corners of a container chassis and on automatic lifting spreaders; used for restraining a container during transport or transfer. (2) Type of positive connector used on most fire service extension cords; may be a two- or three-prong connector.

Two-Stage Centrifugal Pump — Centrifugal pump with two impellers.

Two-Way Radio — Voice network that provides an always-on connection that enables the user to just "push the button and talk;" allows either transmitting or receiving, but not both at once unless it is a full-duplex system. *Also known as* Dispatch Radio or Transceiver.

Tying In — (1) Securing oneself to a ladder by using a rope hose tool or belt, or by inserting one leg between the rungs. (2) Securing a ladder to a building or object. *See* Tie In (1) and (2).

Type A Packaging — Container used to ship radioactive materials with relatively high radiation levels. *See* Excepted Packaging, Industrial Packaging, Packaging (1), Strong, Tight Container, and Type B Packaging.

Type A School Bus — Van conversion-type school bus with a gross vehicle-weight rating of less than 10,000 pounds (4 536 kg).

Type B Packaging — Container used to ship radioactive materials that exceed the limits allowed by Type A packaging, such as materials that would present a radiation hazard to the public or the environment if there were a major release. *See* Excepted Packaging, Industrial Packaging, Packaging (1), Strong, Tight Container, and Type A Packaging.

Type B School Bus — Minibus-type vehicle with a gross vehicle-weight rating in excess of 10,000 pounds (4 536 kg).

Type C School Bus — Conventional school bus vehicle with a gross vehicle-weight rating well in excess of 10,000 pounds (4 536 kg); the engine is found ahead of the cab.

Type D School Bus — Cab-forward style school bus with a gross vehicle-weight rating well in excess of 10,000 pounds (4 536 kg); the engine is found in the front, rear, or midship of the vehicle.

Type I Construction — Construction type in which structural members, including walls, columns, beam, floors, and roofs, are made of noncombustible or limited combustible materials and have a specified degree of fire resistance. *Formerly known as* Fire Resistive Construction.

Type II Construction — Construction type that is similar to Type I except that the degree of fire resistance is lower. *Formerly known as* Noncombustible or Noncombustible/Limited Combustible Construction.

Type III Construction — Construction type in which exterior walls and structural members are made of noncombustible or limited combustible materials, but interior structural members, including walls, columns, beams, floors, and roofs, are completely or partially constructed of wood. *Formerly known as* Ordinary Construction.

Type IV Construction — Heavy timber construction in which interior and exterior walls and their associated structural members are made of noncombustible or limited combustible material; interior structural framing consists of heavy timber with minimum dimensions larger than those used in Type III construction. *Formerly known as* Heavy Timber Construction.

Type V Construction — Construction type in which exterior walls, bearing walls, floors, roofs, and supports are made completely or partially of wood or other approved materials of smaller dimensions than those used in Type IV construction. *Formerly known as* Wood Frame Construction.

Type of Collapse — Manner in which a structure failed; this information is useful in determining possible victim locations and potential for additional collapse.

Type of Occupancy — Nature of business taking place in a given structure or area.

Typical Tool Order — Order in which hand-crew members are assigned tools for varying types of wildland fuels; types of tools that are necessary varies depending on fuel type.

U

UC — *See* Unified Command.

UEL — *See* Upper Explosive Limit.

UFL — *See* Upper Flammable Limit.

UL — *See* Underwriters Laboratories, Inc.

Ullage — Measure of the empty part of a partially-filled tank. *See* Ullage Hole.

Ullage Hole — Opening that leads to a liquid cargo tank, allowing the measurement of liquid cargo; usually located in the hatch cover. *See* Ullage.

Ultimate Capacity — Total capacity of a water supply system, including residential and industrial consumption, available fire flow, and all other taxes on the system.

Ultrahigh Frequency (UHF) — Radio band containing ultrahigh frequencies ranging from 400 MHz to 512 MHz; includes portions that are licensed to broadcast television. Typically used in metropolitan areas.

Ultrasonic Inspection — Nondestructive method of aerial device testing in which ultrasonic vibrations are injected into the aerial device; deviance in the return of the waves is an indication of existing flaws.

Ultraviolet (UV) Wave Spectrum — Wavelengths shorter than visible light, lying at the violet end of the spectrum.

Uncontrolled Airport — Airport having no control tower in operation.

Undeclared Emergency — Aircraft emergency that occurs without prior warning.

Undercarriage — (1) Portion of a vehicle's chassis (frame) that is located beneath the vehicle; consists of the chassis (frame), drive train, and floor pan. (2) Landing gear of an aircraft.

Under Control — Point in a fire incident when the fire's progress has been stopped; final extinguishment and overhaul can begin at this time. *Also known as* Tapped Out.

Undercut Line — Fireline below a fire burning on a slope; should be trenched to catch rolling material. *Also known as* Underslung Line.

Underlayment — Floor covering of plywood or fiberboard installed to provide a level surface for carpet or other resilient flooring.

Underpinning — Process of strengthening an existing foundation.

Underride Collision — Occurs when a striking vehicle collides with another vehicle and comes to rest under the vehicle being struck.

Underslung Line — *See* Undercut Line.

Underwriters Laboratories, Inc. (UL) — Independent fire research and testing laboratory that certifies equipment and materials; equipment and materials are approved only for the specific use for which it is tested. Headquartered in Northbrook, Illinois.

Undetermined Fire Cause — Fire cause classification used when the specific cause has not been determined to a reasonable degree of probability.

Unfriendly Fire — Uncontained and uncontrolled fire of intentional or accidental origin that may cause injury or damage.

Ungrounded Conductor — Conductor in a branch circuit that is energized and supplies current to load devices; the covering will be some color other than white, gray, or green. *Also known as* Hot Conductor.

Unibody — *See* Unitized Body.

Unibody Construction — Method of automobile construction used for most modern cars in which the frame and body of a vehicle is all one integral unit. *Also known as* Bird Cage Construction, Integral Frame Construction, or Unitized Construction.

Unified Command (UC) — In the Incident Command System, a shared command role that allows all agencies with geographical or functional responsibility for the incident, to manage the incident by establishing a common set of incident objectives and strategies. In unified command there is a single incident command post and a single operations chief at any given time.

Uniform — Official dress uniform or work uniform; different from protective clothing.

Uniformly Distributed Load — Load in a building that is evenly distributed over a particular area.

Unincorporated — Portion of a state/province outside the jurisdiction of municipalities that does not provide an inspection program.

Unit — Division of a block within an occupation consisting of an organized grouping of tasks within that block. *See* Block.

Unitized Body — Automobile construction in which a vehicle's stress bearing elements and sheet metal body parts are built together as one unit, instead of attaching the vehicle's body to a frame as in body-on-frame construction. *Also known as* Integral Frame or Unibody.

Unitized Construction — *See* Unibody Construction.

Unit Loading Device — Pallet or container used to facilitate the rapid loading and unloading of aircraft cargo. *Also known as* Unit Load Device.

Unit Lock — Lock designed to be installed in a cutout within the door, without requiring disassembly and reassembly of the lock.

Unit Vents — Vents normally constructed of metal frames and walls and operated by a hinged damper that is controlled either manually or automatically.

Unity of Command — Organizational principle in which workers report to only one supervisor in order to eliminate conflicting orders and the confusion that would result.

Universal Coupling — Coupling device that permits unlike couplings to be connected.

Universal Emergency Telephone Number — Typically an easy to remember and dial 3-digit telephone number that can be used to access emergency services personnel in the event of an emergency. 9-1-1 is the common universal emergency telephone number in the U.S. and Canada. In the United Kingdom, this number is 9-9-9; in other nations in the European Union, it is 1-1-2. *Also known as* Emergency Services Number, Emergency Telephone Number, or Universal Number.

Universal Joint — Multidirectional hinged joint used in the steering system and drivetrain of an automobile.

Universal Precautions — Set of precautions designed to prevent transmission of biological pathogens, especially bloodborne pathogens, when providing first aid or health care.

Universal Priorities — Operational priorities that apply to all emergency incidents. In order of importance (priority) they are: life safety, incident stabilization, and property conservation.

Unlined Hose — Fire hose without a rubber lining; most frequently used in interior standpipe systems and in wildland fire fighting.

Unloading Site — In a water shuttle operation, the place where tankers unload their water into portable tanks. *Also known as* Dump Site.

Unprotected Openings — Openings in floors, walls, or partitions that are not protected against the passage of smoke, flame, and heat; generally used to refer to such openings in fire walls.

Unprotected Steel — Steel structural members that are not protected against exposure to heat.

Unrestricted Grant — *See* General Support Grant.

Unstable Material — Materials that are capable of undergoing chemical changes or that can violently decompose with little or no outside stimulus.

Unsupported Tip — Operation of an aerial device with the tip of the device, or the platform if so equipped, in the air and not resting on another object. *Also known as* Cantilever Operation.

Unwritten Law — *See* Judiciary Law.

U-Pattern — Fire pattern left on a vertical surface from a fire plume some distance away from the vertical surface; similar to a V-pattern but formed higher on the vertical surface.

Upper Airway — Portion of the respiratory system above the epiglottis.

Upper Coupler Assembly — Assembly consisting of an upper coupler plate, reinforcement framing, and a fifth-wheel kingpin mounted on a semitrailer. *Formerly known as* Upper Fifth Wheel Assembly.

Upper Deck — Topmost continuous deck running the entire length and width of a vessel. *See* Deck.

Upper Explosive Limit (UEL) — *See* Upper Flammable Limit (UFL).

Upper Fifth-Wheel Assembly — *See* Upper Coupler Assembly.

Upper Flammable Limit (UFL) — Upper limit at which a flammable gas or vapor will ignite; above this limit the gas or vapor is too *rich* to burn (lacks the proper quantity of oxygen). *Also known as* Upper Explosive Limit (UEL). *See* Flammable Gas, Flammable Limit, Flammable Range, and Lower Flammable Limit (LFL).

Uprights — Planks that are held in place against sections of sheeting with shores. Uprights add strength to the shoring system; they distribute forces exerted by trench walls and counterforces exerted by shores over wider areas of the sheeting.

Upright Sprinkler — Sprinkler that sits on top of the piping and sprays water against a solid deflector; breaks up the spray into a hemispherical pattern that is redirected toward the floor.

Upstream — Direction opposite the flow of a stream or of the airflow; in a self-contained breathing apparatus (SCBA), the regulator is upstream from the face piece.

Urban Search and Rescue (US&R) — Search and rescue efforts involving structural collapse and other urban environments.

Urban/Wildland Interface — *See* Wildland/Urban Interface.

URM — Unreinforced masonry.

U.S. Bureau of Alcohol, Tobacco, Firearms and Explosives (ATF) — *See* Bureau of Alcohol, Tobacco, Firearms and Explosives (ATF).

USCG — *See* U.S. Coast Guard.

U.S. Coast Guard (USCG) — U.S. military, multimission, and maritime service, whose mission is to protect the public, the environment, and U.S. economic interests in U.S. ports and waterways, along the coasts, in international waters, or in any maritime region as required to support national security.

U.S. Department of Defense (DoD) — *See* Department of Defense (DoD).

U.S. Department of Energy (DOE) — *See* Department of Energy (DOE).

U.S. Department of Homeland Security (DHS) — *See* Department of Homeland Security (DHS).

U.S. Department of Housing and Urban Development (HUD) — *See* Department of Housing and Urban Development (HUD).

U.S. Department of Justice (DOJ) — *See* Department of Justice (DOJ).

U.S. Department of Labor (DOL) — *See* Department of Labor (DOL).

U.S. Department of Transportation (DOT) — *See* Department of Transportation (DOT).

U.S. Environmental Protection Agency — *See* Environmental Protection Agency.

USFA — *See* U.S. Fire Administration.

U.S. Fire Administration — U.S. governmental agency charged with reducing the nation's losses from fire through better fire prevention and control, supplementation of existing programs of research, training, and education, and the encouragement of new, improved programs and activities by state and local governments. Administers an extensive fire data and analysis program and co-administers a program concerned with firefighter health and safety. USFA is a division of the Federal Emergency Management Agency (FEMA), which itself is a division of the Department of Homeland Security (DHS). *Formerly known as* National Fire Prevention and Control Administration (NFPCA).

U.S. Occupational Safety and Health Administration (OSHA) — *See* Occupational Safety and Health Administration (OSHA).

US&R — *See* Urban Search and Rescue.

Utilidor — Insulated, heated conduit built below the ground surface or supported above the ground surface to protect the contained water, steam, sewage, and fire lines from freezing.

Utilities — Services such as gas, electricity, and water that are provided to the public.

Utility Rope — Rope that is used in any situation that requires a rope, except life safety applications; can be used for hoisting equipment, securing unstable objects, or cordoning off an area. *See* Non-Lifeline Rope.

UV — *See* Ultraviolet Wave Spectrum.

V

Vaccine — Biological agent given to a person to provide immunization against a specific disease; prepared from the disease-causing biological agent itself or from a synthetic substitute.

Vacuum — Space completely devoid of matter or pressure. In fire and emergency services terms, it is more commonly used to describe a pressure that is somewhat less than atmospheric pressure; a vacuum is needed to facilitate drafting of water from a static source.

Validity — Extent to which a test or other assessment technique measures the learner qualities (knowledge and skills) that it is meant to measure.

Value at Risk — One of several loss control factors considered when planning loss control strategies; a subjective determination of the value of a structure, its contents, the operations associated with it, or its existence.

Valve — Mechanical device with a passageway that controls the flow of a liquid or gas.

Vapor — Gaseous form of a substance that is normally in a solid or liquid state at room temperature and pressure; formed by evaporation from a liquid or sublimation from a solid. *See* Vapor Density, Vapor Dispersion, Vaporization, Vapor Pressure, and Vapor Suppression.

Vapor Barrier — Watertight material used to prevent the passage of moisture or water vapor into and through walls or roofs, or in the case of personal protective equipment, that prevents water from penetrating the clothing.

Vapor Density — Weight of a given volume of pure vapor or gas compared to the weight of an equal volume of dry air at the same temperature and pressure. A vapor density less than 1 indicates a vapor lighter than air; a vapor density greater than 1 indicates a vapor density heavier than air. *See* Physical Properties, Specific Gravity, and Vapor.

Vapor Dispersion — Action taken to direct or influence the course of airborne hazardous materials. *See* Dispersion and Vapor.

Vaporization — Physical process that changes a liquid into a gaseous state; the rate of vaporization depends on the substance involved, heat, pressure, and exposed surface area. *See* Radiative Feedback, Vapor, and Vapor Density.

Vaporizing Liquid Agent — (1) Any liquid that evaporates at elevated temperatures. (2) One of several extinguishing agents used on Class B or Class C fires that produces vapors that are heavier than air and acts as a smothering vapor agent.

Vapor Mitigating Foam — Foam concentrate that is designed solely for use on unignited spills of hazardous liquids and is not effective for fire-suppression operations. *See* Foam Concentrate.

Vapor Pressure — (1) Measure of the tendency of a substance to evaporate. (2) The pressure at which a vapor is in equilibrium with its liquid phase for a given temperature; liquids that have a greater tendency to evaporate have higher vapor pressures for a given temperature. *See* Boiling Point and Vapor.

Vapor Recovery System (VRS) — System that recovers gasoline vapors emitted from a vehicle's gasoline tank during product dispensing.

Vapor Suppression — Action taken to reduce the emission of vapors at a hazardous materials spill. *See* Hazardous Material and Vapor.

Vaportight Fixture — Fixture sealed to prevent an explosive atmosphere from entering the device's electrical contacts, where an ignition spark could be generated.

Variable-Flow Demand-Type Balanced-Pressure Proportioner — Foam proportioning system that is used in both fixed and mobile applications; a variable speed mechanism drives the foam pump and automatically monitors the flow of foam to produce an effective foam solution. *See* Foam Proportioner and Proportioning.

Variable-Flow Variable-Rate Direct-Injection System — Apparatus-mounted foam system that injects the correct amount of foam into the pump piping, thereby supplying all discharges with foam; automatically monitors the operation of the hoselines and maintains a consistent quality of foam solution. *See* Foam Proportioner and Proportioning.

Vaulted Surfaces — Ground above underground vaults such as underground parking structures, utility chases, drainage culverts, basements that extend under sidewalks, or underground transportation systems.

Vector — (1) Quantity in mathematics that has magnitude and direction; commonly represented by a directed line segment or arrow whose length represents the magnitude and whose orientation in space represents the direction. Common quantities with vector representations include force, pressure, and velocity. (2) An animate intermediary in the indirect transmission of an agent that carries the agent from a reservoir to a susceptible host. (3) Compass heading or cours followed by or to be followed by an aircraft.

Vector Diagram — Visual representation of fire movement at a scene, generally from areas of greater damage to areas of less damage.

Vegetation Fire — *See* Wildland Fire.

Vegetation Management — *See* Fuel Management.

Vehicle-Borne Improvised Explosives Device (VBIED) — An improvised explosive device placed in a car, truck, or other vehicle, typically creating a large explosion. *Also known as* Car Bomb or Vehicle Bomb. *See* Explosion, High Explosive, and Improvised Explosive Device.

Vehicle Driving Course — Temporarily or permanently constructed training course intended for training in apparatus and vehicle driving and operation.

Vehicle Identification Number (VIN) — Unique serial number used by automobile manufacturers to identify each individual vehicle.

Vehicle Rescue Technician (VRT) — Firefighter who is specially trained and certified to perform automobile extrications.

Vehicle Stabilization —Process of providing additional support to key places between an object of entrapment (in this case, a vehicle) and the ground or other solid anchor points to prevent unwanted movement.

Vein — Any blood vessel that carries blood from the tissues to the heart.

Velocity — Rate of motion in a given direction; measured in units of length per unit time, such as feet per second (meters per second) and miles per hour (kilometers per hour). *Also known as* Speed.

Veneered Wall — Wall with a surface layer of attractive material laid over a base of a common material.

Veneered Product — Structural product that has an external surface material over an inner core.

Vent — To release enclosed smoke and heat through an opening in the structure; the opening is made by chopping a hole in the roof, allowing for freer passage of air.

Ventilation — (1) Systematic removal of heated air, smoke, gases or other airborne contaminants from a structure and replacing them with cooler and/or fresher air to reduce damage and facilitate fire fighting operations. (2) Process of replacing foul air in any of a vessel's compartments with pure air. *See* Positive-Pressure Ventilation and Supply/Exhaust Ventilation.

Ventilation-Controlled — Describes a fire in which fire development is limited by the air supply.

Ventilation-Generated Pattern — Fire pattern that can vary widely in appearance but is created as a result of some kind of ventilation introduced to a fire.

Vent Sector — Incident command system term for those firefighters assigned to ventilate a structure.

Venturi Meter — Device used to measure water velocity, when coupled with a differential manometer; consists essentially of a piece of pipe in which the cross-sectional area has been constricted.

Venturi Principle — Physical law stating that when a fluid, such as water or air, is forced under pressure through a restricted orifice, there is an increase in the velocity of the fluid passing through the orifice and a corresponding decrease in the pressure exerted against the sides of the constriction. Because the surrounding fluid is under greater (atmospheric) pressure, it is forced into the area of lower pressure. *Also known as* Venturi Effect.

Verdict — Formal finding of fact made by a jury on matters or questions submitted to the jury by a judge. *Also known as* Discovery of Truth.

Vermiculite — Expanded mica used for loose fill insulation and as an aggregate in concrete.

Vertical Deadbolt — *See* Jimmy-Resistant Lock.

Vertically Mounted Split-Case Pump — Centrifugal pump similar to the horizontal split-case, except that the shaft is oriented vertically and the driver is mounted on top of the pump.

Vertical-Shaft Turbine Pump — Fire pump originally designed to pump water from wells; currently utilized when the water supply is from a nonpressurized source. Vertical-shaft pumps ordinarily have more than one impeller and are therefore multistage pumps.

Vertical Shore — *See* Dead Shore.

Vertical Strut — Vertical load-bearing member that receives the load from the header in a vertical shoring system.

Vertical Ventilation — Ventilating at the highest point of a building through existing or created openings and channeling the contaminated atmosphere vertically within the structure and out the top; accomplished by creating holes in the roof, skylights, roof vents, or roof doors. *Also known as* Top Ventilation.

Vertical Zone — Area of a vessel between adjacent bulkheads.

Very High Frequency, High Band (VHF-HI) — Radio band containing very high frequencies (high range), ranging from 150 MHz to 176 MHz; characterized by relatively short radio waves and generally the most widely used band for public safety agencies.

Very High Frequency, Low Band (VHF-LO) — Radio band containing very low frequencies (low range), ranging from 30 MHz to 76 MHz; characterized by long radio waves and generally used by public safety agencies serving large geographic areas.

Vesicant — Agent that causes blistering. *See* Blister Agent.

Vessel — (1) General term for all craft capable of floating on water and larger than a rowboat. (2) Tank or container used to store a commodity that may or may not be pressurized.

VFR — *See* Visual Flight Rules.

Vibration Reduction (VR) — *See* Image Stabilization (IS).

Vibrator — Mechanical device used in placing concrete to make certain that it fills all voids.

Vicarious Liability — Liability imposed on one person for the conduct of another, based solely on the relationship between the two persons; indirect legal responsibility for acts of another, such as the liability of an employer for acts of an employee. *See* Liability.

Victim — Person who suffers death, injury, or loss as a result of an act, circumstance, agency, or condition.

VIN — *See* Vehicle Identification Number.

Violation — Infringement of existing rules, codes, or laws. *See* Citation and Sanction.

Violent Rupture — Immediate release of chemical or mechanical energy caused by rapid cracking of the container.

Virga — Precipitation that evaporates before reaching the ground.

Virus — Simplest type of microorganism that can only replicate itself in the living cells of its hosts. Viruses are unaffected by antibiotics. *See* Bacteria and Rickettsia.

Viscosity — Liquid's thickness or ability to flow.

Visible Damage — Damage that is clearly evident by visual inspection without recourse to optical measuring devices.

Visual Aid — *See* Instructional Materials.

Visual Approach — Approach to landing made by visual reference to the surface.

Visual Flight Rules (VFR) — Rules that govern the operation of an aircraft during visual flight.

Visual Inspection — Observation without recourse to any optical devices except prescription lenses; may include physical and mechanical examination.

Visual Lead Time — Refers to driver/operators scanning far enough ahead of the apparatus to ensure that evasive action can be taken, if it becomes necessary, at the speed it is being driven.

Vital Signs — Indicators of a patient's condition that reflect temperature, pulse, respirations, and blood pressure.

Vitrified Clay Tile — Ceramic tile baked to become very hard and waterproof.

Void Space Nonstructural Entrapment — Victims who are trapped inside a collapsed structure, pinned by furniture or debris, or whose means of escape have been eliminated.

Volatile — Capable of changing into vapor quite readily at a fairly low temperature. *See* Vapor and Vaporization.

Volatility — Ability of a substance to vaporize easily at a relatively low temperature. *See* Vapor, Vaporization, and Volatile.

Volt — Basic unit of electrical potential; difference in potential (electromotive force) needed to create a current of one ampere through the resistance of one ohm. Most commonly abbreviated V, but may also be abbreviated E.

Voltage — Electrical force that causes a charge (electrons) to move through a conductor. Measured in volts (V). *Also known as* Electromotive Force (EMF). *See* Conductor.

Voltmeter — Device used for measuring the voltage existing in an electrical system.

Volume Operation — *See* Parallel Operation.

Volunteer — Anyone inside or outside the fire department who helps with fire and life safety education programs.

Volunteer Fire Department — Organization of part-time firefighters who may receive monetary compensation for on-call time and/or fire fighting duty time.

Volunteer Firefighter — Active member of a fire department who may receive monetary compensation for on-call time and/or fire fighting duty time. *Also spelled* Volunteer Fire Fighter.

Volute — Spiral, divergent chamber of a centrifugal pump, in which the velocity energy given to water by the impeller blades is converted into pressure.

Vomiting Agent — Chemical warfare agent that causes violent, uncontrollable sneezing, cough, nausea, vomiting and a general feeling of bodily discomfort. *See* Chemical Warfare Agent.

V-Pattern — Characteristic cone-shaped fire pattern left on a wall at or near its point of origin.

VRT — *See* Vehicle Rescue Technician.

V-Type Collapse — (1) Situation where the excess weight of heavy loads concentrated near the center of the floor, such as furniture and equipment, cause the floor to give way. A V-type collapse will result in void spaces near the walls. (2) Type of collapse void in which a floor section fails at the center and falls to the floor below; this results in two void spaces along the supporting outer wall.

Vulnerability — Degree to which an asset is exposed or susceptible to damage; depends on an asset's construction, its contents, and the economic value of its functions.

Vulnerability Assessment — (1) Act of predicting what could happen in the future within a given jurisdiction. (2) Extent of injury and damage that may result from a hazard emergency of a given intensity in a given area; should address effects of hazard emergencies on the existing and future-built environments.

W

Wagon — Special piece of fire apparatus that carries a large quantity of hose.

Wake Turbulence — Phenomena that result from the passage of an aircraft through the atmosphere; includes vortices, thrust stream turbulence, jet blast, jet wash, propeller wash, and rotor wash or downdraft.

Wale — Timber placed against sheeting planks in an excavation to keep the sheeting planks in place. *Also known as* Breast Timber.

Wall — (1) Vertical component of a structure or compartment that is intended to enclose, divide, or protect a space. *See* Load-Bearing Wall and Non-Load-Bearing Wall. (2) Side of a trench from the lip to the floor. *Also known as* Face.

Wallboard — Fire-resistive building material that consists of a layer of highly compacted gypsum material sandwiched between two layers of paper. *Also known as* Drywall, Plasterboard, or Sheetrock®.

Wall Footing — Continuous strip of concrete that supports a wall.

Wall Hydrant — Water discharge protruding through and mounted on the wall of a building or pump house; supplied by an interior fire pump and has one or more 2½-inch (6.3 cm) hose valves. Usually used for testing the fire pump.

Wall Ladder — Straight, single-section ladder.

Wallplate — In a raker shore or a flying shore, the continuous sheeting member placed immediately against the vertical surface that is being shored and that collects and distributes the load from the weakened wall.

Wall Post Indicator Valve (WPIV) — Similar to a post indicator valve (PIV) but mounted on the wall of the protected structure.

Wall Sprinkler — *See* Sidewall Sprinkler.

Warded Lock — Simple type of mortise lock that requires the use of a skeleton key to open.

Warm Front — Leading edge of a relatively warm air mass that moves in such a way that warm air displaces colder air; winds associated with warm-frontal activity are usually light, and mixing is limited. The atmosphere within a warm front is relatively stable when compared to cold-front activity.

Warm Gas Inhalator — Device that warms air for a hypothermia patient to breathe.

Warning Devices — Audible or visual devices, such as flashing lights, sirens, horns, or bells, added to an emergency vehicle to gain the attention of drivers of other vehicles.

Warning Lights — Lights on the apparatus designed to attract the attention of other motorists.

Warp Yarn — Threads that run lengthwise in a fabric or woven hose.

Wash Down — To flush spilled liquids from the roadway.

Waste Line — Hoseline that is tied off or otherwise secured and is used to handle water in excess of that being used during a relay operation. *Also known as* Dump Line.

Watch — (1) Period of time during which a firefighter is assigned to the telecommunications center desk. (2) Division of a day that constitutes a period of duty for a crew member on a vessel; a crew member's assigned duty period. *See* Watch Officer.

Watch Desk — Communications desk of a fire station.

Watch Line — Charged hoseline remaining at the scene of a fire with a detail of firefighters to stand guard against possible rekindling after the fire has been extinguished.

Watchman — Employee assigned to patrol and guard a property against fire or theft.

Watch Officer — Officer in charge of a watch; has the responsibility of the safe and proper navigation of the vessel during this time period. *Also known as* Officer of the Watch. *See* Watch.

Water Curtain — Fan-shaped stream of water applied between a fire and an exposed surface to prevent the surface from igniting from radiated heat; for example, the fan-shaped stream of water discharged from beneath an elevating platform to absorb radiant heat and protect the platform's occupants.

Water Department — Municipal authority responsible for the water supply system in a given community.

Water Distribution System — System designed to supply water for residential, commercial, industrial, and/or fire protection purposes; water is delivered through a network of piping and pressure-developing equipment.

Waterflow Alarm — Alarm-initiating device actuated by the movement (flow) of water within a pipe or chamber; most common installation is in the main water supply pipe of a sprinkler system. *Also known as* Sprinkler System Supervision System and Waterflow Detector.

Waterflow Detector — Detector that recognizes movement of water within the sprinkler or standpipe system; once movement is noted, the waterflow detector gives a local alarm and/or may transmit the alarm.

Water Gel — Chemical solution that is gelled or partially solidified to make it easier to use or handle; for example, gelatin dynamite (gelignite).

Water Hammer — Force created by the rapid deceleration of water; causes a violent increase in pressure that can be powerful enough to rupture piping or damage fixtures. Generally results from closing a valve or nozzle too quickly.

Waterline — Level at which a vessel floats; line to which water raises on hull.

Water Main — Principal pipe in a system of pipes for conveying water, especially one installed underground.

Water Mist Extinguisher — Type of fire extinguisher capable of discharging atomized water through a special applicator; pressurized water mist extinguishers use distilled water, whereas back-pump type water mist extinguishers use ordinary water.

Water Motor Gong — Audible local alarm on an automatic sprinkler system; powered by a small water wheel that operates when water begins to flow in the system.

Water-Reactive Material — Substance, generally a flammable solid, which reacts when mixed with water or exposed to humid air. *See* Air-Reactive Material, Reactive Material, and Reactivity.

Water Retention — Foam's ability to retain its water content.

Water Shuttle Operation — Method of water supply in which tenders/tankers continuously transport water between a fill site and the dump site located near the emergency scene.

Water Solubility — Ability of a liquid or solid to mix with or dissolve in water. *See* Dilution, Insoluble, Physical Properties, and Soluble.

Water Superintendent — Manager of the water department.

Water Supply — Any source of water available for use in fire fighting operations.

Water Supply Pumper — Pumper that takes water from a source and sends it to attack pumpers operating at the fire scene.

Water Tank — Water storage receptacle carried directly on the apparatus. NFPA® 1901 specifies that Class A pumpers must carry at least 500 gallons (2 000 L). *Also known as* Booster Tank.

Water Tender — Any ground vehicle capable of transporting large quantities of water. *Also known as* Tanker in some regions.

Water Thief — Any of a variety of hose appliances with one female inlet for 2½-inch (64 mm) or larger hose and with three gated outlets, usually two 1½-inch (38 mm) outlets and one 2½-inch (64 mm) outlet.

Watertight Bulkhead — Bulkhead (wall) strengthened and sealed to form a barrier against flooding. *See* Bulkhead (1).

Watertight Door — Door designed to keep out water; fitted to ensure integrity of the bulkheads (walls).

Watertight Transverse Bulkhead — Bulkhead (wall) that has no openings through it and extends from tank top to the main deck; designed to control flooding. *See* Bulkhead (1) and Watertight Bulkhead.

Water Tower — Aerial device primarily intended for deploying an elevated master stream; not generally intended for climbing operations. *Also known as* Elevating Master Stream Device.

Water Vacuum — Appliance that is similar to a household vacuum cleaner and is designed to pick up water.

Waterway — Path through which water flows within a hose or pipe.

Watt (W) — Basic unit of power; in simple electrical systems, power is equal to voltage times current. One watt is equal to a current of one ampere under the potential of one volt.

Waybill — Shipping paper used by a railroad to indicate origin, destination, route, and product; a waybill for each car is carried by the conductor. *See* Consist and Shipping Papers.

Weaponize — To improve the ability of an agent to be delivered as an effective weapon; for example, reducing the particulate size of the agent in order to increase the likelihood of inhalation.

Weapon of Mass Destruction (WMD) — Any weapon or device that is intended or has the capability to cause death or serious bodily injury to a significant number of people through the release, dissemination, or impact of toxic or poisonous chemicals or their precursors, a disease organism, or radiation or radioactivity; may include chemical, biological, radiological, nuclear, or explosive (CBRNE) type weapons.

Wear Course — External covering on a roof that protects the roof from mechanical abrasion; the typical tar and gravel roof uses gravel as the wear course.

Weather Deck — All parts of the main deck and decks above that are exposed to the weather. *See* Deck.

Web — Wide vertical part of a beam between the flanges.

Webbing — Synthetic nylon, spiral weave, tubular material used for creating anchors and lashings, and for packaging patients and rescuers.

Web Member — Secondary members of a truss that are contained between the chords.

Wedge — Angle-cut piece of timber used to snug up loads, fill in voids, or change the angle of thrust.

Weed Abatement — *See* Fuel Management.

Weep Hole — Small holes in a masonry veneer wall that release accumulated water to the exterior.

Weeping — Giving off or leaking fluid slowly; for example, couplings leaking at the point of attachment.

Weft Yarn — *See* Filler Yarn.

Weld — Joint created between two metal surfaces when they are heated and the two metals run together.

Weldment — Structure formed by welding together two or more pieces.

Western Frame Construction — *See* Platform Frame Construction.

Wet-Barrel Hydrant — Fire hydrant that has water all the way up to the discharge outlets; may have separate valves for each discharge or one valve for all the discharges. This type of hydrant is only used in areas where there is no danger of freezing weather conditions.

Wet Chemical System — Extinguishing system that uses a wet chemical solution as the primary extinguishing agent; usually installed in range hoods and associated ducting where grease may accumulate.

Wet Down — (1) To wet down or dampen debris after fire has been controlled but not completely extinguished. (2) Ceremony used in some departments to celebrate the acquisition of a new piece of apparatus.

Wet Line — Line of water or water and chemical retardant sprayed along the ground that serves as a temporary fire-stop or containment line from which to ignite or stop a low-intensity fire.

Wet-Pipe Sprinkler System — Fire-suppression system that is built into a structure or site. The system's piping contains either water or foam solution continuously; activation of a sprinkler causes the extinguishing agent to flow from the open sprinkler. *See* Deluge Sprinkler System, Dry-Pipe Sprinkler System, and Preaction Sprinkler System.

Wet Standpipe System — Standpipe system that has water supply valves open and maintains water in the system at all times. *See* Dry Standpipe System and Standpipe System.

Wetting Agent — Chemical solution or additive that reduces the surface tension of water (producing wet water), causing it to spread and penetrate more effectively; may also produce foam through mechanical means. Detergent is a mild form of wetting agent. *See* Penetrant.

Wet Water — Wetting agent that is introduced to water to reduce its surface tension and improve its penetration qualities. *See* Penetrant.

Wharf — Place for berthing ships along or at an angle from a shore; constructed by extending bulkheads out from the shore and back-filling the enclosed area to create a flat surface for loading and unloading vessels. *See* Pier.

Wheelbase — Distance between a vehicle's front and rear axles.

Wheel Block — *See* Chock.

Whirlwind — Small rotating windstorm of limited extent containing sand or dust. *Also known as* Dust Devil.

WHMIS — *See* Workplace Hazardous Materials Information System.

Whole-Part-Whole — Method of sequencing instruction; information begins with the complete picture or demonstration of a skill or with an overview of all information, progresses to provide a breakdown of all steps or details on segments of information, and returns to a complete demonstration or overview in a review or summary.

Wicking — Pattern that occurs when quantities of the ignitable liquid are absorbed by the material onto which the liquid is poured.

Wildfire — *See* Wildland Fire.

Wildfire Mop-Up — *See* Wildfire Overhaul.

Wildfire Overhaul — Operations involving extinguishing hot spots and hidden fires after the main body of fire has been knocked down. *Also known as* Wildfire Mop-Up.

Wildland Fire — Unplanned, unwanted, and uncontrolled fire in vegetative fuels such as grass, brush, or timberland involving uncultivated lands; requires suppression action and may threaten structures or other improvements. *Also known as* Ground Cover Fire, Ground Fire, Natural Cover Fire, Vegetation Fire, or Wildfire. *See* Structure Fire and Wildland/Urban Interface.

Wildland Fire Apparatus — Fire department apparatus designed specifically for fighting wildland fires; generally a light, mobile vehicle having limited pumping and water capability for off-road operations. *Also known as* Booster Apparatus, Brush Apparatus, Brush Patrol, Brush Pumper, and Field Unit.

Wildland Firefighter — Person trained to function safely as a member of a wildland fire-suppression crew. NFPA® identifies four levels of progression, Wildland Firefighter I through Wildland Firefighter IV; each level denotes a higher level of capability, supervision, or management.

Wildland/Urban Interface — Line, area, or zone where an undeveloped wildland area meets a human development area. *Also known as* Urban/Wildland Interface.

Wild Line — Uncontrolled hoseline and nozzle or butt that thrash about from the reaction of highly pressurized flowing water.

Winch — (1) Pulling tool that consists of a length of steel chain or cable wrapped around a motor-driven drum; most commonly attached to the front or rear of a vehicle. (2) On a ship, a stationary motor-driven hoisting machine with a vertical drum around which a rope or chain winds as a load is lifted; a special form of this type of winch using a horizontal drum is called a *windlass*.

Wind — Horizontal movement of air relative to the surface of the earth. *See* Crosswind, Downwind, and Headwind.

Winders — Radiating or wedge-shaped treads at the turn of a stairway.

Windpipe — Trachea.

Wind Shakes — Damage done to timber by repeated flexing in the wind.

Windshield Survey — Process of taking a moment to get a 360-degree view of the incident before exiting the vehicle.

Wind Sock — Cone-shaped cloth sock at airports that is used to indicate wind direction and, to some extent, wind velocity.

Wind Tee — T-shaped indicator mounted horizontally on a pivot pole to swing freely in the wind; used as a wind direction indicator or landing direction indicator. May also be in the shape of a tetrahedron.

Windward Side — (1) Unprotected side of the building the wind is striking. (2) Side or direction from which the wind is blowing.

Wing Tank — Tank located well outboard, next to the side shell plating of a vessel; often a continuation of the double bottom up the sides to a deck.

Wire Cutters — Tool with approved, insulated handles to cut wire.

Wired Glass — Flat sheet glass containing an embedded wire mesh that increases its resistance to breakage and penetration; installed in exterior doors, windows, and skylights to increase interior illumination without compromising fire resistance and security. When the glass is exposed to the heat of a fire, it will typically break or crack due to thermal stresses; the wires give the glass dimensional stability, permitting it to act as a barrier to the fire even when the glass has failed. Can be either transparent or translucent.

Wired Telegraph Circuit Box — Alarm system operated by pressing a lever in the alarm box that starts a wound-spring mechanism; the rotating mechanism transmits a code by opening and closing the circuit.

Wire Nut — Approved, solderless, nonconductive connector used to connect one wire to another.

WMD — *See* Weapon of Mass Destruction.

Wooden Short Board — Device used as part of spinal immobilization.

Wood Grain — Stratification of wood fibers in a piece of wood.

Wood Planer — Device used to smooth the surface of wooden boards; commonly found in woodworking shops.

Worker — *See* Working Fire.

Working End — Part of the rope that is to be used in forming the knot. *Also known as* Bitter End or Loose End.

Working Fire — Term used to describe a fire at which considerable fire fighting activity will be required. *Also known as* Worker.

Working Length — Length of a non-self-supporting ladder; measured along the beams from the butt to the point of bearing at the top.

Workplace Hazardous Materials Information System (WHMIS) — Canadian law requiring that hazardous products be appropriately labeled and marked.

Worksheet — Activity sheet that lists tasks to accomplish, guides activities, and enables learners to apply cognitive information in order to practice and develop skills.

Woven-Jacket Hose — Fire hose constructed with one or two outer jackets woven on looms from cotton or synthetic fibers.

WPIV — *See* Wall Post Indicator Valve.

Wrapped Hose — Nonwoven rubber hose manufactured by wrapping rubber-impregnated woven fabric around a rubber tube and encasing it in a rubber cover.

Wrecker — Vehicle that is usually equipped with a small crane, winch, or tilting bed assembly, and is used to transport damaged vehicles; the size and type of the wrecker depends on the type and size of the vehicle to be moved. *Also known as* Tow Truck.

Wristlet — Portion of the coat that prevents fire or water from entering the sleeve.

Wye — Hose appliance with one female inlet and two or more male outlets; the outlets are usually smaller than the inlet, and are usually gated.

Wythe — Single vertical row of multiple rows of masonry units in a wall, usually brick. *See* Course and Header Course.

X

Xiphoid Process — Flexible cartilage at the lower tip of the sternum.

X-Ray — High-energy photon produced by the interaction of charged particles with matter.

X-Type — Type of gypsum wallboard formulated by adding noncombustible fibers to the gypsum, which is required to achieve fire resistance as designated in ASTM C 36.

Y

Yard Hydrant — *See* Private Hydrant.

Y-Branch — Plumbing drainage fitting with a branch or branches that extend at a 45-degree angle.

Z

Zero-Base Budget — Budgetary system in which each department, function, or program theoretically terminates with the budget and must justify its existence in order to receive funding in the next budget.

Zero Mechanical State — State a machine is in when all its power sources are neutralized and all its parts are stabilized.

Zoning Commission — Division of local government that is responsible for managing land use by dividing the area within the jurisdiction into zones in which only certain uses, such as residential, commercial, or manufacturing, are allowed.

Zoom Lens — Lens designed to extend focal length; used for taking close-up pictures from greater distances.

Index

Index by Nancy Kopper